TRANSDUCERS FOR BIOMEDICAL MEASUREMENTS:

Principles and Applications

BIOMEDICAL ENGINEERING AND HEALTH SYSTEMS:

A WILEY-INTERSCIENCE SERIES

***Advisory Editor:* JOHN H. MILSUM, University of British Columbia**

L. A. Geddes and L. E. Baker

Principles of Applied Biomedical Instrumentation

George H. Myers and Victor Parsonnet

Engineering in the Heart and Blood Vessels

Robert Rosen

Dynamical System Theory in Biology

Stanley Middleman

Transport Phenomena in the Cardiovascular System

Samuel A. Talbot and Urs Gessner

Systems Physiology

M. F. Collen

Hospital Computer Systems

Israel Mirsky, Dhanjoo N. Ghista, and Harold Sandler

Cardiac Mechanics: Physiological, Clinical and Mathematical Considerations

Richard S. C. Cobbold

Transducers for Biomedical Measurements: Principles and Applications

Marshall M. Lih

Transport Phenomena in Medicine and Biology

TRANSDUCERS FOR BIOMEDICAL MEASUREMENTS:
Principles and Applications

RICHARD S. C. COBBOLD

Institute of Biomedical Engineering
University of Toronto, Canada

A WILEY-INTERSCIENCE PUBLICATION

JOHN WILEY & SONS
New York • London • Sydney • Toronto

Library of Congress Cataloging in Publication Data:

Cobbold, Richard S C 1931–
Transducers for biomedical measurements.

(Biomedical engineering and health systems: a Wiley-Interscience series)
"A Wiley-Interscience publication."
Includes bibliographical references.
1. Transducers. 2. Function tests (Medicine)
3. Biomedical engineering. I. Title. [DNLM: 1. Biomedical Engineering. 2. Transducers. TJ223.T7 C654t 1974]

R857.T7C6 610'.28 74-2480
ISBN 0-471-16145-4

Printed in the United States of America

10 9 8 7 6 5 4 3 2

Series Preface

> "To love
> is not to gaze steadfast
> at one another:
> it is to look together
> in the same direction"
>
> St. Exupery, *Terre des Hommes*

The provision of good universal health care has only just become a social imperative. Like such other interlocking systems as transportation, water resources, and metropolises, the recognition of the need to adopt a systems approach has been forced upon us by the evident peril of mutual ruin resulting if we do not. The required systems approach is necessarily interdisciplinary rather than merely multidisciplinary, but this always makes evident the very real gulf between disciplines. Indeed, bridging the gulf requires much more time and patience than necessary just to learn the other discipline's "language." These different languages simultaneously represent and hide the whole gestalt associated with any discipline or profession. Nevertheless sufficient bridging must be achieved so that interdisciplinary teams can tackle our complex systems problems for such teams constitute the only form of "intelligence amplification" that we can presently conceive.

Fortunately the existence of urgent problems always seems to provide the necessary impetus to work together in the same direction, using St. Exupery's thought, and, indeed, as a result of this to understand and value each other more deeply.

This series started with its emphasis on biomedical engineering. It illustrates the application of engineering in the service of medicine and biology. Books are required both to educate persons from one discipline in what they need to know of others, and to catalyse a synthesis in the core subject generally known as biomedical engineering. Thus one set of titles will aim at introducing the biologist and medical scientist to the quantitatively based analytical theories and techniques of the engineer and physical scientists. This set covers instrumentation, mathematical modelling, signal and systems analysis, communication and control theory, and computer simulation techniques. A second set for engineers and physical scientists will cover basic material on biological and medical systems with as quantitative and compact a presentation as is possible. The omissions and simplifications necessitated by this approach should be justified by the increased ease of transferring the information, and more subtly by the increased pressure this can bring to bear upon the search for unifying quantitative principles.

A second emphasis has become appropriate as society increasingly demands universal health care, because the emphasis of medicine is now rapidly shifting from individual practice to health care systems. The huge financial burden of our health care systems (currently some 6% of GNP and increasing at about 14% per year) alone will ensure that engineers will be called upon, for the technological content is already large and still increasing. Engineers will need to apply their full spectrum of methodologies and techniques, and, moreover, to work in close collaboration with management professionals, as well as with many different health professionals. This series, then, will develop a group of books for mutually educating these various professionals so that they may better achieve their common task.

This volume on the principles and applications of transducers for biomedical measurements should provide a useful and comprehensive introduction to the field. In treatment it is largely complementary to another volume in the series *Principles of Applied Biomedical Instrumentation* by Geddes and Baker.

JOHN H. MILSUM

Vancouver, 1973

Preface

Measurement systems incorporating transducers play a vital role in both fundamental biomedical research and modern quantitative clinical medicine. New methods and techniques of measurement, often employing recent discoveries in the physical sciences, have not only resulted in improvements in the accuracy and convenience with which certain measurements can be made but also have extended the range of variables to include quantities that were previously inaccessible. It was the need to review these developments in an orderly manner that provided the basic motivation for writing this book.

The purpose of this book is to present a comprehensive and up-to-date account of the theory, design, and application of transducers for biomedical measurements. Not only is it concerned with the physical principles governing transducer operation, it is also concerned with the interaction of the transducer and the system being measured and with the electrical system used to amplify or otherwise process the resulting signal. Through examples of transducer applications in clinical and research practice it is hoped that some of the problems associated with designing a measurement system capable of gathering useful data will be better understood.

I have attempted to present the material in this book in such a way that it will serve the needs of the researcher, the graduate student and, perhaps, the senior undergraduate student. For the researcher, a detailed account of recent developments in input transducers and their applications and a fairly comprehensive, although selective, list of references are included. For the graduate student, sufficient background material has been incorporated so that this book can serve as the basis of a graduate course. Indeed, this book is partially the outcome of such a course given by the author over the past eight years.

The content is divided into two parts. The first consists of four relatively short chapters that are intended to provide the general framework necessary for properly understanding the more specialized material contained in the second. For the reader with a good background in the physical sciences, much of the material in these chapters will be familiar and can either be omitted or briefly reviewed. For the reader with a background in the life sciences, the material will probably be found to form an essential framework for the more detailed and specialized material of the later chapters.

Certainly the "meat" of this book is contained in Part II. It consists of six chapters organized by the type of quantity to be transduced rather than by the principles of the transducer. Although this results in a certain degree of overlap, through the proper choice of chapter ordering and the liberal use of interchapter references, this has been kept to a minimum. Certainly, the topics included in this part do reflect the author's own interpretation of what a transducer is. Some may feel that this is too broad, and others, too narrow, resulting in the omission of certain important topics. I have attempted to strike a balance but perhaps in doing so have fallen between the proverbial stools.

The writing of a book of this kind has necessarily involved the help of many individuals. In particular I would like to thank my colleagues in the Institute for reviewing and discussing many parts of the manuscript, especially Professor N. F. Moody for his encouragement and for providing the atmosphere that made the writing possible. To Mrs. Anna Jamieson, Mr. Jim Butler, and Mrs. Carolyn Nish, I am indebted for their patience in reading, typing, and checking various parts of the manuscript. Finally, to my wife, I am especially grateful for her encouragement and for again tolerating the long periods of evening widowhood that were necessary in all phases of the writing.

For permission to reproduce many of the figures from the literature I wish to thank both the publishers and authors. In particular, I am very grateful to the Year Book Medical Publishers for permission to allow the reproduction of many diagrams and very substantial portions of the text from R. S. C. Cobbold "Biomedical Measurement Systems," in *Medical Engineering*, C. D. Ray, Ed., © Year Book Medical Publishers, Inc., Chicago, 1974.

Toronto, Canada
January 1974

RICHARD S. C. COBBOLD

Contents

TRANSDUCERS FOR BIOMEDICAL MEASUREMENTS:

Principles and Applications

Part I

GENERAL ASPECTS OF BIOMEDICAL TRANSDUCERS

CHAPTER ONE

Measurements and Transducers

The degree of confidence in the results of a measurement is greatly enhanced when all the factors influencing the measurement accuracy are properly understood. Such an understanding requires not only a detailed knowledge of the measurement process itself but also a knowledge of the possible interactions of the measurement process on the system being measured. When the system is inanimate, these interactions are normally relatively straightforward, and provided the effects are not too large, it is fairly easy to make the appropriate corrections and arrive at a reasonable estimate of the accuracy. On the other hand, measurements on living systems can involve a variety of subtle and highly complex interactions arising not only from direct physical influences but also from biochemical, physiological, and even psychological interactions with the measuring process.

The complexity and comparatively elementary knowledge of most biological systems makes it difficult to predict quantitatively the effect of a measurement on the system. As a result, it is most important that the measurement system be designed with a primary aim being a reduction of possible interactions. Although one would like the measurements to be noninvasive and contactless, this is only rarely possible: one must generally accept some degree of interaction. Under such circumstances it is especially important that the properties of the measurement system be thoroughly studied so that one can at least make an educated estimate of the interactions expected. A useful starting point for such a study is a consideration of the general properties of measurement systems (Chapters 1–4) followed by a detailed examination of particular schemes (Chapters 5–10).

1.1 PURPOSE OF MEASUREMENTS

In deciding on the best means of performing a measurement it is most important to keep in mind the primary purpose for which the measurement is made. Too often this is lost sight of and results either in a measurement system that is overly complex, yielding an accuracy far beyond what can be used, or in a system that fails to meet the objectives. Generally, one of the following three purposes can be considered to be of dominant importance: (1) improved understanding, (2) monitoring, or (3) control.

The first arises not only in most basic research work but also in many applied areas and in clinical investigations. For example, a series of tests and measurements on a patient may be carried out to determine the correct diagnosis. Here, the prime objective is to obtain an improved understanding of an individual to determine the best method of treatment.

A second primary objective of certain measurements can best be described as "monitoring." Under such circumstances the desire may be to determine whether or not a variable lies within certain limits: only under unusual circumstances will actual use be made of the data gathered. Such a situation arises, for example, in an intensive care ward, where variables such as temperature, pressure, and ECG are monitored as a means for checking the orderly recovery of the patient.

Finally, a most important objective of certain measurements is that in which the measured quantity serves as a means of controlling a particular process. Here, the measuring system becomes an integral part of a control system designed to govern a particular set of variables. For example, in a myoelectrically controlled artificial arm, the EMG signals arising from certain muscle groups are used to control the position of an arm or the fingers. In such circumstances the prime objective is the control of a process rather than in the measured values themselves. System feedback is provided by visual observation: this in turn controls the EMG signal that controls the position. The system can be further refined through the addition of a pressure-measuring system to control the force with which an object is grasped. Again, the prime purpose of this second measuring system is to control, by a second feedback loop, what was previously a poorly controlled parameter.

1.2 THE PROCESS OF MEASUREMENT

Although the measurement of many physical quantities can be made directly, others require the use of *inferential measurement techniques.* An example of direct measurement is the measurement of skin resistance using a null-type bridge that compares directly the measured skin resistance with a standard. On the other hand, inferential techniques rely on a functional (mathematical) or statistical relationship between the quantity one desires to measure directly (but perhaps cannot) and related quantities that are measurable. The relationship can be established either by theoretical analysis or by empirical techniques using other, but perhaps less convenient, direct measurement methods.

An example of the inferential method arises from the clinical measurement of cardiac output using the indicator dilution principle. Direct measurement of the cardiac output by means of a flow transducer attached to the ascending aorta is evidently impracticable for routine clinical measurements, whereas by means of catheters, it is possible to inject and sample the concentration of a suitable indicator in the cardiovascular system. By measuring the time variation of the concentration of an indicator after passing through the heart–lung system, the cardiac output can be inferred. Since the measurement relies on the mathematical relationship between the cardiac output and the time variation of the indicator concentration, the measurement is said to be inferential. However, it should be noted that such measurements do rely on the *direct* measurement of a quantity, which, in this example, is the time variation of the indicator concentration. Indeed, all measurements do fundamentally involve the quantitative comparison of an unknown quantity with a predefined standard. Such a comparison can be made either directly, as illustrated above for the measurement of skin resistance, or through the use of a measuring system calibrated against a standard.

Often direct comparison is made through the use of null techniques, whereby the *difference* between the standard and the quantity to be measured is detected and the standard is adjusted until this difference is a minimum. One of the simplest illustrations of this is the use of an apothecary's balance, for which zero deflection of the pointer implies that the standard weights and the quantity to be weighed are identical. In general, null measurement techniques are to be preferred because they yield both greater accuracy and precision, especially for the measurement of static or slowly varying quantities. The advantage arises from the ability to *detect* small differences, as compared to the more difficult task of quantitatively measuring them. A major disadvantage of the null method arises from the time delay required to achieve a null, making rapidly varying dynamic measurement more difficult. For this type of measurement a rapid automatic balancing device is required to insure that the balance or null is maintained as the quantity fluctuates. This naturally tends to increase the system's complexity.

1.3 TRANSDUCERS AND TRANSDUCTION OF EVENTS

There are certain features that are common to most scientific measurements. For all but the very simplest of measurements a *measuring system* is required either to compare a quantity with a standard or, by means of a calibrated sys-

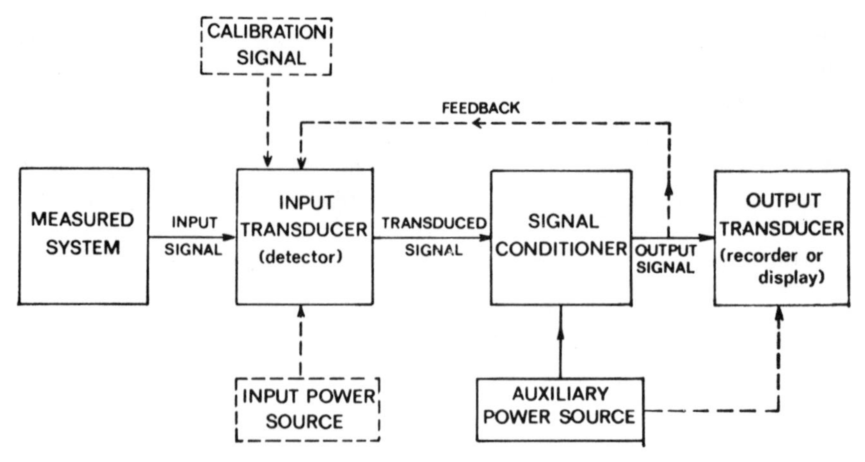

Figure 1.1. General features of a measurement system. The elements and paths in broken lines are not necessarily present in a given system.

tem, to provide an output that can be related to the quantity being measured. Such systems often have the general arrangement illustrated in Figure 1.1.

The quantity to be measured is detected by the *input transducer*, which we define as any sensing device that converts (transduces) energy from one form to another. Input transducers for physiological measurements sometimes convert physical energy directly into an electrical form, as occurs, for example, in the measurement of temperature by a thermocouple. Other transducers may be of the mechanical-to-mechanical conversion type. For example, in a pressure transducer, the pressure change may cause a mechanical displacement that results in a pointer moving over a calibrated scale. Alternatively, this mechanical movement can be detected by a differential transformer displacement transducer, which produces an electrical output signal. The total input transducer then consists of two transducers in series, a pressure-displacement transducer, called the *primary transducer*, and a displacement-voltage transducer, called the *secondary transducer*.

A less obvious form of transducer is the electrode for measuring bioelectric events. Unlike the electrical connection between two conductors that simply enables electrons to be transported, an electrode contacting a biological medium acts as a transducer to convert from ionic current flow in the medium to electronic flow in the electrical circuit. A detailed description is given in Chapter 10.

So far we have been mostly concerned with the measurement of a quantity (e.g., temperature, pressure, flow), but in fact many physiological measurements are not of this form, since they involve the detection of events. To transform a physiological event into an electrical signal, for example, requires that the event possess a *transducible property*. If it has such a property, it is necessary to choose a suitable *principle of transduction*, to enable one to recognize and convert the property into an electrical signal. Geddes and Baker [1] define a transducible property as "that singular characteristic of an event to which a principle of transduction can be applied." They go on to define a principle of transduction as "any one of the many methods that can be employed to convert the transducible property to an electrical signal."

To illustrate these definitions, we suppose that it is desired to measure the density of cells in an electrolyte. A transducible property of the cells is their high electrical resistance compared to the fluid. If the suspension is allowed to pass through a very short narrow tube, whose resistance can be monitored, then every time a cell passes through the tube, the resistance will momentarily increase. The number of such increases for a given flow rate can be recorded, enabling one to calculate the cell density. Here, the principle of transduction is the electrical measurement of the resistance of the tube and the transducible property is the cell resistance.

Returning to Figure 1.1, we note that the input transducer may require external power to drive it. In fact, as discussed in Chapter 4, input transducers can be of two types, active or passive, depending on whether or not they require external power to operate them. Also shown attached to the input transducer is a calibration signal source. Such a source (e.g., a standard pressure) enables one to calibrate properly the complete system, including the input transducer, during use.

So far we have assumed that the input transducer produces an output signal that is directly related to (often proportional to) the input signal and that, after conditioning, produces a proportional output. In practice, many modern measurements entail the use of feedback, in one form or another. The null type of measurement with automatic balancing is of this form: feedback of the difference signal causes the system to adjust itself to a null condition. The quantity adjusted by the feedback is then a direct measure of the quantity being measured. Feedback to the transducer is sometimes used to improve the system linearity and stability and to improve the input characteristics of the transducer itself.

The prime purpose of the signal conditioner stage in Figure 1.1 is to modify the transduced signal in a controlled and well-defined manner so that it will be acceptable to the final stage. It may have to perform several operations such as amplification and filtering. In addition it must be designed in such a way that it is compatible with both the input and output transducers. General aspects of impedance-matching are briefly discussed in Chapter 2, while particular problems associated with an individual input transducer are considered in Part II.

To translate the output of the signal conditioner into a form that can be read or heard is the purpose of the output transducer. It may, in the simplest example, consist of a deflection-type meter or chart recorder calibrated directly in terms of the input signal amplitude. Alternatively, if the elements of the measurement system are physically separate, it will be necessary to use some form of signal-transmission system (e.g., a telemetry system) to link the signal conditioner and the output transducer. A further possibility is that the signal conditioner output is taken directly to a digital or analog computer, where the signal is analyzed and the results printed or stored.

REFERENCE

1. Geddes, L. A., and Baker, L. E. *Principles of Applied Biomedical Instrumentation.* Wiley: New York, 1968.

CHAPTER TWO

The Characteristics of Signals and Systems

2.1 DYNAMIC CHARACTERISTICS OF SIGNALS

Signals may be classified as either static or dynamic. Although the former implies that the signal never changes, and therefore conveys no information, one usually includes in this category signals that change slowly, perhaps from one steady state to another. On the other hand, dynamic signals imply change and require that the measurement system components be sufficiently fast-acting for the output faithfully to follow the input: criteria to insure that this is so will be discussed later in this chaper as well as in Chapter 3.

In discussing the properties and processing of dynamic signals, it is convenient to classify them into *periodic*, *transient*, and *random*. Although ideally each form can occur by itself, more often real signals contain combinations of two or more. The properties of such combinations can usually be treated by considering the individual components and then superimposing the results.

A periodic signal is one that repeats itself in a regular cyclic manner, so that a knowledge of such a signal over one complete cycle enables the signal form to be predicted for all other times. On the other hand, a transient signal, strictly speaking, is isolated in time and is not repeated in any regular manner. But, in practice, a signal whose duration is short compared to the repetition period is generally classified as a transient.

Random signals are characterized by a nonperiodic time variation: the only predictions that can be made regarding the future variations are of a statistical nature. Such signals are always present to some extent in any measuring system and form an ultimate limit to the sensitivity that can be achieved.

The properties and characteristics of each of the above three signal forms will be discussed in detail below.

2.1.1 Periodic Signals

Fourier Series. The simplest mathematical form of a periodic signal is the sinusoidal wave described by

$$V = V_m \sin \omega t,$$

where V_m is the peak amplitude, ω is the angular frequency, and the period of the wave $T = 2\pi/\omega$. It is from such signals that we can *synthesize* any periodic signal no matter how complex its form. Conversely, any periodic signal can be *analyzed* into a series of sinusoidal signals. One reason for the importance of such an analysis is that it is often much simpler to examine how the individual sinusoidal components are affected by the measurement system rather than to treat the periodic signal as an entity.

It can be shown that any periodic signal $f(t)$ of period T can be analyzed into a series of discrete sinusoidal waves given by

$$f(t) = \tfrac{1}{2}a_0 + \sum_{n=1}^{\infty} a_n \cos n\omega t + b_n \sin n\omega t, \tag{1}$$

in which the harmonic amplitudes are given by

$$\begin{aligned} a_n &= \frac{2}{T}\int_0^T f(t) \cos n\omega t \, dt \\ b_n &= \frac{2}{T}\int_0^T f(t) \sin n\omega t \, dt. \end{aligned} \tag{2}$$

This series, called a Fourier series, consists of a term $a_0/2$ equal to the average value of $f(t)$ over one period, plus the sum of a series of sine and cosine terms the frequency components of which increase in integral steps from the fundamental frequency ω up to infinity.

That the series given by Eq. (1) can exactly represent any periodic wave is at first sight somewhat surprising. But on examining the components of a complex wave, such as the square wave illustrated in Figure 2.1, it becomes more evident how, through a judicious choice of the magnitude and sign of the amplitude factors, the harmonic components add to give a complex waveform.

It can be shown that if the signal is an odd function—that is, $-f(t) = f(-t)$—the series contains only sine terms. Further, if the signal is even—that is, $f(t) = f(-t)$—the series contains only cosine components. From the examples of even and odd functions given in Figure 2.2, it will be noted that a simple

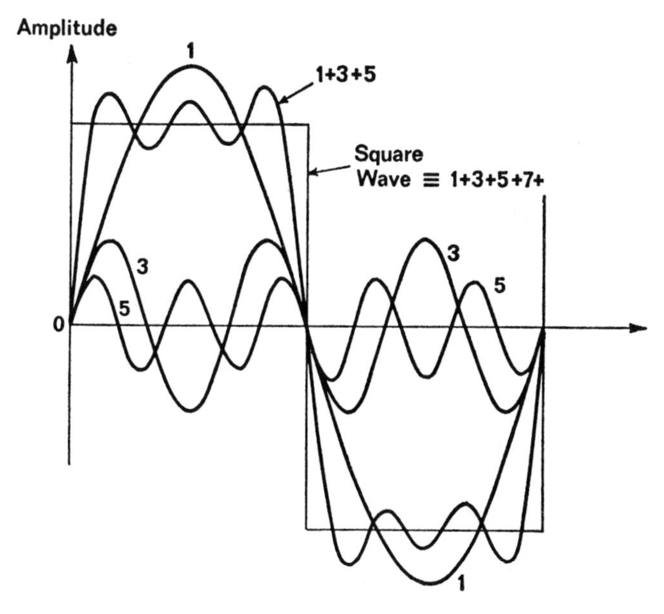

Figure 2.1. Fourier synthesis of a square wave. The waves marked 1, 3, 5 are the fundamental, third, and fifth harmonic components. The sum of these three components can be seen to be beginning to approximate the shape of the square wave. An infinite number of harmonics is required to exactly add up to the square wave.

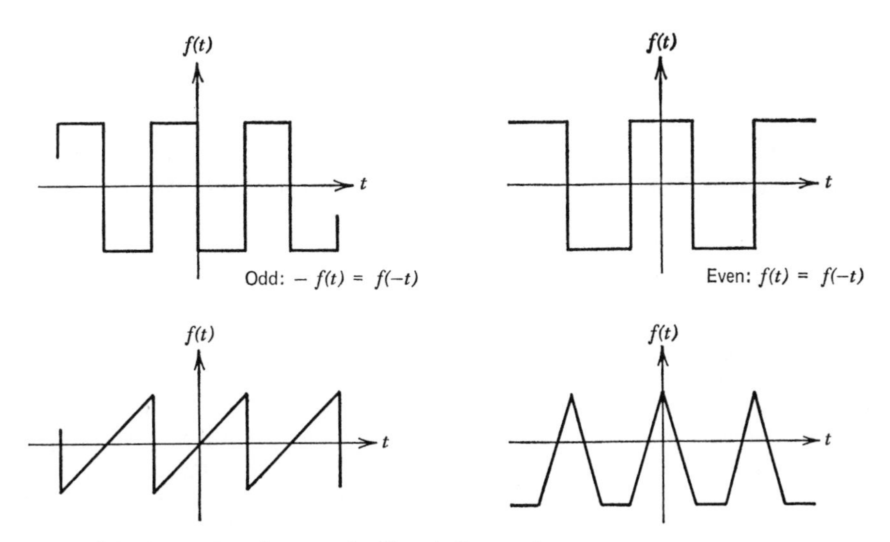

Figure 2.2. Examples of even and odd periodic waveforms.

inspection of the waveform enables one to decide if either set of terms a_n or b_n are zero.

An alternative form of Eqs. (1) and (2) can be obtained by expressing $(a_n \cos n\omega t + b_n \sin n\omega t)$ as a sine or cosine function with a phase term ϕ_n. If the sine function is used, we find

$$f(t) = \tfrac{1}{2}a_0 + \sum_{n=1}^{\infty} c_n \sin (n\omega t - \phi_n), \tag{3}$$

where

$$c_n = \sqrt{a_n^{\,2} + b_n^{\,2}} \qquad \text{and} \qquad \phi_n = \tan^{-1} \frac{a_n}{b_n}. \tag{4}$$

Thus, $f(t)$ can be expressed in terms of a series of sine waves and phases of which vary. This form is particularly valuable for examining the effect of frequency-dependent phase shifts on the waveform.

When Eq. (1) is evaluated for some simple wave shapes, it is found that the harmonic amplitudes for smoothly varying curves decrease rapidly with increasing harmonic number, while those with abrupt changes contain higher-frequency harmonics. Thus, we find in Table 2.1 that the harmonic amplitudes for the triangular wave shown in the third column decrease relatively rapidly compared with those for the square wave. In fact it is generally true that the more abrupt and discontinuous the waveform, the larger is the number of terms that must be included to obtain a reasonable approximation to the wave shape.

Although the Fourier series, with an infinite number of terms included, can exactly represent any periodic waveform, in practice it is only desired to approximate the wave shape closely. The number of terms to be included depends on the nature of the waveform as well as the accuracy desired. Thus, although an arterial pressure waveform (which is a relatively smooth curve) may only require 10 harmonics, an ECG waveform, with its abrupt QRS complex, may require some 30–60 harmonics for the same degree of approximation. Examples of the synthesis and analysis of some physiological signals are shown in Figures 2.3 and 2.4.

A most important concept, especially in dealing with nonsinusoidal waveforms, is that of the frequency spectrum. Column 3 in Table 2.1 shows the frequency spectrum of certain periodic waveforms: each vertical line indicates the amplitude of a specific harmonic. It is a characteristic of all perfectly periodic waves that they have a *line spectrum* of this form, which should be contrasted to the *continuous spectrum* (all frequencies present) for random or transient signals. A waveform that is nearly periodic or a periodic waveform that contains a small amount of noise will exhibit a spectrum in which the lines are broadened and a small-amplitude continuous spectrum is present. Many physiological signals are of this form.

Table 2.1 Fourier Series and Frequency Spectrum for Some Simple Periodic Waves

Type of wave	Waveform	Harmonic amplitudes (frequency spectrum)	Equation
Square wave	$f(t)$, A_0, 0, $\frac{2\pi}{\omega}$, t	$\frac{4A_0}{\pi}$; 1, 3, 5, 7, n	$f(t) = \frac{4A_0}{\pi}(\sin \omega t + \frac{1}{3}\sin 3\omega t + \frac{1}{5}\sin 5\omega t + \cdots)$
Saw-tooth wave	$f(t)$, A_0, 0, $\frac{2\pi}{\omega}$, t	$\frac{2A_0}{\pi}$; 1, 2, 3, 4, 5, 6, 7, 8, n	$f(t) = \frac{2A_0}{\pi}(\sin \omega t - \frac{1}{2}\sin 2\omega t + \frac{1}{3}\sin 3\omega t - \frac{1}{4}\sin 4\omega t + \cdots)$
Triangular wave	$f(t)$, A_0, 0, $\frac{2\pi}{\omega}$, t	$\frac{8A_0}{\pi^2}$; 1, 3, 5, 7, n	$f(t) = \frac{8A_0}{\pi^2}(\sin \omega t - \frac{1}{3^2}\sin 3\omega t + \frac{1}{5^2}\sin 5\omega t - \cdots)$
Half-rectified wave	$f(t)$, A_0, 0, $\frac{2\pi}{\omega}$, t	$\frac{A_0}{2}$; 1, 2, 4, 6, 8, n	$f(t) = \frac{A_0}{2}(\frac{2}{\pi} + \cos \omega t + \frac{4}{3}\cos 2\omega t - \frac{4}{15}\cos 4\omega t + \frac{4}{35}\cos 6\omega t - \cdots)$

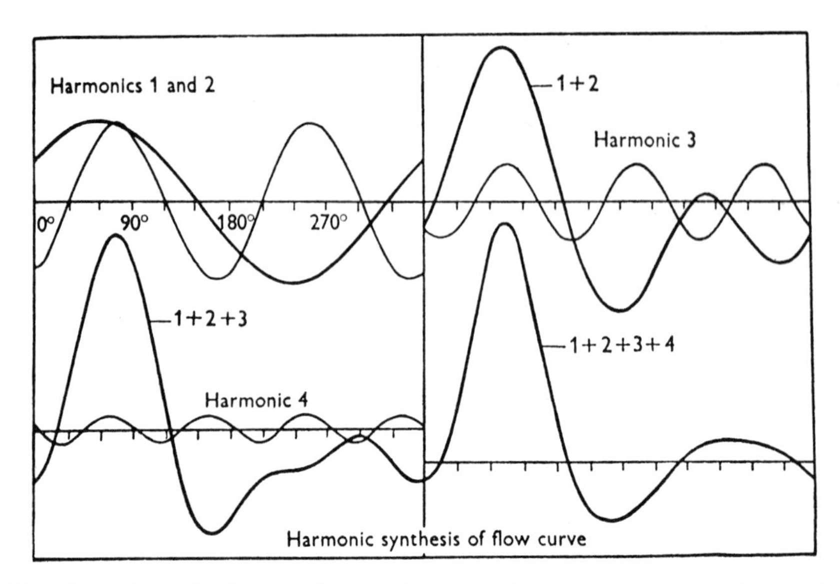

Figure 2.3. Synthesis of a blood-flow waveform in the femoral artery of a dog, showing the addition of the fundamental and three harmonics. The term $a_0/2$ (average flow) has been added to the final graph (reproduced, with permission, from D. A. McDonald, *Blood Flow in Arteries*, Arnold: London, 1960).

Methods of Analysis. The analysis of signals, and in particular the determination of the frequency spectrum of waveforms, provides important and often essential information for the proper design of a measuring system. It can also provide information about the system being measured in a form that can be more readily interpreted in terms of the physical processes involved. The applicability of the various methods developed for spectral analysis depends on the frequency range involved, the form in which the signal is available (analog or digital), and the nature of the signal (periodic or random). A brief discussion will be presented on the following four methods: (1) systems based on narrow-band analog filters, (2) systems based on the Fourier transform of the autocorrelation function, (3) digital techniques based on the fast Fourier transform (FFT), and (4) systems based on optical data processing.

The use of a series of narrow-band filters arranged to cover the frequency range of interest is perhaps the most straightforward (although expensive) means of spectral analysis and one that enables both random and periodic analog signals to be analyzed in real time. One such instrument of this type*

* General Radio 1921, Real-Time Analyzer: see *GR Experimenter*, **43**, May–June 1969.

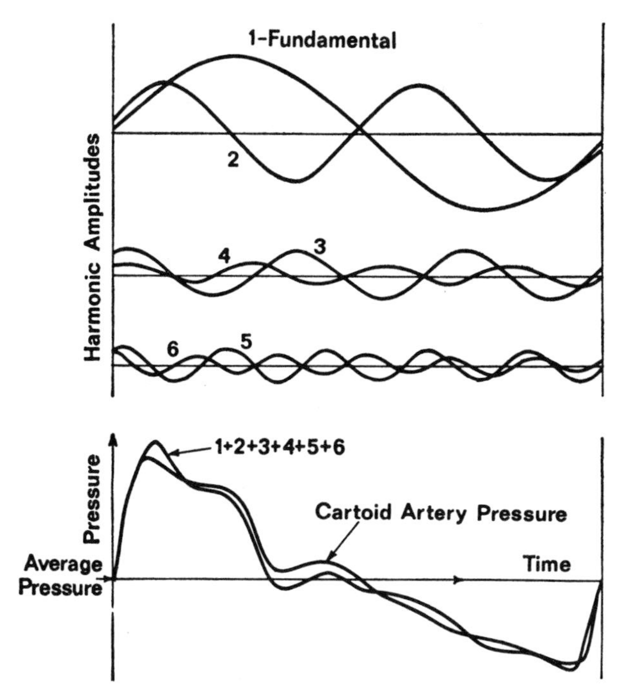

Figure 2.4. First six Fourier components obtained by analyzing the carotid artery pressure recording shown at the bottom. The synthesis of the six components is also shown to indicate how closely the six harmonics approximate the original recording (redrawn from A. T. Hansen, *Acta Physiol. Scand.*, **19**, Suppl. 68, 1–230 [1949]).

uses a series of $\frac{1}{3}$-octave filters to cover the range 3.15 Hz–80 kHz and employs a multiplexer and digital detector to measure the output from each filter in turn.

The need for a large number of precision filters can be avoided, at the expense of some increase in analysis time, by using a frequency-change system. In such a system the incoming signal is mixed with a signal from a variable-frequency oscillator. The sum or difference frequencies that result are then passed through a single narrow-band filter whose output is recorded. By changing the local oscillator frequency, various components of the signal spectrum can be selected and measured. In essence, such a system behaves like a tunable narrow-band filter, the center frequency of which is determined by the local oscillator. Through the use of a programmable local oscillator,*

* Hewlett-Packard Spectrum Analyzer Model 3580A; minimum bandwidth 1 Hz over a 5 Hz–50 kHz range: see *Hewlett-Packard Journal*, Sept. 1973.

the system can be automated, so that the center frequency of the "filter" is swept over the range of interest and a graph is produced showing the spectral characteristics of the signal.

In the second analysis scheme listed above, the spectrum is determined from the Fourier transform of the autocorrelation function. Now, the autocorrelation function of a periodic waveform of period T can be defined as

$$\phi(\tau) = \frac{1}{T}\int_0^T f(t) \cdot f(t - \tau)\, d\tau. \tag{3}$$

If $f(t)$ is given by Eq. (1), then it can be shown by substituting Eq. (1) into Eq. (3) that

$$\phi(\tau) = \frac{a_0{}^2}{4} + \frac{1}{2}\sum_{n=1}^{\infty} (a_n{}^2 + b_n{}^2) \cos n\omega\tau. \tag{4}$$

Now, the cosine Fourier transform of $\phi(\tau)$ is, by definition, given by

$$\Phi(n) = \frac{1}{T}\int_0^T \phi(\tau) \cos n\omega\tau\, d\tau. \tag{5}$$

By substituting Eq. (4) into Eq. (5), we find that

$$\Phi(n) = \frac{a_n{}^2 + b_n{}^2}{4}, \tag{6}$$

which is simply half the mean-square value of the nth harmonic amplitude. Hence, the process of finding the autocorrelation function and taking its Fourier transforms enables the spectral amplitudes to be determined. A commercial system,* based on these two operations, enables one to analyze a waveform in less than a minute.

Digital techniques that make use of either a general-purpose digital computer and an appropriate program or a machine designed specifically for the type of computations involved provide a powerful means for both one-line and off-line spectral analysis. Conversion of an analog input signal to digital form is usually accomplished by sampling the analog signal at regular intervals and converting the sampled amplitude to a digital form. Accurate results can be achieved if the sampling frequency is greater than twice the highest harmonic frequency of practical interest (see Section 3.4). The discrete Fourier transform, evaluated by means of the FFT algorithm, enables one to derive the spectrum from the sampled information. Although a full understanding of this technique is beyond the scope of this chapter, a qualitative understanding can be obtained from the following considerations [1, 2].

* Princeton Applied Research, Signal Correlator Model 100 combined with Model 102 Fourier Analyzer.

Equation (1) can be expressed in terms of complex numbers by making use of the relations

$$\begin{aligned} \cos n\omega t &= \tfrac{1}{2}(e^{jn\omega t} + e^{-jn\omega t}) \\ \sin n\omega t &= \tfrac{1}{2}(e^{jn\omega t} - e^{-jn\omega t}) \end{aligned} \tag{7}$$

which yields a compacted form of the Fourier series

$$f(t) = \sum_{n=-\infty}^{+\infty} A_n e^{jn\omega t}, \tag{8}$$

where the complex amplitudes A_n are given by

$$A_n = \frac{1}{T}\int_0^T f(t)e^{-jn\omega t}\,dt. \tag{9}$$

It can quite easily be shown that these amplitude terms are related to the real amplitude terms in Eq. (1) by

$$A_0 = \tfrac{1}{2}a_0, \qquad A_n = \tfrac{1}{2}(a_n \pm jb_n), \qquad |n| > 0,$$

where the minus sign applies for positive n and the plus sign applies when n is negative.

If N samples whose amplitudes are $x_k(k = 0, 1, 2, \ldots, N-1)$, are taken at regular intervals Δt, then Eq. (9) must be replaced by the sum

$$A_r = \frac{1}{N}\sum_{k=0}^{N-1} x_k \exp\left(\frac{-2\pi jkr}{N}\right), \tag{11}$$

where $r = 0, 1, 2, \ldots, N-1$. Evaluation of the amplitude A_r using Eq. (11) involves a series of multiplications and additions, in fact for $N/2$ harmonics it requires N^2 multiplications and additions. The FFT is an ingenious method for reducing the number of computations to $N \log_2 N$. The reduction is very significant when N is large, resulting in large savings in computer time. For example, with 1024 samples the number of calculations is reduced by more than 200 times. A number of special-purpose computers are commercially available that have an FFT algorithm built in and that can complete a spectral analysis in a matter of seconds—fast enough to meet the requirements of many real-time problems [3].

The final method to be discussed concerns the use of optical techniques, which potentially offer an economical means for the spectral analysis of recorded data. The method uses the Fourier transformation properties of optical lenses [4, 5]. Using either a photographic transparency or an accoustical diffraction cell, one can introduce the signal waveform to be analyzed at the input focal plane of the instrument. An output is obtained whose optical intensity is a measure of the spectral amplitude and whose displacement is a measure of the harmonic number.

2.1.2 Transient Signals

Like complex periodic waves, transients can also in principle be synthesized from sinusoidal waves. The major differences are that the spectrum is continuous instead of discrete and that although the amplitude of any individual frequency is zero, the "amount" of signal within a finite frequency range is nonzero. For a periodic signal the energy contained in the signal is composed of the energy content of a finite number of discrete frequencies that are harmonics of the fundamental. For a transient signal, if the energy content of a discrete frequency were nonzero, then, because of the infinite number of frequencies present, the energy content of the signal would be infinite. Hence, it follows that the amplitudes are zero, while the amount of signal within a bandwidth $\Delta\omega$ will be nonzero. We call the amount of signal the spectral density $g(\omega)$: it is analogous to the amplitude terms A_n contained in Eq. (9) and is, in general, a complex quantity defined by

$$g(\omega) = \int_{-\infty}^{+\infty} f(t)e^{-j\omega t}\,dt, \tag{12}$$

where $f(t)$ is the transient signal. Just as for the periodic signal, a transient can be reconstructed by integrating the spectral density over all frequencies; that is,

$$f(t) = \frac{1}{2\pi}\int_{-\infty}^{+\infty} g(\omega)e^{j\omega t}\,d\omega. \tag{13}$$

This expression is analogous to the complex Fourier series of a periodic wave as given by Eq. (8). Equations (12) and (13) form a Fourier transform pair [6]: Eq. (12) enables one to determine the frequency spectrum of a signal and perhaps to modify it by a filter, and Eq. (13) enables one to determine how the altered spectrum affects the signal shape. In brief, Eqs. (12) and (13) form the basis of examining the effects of a signal-conditioning system on the signal itself.

To illustrate the use of Eq. (12), we consider the unit amplitude square-wave transient pulse of duration $2T$ shown in Figure 2.5. By carrying out the integration demanded by (12) we find that the spectral density is given by

$$g(\omega) = 2T\left(\frac{\sin \omega t}{\omega t}\right),$$

which is sketched in Figure 2.5(*b*).

It will be noted that although both positive and negative frequencies are included in the graph, only the former have a physical meaning; negative frequencies are included for mathematical convenience.

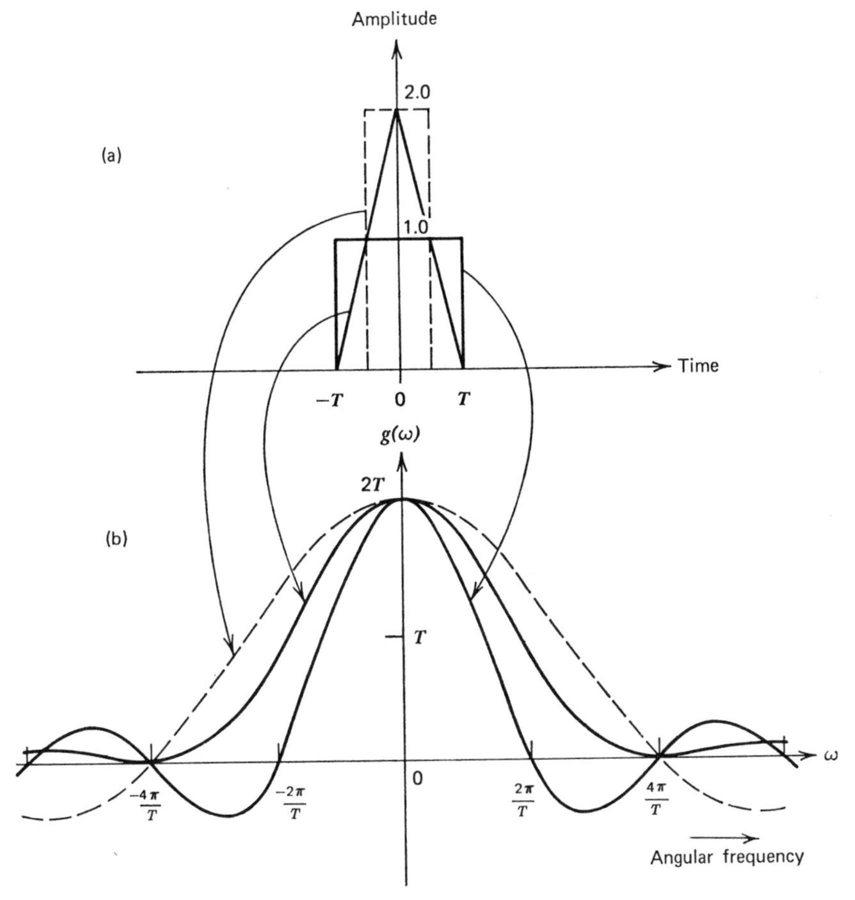

Figure 2.5. Comparison of the spectral densities of various transient pulses. The square pulses and triangular pulse have the same total energy: (a) pulse waveforms; (b) spectral densities.

Comparison of the spectrum of the triangular waveform with the square wave demonstrates the general feature that sharp changes in the waveforms tend to produce high-frequency components, thereby requiring larger signal bandwidths for proper signal processing.

2.1.3 Noise

Noise is present, at least to some extent, in all measuring systems and in all signal sources. It is usual to distinguish between noise of a random nature arising from basic physical processes [7] and noise caused by interference [8], which may or may not be correlated with the signal being measured. For example, one source of fundamental noise arises from statistical variations in the electron density in a conductor and will be present in all resistive elements. A frequent cause of interference noise is the electromagnetic or electrostatic interference arising from the presence of 60-Hz driven components.

Interference can usually be reduced and often virtually eliminated by careful electrostatic and magnetic shielding [7]; however, noise arising from basic physical phenomena usually sets a fundamental limit to the precision with which a given measurement can be performed. Generally the noise content increases as the signal bandwidth increases, so that for dynamic signals requiring large bandwidths special care may be required in the design to insure that the measurement system has an optimum noise performance.

If the sources of noise are uncorrelated to the signal, very significant reductions in the noise content of periodic signals can be achieved by using an averaging process. Averaging computers generally operate by sampling the signal a large number of times over its period and storing the results in digital form. The process is repeated for successive cycles and the new amplitudes

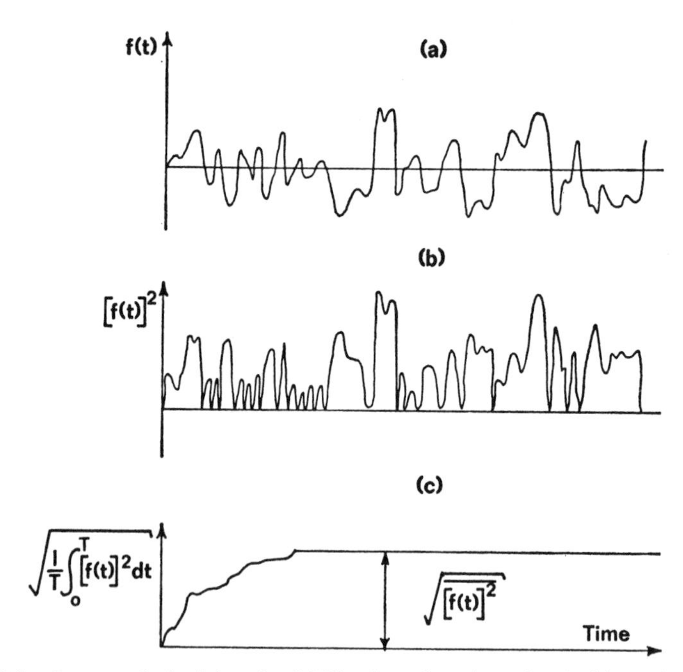

Figure 2.6. Process of obtaining the RMS value of random signal: (a) random signal; (b) square of (a); (c) RMS value.

are added to the previous ones, thereby enabling one to find the average sampled amplitude. Now random noise and uncorrelated interfering signals have an average value of zero, so that as the number of periods over which the signal is averaged is increased, so the signal–noise ratio is improved. In fact it can be shown that the ratio can be improved by as much as the square root of the number of sampling cycles. However, such an improvement can only be realized if the sync pulse responsible for initiating each cycle is properly locked to the signal being extracted.

A convenient measure of the noise amplitude is obtained by finding the square root of the mean-square value of the amplitude (RMS amplitude). By squaring the amplitude, all negative amplitudes become positive, so that the mean value of the amplitude squared is a nonzero quantity. This process is illustrated in Figure 2.6.

Although the RMS value indicates the noise amplitude it says nothing about its frequency content. This can be specified by a graph of the spectral density such as that shown in Figure 2.7. The graph is typical of many practical measurement systems in that it displays three distinct regions: a low-frequency region in which the mean-square noise varies as $1/f$, an intermediate-frequency region in which the noise spectrum is essentially flat, and a high-frequency region displaying an increasing noise spectrum. It is generally found that most components and systems display a low-frequency region in which the noise varies as $1/f^n$ (n is approximately unity). Typically, an amplifier may exhibit a noise spectrum in which the $1/f$ noise is dominant for frequencies less than a few kilohertz. At intermediate frequencies the noise may well be governed by thermal fluctuations in the electron density, giving rise to Johnson noise, which has a flat spectrum [7]; noise of this type is commonly referred to as *white noise*. As the frequency approaches the cutoff frequency

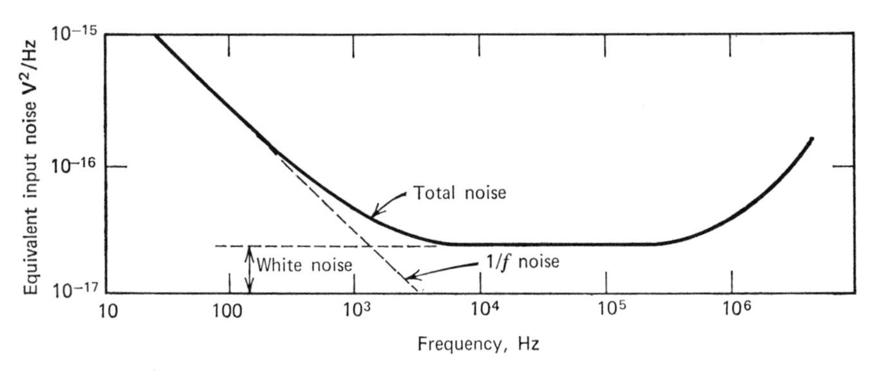

Figure 2.7. Frequency spectrum of the equivalent mean-square input voltage noise per cycle of bandwidth (spectral density) typical of a wide-band signal amplifier. The $1/f$ and white-noise components add to give the total spectral density.

of the amplifier, other processes come into play and an increasing noise amplitude is generally observed.

Of particular importance in the amplification of low-frequency signals or signals in which the dc component must be preserved is the $1/f$ noise. By modulating the input signal so as to convert it to a higher frequency, the amplifier can be used in a region where the $1/f$ component is less important. Once the signal has been amplified to an extent such that the noise generated by subsequent conditioning elements is no longer significant, the signal can be demodulated and the original, but amplified, signal can be recovered.

2.2 DYNAMIC CHARACTERISTICS OF SYSTEMS

A discussion of the characteristics and properties of signals leads naturally to a discussion of the systems or subsystems that are used to detect, process, and record them. Evidently it is of great importance to identify and quantify those system properties that affect the signal we are trying to measure, and to understand the possible interaction of one subsystem on another. To avoid the many sources of measurement error, it is necessary to specify a set of criteria to be met by the various subsystems. But before we can do this, methods must be discussed for quantitatively evaluating a system in terms of how it modifies the input signal, how it interacts with the signal source, and how it is affected by any output load.

For systems in which the input and output are linearly related (linear systems), such evaluations can best be performed by specifying the system *input impedance*, *output impedance*, and *input–output transfer function*. These quantities, which are the prime topic of this section, are most frequently employed in connection with electrical circuits and systems; however, they are also useful when applied to purely mechanical systems or systems of a hybrid nature.

By restricting our discussion to linear systems, the mathematical difficulties arising from the dynamic analysis of nonlinear systems are avoided. Nonlinearity, hysteresis, and backlash will be considered in Chapter 3 primarily as quasi-static phenomena; by superimposing the quasi-static and dynamic characteristics a rough measure of the overall system performance can be obtained.

2.2.1 Input–Output Transfer Function

The transfer function of a system, subsystem, or component relates the signal input to the signal output and provides a means whereby the output can be quantitatively evaluated for any given input. For a complex system made up of a number of interconnected parts, the transfer function of each part and a knowledge of their input and output characteristics enables one to calculate the complete system transfer function.

The transfer function can be expressed in two equivalent forms: an operational form and a sinusoidal form. In the operational form the transfer function can be used directly for calculating the response to transient input signals. On the other hand, the sinusoidal form is more appropriate for dealing with periodic waveforms. The general approach for this type of waveform is to analyze the input into its frequency components in the manner described in the previous section. Using the sinusoidal transfer function, the effect of the system on each component can be calculated, and by summing all the modified output components, the net output signal waveform can be predicted. This procedure is illustrated in Figure 2.8. Of course, the same type of approach can be used for a transient input; however, it turns out that it is simpler to make use of the operational form, for which type of problem the technique is expressly designed.

The sinusoidal transfer function of the system shown in Figure 2.9(a) can be measured by applying sinusoidal test inputs to the system and measuring the magnitude and phase of the output signal. The frequency-dependence of these quantities enable one to construct the two graphs shown in Figure

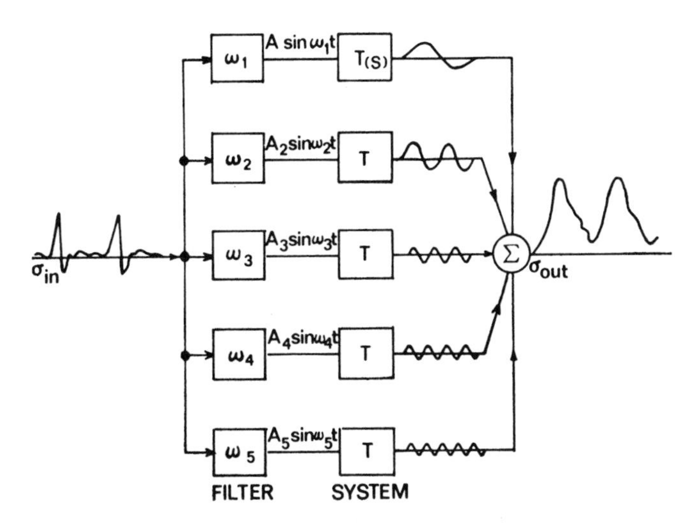

Figure 2.8. Effect of a system on a periodic input signal. The input is analyzed into its Fourier components; the effect of the system on each component is calculated and the system output is obtained from the component sum (from W.B. Blesser, *A Systems Approach to Biomedicine*; © 1969, McGraw-Hill Book Co.; used with permission of McGraw-Hill Book Co., New York).

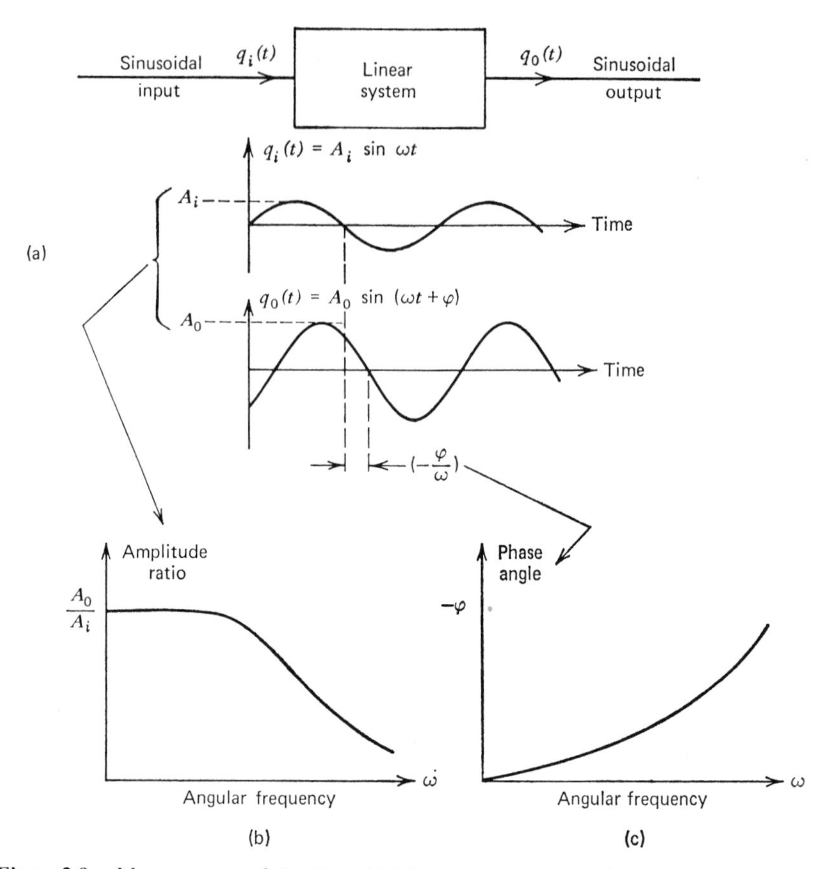

Figure 2.9. Measurement of the sinusoidal frequency response of a linear system. Curves (b) and (c) are obtained by repeating the measurement illustrated in (a), for various frequencies.

2.9(b) and (c). Taken together, these are called the *Bode plot* for the system, and they completely specify the system transfer function. Curve (b) is the *amplitude response* and curve (c) is the *phase response*.

Often the input–output relationships can be expressed in the form of a mathematical equation derived from a detailed analysis of the system components. In this form, the transfer function can be used to predict analytically the output for certain simple forms of input signal, and from this point of view, it is rather more convenient than the Bode plot.

The use of complex numbers enables the transfer function to be expressed in a compact, and often more convenient, form. For example, the transfer function of a pen-recorder system can be given by two expressions: one giving the magnitude of the pen-deflection–input-voltage ratio and the other giving the frequency-dependence of the phase angle between the input voltage and output deflection. Since a complex number can represent both the magnitude and phase angle of a quantity, it is not surprising that these two expressions can be combined to yield a single expression for the transfer function. Such an expression generally contains terms of the form $j\omega$; it can, if required, be readily split into its two component forms.

Zero-order Systems. Linear systems and their component parts can be classified, according to the complexity of their transfer function, into zero first, second, and higher-order systems. In general, the higher the order, the more complex will be the system's frequency response. A zero-order system, by definition, is a frequency-independent system in which the output and input are proportional. An example is the angular displacement-type transducer shown in Figure 2.10, which makes use of a variable resistor to attenuate the voltage by an amount proportional to the angular deflection. The transfer function is given by

$$\frac{V}{\theta} = \frac{V_B}{180}.$$

It can be considered to be a zero-order system if the changes in θ are sufficiently slow for the capacitive and inductive effects associated with the resistance to be neglected. Thus, while the system is, in fact, of a higher order, for the frequencies involved it can be considered a zero-order system. In fact, many higher-order systems can be approximated by a zero-order system if changes do not occur too rapidly or the frequencies involved are not too high.

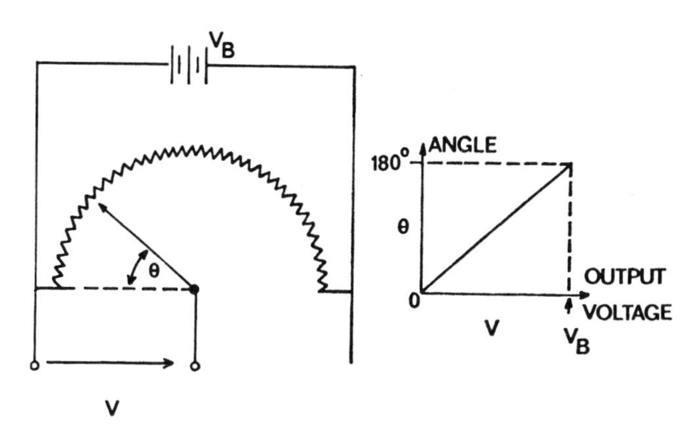

Figure 2.10. Angular displacement transducer: an example of a zero-order system.

First-order Systems. First-Order Systems generally contain a single energy-storage element and have a transfer function that can be expressed in the form,

$$F(j\omega) = \frac{k}{1 + j\omega\tau}, \tag{14}$$

where τ is the system time constant and k is a constant. From this equation we can find the magnitude of the output–input ratio and the phase angle. They are

$$|F(j\omega)| = \frac{k}{\sqrt{1 + \omega^2\tau^2}} \qquad \phi = \tan^{-1}(-\omega\tau), \tag{15}$$

which are plotted in Figure 2.11 on a log frequency scale.

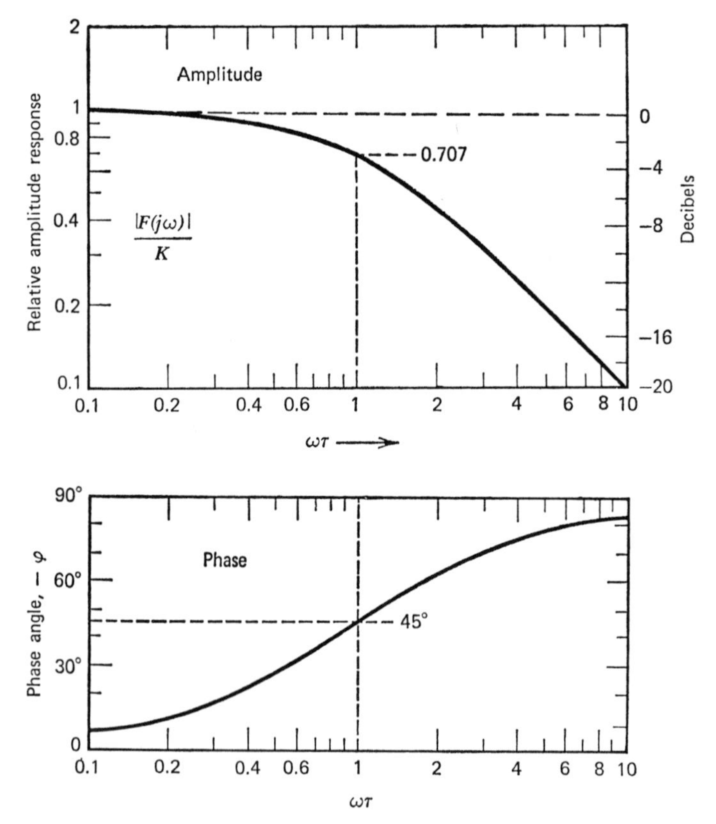

Figure 2.11. Amplitude and phase characteristics of a first order system.

A glass thermometer is a good example of a system that behaves in a first-order manner. If a thermometer is suddenly placed in a fluid at a higher temperature, heat will be transferred through the bulb and result in expansion of the filling fluid. Such a process takes time, resulting in a lag between the *step change* in temperature and the indicated change. In fact this transient process, like all first-order processes, involves an exponential dependence of the output quantity on time:

$$(\Delta T)_{\text{ind}} = \Delta T(1 - e^{-t/\tau}) = \Delta T - \Delta T e^{-t/\tau}, \tag{16}$$

which is plotted in Figure 2.12. The response to a step change in temperature ΔT is exponential, the exponent being determined by the thermal *time constant* τ for the system. The first term on the RHS of Eq. (16) is the *forced* response, and the second term, the *natural* response. It is generally true that the natural response of a first-order system is exponential in form, the time constant being given by the transfer-function expression. The forced response term is determined by the boundary conditions (i.e., the magnitude and direction of the step change in temperature). In fact, the forced term can be zero if the proper boundary conditions are present. Such occurs when the thermometer is plunged into a bath at 0°C, resulting in an indicated temperature

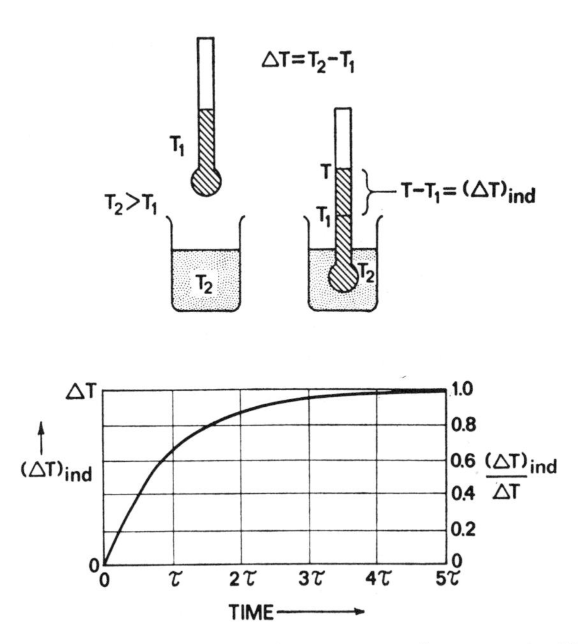

Figure 2.12. Example of a first-order transient process: a thermometer subjected to a step change in temperature $\Delta T = T_2 - T_1$.

that has an initial value of $(T)_{\text{init}}$ a final value of 0°C, and time variation given by

$$(T)_{\text{ind}} = (T)_{\text{init}} e^{-t/\tau}.$$

Although the time taken to reach exactly 0°C is infinite, in practice one is concerned with the time to reach a given percentage of the initial value, perhaps 1%. In fact, to reach this value takes approximately five time constants.

Second-order Systems. Although a number of practical examples of first-order systems exist, most systems are of a second or higher order. Fortunately, however, these higher-order systems can generally be approximated by an equivalent second-order system, making the analysis of second-order systems doubly important. Basically, second-order systems have a sinusoidal transfer function of the form

$$F(j\omega) = \frac{k}{(j\omega/\omega_n)^2 + 2\xi j(\omega/\omega_n) + 1}, \tag{17}$$

where ω_n is the *natural angular frequency* of the system and ξ is the *damping ratio.* Physical insight into the meaning of ω_n and ξ can be obtained by considering a specific example. One such example is a car suspension system in which the springs of the suspension tend to restore the car back to an equilibrium position after it has hit a bump in the road. If the shock absorbers are not working, the car tends to oscillate after hitting a bump, with a frequency that is independent of the magnitude of the bump. However, if the shock absorbers are operating, the system quickly restores equilibrium; that is, the system is damped by the shock-absorber action, the degree of damping being measured by the value of ξ.

Before examining the transient response in any more detail, we shall first take a brief look at the frequency response by expressing Eq. (17) in terms of the magnitude and phase of the transfer function:

$$\begin{aligned} |F(j\omega)| &= \frac{k}{\{[1 - (\omega/\omega_n)^2]^2 + 4\xi^2(\omega/\omega_n)^2\}^{1/2}} \\ \phi &= \tan^{-1}\left\{\frac{2\xi}{\omega/\omega_n - \omega_n/\omega}\right\}. \end{aligned} \tag{18}$$

These two equations are plotted in Figure 2.13 for various values of the damping constant ξ, using a logarithmic scale to plot the ratio ω/ω_n. It will be noted that as the damping constant approaches zero, the amplitude ratio becomes very large in the neighborhood of the natural frequency ($\omega/\omega_n \simeq 1$). Under these circumstances the exciting frequency causes resonance to occur

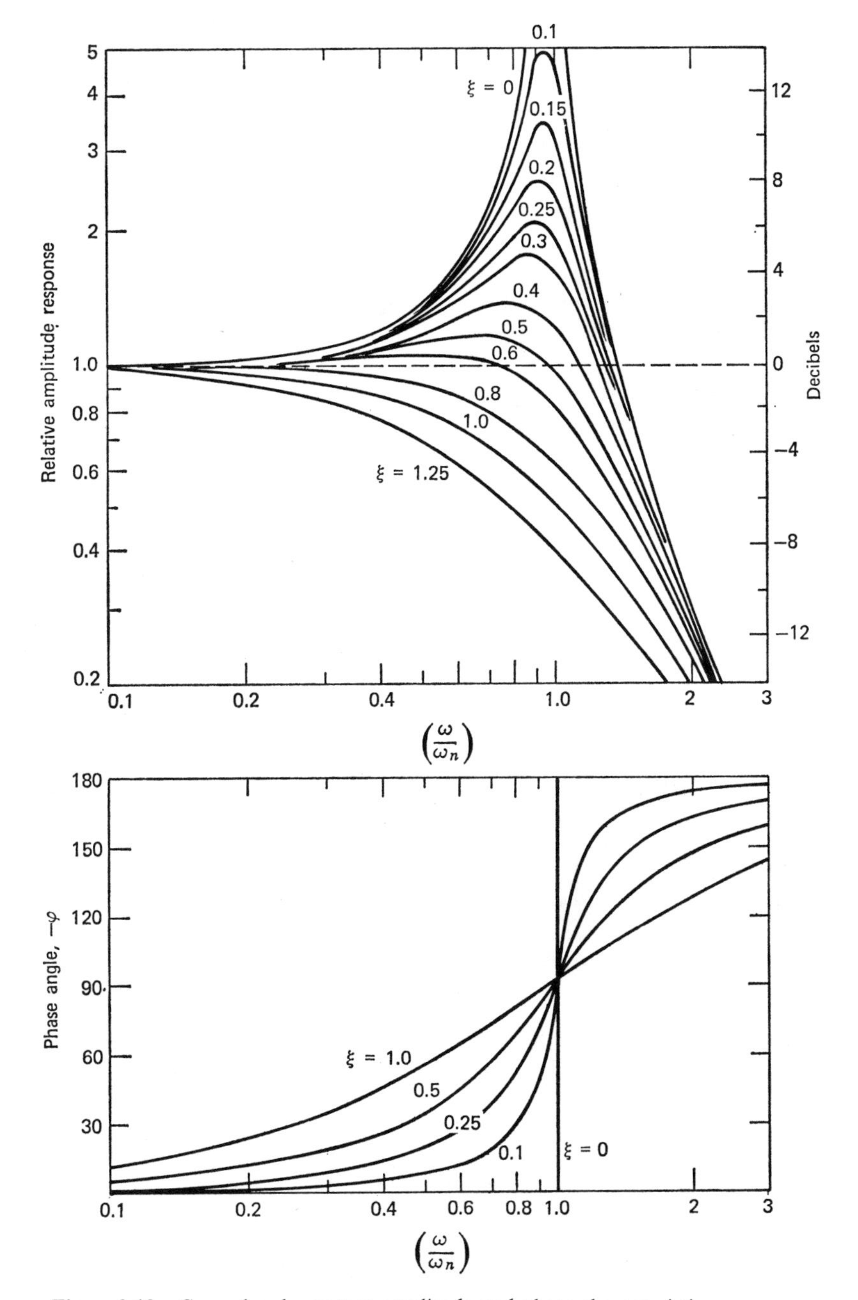

Figure 2.13. Second-order system amplitude and phase characteristics.

in the system. This can be avoided by increasing ξ, in fact, all traces of this resonance effect disappear when $\xi \geqslant 1$.

Perhaps the response of a second-order system to a transient, such as a step function, gives a better insight into the significance of ξ and ω_n. Like the first-order system, the transient response of the second-order system consists of a natural response and a forced response; however, in general, the natural response is rather more complex. As an example, we consider an ammeter consisting of a moving coil suspended in a fixed magnetic field. If such a system has no damping other than that resulting from friction at the bearings, the sudden application of a current to the meter will result in an angular rotation of the pointer. The total movement can be considered to be composed of a damped oscillatory change (the natural response) superimposed on a step change (forced response), as illustrated in Figure 2.14. The time taken for the deflection to settle to its final value is evidently greatly increased by the poorly damped oscillation. It can be reduced by increasing the system damping through the addition of a resistance across the meter (resistive damping) or by using eddy currents induced in a metal plate (eddy-current damping).

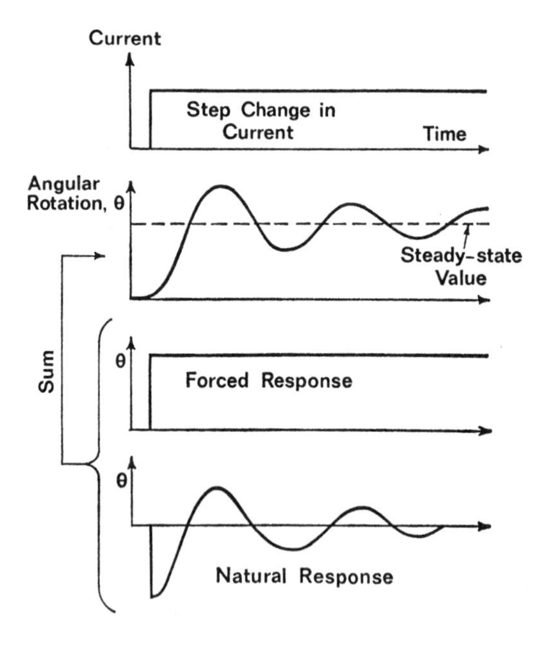

Figure 2.14. Response of a poorly damped meter to a step change in current. The forced component of the meter angular deflection determines the final steady-state value; the natural response gives the decaying oscillatory motion.

The general step response characteristics of a second-order system are shown in Figure 2.15 for various damping constants: when $\xi > 1$, the system is overdamped; when $\xi = 1$, it is critically damped (no overshoot); and when $\xi < 1$, it is underdamped. Such a wide variation in the step-response characteristics suggests that some carefully chosen definitions are required to provide a practical measure of the transient response. These are explained in Figure 2.16.

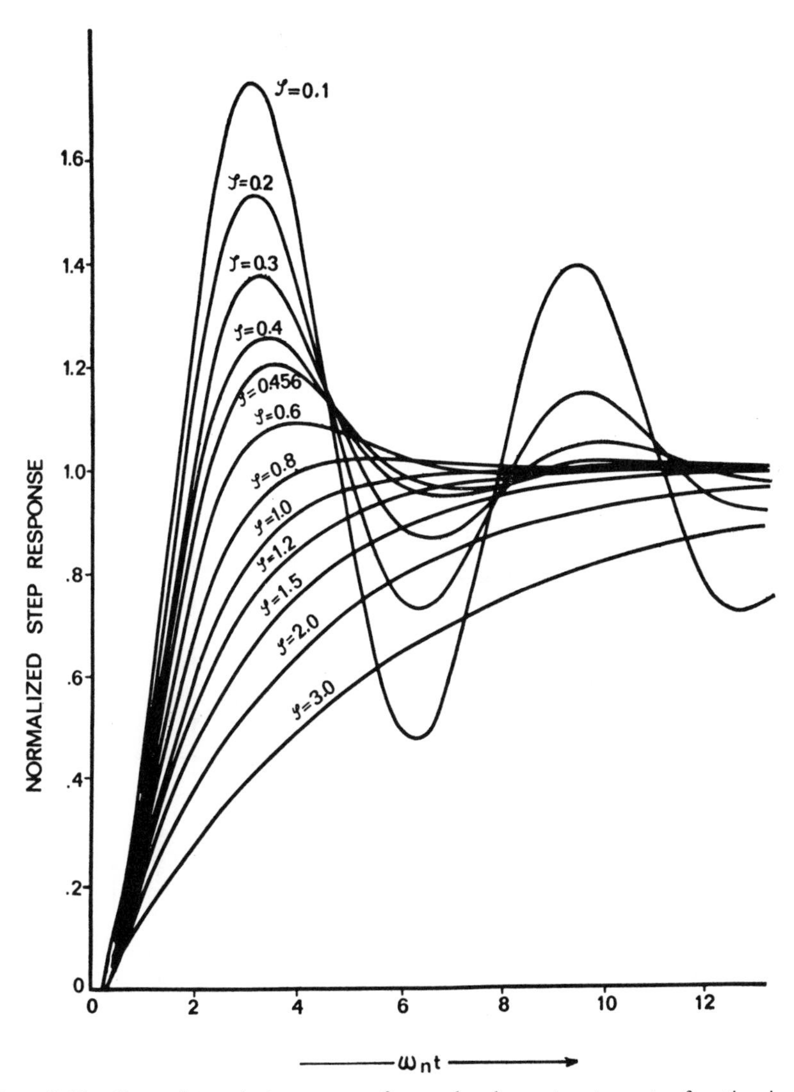

Figure 2.15. General transient response of second-order system to a step-function input waveform.

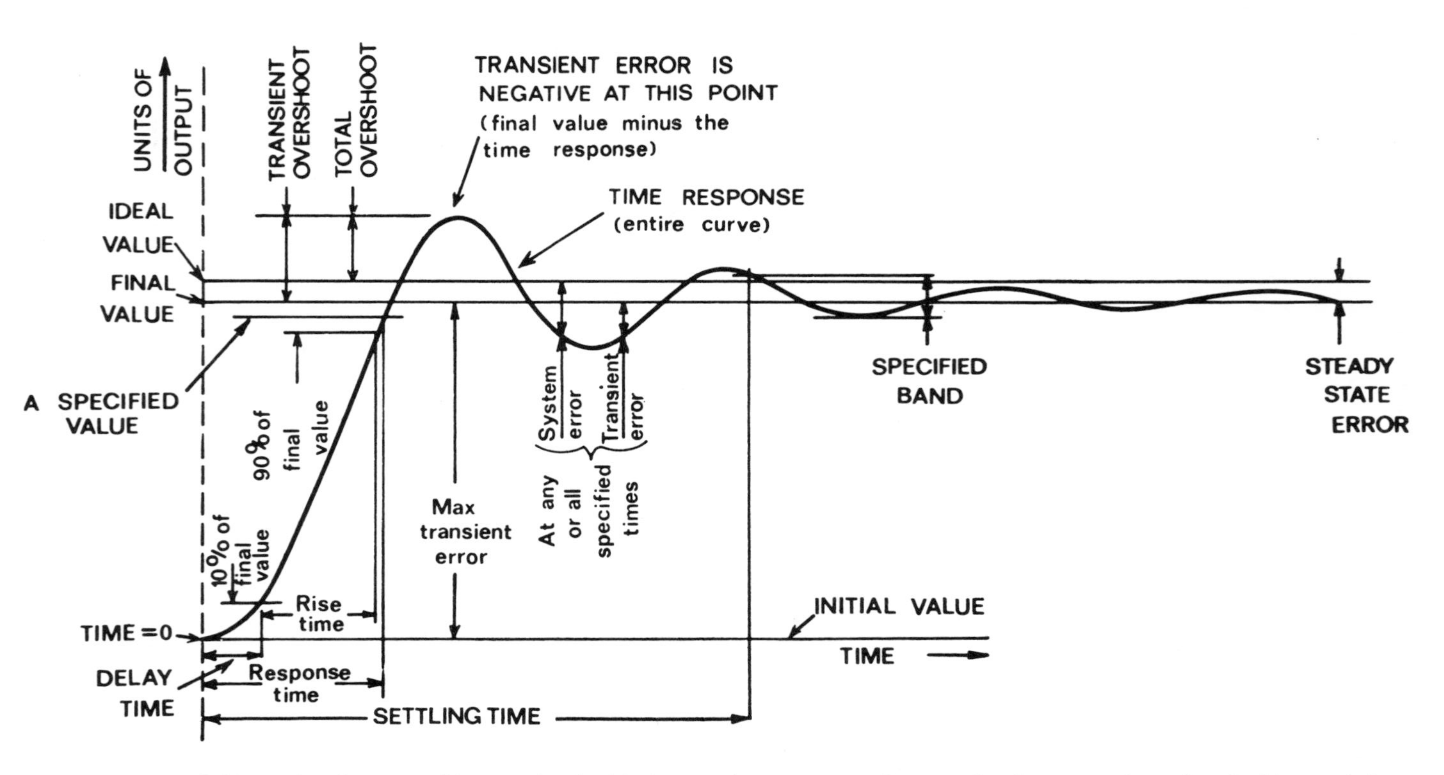

Figure 2.16. Definitions of various quantities associated with the transient response of a second-order system (reproduced with permission, from R. H. Cerni and L. E. Foster, *Instrumentation for Engineering Measurement*, Wiley: New York, 1962).

The *settling time* is defined as the time required for the system to settle within a given percentage of its final value. For the basic second-order system the settling time for a $\pm 5\%$ margin is a minimum when $\xi \simeq 0.7$ and is approximately equal to $3/\omega_n$. Another commonly used parameter that indicates how quickly a system responds is the *rise time*, defined as the time for the system to change from 10% to 90% of the final value. For a first-order system it is very nearly equal to 2τ, but for a basic second-order system it increases as ξ is increased, being approximately $2/\omega_n$ when $\xi = 0.7$. Since the rise time for a second-order system does not indicate the degree of overshoot, the $\pm 5\%$ settling time is a rather more meaningful way of indicating the transient response.

2.2.2 Input and Output Impedances

In general, the input–output transfer function of a system is affected by the conditions existing at the input and output ports, so that a meaningful specification of the transfer function must also include a statement as to what these conditions are. In a pump, for example, the throughput may well be affected by changes in pressure at the input and output ports. Thus, a proper specification of the performance should include graphs showing the variation of throughput with input and output port pressures. In a generalized system these pressures correspond to the input and output load conditions.

To avoid errors arising from improper matching between systems, it is essential that the terminal properties of each component system be properly understood. Mismatch errors commonly take the form of a frequency-dependent signal attenuation, but under extreme conditions nonlinear distortion can also occur. While attenuation between parts of a system arising from improper matching can usually be corrected, improper matching between the signal source and the transducer can be especially troublesome when the source impedance is unstable. The reason for this is simply that it becomes impossible to distinguish whether an apparent signal variation is caused by a source impedance variation or a true signal variation. In such a situation it is important to design the transducer in such a way that its effect on the signal source can be neglected.

Quantities that conveniently characterize the input and output properties of most systems are the generalized *input impedance* and *output impedance*. Although these quantities are usually associated with purely electrical systems, they can also be conveniently applied to mechanical and hydraulic systems. Thus, one speaks of the mechanical input and output impedances. Formally, the generalized impedance Z is defined by

$$Z = \frac{\text{Generalized effort}}{\text{Generalized flow}}, \tag{19}$$

which, in general, is a complex quantity, since the effort and flow may be out of phase. Thus, Z has a magnitude and phase the values of which may be frequency-dependent.

For an electrical system, Z is the ratio of the voltage (effort) to the current (flow), and the input impedance can be found by applying a known sinusoidal emf to the input and measuring the input current. Similarly the output impedance can be found by applying an emf to the output terminals and measuring the output current.

In the case of a hydraulic system the impedance is the ratio of the pressure (effort) to the volumetric flow rate (flow). Thus, for example, the input impedance of a pressure transducer system using hydraulic coupling via a catheter can be measured by applying a sinusoidal pressure to the fluid and measuring the resultant sinusoidal fluid flow. Since the presence of fluid flow causes distortion, it is evidently desirable that such a system should have a large input impedance. At very low frequencies the volumetric flow rate becomes small and difficult to measure, so that it is useful to define another quantity, the *static compliance*, which can be readily measured and which also characterizes the transducer input property. The static compliance for this system is simply the volumetric fluid displacement divided by the pressure and is the direct analog of the electrical capacitance ($C = Q/V$). Just as for an electrical system that has a purely capacitive input impedance, it is sufficient, when specifying the input characteristics, simply to state the input capacitance, so with the hydraulic system described above it is sufficient to state the input compliance.

To illustrate the effect of the measuring system on the quantity being measured we consider the measurement of a periodic bioelectric signal by means of electrodes connected to an amplifier having an input impedance Z_{in}. If the electrodes and conducting path through the tissue can be represented by an impedance Z_s as illustrated in Figure 2.17, then the ratio of the measured

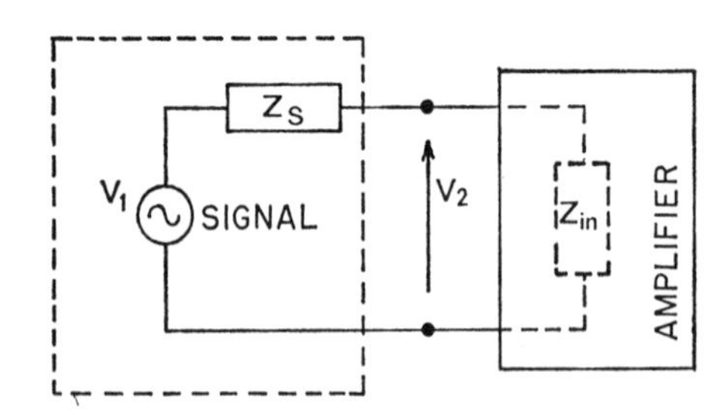

Figure 2.17. Biopotential measurement illustrating the loading effect of Z_s and Z_{in} on the voltage V_2.

voltage (voltage at the amplifier terminals) to the undisturbed voltage is given by

$$\frac{\text{Measured voltage}}{\text{Undisturbed voltage}} = \frac{1}{(Z_s/Z_{in}) + 1} \tag{20}$$

if V_1 is sinusoidal. Since the signal is periodic, it can be represented by the sum of a series of sinusoidal voltages. For each component Eq. (20) can be evaluated enabling the resultant voltage V_2 to be found by summation. When both Z_s and Z_{in} are purely resistive, Eq. (20) gives the instantaneous measured voltage directly.

An important point to be noted from Eq. (20) is that to avoid any measurement correction Z_{in} must be much greater than Z_s for all frequencies of practical interest. If this is not possible, then it is important that Z_s be constant during the course of the measurement and that its value be known to an accuracy that increases as Z_s approaches Z_{in}.

REFERENCES

1. Cochran, W. T.; Cooley, J. W.; Favin, D. L.; Helms, H. D.; Kaenel, R. A.; Lang, W. W.; Maling, G. C.; Nelson, D. E.; Rader, C. M.; and Welch, P. D. "What is the Fast Fourier Transform." *Proc. IEEE*, **55**, 1664–1674 (October 1967).
2. Bergland, G. D. "A Guided Tour of the Fast Fourier Transform." *IEEE Spectrum*, **7**, 41–52 (July 1969).
3. Bergland, G. D. "Fast Fourier Transform Hardware Implementations—A Survey." *IEEE Trans. Audio Electroacoustics*, **AU-17**, 109–119 (June 1969).
4. Preston, K. "Use of the Fourier Transformable Properties of Lenses for Signal Spectrum Analysis," in J. T. Tippett et al., Eds., *Optical and Electro-optical Information Processing*. MIT Press: Cambridge, Mass., 1965, pp. 59–68.
5. Goodman, J. W. *Introduction to Fourier Optics*. McGraw-Hill: New York, 1968
6. Papoulis, A. *The Fourier Integral and Its Application*. McGraw-Hill: New York 1962.
7. MacDonald, D. K. C. *Noise and Fluctuations: An Introduction*. Wiley: New York, 1962.
8. Morrison, R. *Grounding and Shielding Techniques in Instrumentation*. Wiley: New York, 1967.

CHAPTER THREE

Criteria for Error-Free Measurements

In making a biomedical measurement with the help of a transducer, one can identify three basic sources of possible error. The first arises from the procedure required to place the transducer in the required position for making the measurement. For instance, the placement of a pressure transducer within the vessel of an animal may require surgery involving anesthesia. If the measurement has to be carried out while the animal is anesthetized, the physiological effects of the anesthesia may seriously disturb the pressure from its normal value. A second source of error arises from the presence of the transducer itself. In the case of an implanted pressure transducer, this can arise from the transducer size interfering with the flow and thereby affecting the pressure. Finally, errors can arise from the characteristics of the transducer itself and subsequent signal conditioning circuits. It is this latter source of error that will be examined most closely in this chapter.

Our previous discussion of the input–output transfer function and the input and output impedances enables us to consider in a meaningful way the criteria to be satisfied for the faithful measurement of dynamic signals using a perfectly linear system. Generally speaking, it is difficult to account fully for dynamic effects arising from system nonlinearities, but what can be done is to consider the nonlinearity as a quasi-static phenomenon and to superimpose the resulting effects on the linear dynamic effects. In essence, this assumes that the nonlinear effects are small.

3.1 QUASI-STATIC EFFECTS

3.1.1 Linearity

A useful measure of the performance of a system can be obtained by measuring the input–output *amplitude characteristics* at a sufficiently low frequency for any frequency-dependent effects to be unimportant. Such a measurement may yield a static calibration curve similar to that illustrated in Figure 3.1. The slope of this curve at any point is the *sensitivity*. It is usually desirable that the curve be linear so that the sensitivity will be independent of the input amplitude. For a static calibration curve that is close to linear, it is usual to define the sensitivity as the slope of the least-squares fit straight line.

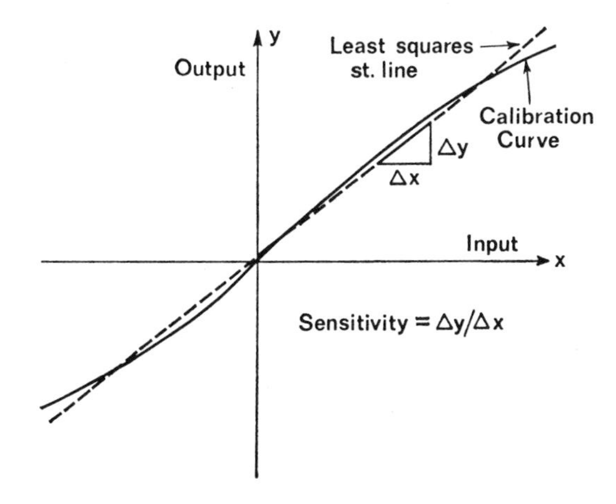

Figure 3.1. Static calibration curve: definition of sensitivity.

Since most systems depend to some degree on environmental factors such as temperature, pressure, humidity, it may also be necessary to specify the change in sensitivity with the most significant of these factors. Thus, for example, as illustrated in Figure 3.2, the change in sensitivity of a pressure transducer might be quoted for a change in nominal operating temperature, thereby enabling the sensitivity to be calculated for a different temperature.

An additional important aspect of the static calibration curve is the zero offset and the change in zero offset with environment. Many instruments have a means of zero-offset correction to enable the calibration curve to be shifted so that, for example, it passes through the origin. Naturally one is interested

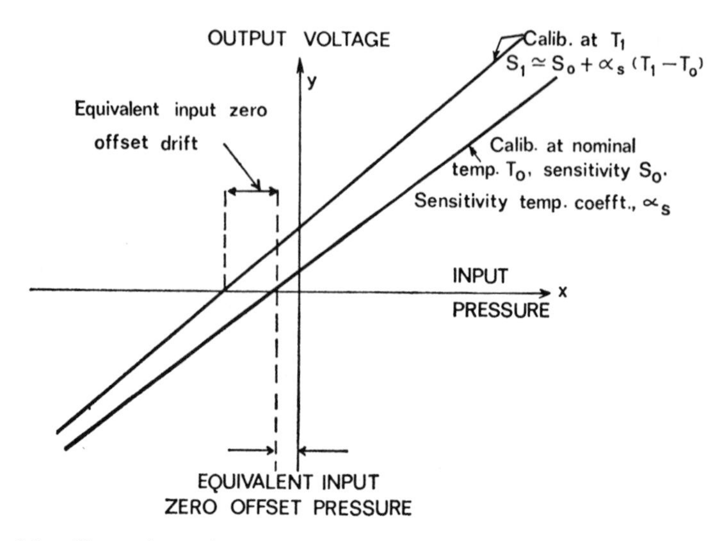

Figure 3.2. Change in sensitivity and offset with temperature for a pressure transducer.

in knowing how this can be expected to change in the course of time, and so, it is often appropriate to quote its temperature coefficient and perhaps stability. This can be most conveniently done by expressing it in terms of the equivalent input drift. Thus, for example, a pressure transducer might have an equivalent offset drift of 0.1 mmHg/°C, and a long-term stability at the same operating temperature of 0.05 mmHg/h. To be meaningful, such figures must also be accompanied by a statement specifying the conditions under which the transducer is operating.

The nonlinearity of a static calibration curve is evidently of considerable importance. A convenient way in which it can be defined is, as illustrated in Figure 3.3, through the maximum deviation of the calibration curve from the least-squares straight line, expressed as a percentage of the full-scale input:

$$\% \text{ nonlinearity} = \left(\frac{\text{Maximum input deviation}}{\text{Full-scale input}}\right) \times 100. \tag{1}$$

Although this is a useful measure of a system performance, it does not enable the effects of the nonlinearity to be quantitatively evaluated for dynamic signals. To do so requires a more detailed knowledge of the nonlinearity.

If hysteresis effects are absent, the amplitude characteristics can generally be represented by an equation of the form

$$y = a_0 + a_1 x + a_2 x^2 + a_3 x^3 + \cdots, \tag{2}$$

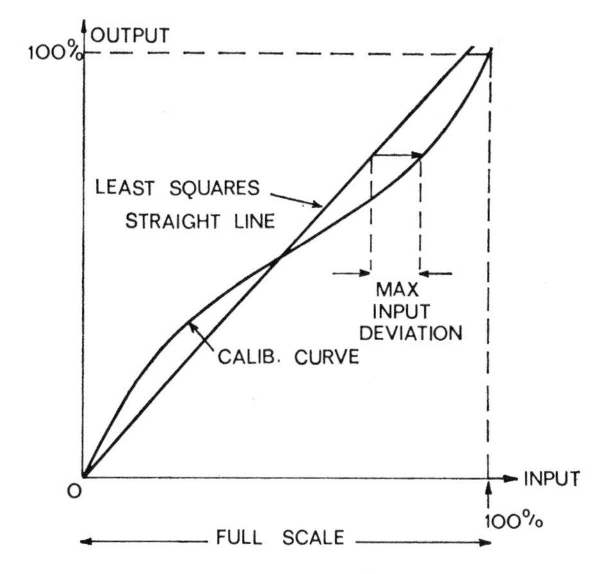

Figure 3.3. Definition of nonlinearity.

where x and y are the input and output amplitudes, respectively, and a_0, $a_1, \ldots$ are constants whose values depend on the exact form of the characteristics. The term a_0 is the output zero offset, a_1 is the sensitivity at $x = 0$, and the terms $a_2, a_3, \ldots$ express the nonlinearity of the characteristic. As illustrated in Figure 3.4, the presence of only odd powers of x results in a symmetrical curve: $y(x) = -y(-x)$; even terms always result in asymmetry.

To examine the effects of this type of characteristic on a dynamic signal we consider the sinusoidal input waveform $x = x_m \sin \omega t$. By substituting this into Eq. (2) and expanding the power terms, we find that the output contains harmonics of ω according to the relation

$$y = a_0 + A_0 + A_1 \sin \omega t + A_2 \sin 2\omega t + A_3 \sin 3\omega t + \cdots + A_n \sin n\omega t + \cdots, \qquad (3)$$

where the constants $A_2, A_4, A_6, \ldots$ are zero if the even powers of x are zero in Eq. (2) and $A_3, A_5, \ldots$ are zero when the odd powers of x are zero.

The presence of nonlinearity can be particularly serious if it is desired to carry out Fourier analysis of a periodic waveform. The harmonics generated by the lower-frequency components can seriously affect the measurements at the higher frequencies, where it is impossible to distinguish between harmonics generated by nonlinear effects and the true harmonics of the signal waveform.

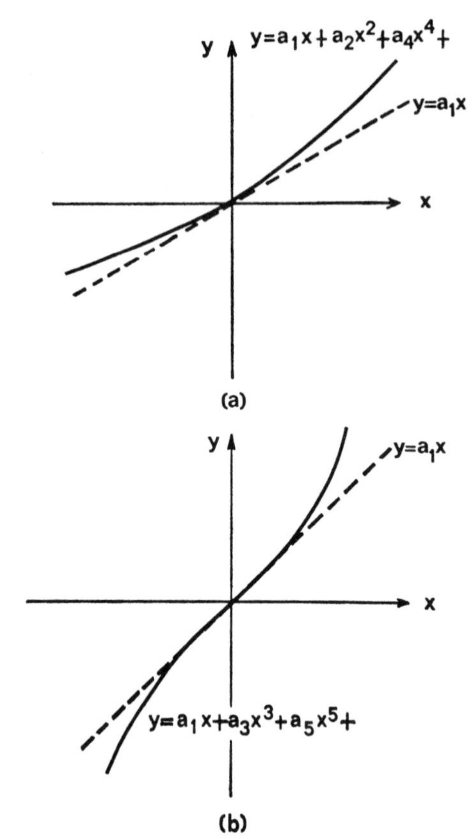

Figure 3.4. Examples of (a) asymmetrical and (b) symmetrical static calibration curves.

A useful measure of the harmonic distortion is the *distortion factor* defined by

$$D = \sqrt{\left|\frac{A_2}{A_1}\right|^2 + \left|\frac{A_3}{A_1}\right|^2 + \left|\frac{A_4}{A_1}\right|^2 + \cdots}. \tag{4}$$

It is zero in the absence of distortion and increases as the harmonic distortion increases. When multiplied by 100, it gives the total percentage of harmonic distortion.

The nonlinearity of a measurement system can sometimes be significantly reduced by making use of a differential measurement system. For example, suppose a displacement transducer has an output given by

$$Y_1 = a_0 + a_1 x + a_2 x^2 + a_3 x^3 + a_4 x^4 + \cdots.$$

If a second, identical transducer is used but is connected so that it is displaced in the opposite direction, then its output for the same displacement will be

$$Y_2 = a_0 - a_1 x + a_2 x^2 - a_3 x^3 + a_4 x^4 - \cdots.$$

The difference in the two outputs is

$$\Delta Y = Y_1 - Y_2 = 2(a_1 x + a_3 x^3 + a_5 x^5 + \cdots). \tag{5}$$

Thus, by using the transducers in a differential mode the linearity is improved through the elimination of the even terms (and even harmonics), the zero offset is eliminated, and the sensitivity is doubled. Such advantages make differential-type transducers very desirable.

3.1.2 Hysteresis

To describe the multitude of effects that result in the output of a system depending on the past history of the input, the concept of *hysteresis* is introduced. It can occur in both electrical and mechanical systems. Electrically, it may result from the B–H curve hysteresis of magnetic material, though it can result from instability effects in other nonmagnetic components. In mechanical systems, hysteresis results from energy being absorbed by the system during loading and not being recovered during unloading; that is, the loading and unloading characteristics differ as illustrated in Figure 3.5. Hysteresis characteristics also result from backlash in mechanical coupling; elastic aftereffects; and viscous flow, or creep.

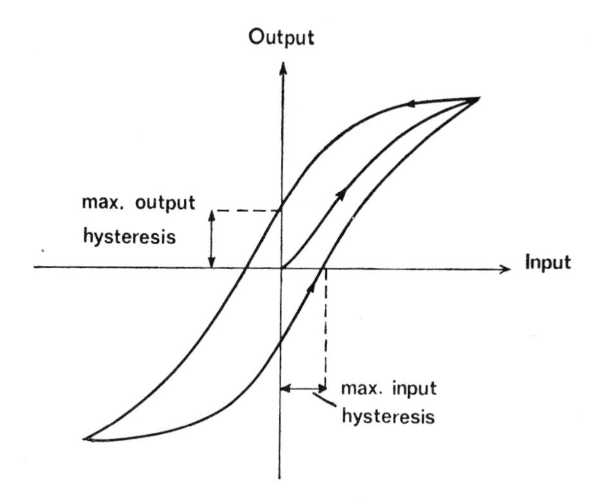

Figure 3.5. An example of hysteresis effect.

In the absence of backlash, hysteresis losses generally decrease rapidly with decreasing signal amplitude. Hence, it would seem desirable to design the system with a small full-scale input amplitude. On the other hand, both noise and backlash are normally independent of the signal level, so that their effect on the output signal becomes more significant as the full-scale amplitude is decreased. Evidently a compromise is necessary to minimize the total distortion. A further effect of considerable importance arises from transient overloads. Even with the most carefully designed experiment, it is sometimes impossible to avoid transient input signals that grossly overload the system. In the presence of hysteresis, such signals can permanently affect the static calibration. Their effects can be avoided by providing a means of limiting the input excursion to a value just beyond the design value of the full-scale input amplitude.

3.2 AMPLITUDE DISTORTION

In general the frequency bandwidth of the system should be somewhat greater than that of the signal. Further, the amplitude response should normally be flat and reasonably free of resonant peaks, preferably with a damping factor in the range 0.6–0.8. This gives a reasonable compromise between a fast rise time and freedom from amplitude distortion.

For measurements in which significant noise originates either from the signal source or the transducer–signal-conditioner system, too wide a bandwidth can be a disadvantage in that the extra bandwidth contributes little to the signal but lets through extra noise, thereby making the signal–noise ratio worse. It would thus seem desirable to tailor the system bandwidth so as to carefully match that of the signal. However, this solution is not without its difficulties. It will be noted that in the region in which the amplitude response of a system decreases, the phase angle between the input and output also undergoes a rapid change. Such a phase shift can by itself introduce distortion of the signal waveform. A simple method to avoid this is to insure that the system bandwidth is much greater than the signal. If noise considerations dictate that this is not possible, careful consideration must also be given to the *phase distortion*.

3.3 PHASE DISTORTION

Phase distortion occurs when the phase angle between the input and output depends nonlinearly on frequency. A linear phase angle versus frequency characteristic by itself introduces no distortion of a signal: it simply serves to displace the output in time. As illustrated in Figure 3.6, the output will

AMPLITUDE

PHASE ANGLE

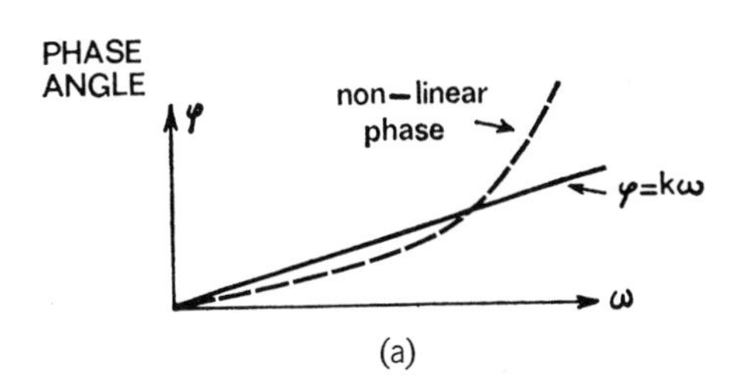

(a)

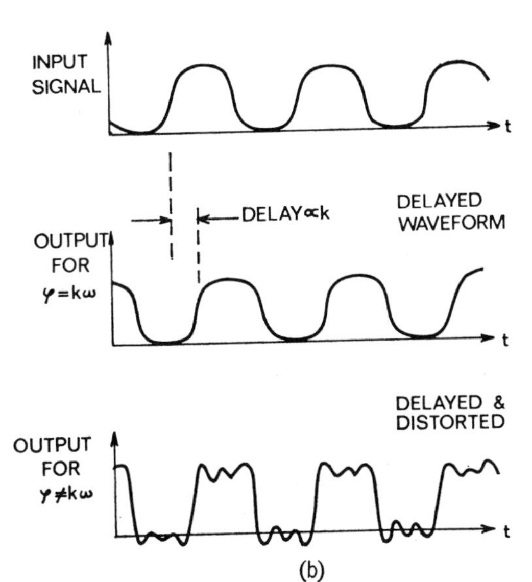

(b)

Figure 3.6. Illustrating the effect of phase distortion in the absence of amplitude distortion: (a) system characteristics; (b) showing the effects of a linear and nonlinear phase characteristic on a periodic signal.

then be identical to that with zero phase angle but delayed in time by an amount that depends on the slope of the phase characteristic. A nonlinear phase characteristic results in the output-signal spectral components having the wrong time relationship, thereby distorting the output signal, as demonstrated by the lower waveform in Figure 3.6(b).

In multichannel recordings in which the time relationship between the signals recorded on separate channels is significant (such as occurs in EEG measurements), it is important that each channel have exactly the same amplitude and phase characteristic. This is especially important if the signal frequency spectrum is greater than that of the output transducer.

3.4 SAMPLING ERRORS

The process of digitizing an analog signal normally involves sampling the signal at a fixed frequency and converting the sampled amplitude into the required digital format. To convert the digital signal back into analog form requires the reconstruction of the sampled amplitude and the use of a filter or other means for interpolating between successive sampled amplitudes. If the error involved in converting the sampled amplitude into digital code and back again into an amplitude can be neglected, then the only sources of error are those arising from the sampling process and from the means of reconstructing the analog signal from the sampled amplitudes. Under these circumstances it is important to know what sampling frequency should be chosen so that the RMS error between the original signal and that reconstructed will not exceed a given value.

Although the sampling theorem dictates the minimum sampling frequency to be used (two f samples per second for a frequency f) under ideal conditions, it is of little use in determining the sampling frequency required for a practical system and for a signal that contains a spectrum of frequencies. Furthermore, if a signal has spectral components beyond those of practical interest, aliasing or foldover errors can occur that result in errors in the reconstructed waveform at the frequencies of interest.

Aliasing errors can perhaps best be understood through the use of a graphical example of the sampling and reconstruction of two sinusoidal waveforms. Figure 3.7 shows two sine wave signals, one having a frequency of 1/8 of the sampling frequency, f_s, the other being $7f_s/8$. It can be seen that both waveforms give rise to identical sampled data, which reconstructs to a frequency of $f_s/8$. The frequency at which the erroneous signal is produced can be found by simply "folding over" all frequencies of greater than $f_s/2$ on the frequency spectrum of the signal. Thus, $7f_s/8$ gives rise to a frequency of $f_s - 7f_s/8 = f_s/8$, as shown in the figure. Such errors can be avoided either by

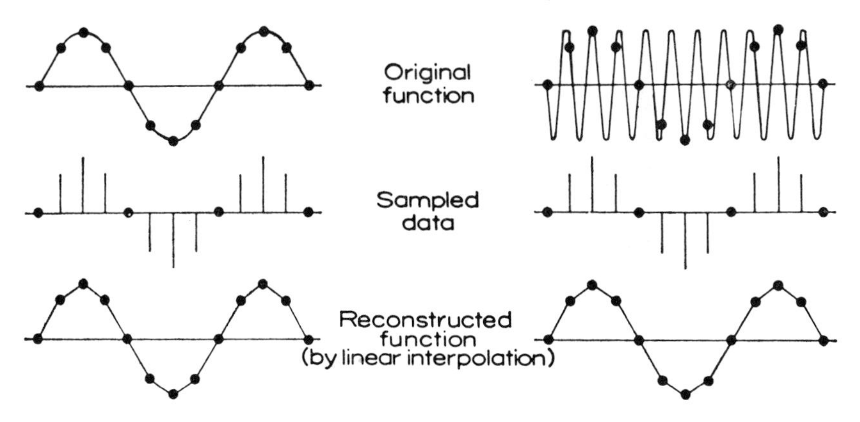

Figure 3.7. Illustrating aliasing errors. The left-hand signal is sampled at a rate of greater than two per cycle, while the other signal is sampled at 7/8 of the sampling frequency. Both give rise to the same reconstructed waveforms (reproduced, with permission, from Gardenhire [2]).

inserting a filter in the signal path to cut out the higher unwanted components or by using a higher sampling frequency.

The minimum sampling frequency necessary to insure that a given RMS error is not exceeded depends on the manner in which the frequency spectrum of the signal falls off at high frequencies and the manner in which the analog signal is reconstructed from the sampled amplitudes. The signal spectrum can be approximately characterized by assuming that the spectrum is flat to a frequency f_1, and that beyond this the power spectrum falls off at some multiple of 6 dB/octave—that is, $(f_1/f)^{2m}$ where $m = 1, 2, \ldots$, as illustrated in Figure 3.8(a). Using this signal spectrum, Gardenhire [2] has published computed values for the required sampling rate to achieve a given percentage error for various types of signal reconstruction schemes. Some of these results are shown in Table 3.1.

With an optimum Wiener filter and an ideal signal ($m = \infty$), the sampling frequency is, as expected, the same as that given by the sampling theorem. For a practical analog filter (e.g., a Butterworth 4-section filter) and an input-signal spectrum corresponding to $m = 2$, the sampling frequency must be $16f_1$ for a 5% error, and $290f_1$ for a 0.2% error. By using a simple linear interpolation between successive sampled amplitudes, the corresponding results are $13f_1$ and $120f_1$. The large increase in the sampling frequency required to achieve small percentage errors is further illustrated in Figure 3.8(*b*), where for various digital interpolation orders the percent error is plotted as a function of the sampling frequency.

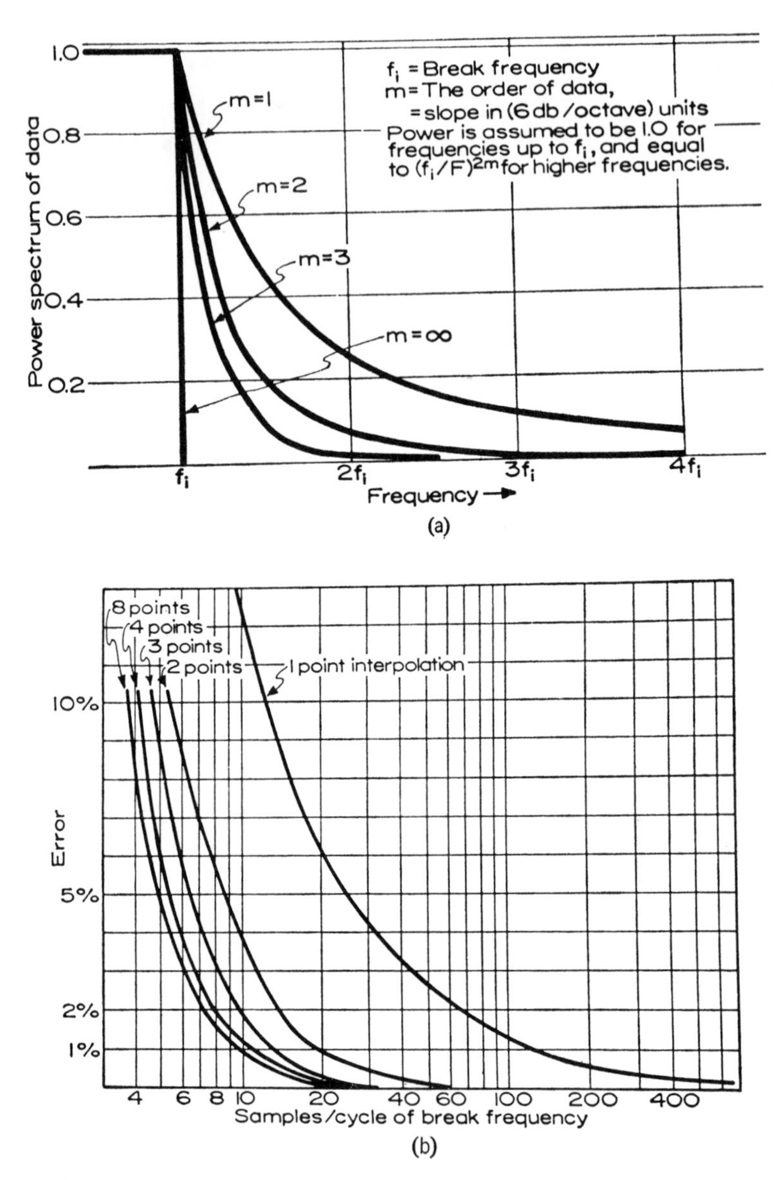

Figure 3.8. Influence of the sample rate on the RMS error between the sampled signal and that reconstructed from the sampled amplitudes: (a) approximation to the signal spectrum; (b) RMS error versus sampling frequency for various orders of interpolation (reproduced, with permission, from Gardenhire [2]).

Table 3.1 The Sampling Frequency Required Expressed as a Multiple of the Signal "Break" Frequency, for 5% and 0.2% RMS Error, for Various Signal Reconstruction Methods and Various Values of the Signal Spectrum Roll-Off [a]

Interpolation method	$m = 1$		$m = 2$		$m = 3$		$m = \infty$	
	5%	0.2%	5%	0.2%	5%	0.2%	5%	0.2%
Wiener optimum filter	640	410,000	11	93	5.1	19	2.0	2.0
Butterworth, 4-section	—	—	16	290	8.3	61	5.5	26
R–C filter	12,000	—	220	2000	130	850	91	540
Step interpolation	910	600,000	37	890	26	630	21	510
Linear interpolation	640	410,000	13	120	8.3	42	5.9	29

[a] Data extracted from L. W. Gardenhire [2].

3.5 INPUT AND OUTPUT IMPEDANCE EFFECTS

In the earlier discussion of input and output impedances it was noted that the loading effect imposed by the input impedance of a transducer can cause the measured signal to differ from the undisturbed value. If the signal source impedance is known, corrections can be made: however, with many physiological measurements this is not possible since the signal impedance can only be very roughly estimated. In addition it frequently happens that the signal source impedance is nonlinear and varies over the time course of the measurement. For both these reasons it is desired that the transducer-system loading effects be small.

Changes in the input and output impedances of a measurement system to meet the specifications demanded by the source of the measured quantity or the load into which the system delivers its output can be achieved in several ways. Sometimes it is possible to achieve the required values through modifications to an existing design; but at other times this cannot be achieved without compromising other significant system parameters. In the latter case it is worthwhile examining the use of feedback, since it enables one to obtain very large changes in the input and output impedances.

In electrical measurements it is generally found that current feedback from the output lowers both the input and output impedances. On the other hand, voltage feedback increases the input impedance and lowers the output impedance. If the feedback is large, the input transducer acts simply as a sensitive null detector to detect if a difference between the feedback quantity and the quantity being measured exists, and if it does, to alter the feedback quantity in such a way as to improve the null.

Feedback can be advantageous in mechanical and hydraulic types of measurements. For example, suppose it is desired to measure a force whose true value can only be obtained when the displacement it is required to produce is negligibly small. Such a measurement can be made by using a force generator to exactly balance the measured force. The difference between the two forces is detected by a displacement transducer and associated amplifier whose output drives the force generator. The more sensitive the displacement transducer–amplifier system, the smaller will be the null displacement and hence the more accurate will be the measurement.

As mentioned above, feedback from output to input lowers the output impedance. The reason for this is that when the output of a feedback measurement system is more heavily loaded, the amount of signal feedback decreases, thereby tending to increase the net input signal to compensate for the loading effect. If the compensation is perfect, the output impedance will be zero.

REFERENCES

1. Doebelin, E. O. *Measurement Systems: Application and Design.* McGraw-Hill: New York, 1966.
2. Gardenhire, L. W. "Selecting Sample Rates." *ISA J.* **11**, 59–64 (April 1964).

CHAPTER FOUR

General Properties of Input Transducers

4.1 ACTIVE AND PASSIVE

From a functional standpoint, transducers can be classified as *passive* or *active*, according to whether or not the output signal energy is supplied by the input.* Thus, an active transducer is one in which the output energy is supplied primarily by an auxiliary power source controlled by the input signal. A resistive displacement transducer is an example. The output voltage is supplied by an emf applied to the resistor; it is the displacement of the sliding contact that determines the output voltage.

In a passive transducer the primary source of output energy is the input signal. A thermocouple is classified as a passive transducer because the difference in temperature between the junctions creates an emf. On the other hand, a thermistor is an active transducer because it requires an auxiliary power source (e.g., a bridge emf) to indicate its output. Additional examples are given in Table 4.1, which lists a variety (not exhaustive) of physical effects useful or potentially useful for transducer action (see Refs. 1–4 for an exhaustive account of input transducers).

* Some authors use the reverse definition. The definition adopted here is consistent with the generally accepted view of a transformer as a passive device and a transistor as an active device.

Table 4.1 List of Physical Effects Used in Passive and Active Transducers[a]

Passive	Active
Electromagnetic	Resistance }
Piezoelectric	Inductance } Geometry controlled
Magnetostrictive (as a generator)	Capacitance }
Thermoelectric	Mechanoresistive (strain)
Photoemissive	Magnetoresistive
Photovoltaic	Thermoresistive
Electrokinetic (streaming potential)	Photoconductive
Pyroelectric	Piezoresistive
	Magnetostrictive (as a variable inductance)
	Hall effect

[a] Adapted, with changes, from Neubert [2].

4.2 PRIMARY AND SECONDARY

From an operational standpoint, it is worthwhile recalling that input transducers can be employed in either a *primary* or a *secondary* transducing role, as occurs, for example, in a diaphragm-type pressure transducer. Here the primary transducer is the pressure–displacement action of the diaphragm, while the secondary transducer is the device designed to measure the diaphragm displacement and to give an output that is usually in the form of an electrical signal. It happens that many mechanical–electrical transducers are of this form.

4.3 DIGITAL AND ANALOG

An additional classification that is sometimes useful in describing a transducer is determined by the form of the output signal. Although most transducers give an output in an analog form, some are specifically designed to yield an output that either is in a digital form or can be readily encoded into one.

It is questionable whether a true digital transducer really exists, for most transducers of this form fundamentally consist of an analog–analog transducer with a built-in analog–digital converter. However, it is generally accepted that for a transducer to be described as digital, its output must either be in digital form or be in a form that is very readily converted to it. For example, a temperature transducer that relies on the change in resonant frequency of a quartz crystal with temperature is usually classified as a digital transducer. Here, the frequency of oscillation is measured with a digital counter. A more clear-cut case of a digital transducer is a displacement transducer that uses an encoded plate with transparent and opaque regions. If such a plate is moved past a set of optical detectors, a digital output proportional to the displacement can be obtained. This type of system is most frequently used for shaft-angle (rotation) measurements.

Schuler [5] has reviewed the problem of digital transducer classifications and has suggested the following four subcategories: (1) direct digital transducers, (2) indirect digital transducers, (3) quasi-digital transducers, and (4) analog–digital transducers. He points out that although examples of category 1 are not currently available, it seems likely that true digital transducers may well be developed in the future. An example of category 2 is the optical encoder referred to previously. Transducers with frequency-, pulse-duration-, or pulse-rate-dependent outputs, such as the quartz crystal thermometer, are examples of the quasi-digital transducer category. The final category includes transducers that use an analog sensing device but that have a built-in analog–digital converter.

4.4 SPECIFICATION AND CHOICE

In designing a biomedical measurement that uses a transducer, one basic decision to be made concerns the choice of either invasive or noninvasive techniques. Although noninvasive techniques generally require certain compromises to be made (such as a reduction in the measurement accuracy), they do normally result in the least interference with the system being measured. When this decision has been made, it is possible to consider the factors entering into the choice and design of a suitable transducer. Although some of these factors are difficult to isolate and categorize, most can be lumped under the three headings shown in Figure 4.1—namely, economic, signal, and environmental factors. These lead to a first-order set of transducer specifications, which, if one is fortunate, may lead immediately to the choice of a commercially available item. But often as not, the specifications are too tight, requiring compromise. An initial search of available transducers may lead to one or more that nearly meet the requirements; by taking a second look at the specifications demanded and modifying the less critical ones, a satisfactory transducer may be found.

An additional aspect that sometimes plays an important role in the eventual choice is the specifications to be met by the signal-conditioning system. While one transducer may be clearly superior on the basis of achievable performance it may necessitate a signal-conditioning system that is far more complex than that required with an alternative transducer type whose specifications are inferior. On the basis of system cost, MTBF, and size the somewhat inferior transducer may in fact turn out to be the best from the overall viewpoint, even though it may result in some loss of information.

To illustrate the use of some of the physical effects listed in Table 4.1 for the measurement of some primary hydraulic, thermal, and mechanical

Table 4.2 Methods for Transducing Some Primary Physical Quantities

Quantity	Physical effect	Examples and Comments
Temperature	Thermoelectric	Thermocouple; thermopile
	Thermocapacitive	Change of capacitance
	Thermoresistive	Thermistors; platinum resistance thermometer
	Thermal expansion	Glass thermometer; bimetallic strip; quartz crystal digital thermometer
	Radiation	Thermopile; thermistor; photovoltaic and photoconductive semiconductor detectors
	Thermochemical	Liquid crystals (temperature sensitive chemical changes)
	Pyroelectric	Lead zirconate-titanate materials (polarization changes strongly with temperature)
Displacement: Low mechanical impedance types	Resistive	Potentiometer (e.g., rotational and linear displacement types)
	Capacitive	Change in capacitance
	Inductive	Change in inductance
	Transformer	AC-excited differential transformer
	Electromagnetic	Movement of a coil through a magnetic field (lacks dc response)
	Optical	Interferometry; Moire fringes; reflection change
	Ultrasonic	Pulse transit time
Higher impedance types	Piezoresistive	Semiconductor strain gauge
	Mechanoresistive	Metal-foil and wire strain gauge; mercury gauge
Velocity	dx/dt	Differentiation of the output from a displacement transducer
	Magnetic induction	Moving coil (gives an output proportional to the velocity)
	Doppler effect	Ultrasonic or optical frequency change
	$\int a\, dt$	Integrating the output from an accelerometer

Table 4.2—*cont.*

Quantity	Physical effect	Examples and Comments
Acceleration	dv/dt	Differentiating the output from a velocity transducer
	$F = ma$	Measurement of the force due to the movement of a known mass (e.g., piezoelectric, magnetostrictive, mechanoresistive transducers)
Force	Elastic displacement	Primary: displacement of elastic member Secondary: displacement transducer as described above
	Piezoresistive	Semiconductor (e.g., silicon)
	Piezoelectric	Barium titanate (ferroelectric ceramic; lacks dc response)
	Magnetostrictive	Induced voltage type (lacks dc response); change of inductance type
	Balance	Electromagnetic force balance (null-type system)
Pressure (force/unit area)	Elastic displacement	Diaphragm deflection; Bourdon tube; bellows: measured with a displacement-type transducer
	Force balance	Manometer; electromagnetic force balance.
Flow	Pressure difference	Orifice type
	Mechanical	Rotameter, driving an electromagnetic emf-generating secondary transducer
	Thermal	Heat transport from a heated element (e.g., a self-heated thermistor)
	Electromagnetic	Electromagnetic flow emf, generated by flow through a magnetic field
	Ultrasonic	Pulse transit time; Doppler shift
	Optical	Laser Doppler shift
	Indicator	Dye dilution; thermal dilution; conductivity dilution methods
	Transit time	Small-bubble (or other fixed marker) transit-time measurement

quantities, Table 4.2 is presented. Since this table summarizes much of the material given detailed consideration in Part II of this book, there seems little point in further elaboration. However, it should be pointed out that surveys of this type can be very useful for insuring that no important physical effect has been overlooked in searching for a suitable method to solve a particular transduction problem.

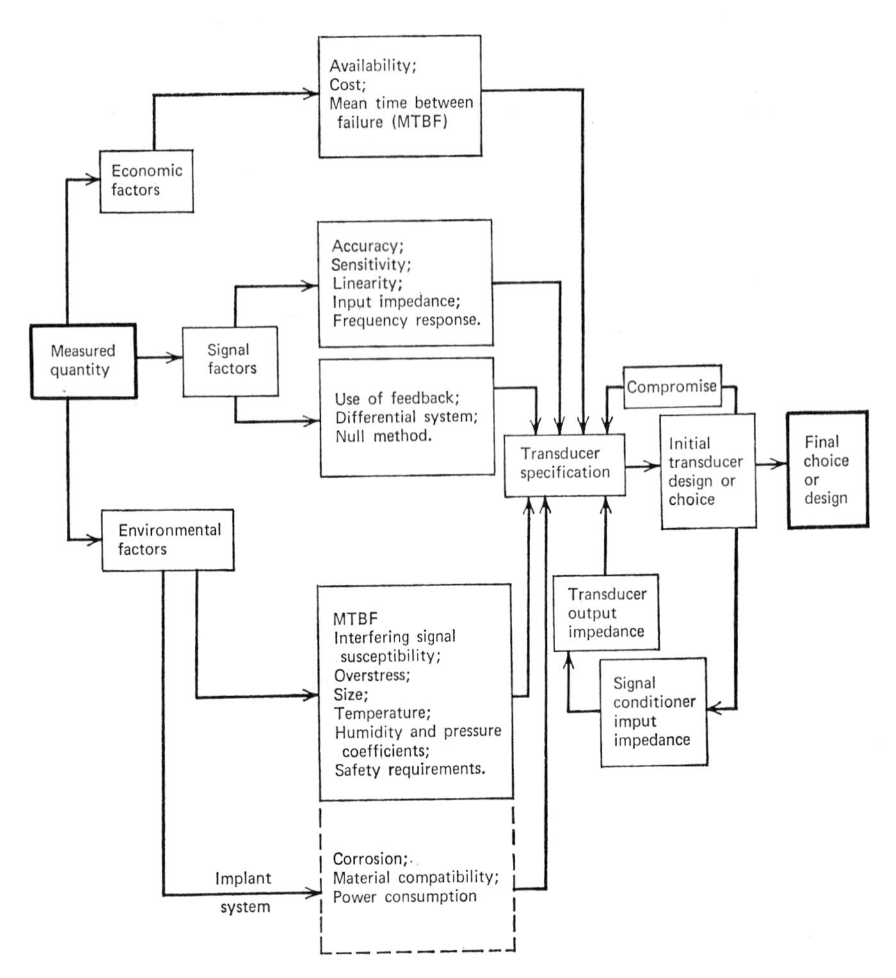

Figure 4.1. Factors influencing the choice and design of an input transducer for biomedical measurements.

REFERENCES

1. Doebelin, E. O. *Measurement Systems: Application and Design.* McGraw-Hill: New York, 1966.
2. Neubert, H. K. P. *Instrument Transducers.* Clarendon: Oxford, 1963.
3. Lion, K. S. *Instrumentation in Scientific Research: Electrical Input Transducers.* McGraw-Hill: New York, 1959.
4. Harvey, G. F., Ed. *ISA Transducer Compendium*, 2nd ed. Pts. 1–3. Instrument Society of America: Pittsburgh, 1969–1972.
5. Schuler, A. E. "Digital Transducers" (Paper 662), in *Advances in Instrumentation,* Vol. XXIV pt. 4. Proc. 24th Ann. ISA Conf., 1969, Instrument Society of America, Pittsburgh, 1969, pp. 1–8.

Part II

THEORY AND APPLICATIONS

CHAPTER FIVE

Temperature Transducers

Most physical processes are influenced, at least to some extent, by temperature changes so that it is hardly surprising to find a wide variety of phenomena employed as the basis of temperature transducers.* In selecting the most appropriate to meet a given design, objectives, linearity, range, reproducibility, and ease with which it can be converted into an electrical signal are evidently of considerable importance. Also of importance are the size and thermal mass of the probe, for these determine the disturbance imposed by the measurement and the speed of response.

Perhaps the simplest, and certainly the most widely used, phenomenon for temperature sensing is thermal expansion. This, of course, forms the basis of the mercury-in-glass thermometer as well as a variety of other sensing elements used in measurement and control. For electrical temperature recording and display, transducers based on the thermoresistive and thermoelectric effects are most frequently used for biological and medical applications. A discussion of these effects and the way in which they are applied for temperature measurements forms the first two sections of this chapter.

* Refs. 1–3 contain useful general accounts of temperature transducers and extensive bibliographies; Ref. 4 contains a large number of specialized papers covering most aspects of measurement and control.

5.1 THERMORESISTIVE TRANSDUCERS

The change in resistance of certain metals and semiconductors constitutes the basis of thermoresistive temperature transducers. For most metals, over moderate ranges of temperature, the change in resistivity is very nearly proportional to the temperature change, so that the resistance can be written as

$$R_T = R_0[1 + \alpha(T - T_0)], \tag{1}$$

where R_0 is the resistance of the element at a temperature T_0 and α is the temperature coefficient of resistance at T_0. As shown in Table 5.1, the temperature coefficient of metals is normally positive, corresponding to an increase in resistance with temperature. For single-crystal semiconductors α is also positive but decreases with increasing doping. On the other hand, ceramic semiconductors (thermistors) generally have a highly nonlinear temperature characteristic and α can be either positive or negative depending on the composition.

Table 5.1 Temperature Coefficients and Resistivities of Certain Metals and Semiconductors at Room Temperature

Material	α, (°C^{-1})[a]	ρ, Resistivity (Ω-cm)
Gold	+0.0040	2.4×10^{-6}
Nichrome	+0.0004	1.0×10^{-4}
Nickel	+0.0067	6.84×10^{-6}
Platinum	+0.00392	1.0×10^{-5}
Silver	+0.0041	1.63×10^{-6}
Silicon (10^{16} cm^{-3} doping)	~+0.007	1.4 (p-type)
		0.6 (n-type)
Thermistors	−0.04	~10^3 (neg. coefft. type)
	+0.1	— (pos. coefft. type)

[a] Multiplying α by 100 gives the percent change in resistance per 1°C.

5.1.1 Metallic Elements

Certain metals have particularly stable electrical characteristics and such small nonlinearities that if the temperature range is not too large and the accuracy demanded not too great, linearity can be assumed. Platinum, in particular, has excellent stability over a wide temperature range; in fact, the platinum resistance thermometer is used to define the International Temperature Scale between the oxygen boiling point of −183.962°C and the antimony melting point of +630.74°C. Over the range 0–100°C, platinum resistance thermometers have a linearity of ±0.2% and are capable of an accuracy of 0.001°C. To achieve this accuracy requires wire of very high purity, a probe designed to eliminate thermal stresses, and careful attention to the nonlinearities.* Less-stringent accuracy demands (0.05°C) still require nonlinear corrections. Over the range 0–630°C the simple quadratic relation

$$R_T = R_0(1 + AT + BT^2)$$

can be used. In this equation $A = 3.983 \times 10^{-3}(°\mathrm{C})^{-1}$, $B = -0.586 \times 10^{-6}$ $(°\mathrm{C})^{-2}$, T is the temperature in degrees centigrade and R_0 is the resistance at the ice point.

The relatively small temperature coefficient (0.4%/°C) of platinum requires very careful attention to what might normally be considered insignificant sources of error in the bridge measuring circuit. One such source is the lead wires to the sensing element, which will be subject to a temperature gradient of undefined value, leading to a resistance error. This effect can be eliminated through the use of the three-lead-wire bridge arrangement shown in Figure 5.1. Since the leads R_{L1} and R_{L2} are identical and appear on opposite arms of the bridge, changes in the lead resistance have no effect on the balance. A special feature of the bridge circuit is that the contact resistance of the slider element on R_X and R_Y has no effect on the balance. By using the two mechanically coupled variable resistors such that $R_X = R_Y/2$, it can be shown that the null occurs at a position directly proportional to the value of R_T.

A second source of possible error is the thermoelectric emf's generated at the various contacts. These can be reduced by insuring that all contacts are at the same temperature. Their effects can be avoided by using ac bridge excitation coupled with a narrow-band amplifier, preferably with a phase-sensitive null detection scheme.

A further effect of significance in thermoresistive thermometry is the self-heating effect of the current through the resistive element. The magnitude of the error depends on I^2R_T as well as the heat-transfer conditions. It can be reduced without decreasing the bridge sensitivity by employing a pulsed source; however, the added complexity is not normally required, since the simple expedient of decreasing the supply voltage and increasing the null amplifier gain is all that is required to reach a condition where the resulting error is negligible.

* See Section 6 in Ref. 4a for a discussion of various aspects of platinum resistance thermometry above −183°C.

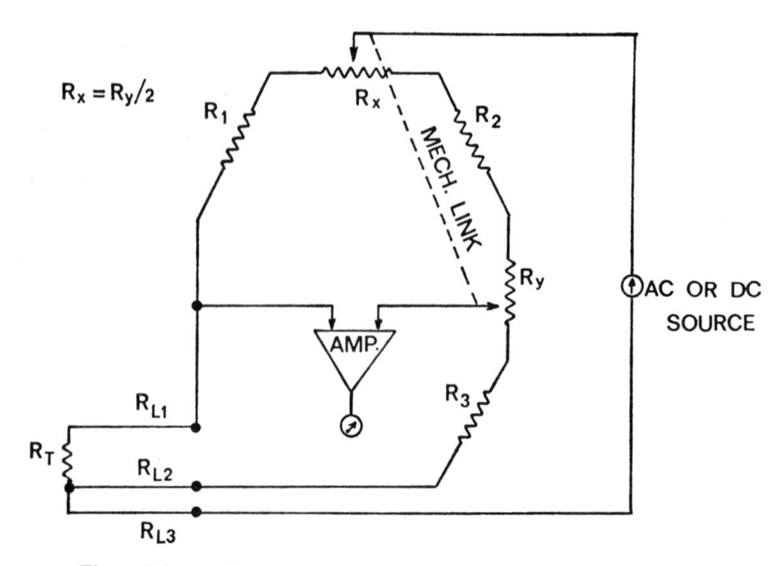

Figure 5.1. Null-type bridge for platinum resistance thermometry.

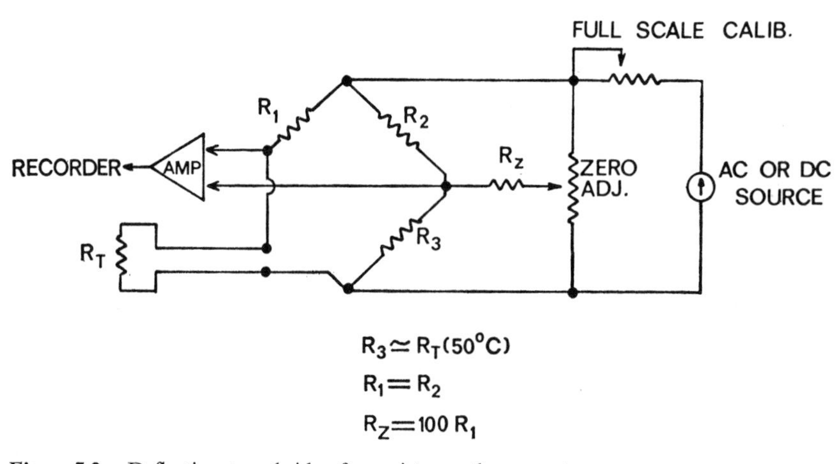

Figure 5.2. Deflection-type bridge for resistance thermometry.

If the temperature range is not too large and the accuracy demanded not too great, a linear indication of the temperature can be achieved by using a bridge in the deflection mode, as illustrated in Figure 5.2. With this scheme the arms of the bridge are fixed at values such that the bridge is balanced at the lower end of the range, so that, for example, 0°C corresponds to zero output. The linearity of this arrangement can be improved by balancing the bridge at the mid-temperature point and also by making R_1 and R_2 some 10 times greater than R_T. Although, some loss in sensitivity results from the latter scheme, it can be readily compensated by increasing the amplifier gain. Using both these linearity improvements for a platinum wire sensor, a nonlinearity of $\pm 0.5°C$ over a 0–100°C span can be achieved.

When accurate temperature measurement is required over a wide range with direct read-out of the actual temperature, a linearization technique can be employed to compensate for the inherent nonlinearity of the sensor. Diamond [5] has discussed the various approaches to this problem and has categorized the linearization techniques employed by various workers. One category includes the use of a bridge arm network that varies in a nonlinear manner with the balance potentiometer setting. The bridge described by van der Wal and Struik [6] is of this type and is illustrated in Figure 5.3. Here, the network R_V–R_1–R_2 generates a bridge arm resistance that varies nonlinearly with the angular rotation of the multiturn balance potentiometer in such a way that it compensates for the platinum resistance sensor nonlinearity. The bridge is of the null-balance type, with the bridge unbalance being applied to the input amplifier of a servo-driven strip-chart recorder. A mechanical coupling to the balance potentiometer R_V serves to bring the bridge into balance and thereby to produce an output proportional to the angular rotation. The authors claim that apart from any inaccuracy in the sensor itself, the reading accuracy for a temperature range of 0–500°C is better than $\pm 0.1°C$.

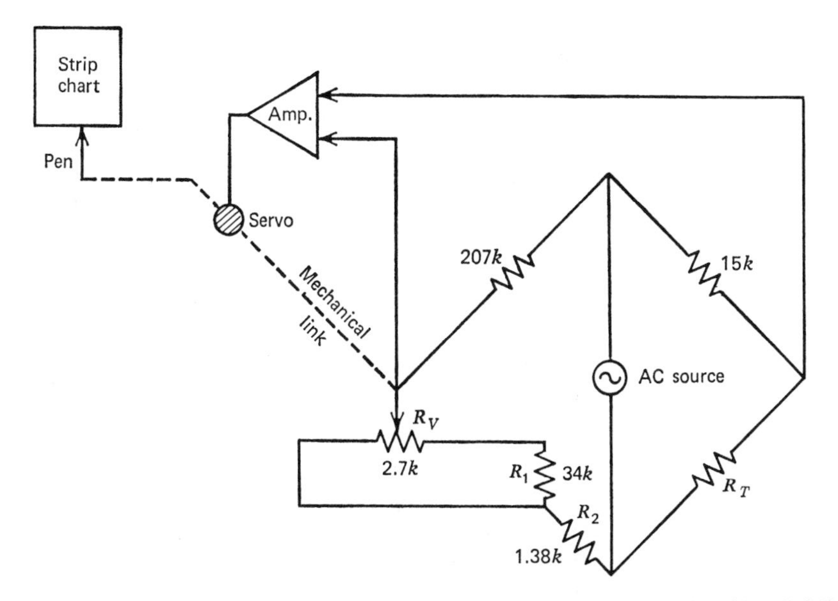

Figure 5.3. Linearized null bridge using a servo balance (after van der Wal and Struik [6]).

A second example of linearized resistance wire thermometry using a null bridge is the dual-element scheme described by Massey [7]. The probe contains two resistance wires of the same material: one acts as the temperature sensor; the other, which is in the opposite side of the bridge, acts as a compensator to correct the nonlinearities of the sensor. By careful design excellent accuracy can be achieved. For example, the author cites the performance obtained with a direct-reading portable thermometer using either nickel or platinum probes. Over the range 0–100°C the worst-case total error for nickel is 0.02°C and that for platinum is 0.01°C.

In practice, the probe resistance values range from a few ohms to greater than 10 kΩ, the lower values being typical for platinum elements. For high-accuracy thermometry the physical size is largely determined by mechanical stability considerations. But, when this is not so important, wire probe elements can be made as small as 1 mm in diameter, with thermal time constants of less than 1 sec. Much smaller thermoresistive elements can be fabricated by vacuum deposition onto a suitable substrate either through a fixed mask or by subsequent photolithographic processing and etching [8]. Resistive sensors fabricated in this way on a flexible substrate are particularly convenient for surface temperature studies.

Table 5.2 Some Properties of Oxide Thermistors[a]

Manufacturer and model	Temperature range (°C)	α at 25°C (%/°C)		Stability
Fenwall				
A-B-C	−60 ÷ +300	−3.9		Better than 0.4 percent (year) at maximum temperature
D-E	−60 ÷ + 300	−4.4		
AK	−20 ÷ +175	−3.7		
EM 28	+90 ÷ −650	—		
Gulton Industries				
A	−60 ÷ +300	−4.6		—
B	−60 ÷ +300	−3.9		—
G	−60 ÷ +150	−5.4		—
M	−60 ÷ +150	−6.8		—
Philips		from	to	
610	0 ÷ +120	−2.98	−6.13	
634	−25 ÷ +200	−2.64	−4.8	<1% (1000 h at 200°C)
635	−25 ÷ +150	−3.66	−4.73	<5% (1000 h at 150°C)
636-637	+25 ÷ +150	−3.66	−4.73	
642-643-644	+25 ÷ +150	−2.93	−4.73	

Table 5.2—*cont.*

Manufacturer and model	Temperature range (°C)	α at 25°C (%/°C)			Stability
Siemens					
K11-K13-K252	0 ÷ +120	−2.9		−5.2	—
K15	0 ÷ +150	−2.9		−4.8	—
K17-K29	0 ÷ +250	−3.8		−4.4	—
K18-K19-K22	0 ÷ +200	−3.9		−5.1	—
K172-K292	0 ÷ +350		−4.4		—
K273	0 ÷ +100		−4.4		—
Victory Engineering					
A	−50 ÷ +300	−3.2		−3.3	Between 0.05 and 0.2% (year) if glass enclosed; between 0.2 and 2.5% if wafers, disks, rods, etc.
B-C-D-E-F	−50 ÷ +300	−3.3		−4.4	
G-H-I-J-K-L	−50 ÷ +300	−4.5		−5.6	
Yellow Spring Industries					
44001	−80 ÷ +120		−3.1		—
44002	−80 ÷ +140		−3.5		—
44003-4-5-6	−80 ÷ +150	−3.68		−4.025	—
44008-440011	−40 ÷ +150	−4.3		−4.5	—
44014-44015	0 ÷ +150	−4.83		−5.16	—
Standard Telephones and Cables					
D-F-FS-G	+20 ÷ +300	−2.8		−5.6	—
G	+20 ÷ +155	−2.9		−4.8	—
GT	+20 ÷ +125	−2.9		−4.8	—

[a] Reproduced, with permission, from Prudenziati, Taroni, and Zanarini [14].

5.1.2 Semiconductor Elements

Thermoresistive transducers based on the properties of certain ceramic like semiconductors are of special importance: their small size, excellent long-term stability, and relatively large temperature coefficient make them particularly useful for biomedical temperature measurements. Transducers of this type are called *thermistors*—an acronym for *therm*ally sensitive res*istors* [9]. There are in fact three categories of thermistor: the ceramic negative temperature coefficient (NTC) type, fabricated by high-temperature sintering of certain metallic oxide mixtures [10]; the positive temperature coefficient (PTC) type, made by sintering barium and strontium titanate mixtures [11]; and the single-crystal doped semiconductor (usually silicon) type, which also has a positive temperature coefficient.

As shown in Table 5.2, the NTC thermistors typically have coefficients in the range −3 to −5%/°C—some 10 times larger than for metals. They can be made with maximum dimensions of less than 0.5 mm and with resistance values ranging from a few ohms up to several megohms. For certain glass-encapsulated devices, the stability may be ±0.2% of the nominal resistance value per year, corresponding to a temperature stability of around ±0.05°C/yr [12–14]. Even larger temperature coefficients are achieved with the PTC sintered barium titanate thermistors (10–60%/°C); however, little information is available on their long-term stability. For the single-crystal silicon thermistors, which should have excellent stability, the temperature coefficient is around 0.7%/°C, depending on the doping.

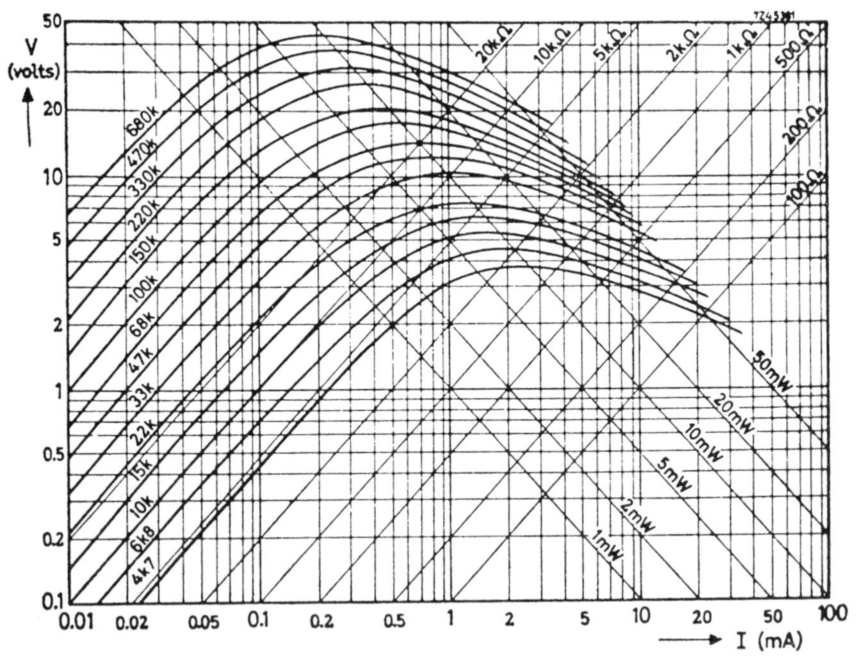

Figure 5.4. Typical current versus voltage characteristics of bead-type thermistors having various 25°C resistance values. The positive-slope 45° lines indicate the degree of linearity at low currents: they correspond to linear resistance values. The negative-slope lines are equipower dissipation lines whose intersection with the characteristics give the device power dissipation (from Philips Electronics data sheet, 1967).

Thermistor Characteristics. Figures 5.4 and 5.5 show the current versus voltage and resistance versus temperature characteristics for a set of NTC bead thermistors. It will be noted from Figure 5.4 that at low currents, where the power dissipated in the thermistor is small, the characteristics are essentially linear. Under these conditions the thermistor temperature will be equal to ambient temperature. At higher current levels the increased power dissipated causes the thermistor temperature to rise above ambient, and because of the NTC this results in a decreasing incremental resistance. Eventually, when the current is large enough, the incremental resistance drops to zero (the turn-over point) and then becomes negative. When operating a thermistor in this region, care must be taken to limit the current so that thermal destruction is prevented.

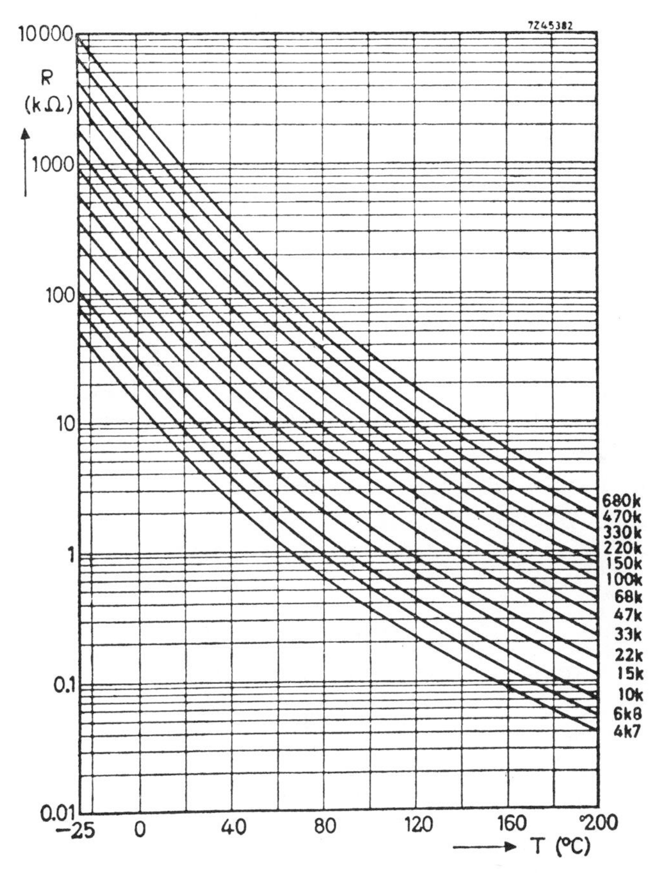

Figure 5.5. Resistance versus temperature characteristics of the bead thermistors whose I–V characteristics are shown in Figure 5.4 (from Philips Electronics data sheet, 1967).

From the resistance-versus-temperature characteristics of Figure 5.5, it will be noted that the resistance decreases in a highly nonlinear manner with increasing temperature (the log–linear plot tends to deemphasize the nonlinearity). An expression for the characteristics can be obtained in a semiquantitative manner if it can be assumed that the behavior is similar to that of a single-crystal semiconductor.

For an intrinsic semiconductor the electron density n increases with temperature according to

$$n \propto T^{3/2} \exp\left(\frac{-E_g}{2kT}\right),$$

where E_g is the band gap and T is the absolute temperature. Furthermore, the mobility of both holes and electron in the absence of impurities varies as $T^{-3/2}$; hence, the resistivity temperature-dependence will be given by

$$\rho \propto \exp\left(\frac{E_g}{2kT}\right).$$

Thus, the resistance of a thermistor can be expressed as

$$R_T = R_C\, e^{\beta/T}, \tag{2}$$

where $\beta = E_g/2k$ is a characteristic temperature that varies somewhat with composition. A somewhat more convenient form of this equation is

$$R_T = R_0 \exp\left[\beta\left(\frac{1}{T} - \frac{1}{T_0}\right)\right], \tag{3}$$

where R_0 is the resistance at T_0 in degrees Kelvin, which is usually taken to be 298°K (≡25°C). A typical value of β is 4000°K, but depending on the composition and method of fabrication, it can vary from 1500° to 6000°K.

An expression for the temperature coefficient α can be found by differentiating Eq. (2), yielding

$$\alpha = \frac{1}{R_T}\left(\frac{dR_T}{dT}\right) = -\frac{\beta}{T^2}. \tag{4}$$

It follows, that α is temperature-dependent and decreases with increasing temperature. Typically, at 300°K (27°C),

$$\alpha = -0.044(°\text{C})^{-1}$$

or

$$\alpha = -4.4\%/°\text{C}.$$

Thermistor Linearization In designing a linear-reading thermometer the inherent nonlinearity of the resistance-versus-temperature characteristics of thermistors is rather troublesome when a wide temperature range is required.

Over a limited temperature span two approaches can be used to achieve approximate linearization [15,16]. If the thermistor is fed from a constant-current source and the voltage across the thermistor is used to indicate the temperature, linearization can be achieved by shunting the thermistor with an appropriately chosen resistor R_P, as shown in Figure 5.6(a). Alternatively, when the current through the thermistor, for a fixed applied emf, is used to indicate the temperature, the series arrangement of Figure 5.6(b) may be employed.

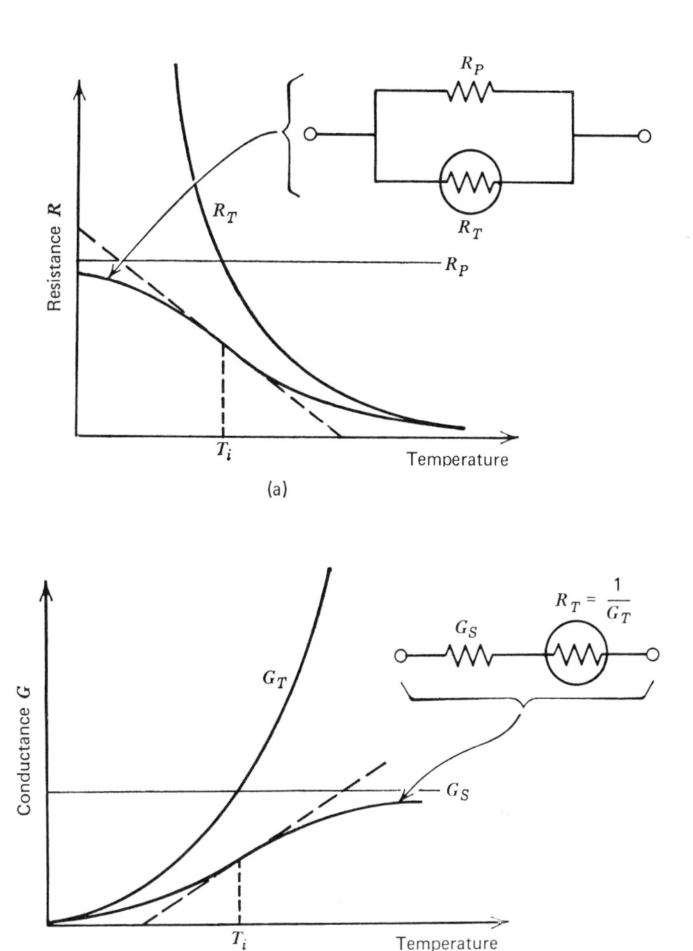

Figure 5.6. Thermistor linearization: (a) shunt network giving improved resistance–temperature linearity; (b) Series network giving improved conductance—temperature characteristics.

For the shunt arrangement, the objective is to make the point of inflection of the parallel combination coincide with the midscale temperature. The value of R_P required to achieve this can be found by differentiating

$$R = \frac{R_P R_C e^{\beta/T}}{R_P + R_C e^{\beta/T}},$$

twice and equating to zero. This yields

$$R_P = R_{T_i}\left(\frac{\beta - 2T_i}{\beta + 2T_i}\right), \tag{5}$$

where R_{T_i} is the thermistor resistance at the midscale temperature T_i. In a similar manner it can easily be shown that the value of the series resistance R_S required to make the conductance-versus-temperature characteristic approximately linear is given by

$$\frac{1}{R_S} = G_S = G_{T_i}\left(\frac{\beta - 2T_i}{\beta + 2T_i}\right), \tag{6}$$

where G_{T_i} is the thermistor conductance at T_i.

With the latter arrangement, assuming $\beta = 3000°\text{K}$ and setting the midscale temperature to 300°K, we find from Eq. (6) that $G_S = 1.5\, G_{300}$. Beakley [15] has shown that with these values, for a ±10°C span, the maximum deviation from linearity is 0.03°C. When the span is increased to ±15°C the deviation increases to 0.1°C.

The penalty incurred in achieving the improved linearity is a decrease in the effective temperature coefficient of the combination. It can readily be shown that the coefficients for the parallel and series linearization circuits are given by

$$\alpha_{\text{eff}} = \frac{(\beta/T_i^2)}{[(R_{T_i}/R_P) + 1]} \qquad \text{(Parallel)}$$

$$\alpha_{\text{eff}} = \frac{(\beta/T_i^2)}{[(G_{T_i}/G_S) + 1]} \qquad \text{(Series)}$$

For example, using the values given in the previous paragraph, we find that α_{eff} decreases from 3.3%/°C (with $R_S = 0$) to approximately 2%/°C when the optimum linearization resistance is employed.

More complex circuit arrangements can be devised to achieve better linearization over wider temperature ranges. For example, Trolander and Harruff [17] have described a combination of two thermistors in a single-package three-terminal configuration. When used with the appropriate linearizing network, a maximum deviation from linearity of 0.2°C can be achieved for a span from −30° to +50°C.

Thermistor Thermometry. Two types of thermistor thermometry systems can be identified: those in which the voltage across, or the current through, the thermistor is measured directly and those in which the thermistor forms part of a bridge operating in either the null or deflection modes. As an example of the first type of system, consider the circuit shown in Figure 5.7. Here the conductance versus temperature characteristic has been linearized by means of the resistor R_S. In order to effectively eliminate any self-heating errors, the series circuit is driven from a voltage source of only 50 mV.

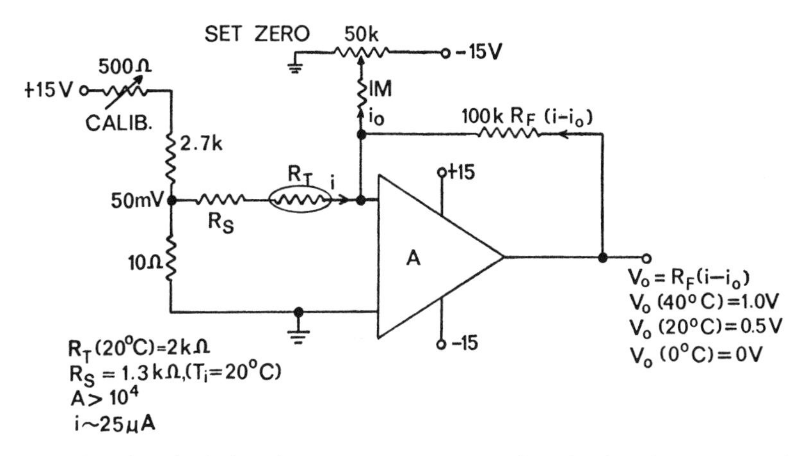

Figure 5.7. Linearized thermistor temperature measuring circuit using an operational amplifier.

Current feedback to the input of the operational amplifier creates a virtual earth at the input terminals, thereby enabling the thermistor current to be measured without affecting the voltage across it. If the amplifier input impedance is large, the current through the feedback resistor R_F will be equal to the thermistor current minus the offset current i_0. Thus, the output voltage will be linearly related to the thermistor current, and by virtue of the series combination having a conductance linearly related to the temperature, the output voltage should also vary linearly with temperature. Such a system when operating over a 0–40°C range should have a maximum linearity deviation of around 0.15°C.

When good accuracy and high sensitivity are required, bridge circuits are usually preferred. Priestly [18] has described one such system in which a servo motor is used to automatically null the bridge and indicate the temperature on a mechanically coupled digital display. A commercial version* of

* Digitec, United Systems Corp., Dayton, Ohio.

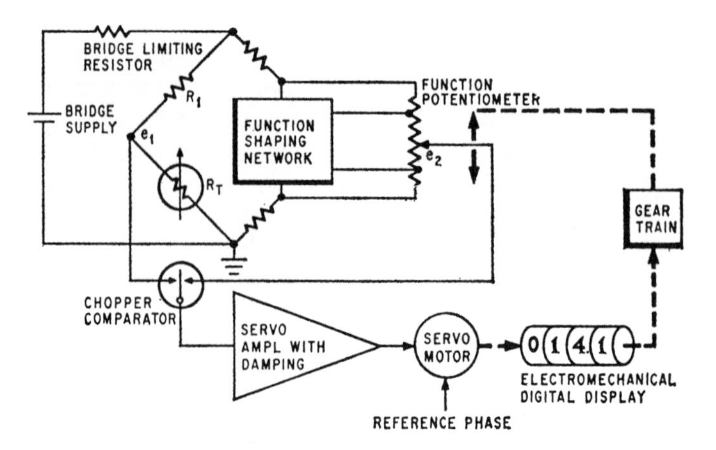

Figure 5.8. Servo-balanced thermistor thermometry system with digital readout (reproduced, with permission, from United Systems Corp., Dayton, Ohio).

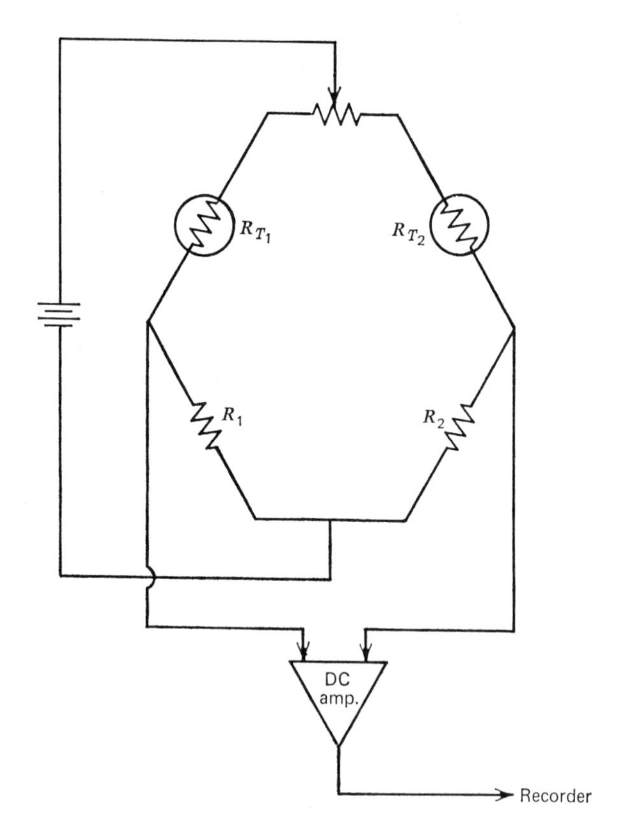

Figure 5.9. Differential temperature bridge of the deflection type using dc excitation.

this system, illustrated in Figure 5.8, uses a special function-shaping network shunting the balance potentiometer, to achieve improved linearity. This thermometer, which is especially designed for biological applications, has a wide range of interchangeable thermistor probes. Instrument accuracy is claimed to be $\pm 0.05°C$ in a 20°C span, with a repeatability of 0.01°C.

In biological work it is often necessary to accurately determine very small temperature differences [4c]. For example, it may be necessary to measure the heats of reaction of certain cellular or subcellular constituents by differential calorimetry or to determine the difference in temperature between two regions of an organ. By using two thermistors in a differential arrangement, it is possible to achieve a very high sensitivity. For example, Nancollas and Hardy [19] have described a differential calorimetric system capable of detecting temperature differences as small as 10^{-5}°C.

For this type of measurement, bead thermistors matched to $\pm 1\%$ of each other at 25°C are commonly used. If the temperature differences are fairly small (less than 1°C) a dc-excited Wheatstone bridge operated in the deflection mode will normally give adequate linearity (better than 1% of the full-scale output). For the system shown in Figure 5.9, amplifier dc stability is not normally a significant problem, since, even for temperature differences of 0.01°C, the bridge output is still fairly large compared to the equivalent input drift of a good integrated-circuit operational amplifier.

When a very high sensitivity is required it is usually better to use ac bridge excitation together with a phase sensitive demodulation system (Figure 5.10). In such a system the problem of parasitic thermoelectric emf's generated within the bridge is avoided. Since the signal bandwidth required is normally less than 10 Hz, a narrow-bandwidth amplifier with its lower inherent noise can be used. Furthermore, by using a carrier frequency well away from the low-frequency end of the spectrum the $1/f$ noise, generated by both the thermistors and the input stage of the amplifier, is largely avoided. A problem does arise, especially at higher excitation frequencies, from the unbalanced capacitance of the two thermistors. One solution, as shown in the circuit diagram, is to place a fixed capacitor across one of the thermistors and to use a variable across the other, which is adjusted to achieve bridge balance when the temperature difference between the thermistors is zero.

Of considerable importance in achieving accurate temperature measurement is the physical design of the thermistor and the probe assembly. Glass-encapsulated thermistors of the type shown in Figure 5.11(a) are generally preferred for most biomedical measurements. The protection afforded by the glass coating against environmental effects insures good long-term stability without significantly affecting the thermal response time. A subminiature version, measuring only 0.32 mm in diameter, was used by Guadagni et al. [20] as the sensor for an accurate skin thermometer. The thermistor was mounted in

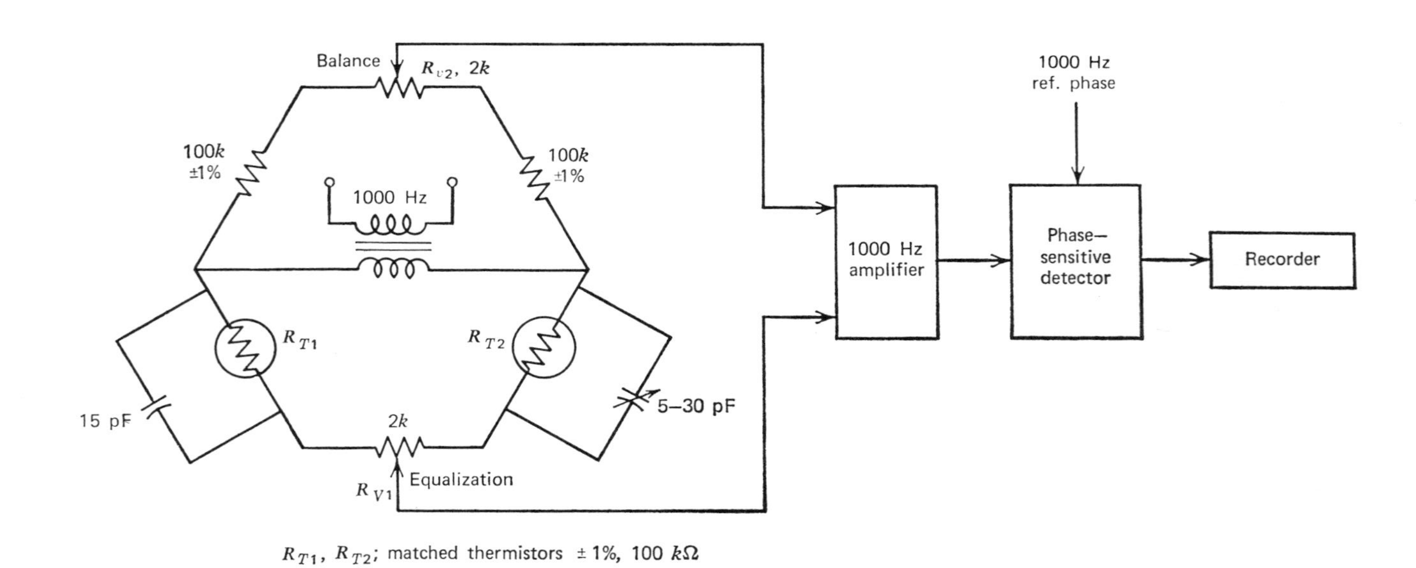

R_{T1}, R_{T2}; matched thermistors ± 1%, 100 $k\Omega$

Figure 5.10. AC-excited differential bridge system for measuring very small temperature differences [19].

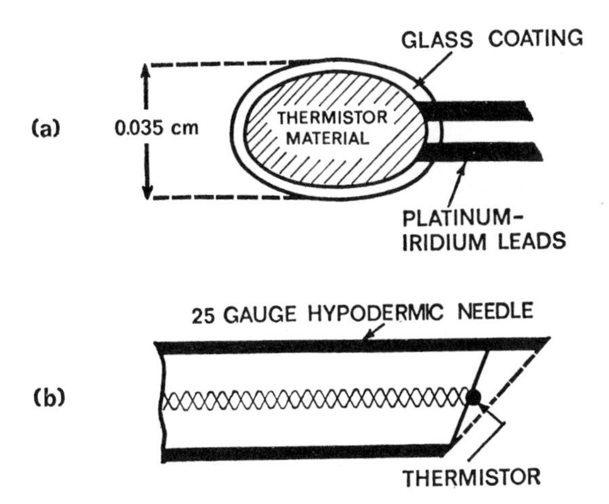

Figure 5.11. Examples of thermistor probes: (a) bead thermistor construction; (b) bead thermistor mounted at the end of a hypodermic needle.

a special probe assembly designed to achieve a constant contact pressure and to insure that the true skin temperature was measured following the disturbance caused by the initial contact of the thermistor on the skin. The authors reported that the measurement system had a reproducibility of $\pm 0.01^\circ$C and a drift of 0.01°C/wk.

The small size of glass encapsulated thermistors enables them to be mounted, for example, at the tips of either hypodermic needles [Figure 5.11(b)] [21] or catheters. Specially designed probe assemblies are manufactured for use in oral and rectal thermometry as well as for a variety of other applications. With regard to oral thermometry a variety of pocket-size electronic thermometers designed for clinical use are commercially available. They use thermistor probes contained in a sterile plastic disposable sheath. Typically, they have a range of 35–42°C, an accuracy of 0.1°C, and, when used with the disposable sheath, reading times of around 20 sec.

5.2 THERMOELECTRIC TRANSDUCERS

5.2.1 Basic Principles [22–24]

If, as shown in Figure 5.12(a), two dissimilar metals are connected in a closed circuit with their two junctions at differing temperatures, a current flows. This phenomenon, first reported by Seebeck in 1823, involves the absorption of heat by the hot junction and release of heat from the cold one.

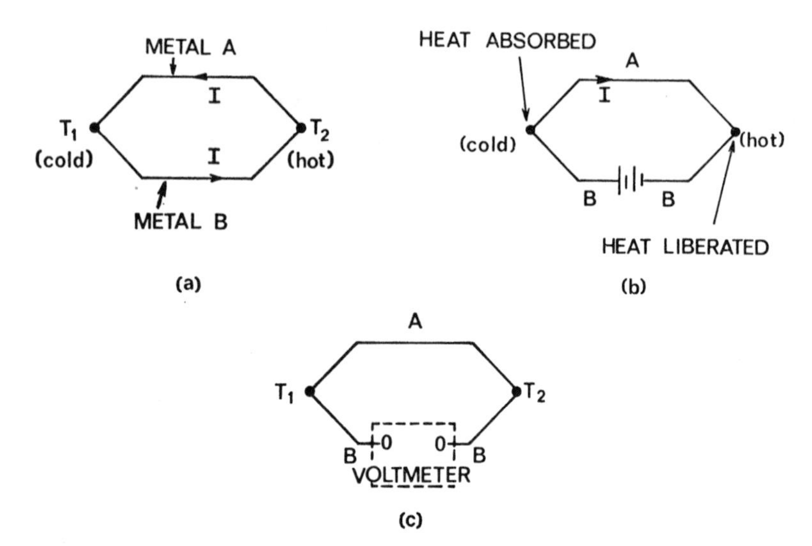

Figure 5.12. Illustrations of (a) the Seebeck effect; (b) the Peltier effect; and (c) the measurement of the Seebeck thermoelectric emf.

The Seebeck thermal emf, responsible for the current flow, depends on the types of metal involved and is approximately proportional to the temperature difference between the two junctions. Peltier demonstrated the inverse effect by inserting a battery into a closed circuit of two dissimilar metals [Figure 5.12(b)]. The resulting current flow causes heat to be absorbed at one junction and released at the other. This effect forms the basis of thermoelectric refrigeration.

In its simplest form a thermocouple consists of the two dissimilar metals A and B shown in Figure 5.12(c) electrically joined to form junctions at both ends of A but open-circuited so that the thermal emf can be measured. Since the output impedance of the thermocouple is very small, an amplifier with a low input impedance can be used. However, it must not be so small that the input current causes significant ohmic drops or that it causes appreciable Peltier heating or cooling of the junctions.

The Seebeck emf is approximately related to the absolute junction temperatures T_1 and T_2 by

$$V = \alpha(T_1 - T_2) + \gamma(T_1^2 - T_2^2), \qquad (7)$$

where α and γ are constants for the thermocouple pair. It follows from Eq. (7) that the emf depends not only on the difference in junction temperatures but also on the absolute values. However, since the quadratic dependence is not too strong, Eq. (7) can usually be closely approximated by a linear relation if the temperature difference $(T_1 - T_2)$ is not too great. Thus, for example a copper–constantan thermocouple for the range 0–50°C gives a linearity corresponding to $\pm\frac{1}{2}$°C.

The differential coefficient of Eq. (7) is the sensitivity, or *thermoelectric power*, of the thermocouple:

$$S = \frac{dV}{dT_1} = \alpha + 2\gamma T_1. \tag{8}$$

It is usually expressed in microvolts per degree centigrade and forms a useful basis for the comparison of various thermocouple types. As shown in Table 5.3, the sensitivity varies from 6.2 to 80 μV/°C for the most commonly used pairs.

Table 5.3 Properties of Some Common Thermocouples

Thermo-couple	Sensitivity at 20°C, μV/°C	Useful range, °C	Remarks: accuracy
Copper/Constantan ($Cu_{100}/Cu_{57}Ni_{43}$)	45	−150 to +350	Approx. $\pm\frac{1}{2}$%
Iron/Constantan	52	−150 to +1000	Approx. ±1%
Chromel/alumel ($Ni_{90}Cr_{10}/Ni_{94}Mn_3Al_2Si_1$)	40	−200 to +1200	Good in a hostile environment: approx. $\pm\frac{1}{2}$%
Chromel/constantan	80	0 to 500	Good stability: highest sensitivity of common materials.
Platinum/platinum–rhodium ($Pt_{100}/Pt_{90}Rh_{10}$)	6.5	0 to +1500	Highly stable, expensive, small sensitivity: approx. $\pm\frac{1}{4}$%

Since Eq. (7) is not exact, it cannot be used as the basis of calibration over wide temperature ranges. For most of the common thermocouple pairs, calibration data in tabular form is available using the ice point (0°C) as the reference temperature. However, it should be noted that this presupposes that the purity and uniformity of the thermocouple material is held to a high standard. To achieve accuracies of better than $\frac{1}{2}$%, it is normally necessary to calibrate each thermocouple individually.

The proper application of thermocouples requires an understanding of the laws governing their behavior. These can be stated as follows:

1. Temperature gradients along a homogeneous wire will not affect the thermal emf if the junction temperatures remain the same. Thus, in Figure 5.13(a), the fact that portions of wire B are at a different temperature has no effect on the emf.

2. If a third metal C is introduced into the circuit as shown in Figure 5.13(b), then if the two new junctions so formed are at the same temperature, the net emf is the same as if metal C were absent. This important law enables materials other than the thermocouple materials to be used in the measuring circuit, with the stipulation that the materials be homogeneous and that any junctions so formed be at the same temperature.

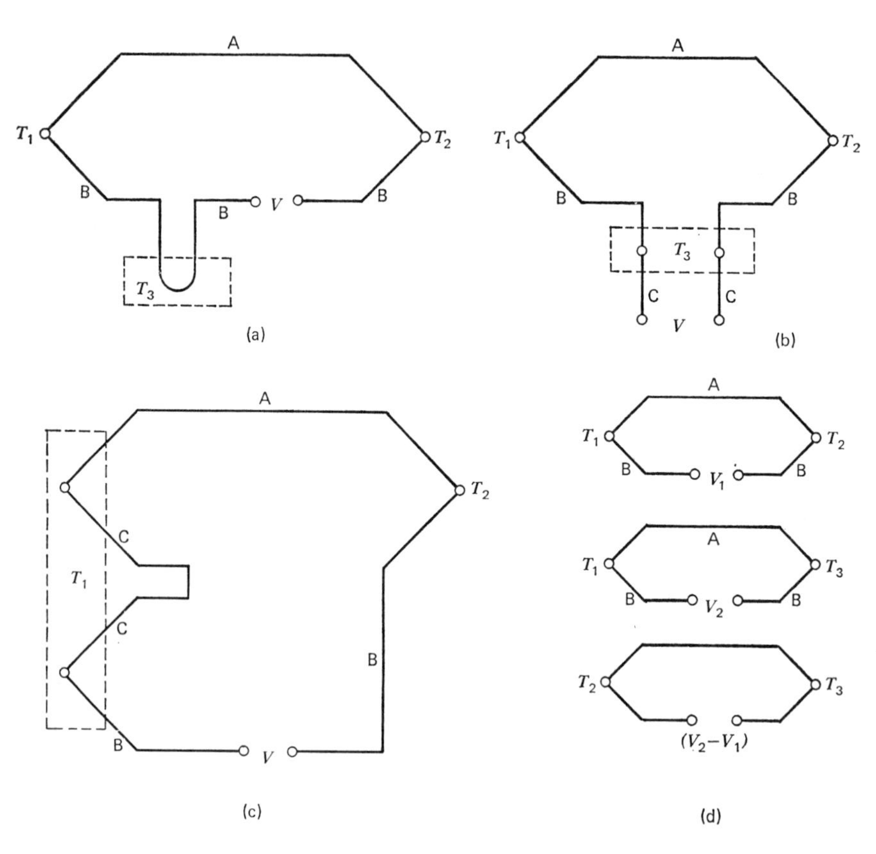

Figure 5.13. Thermocouple circuits illustrating the thermoelectric laws.

3. If a third metal C is introduced between metals A and B, as shown in Figure 5.13(c), then if the junctions AC and BC are both at the same temperature T_1, the net emf is unchanged.

4. If, as shown in Figure 5.13(d), a thermocouple produces an emf V_1 when its junctions are at temperatures T_1 and T_2 and an emf V_2 when the temperatures are T_1 and T_3, then it will produce an emf of $(V_2 - V_1)$ when the temperatures are T_2 and T_3. The practical importance of this law arises from the fact that it enables the calibration curves for a certain reference temperature T_1 to be used to derive the calibration curve for a reference temperature T_2. It should be pointed out that this is an approximate law holding only if the difference between T_1 and T_2 is not too large.

5.2.2 Practical Aspects

The temperature of the measuring junction can only be determined from the thermoelectric emf if the absolute temperature of the reference junction is known. This can be achieved either by measuring the reference temperature with a standard direct-reading thermometer or by containing the reference junction in a bath of well-defined temperature. Such a bath, for the most accurate work, consists of a triple-point-of-water apparatus for which the temperature is $+0.01 \pm 0.0005$°C. A less complex procedure is to use an ice bath; this, when carefully constructed and used, is capable of achieving an accuracy of 0.05°C with a reproducibility of 0.001°C.

A far simpler, although less accurate, solution to the reference-temperature problem is to use a reference-temperature compensator. The basic idea of such a circuit is to generate an emf that will exactly compensate for variations in the reference-junction temperature. In the compensator circuit shown in Figure 5.14, the thermally sensitive bridge is designed to generate an emf that varies with the enclosure temperature T_2 (normally ambient) in such a

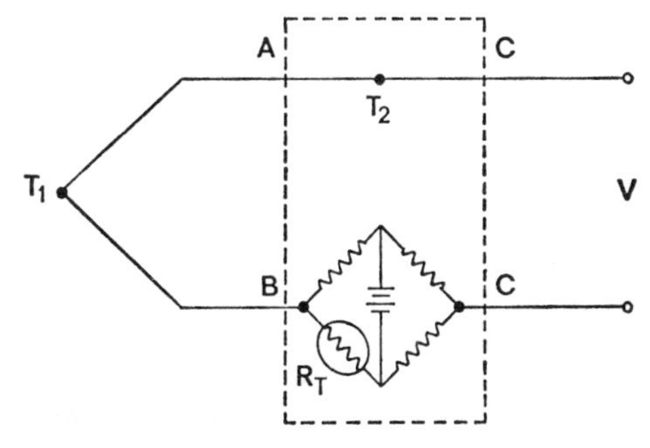

Figure 5.14. Bridge-type reference-junction compensator.

way that variations in the junction AC (also at T_2) are nullified. If the reference-temperature compensator is designed to simulate the ice point, the bridge will be adjusted so that the total circuit emf is zero when T_1 is at the ice point. Naturally, such a system introduces errors if the enclosure temperature undergoes wide variations. However, for moderate fluctuations ($\pm 5°C$) a well-designed compensator enables an effective reference-temperature stability of $\pm 0.2°C$ to be achieved.

A digital voltmeter is one of the simplest means for directly registering thermoelectric emf's. It also has the possible advantage of generating a binary coded output for direct digital recording or computer processing. When accurate chart recording is required, the self-balancing potentiometric recorder shown in Figure 5.15 can be used. This instrument has the advantage that its linearity is independent of the amplifier and motor and depends only on the linearity of the thermocouple and potentiometer.

Many examples exist of the application of thermocouples in biological work [4c]. Their small size, the ease with each they can be fabricated and good long-term stability are some of the factors favoring their choice. On the other hand, compared to thermistor sensors, they suffer from the disadvantages of a small output voltage and the need to provide a reference temperature or reference compensator. Like thermistors, thermocouples can be inserted into catheters and hypodermic needles. Special needles are commercially available that permit a thermocouple to be subcutaneously implanted, the needle being withdrawn to leave the thermocouple in place.

Very small diameter wire can be successfully used to fabricate thermocouples for applications where freedom from conduction and radiation errors, speed of response, and good spatial resolution are demanded. Battist et al. [25], for example, have described the fabrication of chromel-constantan thermocouples from 13 μm wire. To spot weld the two wires, they used a pulsed laser focused through a microscope. In this way they were able to achieve a bead diameter of around 30 μm and a thermal time constant of less than 1 msec in still water. Micron size thermocouples can also be fabricated by vacuum deposition of the two metal types onto a suitable substrate. Reed [26], for example, has described thermocouples fabricated by this means on quartz fibers. Their small size and very fast response ($\sim \mu$sec) make them suitable for intracellular transient temperature measurements.

To increase the sensitivity of a thermocouple a number of thermocouples can be connected in series. Such an arrangement, called a *thermopile*, has a sensitivity that is simply the individual thermocouple sensitivity times the number of pairs involved. Thermopiles fabricated by vacuum deposition of the metal array can be made having very small dimensions and fast response times [27]. As discussed in Section 5.6.3, they are particularly useful for infrared energy measurements.

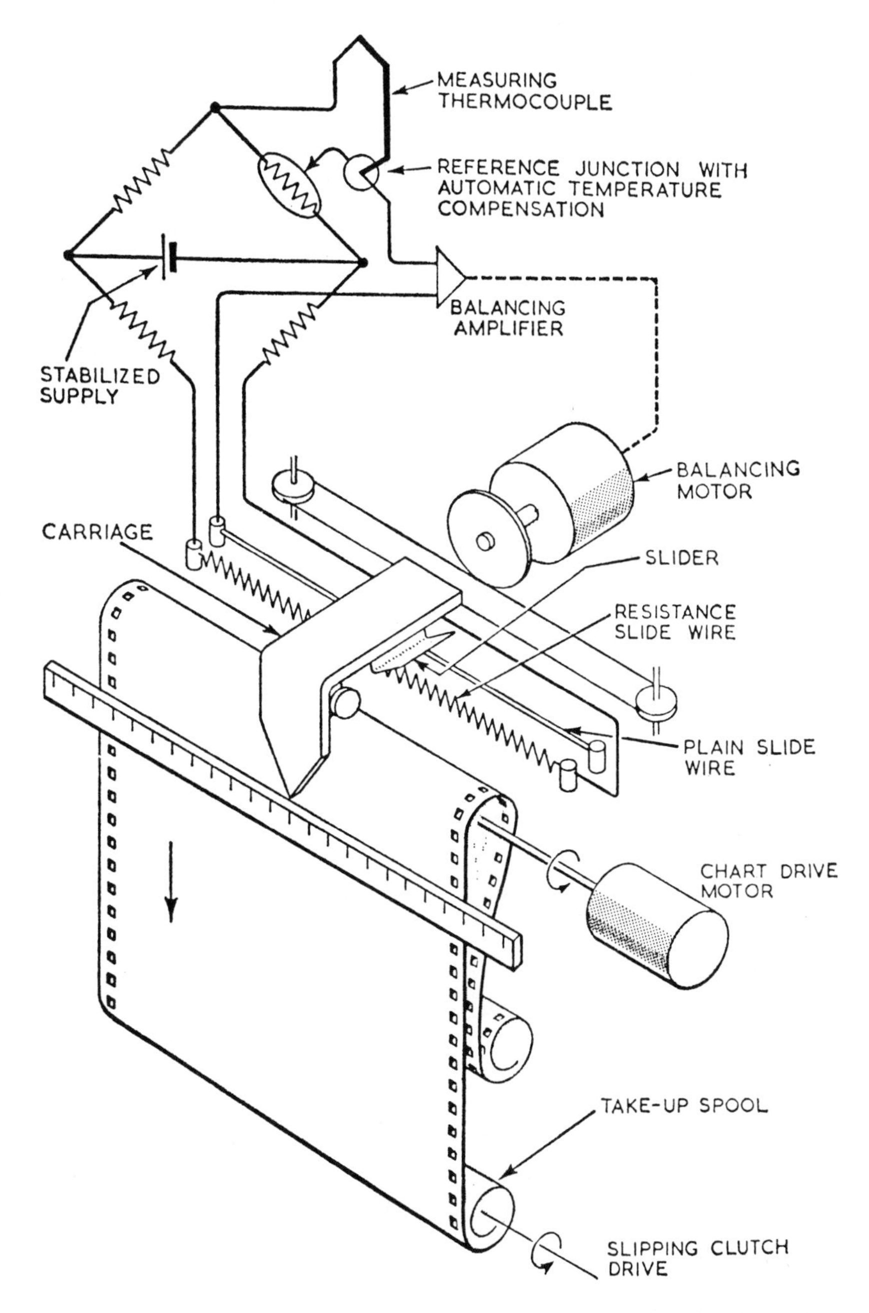

Figure 5.15. Strip-chart self-balancing potentiometer system (reproduced, with permission, from A. F. Giles, *Electric Sensing Devices*, Newnes: London, 1966).

5.3 P–N JUNCTION DIODE THERMOMETERS

It is generally found that a p–n junction diode when supplied with a constant current exhibits a terminal voltage that varies linearly with temperature (see Figure 5.16). The high degree of linearity normally observed is a particularly attractive feature of this type of transducer, for it allows calibration to be carried out using only two fixed temperature points.

Germanium [28–30], silicon [30, 31], and gallium arsenide [32] diodes have all been investigated over wide temperature ranges. Barton [29] reported that commercial germanium diodes exhibited linear temperature characteristics from 20°K to more than 30°C. Both silicon and germanium diodes were investigated by McNamara [20] and were found to be highly linear with only small variations in sensitivities between diodes of the same kind, over the range −40° to +100°C. A more recent detailed investigation of silicon diodes by Scalar and Pollock [31] revealed that the linearity extended down to 40°K and that with individual calibration, they perform usefully as thermometers down to 4°K.

An understanding of the temperature characteristics of p–n junction diodes can be gained by considering the current–voltage equation for a silicon diode in an intermediate forward-biased range of operation. This equation can be expressed as

$$I = I_0\, e^{qV/2kT}, \tag{9}$$

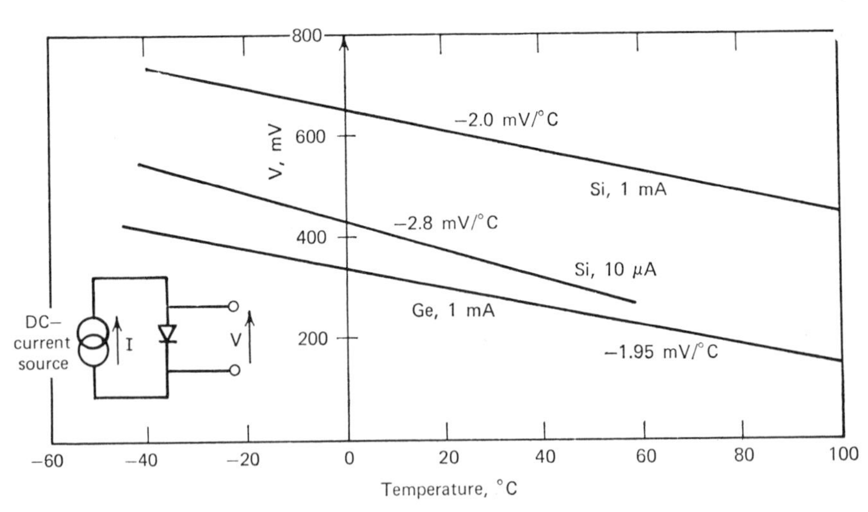

Figure 5.16. Measured temperature characteristics of Ge and Si diodes operated under constant current conditions (data taken from Refs. 30 and 31).

where I_0 is the saturation current, which is itself a strong function of temperature. It can be shown that the temperature-dependence of I_0 for high-level injection conditions of operation can be written as

$$I_0 = f(T)\, T^{3/2} \exp\left(\frac{-E_g}{2kT}\right). \tag{10}$$

where E_g is the energy band gap for silicon at 0°K. It turns out [31] that the function $f(T)$ has a dependence that essentially cancels out the $T^{3/2}$ term, with the result that Eqs. (9) and (10) can be combined to yield

$$V = \frac{E_g}{q} - \frac{2kT}{q}[\ln K - \ln I], \tag{11}$$

where K is a constant, independent of temperature, for a diode of a given type. From Eq. (11), it follows that when the diode is operated under constant-current conditions, the diode voltage is linearly related to the temperature, and the sensitivity is given by

$$\frac{dV}{dT} = -\frac{2k}{q}[\ln K - \ln I].$$

Typically, for a silicon diode operated at 10 μA, the sensitivity is approximately −2.8 mV/°C; it drops to about −2.0 mV/°C for a current of 1 mA.

Griffiths and Hill [33] have described the design of a silicon-diode body-temperature thermometer that uses an operational amplifier to obtain a closed loop voltage gain of 500 and has an output sensitivity of about 1 V/°C. A chronically implanted diode probe for measuring the brain temperature of cats has also been reported by Granfield and Smaha [34].

5.4 FREQUENCY-CHANGE TEMPERATURE TRANSDUCERS

Although all the methods for temperature measurement discussed so far can be adapted to digital read-out by using an analog–digital converter, certain methods of transduction exist that, although they are not true digital transducers, are much more readily and economically adapted to give a digital output. Transducers that produce a frequency change are of this type, and two examples will now be briefly discussed.

The first example makes use of the capacitance temperature dependence of certain ceramic-type capacitors whose temperature coefficient can be reasonably well controlled in the manufacturing process. When such a capacitor is used in an L–C resonant circuit, it is found that if the temperature range is reasonably small (±5°C), the resonant frequency is linearly related to the

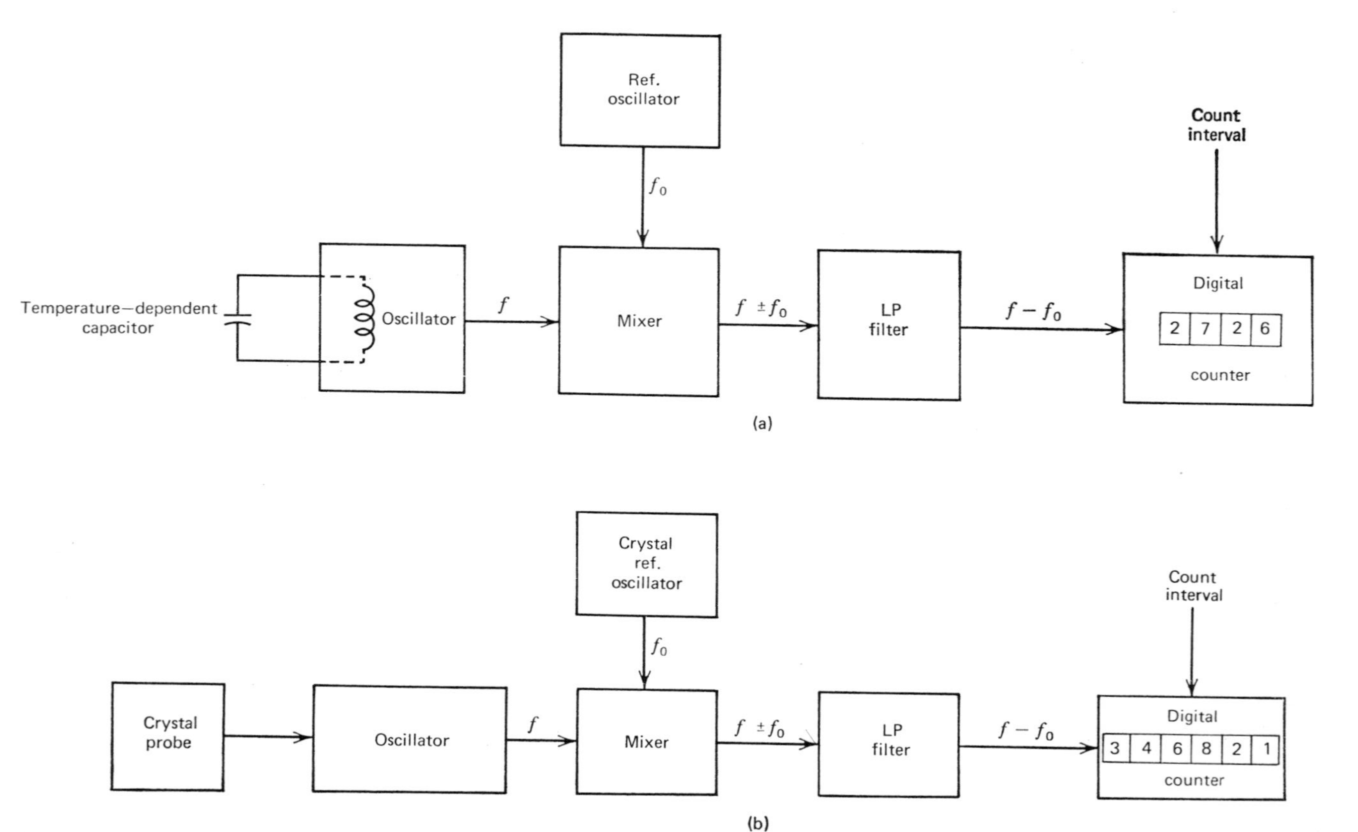

Figure 5.17. Digital temperature transducers: (a) temperature-dependent capacitor; (b) quartz-crystal thermometer.

temperature. Thus, by using this L–C circuit as the frequency-determining element of an oscillator, an output can be obtained in the form of a frequency, the change in frequency being proportional to the temperature change. A digital output can be obtained in the manner illustrated in Figure 5.17(a). In this system the outputs from the temperature-dependent oscillator and that from a reference oscillator are mixed; the difference between the two frequencies is selected by a filter and passed to a digital counter. By proper design, the counter can be arranged to give a direct indication of the temperature.

The second example presented is the quartz-crystal digital thermometer system illustrated in Figure 5.17(b). For this system the temperature-dependence of a quartz-crystal resonator is the means by which temperature is converted into a linearly related frequency.

The resonant frequency of a quartz crystal over the range -50 to $+250°C$ can be represented by the third-order polynomial [35, 13]

$$f(T) = f(0)[1 + aT + bT^2 + cT^3],$$

where $f(T)$ is the resonant frequency at a temperature T; $f(0)$ is the resonant frequency at 0°C; and a, b, and c are constants. It is found that the coefficients expressing the nonlinearity, b and c, can be made zero when a certain crystallographic orientation and the lowest-frequency shear mode of operation are used. Under these conditions, the frequency–temperature characteristic is essentially linear and the temperature coefficient is 35.4 ppm/°C. More specifically, over the range -40 to $+250°C$, the device is linear to within $\pm 0.05\%$.

To use the quartz crystal as a temperature transducer, the probe forms the controlling element of an oscillator. To measure the change in frequency, a temperature-controlled reference oscillator is mixed with the probe oscillator. The difference frequency is filtered out and counted over a fixed time interval to yield a digital output proportional to the temperature.

In a commercial version,* the reference oscillator frequency is 28.2 MHz and the sensor oscillator is designed to give an identical frequency at 0°C. A change of 1°C causes a frequency change of $28.2 \times 10^6 \times 35.4 \times 10^{-6} = 1000$ Hz. Hence, by counting for 0.1 sec, on a five-digit counter the temperature will be correctly indicated, with a resolution of 0.01°C. Increased resolution can be achieved by simply counting for a longer period of time (e.g., a 10-sec counting interval increases the resolution to 0.0001°C). An absolute accuracy of 0.02°C can be achieved with a linearity that is some 10 times better than that for a platinum resistance thermometer.

* Hewlett-Packard Co., Palo Alto, Calif.

5.5 CHEMICAL THERMOMETRY

5.1.1 Liquid Crystals

Liquid crystals are a class of substances that resemble a liquid in so far as the mechanical properties are concerned, yet they possess many of the optical properties of a single crystal [36–40]. In molecular arrangement the liquid–crystal phase can be thought of as a collection of one- or two-dimensional crystals organized in a particular manner that is a characteristic of the substance. Three classes of this organization can be identified: the nematic, the semitic, and the cholesteric phases. Of particular interest for temperature measurements are substances that can exist in the cholesteric phase. These materials, as will be seen, exhibit some remarkable changes in their optical properties when the temperature is varied [39].

In structure, the cholesteric phase consists of a two-dimensional layered arrangement in which the molecules in a particular layer lie parallel to one another with their longitudinal axes in the plane of the layer. Adjacent layers are aligned at a small angle to one another in such a manner that a helical path is traced out by the molecular direction as one moves normal to the planes. When illuminated by white light, it is found that a liquid crystal in the cholesteric phase breaks up the incident light into a circularly polarized transmitted component and an oppositely polarized reflected (scattered) component. The scattered intensity is strongly wavelength-dependent, so that a characteristic color may be observed, depending on the substance and its temperature. Since the molecular arrangement, and in particular the pitch of the helix, is strongly temperature-dependent, it is not surprising to find a rapid change in the characteristic color of cholesteric substances when heated or cooled through certain temperature ranges. For example, certain mixtures of cholesteric esters exhibit a change in iridescence through red, yellow, green, and blue as the substance is heated from 38°C through to 40°C. The range in temperature over which the color change occurs can be controlled by adjusting the mixture proportions. A further feature of certain cholesteric esters is the existence of several phases with well-defined transition temperatures. For example, cholesteryl-*n*-nonanoate exhibits the following phase transitions [38]:

$$\text{Solid} \xleftrightarrow{74^\circ\text{C}} \text{Semitic liquid} \xleftrightarrow{76.3^\circ\text{C}} \text{cholesteric liquid} \xleftrightarrow{92.1^\circ\text{C}} \text{Isotropic liquid.}$$

The rapid color changes that occur with relatively small temperature changes enables one to measure surface temperatures either by painting or spraying onto the surface the liquid-crystal substance or by using a plastic-film-encapsulated liquid crystal* that can be applied directly to the surface [39b]. A color photograph of the surface then reveals the temperature distribution in the form of contours containing areas of the same color. By means of a calibration chart, the absolute temperature can be determined at any given point. By this means it is possible to discriminate temperature differences of around 0.1°C. These techniques have been usefully applied for nondestructive testing of aerospace materials [41]; they have also been used on an experimental basis for determining skin-surface temperature distributions [42, 43].

5.2.2 Solid–Liquid Transition Thermometers

Another chemical method for temperature indication is based on the well-defined solid–liquid phase transition temperatures of certain substances. For example, a mixture of 1-bromo-2-nitrobenzene and 1-chloro-2-nitrobenzene displays a precisely defined melting point that depends in a well-defined manner on the proportions of the mixture. Such a substance is called a solid solution, because on lowering the temperature below the melting point a crystalline phase is formed in which the composition of each crystallite has the same mixture proportions as the liquid phase. A further important feature of this particular mixture is the fact that the range of melting points covers the range demanded for a clinical thermometer. Thus, the temperature range 96–104.8°F can be covered in 0.2°F steps by a matrix of 45 elements, each element differing from its neighbor by having a composition whose melting point differs by 0.2°F. A disposable clinical thermometer of this form, having digital read-out, is illustrated in Figure 5.18.

To provide a permanent visual indication of the change in state the design illustrated in Figure 5.18(c) can be used [44, 45]. In this arrangement, the solid solution contained within the depression in aluminum foil is separated (prior to activating the sensor) from a dye-containing layer by a thin membrane. This membrane insures that the solid solution stays in a reversible state prior to withdrawing the thermometer strip from the dispenser. When the strip is withdrawn, rollers in the dispenser cause the membrane to be punctured, so that when the melting point of a particular element is exceeded, the liquid flows into the dye-containing layer, causing the dye to be dissolved. The upper layer of each well consists of a opaque white absorbent layer (e.g., filter paper) that changes color when in contact with the dissolved dye, thereby providing a permanent visual indication of the phase change in the solid solution. Thus, as shown in Figure 5.18(a), when used to measure oral temperatures, all elements of the strip thermometer whose melting points lie below the oral temperature change color, so that a permanent record of the temperature is obtained.

* An adhesive disc containing a cholesteric liquid-crystal, designed for monitoring temperature ranges in the newborn, is available from Hoffman-La Roche, New Jersey.

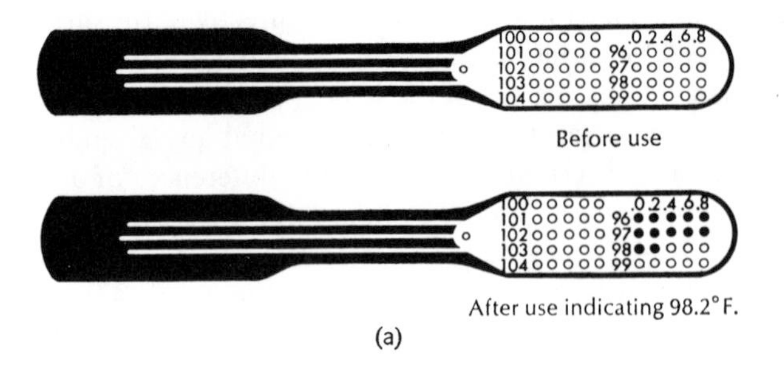

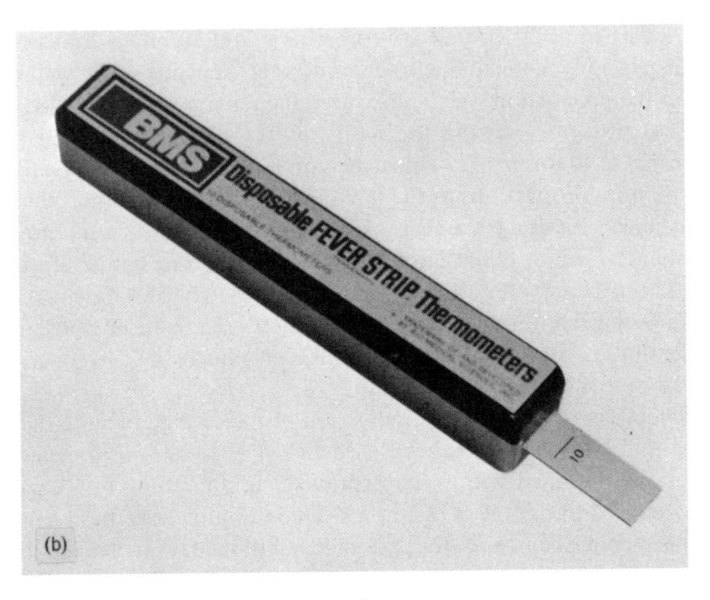

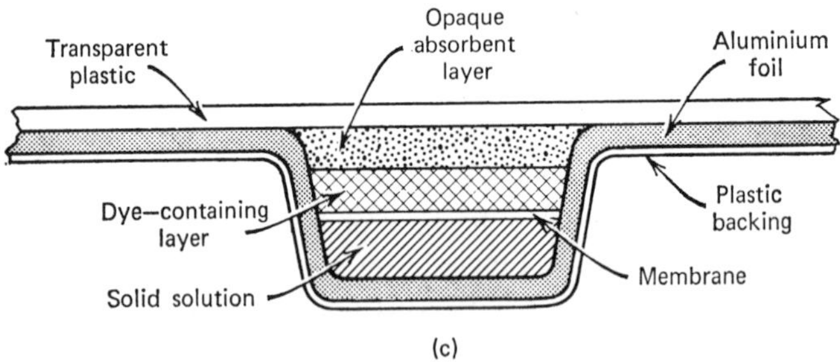

Figure 5.18. Disposable temperature thermometer with digital readout: (a) strip thermometer; (b) thermometer dispenser (reproduced, with permission, from Bio-Medical Sciences Inc., N.J.); and (c) details of sensor.

5.6 RADIATION THERMOMETRY

All bodies radiate energy in the form of electromagnetic waves, the wavelength of which, for moderate temperatures, is dominantly in the far and extreme infrared regions. Only for temperatures above about 800°C is there sufficient short-wavelength energy to make visual observation possible. The relation between the energy emitted from a surface and the surface temperature forms the basis of radiation thermometry. Measurement of the radiant emission either over a restricted bandwidth or over the full spectrum enables the temperature to be found.

For many years optical pyrometers have been used for measuring very high temperatures (e.g., blast-furnace temperatures). In such applications the method's prime advantages stem from the fact that it is contactless, thereby avoiding the necessity of requiring that the temperature probe withstand the hostile environment. Further advantages of its noncontacting nature are the ability to make the measurements at a considerable distance from the source, and the ability to scan the surface of the object and thereby produce a visual map of the temperature distribution. This latter technique, when applied for measuring the temperature distribution of the skin is called *medical thermography* [46–48].

The temperature of human skin is influenced by factors such as surface blood flow, heat generation in the underlying tissue, and surface heat loss. Thus, the temperature distribution on the skin is a window that allows one to view, in a somewhat distorted manner, many of the underlying vascular and tissue changes. The variation of the temperature distribution from the normal pattern or the variation over a period of time has proved to be a significant technique for clinical investigation. Thermography has been found particularly useful in the early detection of carcinoma of the breast, in the study of peripheral vascular diseases, in the detection of carotid artery insufficiency, and in a variety of research studies. But before describing the manner in which such measurements can be made we shall briefly review some of the relevant fundamentals of infrared emission and detection.

5.6.1 Basic Principles [49, 50]

The flux emitted by a body at an absolute temperature T is given by the well-known Planck equation multiplied by the emissivity ε of the surface, i.e.,

$$W_\lambda = \frac{\varepsilon(\lambda)C_1}{\lambda^5}\,[e^{C_2/\lambda T} - 1]^{-1}, \tag{12}$$

where W_λ is the radiant flux emitted per unit area per unit wavelength centered at a wavelength λ, and the constants C_1 and C_2 are given by

$$C_1 = 2\pi hc^2 = 3.74 \times 10^{-12} \text{ W-cm}^2$$

$$C_2 = \frac{hc}{k} = 1.44 \text{ cm-}^\circ\text{K}.$$

The emissivity ε, which expresses the degree by which the surface deviates from an ideal black body ($\varepsilon = 1$), is generally found to be wavelength-dependent.

By differentiating Eq. (12) and equating to zero, the wavelength at which E_λ is a maximum can be found. When ε remains constant this is given by

$$\lambda_m = \frac{2898}{T} \ \mu\text{m}, \tag{13}$$

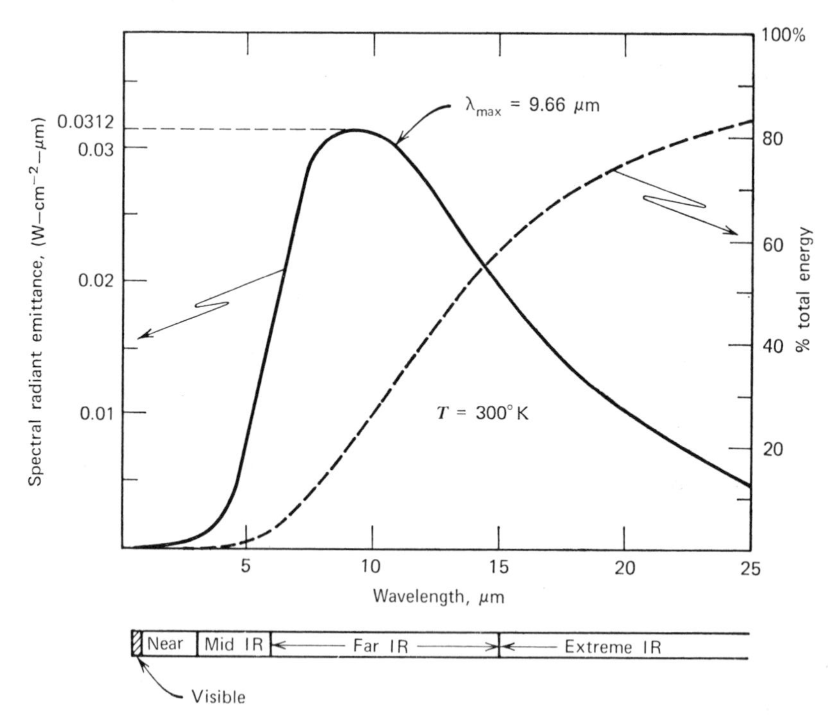

Figure 5.19. Infrared emission from a black body at 300°K. The right hand scale shows the percentage of the total energy that lies below λ.

which is known as Wien's displacement law. In addition, by integrating Eq. (12) from $\lambda = 0$ to ∞ the total radiated energy can be determined. The result known as the Stefan–Boltzmann equation, can be expressed as

$$W_T = \int_0^\infty W_\lambda \, d\lambda \qquad (14)$$
$$= \varepsilon \sigma T^4,$$

where $\sigma = 5.7 \times 10^{-12}$ W-cm^{-2}-°K^{-4} is the Stefan–Boltzmann constant and ε has been assumed independent of wavelength.

Equation (12), expressing the manner in which the radiant energy varies with wavelength, is plotted in Figure 5.19 for $T = 300$°K (27°C) and $\varepsilon = 1$. Also plotted on the same graph is the integral

$$W_{\%} = \frac{100}{W_T} \int_0^\lambda W_\lambda \, d\lambda,$$

which is the energy emitted up to a wavelength λ expressed as a percentage of the total energy as given by Eq. (14). From this graph it will be noted that at 27°C the peak emission occurs at 9.7 μm and that approximately 90% of the total energy is emitted in the range 4–30 μm.

5.6.2 The Emissivity

Measuring W_λ or its integral enables the temperature of the source to be found if the surface emissivity is known. The influence of ε on such a measurement can be examined by calculating the change in temperature that is equivalent to a change in emissivity of $\Delta\varepsilon$. If $C_2/\lambda T > 1$, then Eq. (12) can be approximated by

$$W_\lambda = \frac{\varepsilon(\lambda) C_1}{\lambda^5} \exp\left(\frac{-C_2}{\lambda T}\right).$$

Differentiating and setting $dW = 0$, we find that

$$\Delta T = \frac{\Delta\varepsilon}{\varepsilon(\lambda)} \left(\frac{-\lambda T^2}{C_2}\right).$$

Thus, for example, if $\lambda = 3$ μm and $T = 300$°K, then for a 5% change in ε, the equivalent temperature change is nearly 1°C. It follows, therefore, that if absolute temperatures are important, a knowledge of the variation of ε with wavelength is required. However, if relative variations in temperature over a surface are of prime importance, the value of ε is of less significance if it remains constant over the surface area examined.

Measurements of the emissivity of human skin and its variation with wavelength have been made by various researchers:* some have involved measurements on excised skin; others have been of the in vivo type. By measuring the total energy emitted in the range 0.2–20 μm, Mitchell et al. [51] concluded that for both excised European and African skin the emissivity was within 1% of unity. Such a measurement does not of course indicate the variation of ε with wavelength: the value of ε is an average value weighted by the Planck distribution function. The result is useful for measurement systems involving a broad-band detector such as a thermopile, but for the narrow-band cooled detectors such as indium antimonide, it is of little help. From in vivo measurements using a detector that was sensitive in the range 2–5.4 μm, Watmough and Oliver [52] concluded that at normal incidence the emissivity was within 2% of unity. In a subsequent paper [53] the same authors discussed some earlier results presented by Elam et al. [54] showing very large variations in ε over the range 1–6 μm and pointed out that the apparent variation was probably caused by an interpretive error. Making use of the reflection data of Derksen et al. [55] and Hardy and Muschenheim [56], Watmough and Oliver concluded that ε increased monotonically from a value of 0.95 at 2 μm to unity at about 6 μm.

5.6.3 Infrared Detectors [49, 50, 57, 58]

Infrared detectors can be classified into two categories—namely, thermal detectors and photon detectors. The most useful forms of these are as follows:

Thermal Detectors	*Photon Detectors*
Radiation thermopiles	Photoconductive cells
Thermistor bolometers	Photovoltaic cells
Pyroelectric detectors	
Golay cell detectors	

Before discussing these, it is necessary to consider a means by which their performance can be compared.

Of importance in an infrared detector is the ability to detect weak signals, the ability to respond quickly to changes in intensity, and the range of wavelengths over which the detector is sensitive. With regard to the first, it is helpful to define a quantity P_N, the noise equivalent power. This is the signal power that produces an output from the detector that is equal to the output produced by all sources of noise that affect the detector. In many infrared measurement systems the source of radiation is modulated at a frequency f by using, for example, a mechanical chopper. This enables an ac amplifier to be

* Ref. 51 contains a fairly complete list of papers on this subject prior to 1967.

used having a bandwidth Δf centered at f. Such a system has a much better noise performance than a dc-coupled system since the amplifier operates in a frequency range where the $1/f$ noise produced by the detector and amplifier input stage is fairly small, and the bandwidth can be altered easily to reduce the noise at the expense of a loss in frequency response. Thus, the noise equivalent power depends on both f and Δf. In addition, P_N also depends on the temperature of the radiation source, since its spectral distribution varies with temperature. To provide a common basis for detector comparison, a black body at 500°K is chosen as a reference source. Differences in detector area A, and amplifier bandwidth Δf can be eliminated by normalizing P_N to a 1-Hz bandwidth and a 1-cm^2 area. For most detectors it is found that $P_N \propto (A\Delta f)^{1/2}$, so that the specific detectivity D^*, defined by

$$D^* = \frac{(A\Delta f)^{1/2}}{P_N}$$

is a figure of merit, with units of cm-W^{-1}-(Hz)$^{1/2}$, that provides a most useful means of comparing the performance of detectors. Not included in the figure of merit is the response time, which, for certain applications, is of crucial importance in governing the choice of detector.

Shown in Figure 5.20 is a comparison of the specific detectivities of various detector types as a function of wavelength. It will be noted that the thermal detectors exhibit a flat response and can be satisfactorily operated at room temperature. On the other hand, the photon detectors have a highly selective response with a peak detectivity considerably greater than the thermal detectors if they are cooled to liquid-nitrogen temperatures or thereabouts.

A graph of the detectivity ($1/P_N$) measured at the wavelength of peak D^*, as a function of the modulation frequency is shown in Figure 5.21. It indicates that in comparison with the photon detectors, the thermal detectors rapidly deteriorate in performance as the frequency is raised.

Thermal Detectors. Thermal detectors make use of a blackened element to absorb all the incident radiation and thereby produce a temperature increase that can be measured. The manner in which the increase is registered depends on the form of detector: in a thermopile it is the generation of an emf; in a thermistor it is a change in resistance; in a pyroelectric detector it is the generation of a charge; and in the Golay cell it is the expansion of a gas. Since such detectors rely on thermal transport and achieving an equilibrium between the incoming radiative energy and the heat lost by conduction or radiation, they tend to respond rather more slowly than photon-based detectors.

Radiation Thermopiles [27]. Thermopiles consist of a series connection of a number of thermocouple pairs in the manner shown in Figure 5.22. Although

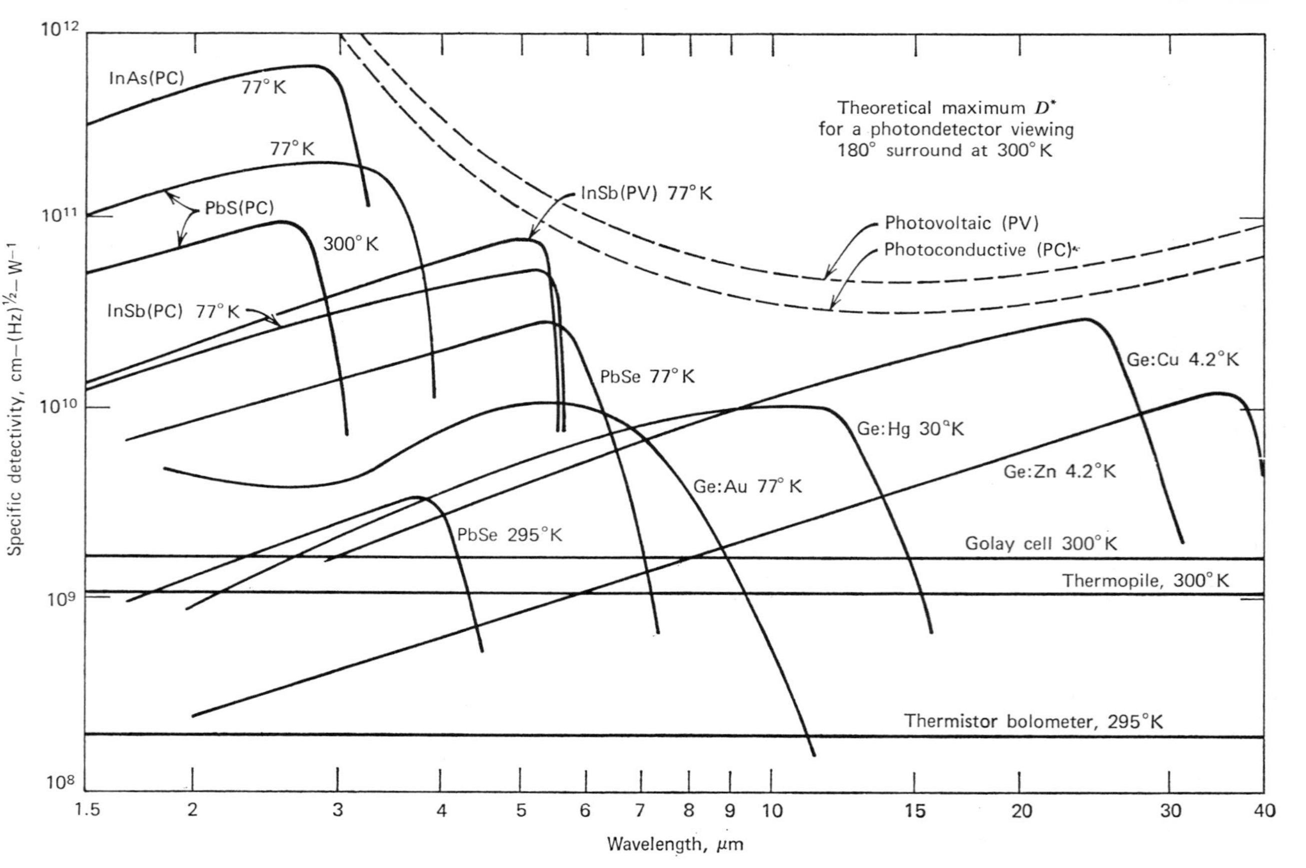

Figure 5.20. Comparison of the performance of a number of useful detectors for the far infrared region of the spectrum. The detectivity is calculated assuming an 1800-Hz chopping frequency for the photon detectors and 10 Hz for the thermal detectors (adapted from R. D. Hudson, *Infrared System Engineering*, Wiley: New York, 1969).

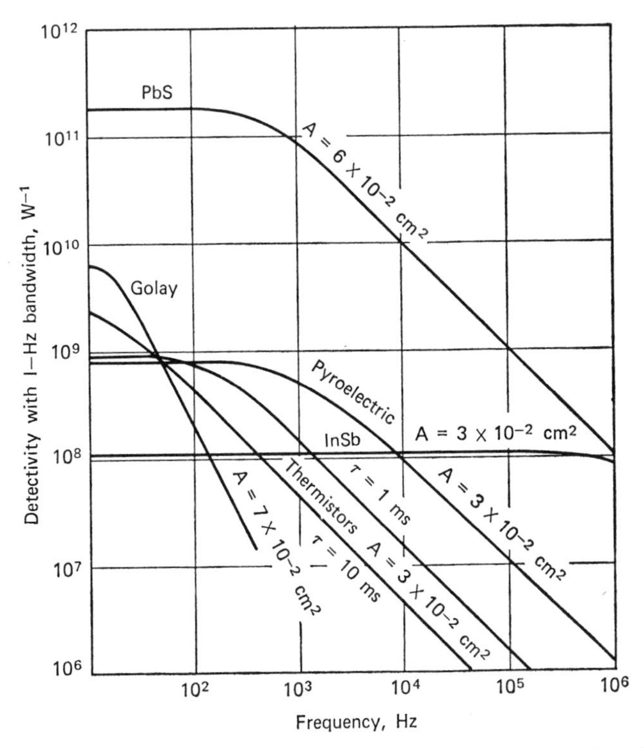

Figure 5.21. Detectivity as a function of frequency measured at the wavelength where D^* is a maximum, for various detectors operated at room temperature (reproduced, with permission, from Putley [60]).

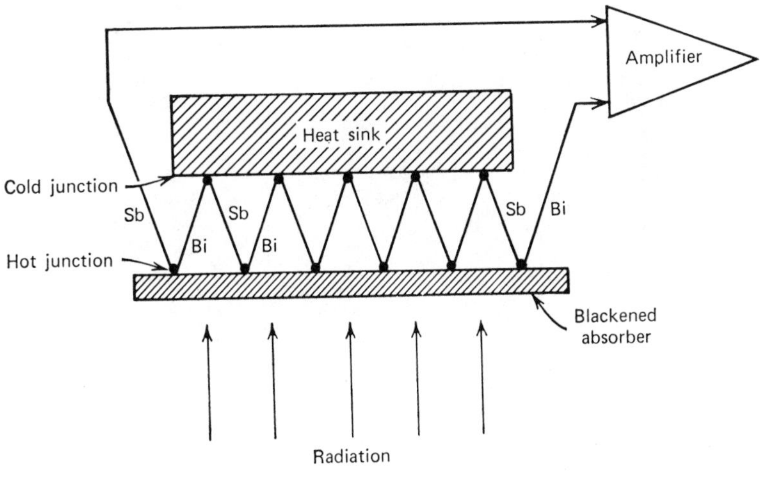

Figure 5.22. Schematic representation of a radiation thermopile.

radiation thermopiles can be fabricated from spot-welded fine wires, such devices have a long response time and a comparatively large active area. By using vacuum evaporation and photolithographic techniques, thin-film radiation thermopiles can be fabricated with a high packing density and a fast response time

A recently developed thermopile configuration [59] consists of an 8 × 8 array of antimony–bismuth thermocouple pairs in an area of 0.19 cm². Antimony–bismuth thermocouples are particularly sensitive, giving approximately 100 μV/°C, so that the 64-thermocouple array has a sensitivity of close

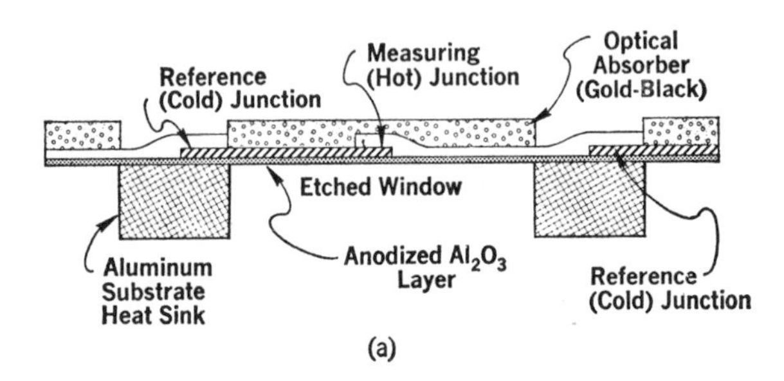

Figure 5.23. A thin-film thermopile: (a) details of the fabrication of an antimony–bismuth thermopile showing a single element of an 8 × 8 array; (b) completed thermopile with an active area containing gold-black absorbing squares having a total area of 0.1 cm² (reproduced, with permission from the Hewlett-Packard Co. [59]).

to 6.4 mV/°C. As illustrated in Figure 5.23, the thermopile makes use of the nearly perfect absorbing properties of gold-black (roughened gold) to form an absorbing surface for the incoming radiation. Each thermocouple pair consists of a thin film deposit of the two metals onto an aluminum oxide window whose thickness is only 750 Å. One junction is formed at the center of the window; the other is formed over the aluminum-substrate heat sink. This particular design is claimed to have a 10-msec response time and a wavelength response that is flat to 40 μm. Other evaporated thermopiles using as many as 89 series-connected junctions have been described by Stevens [27]. The specific detectivity achieved depends on the design; for example, one of the thermopiles described by Stevens, with an active area of 0.12 mm by 0.12 mm and a time constant of 13 μsec, has a D^* of 3.6×10^9 cm-W^{-1}-(Hz)$^{1/2}$.

Thermistor Bolometers [9, 58]. Two infrared detectors using thermistors as the temperature sensing elements are shown in Figure 5.24. In both arrangements the thermistor is in the form of a thin flake, perhaps 10 μm thick, with either a square or rectangular geometry, having linear dimensions ranging from 0.05 to 2.5 mm. A second thermistor, shielded from the incoming radiation, provides compensation, so that small changes in the heat-sink temperature will not produce an output. In the arrangement shown in Figure 5.24(a) both thermistors are mounted on electrically insulating and thermally conducting sapphire blocks. These insure good thermal transport between the thermistors and good control of the thermal time-constant. In the other arrangement shown, the flake is in direct optical and thermal contact with the lens (such a detector is of the optically immersed variety [49, p. 289]). The improved optical coupling results in a reduction in the image area of 16, and this enables a smaller detector element to be used [58]. Since $P_N \propto A^{1/2}$, this leads to the noise equivalent power being reduced by a factor of 4 over the other design.

Currently available thermistor bolometers have time constants in the range 1–15 msec (see Figure 5.21). It is usually found that the best detectivity is achieved when the modulation frequency is in the 10-Hz range. Much higher frequencies result in a decreased sensitivity, while the use of lower frequencies results in an increased $1/f$-noise component.

Pyroelectric Detectors [60]. Certain types of materials with a noncentrosymmetric structure exhibit spontaneous electric polarization. Under steady-state conditions, the surface charge created by the polarization is neutralized by external charges (due to leakage currents) and no emf is observed across the specimen. However, if the temperature of the material is changed, the state of polarization is generally altered, and as a result, an emf will be observed. This is known as the *pyroelectric effect*.

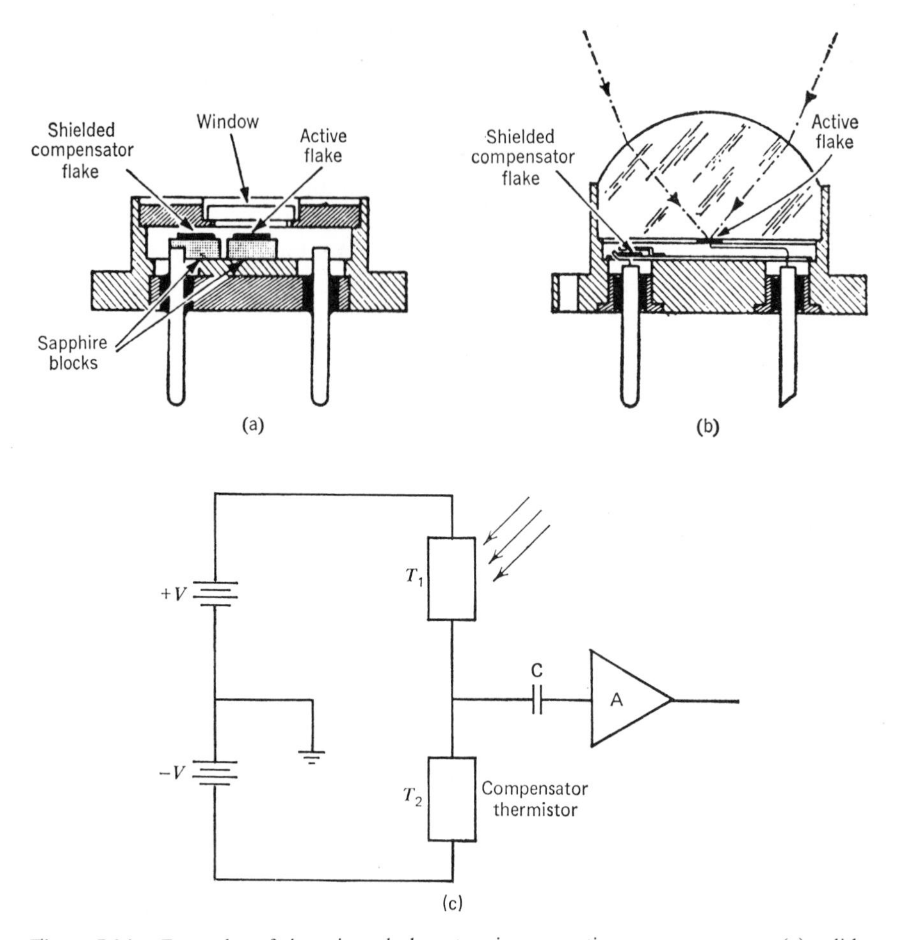

Figure 5.24. Examples of thermistor bolometers incorporating a compensator: (a) solid-backed type; (b) optically immersed type; (c) typical bias arrangement (reproduced, with permission, from F. J. Hyde, *Thermistors*, Iliffe: London, 1971).

A pyroelectric infrared detector consists of a sandwich of the material in a capacitorlike configuration, with a transparent metal electrode on the top and a thick electrode on the bottom. The incoming radiation is absorbed either within the material or, if the top surface has been blacked, on the surface. The resulting temperature change generates a surface charge that either can be measured directly using a charge-sensitive amplifier or can be detected as a change in voltage. Since the charge eventually becomes neutralized, such a detector lacks a dc response, but for a modulated radiation source this is not a disadvantage.

The ferroelectric materials used in pyroelectric detectors include barium titanate [61], triglycine sulfate (TGS) [60], polyvinylfluoride [62] and $LiTaO_3$ [63]. The last mentioned material is particularly attractive, for it is nonhygroscopic and can be polished to yield very thin slices. Theoretical evaluations [60, 64, 65] and recent experimental work indicate that pyroelectric detectors are capable of achieving a superior performance to other noncooled thermal detectors, especially when the modulation frequency is fairly high. An example of the use of a pyroelectric detector is that reported by Astheimer and Schwarz [66], who used a TGS crystal in a thermal scanning system.

Golay-Cell Detectors. The Golay cell [67, 68] is a pneumatic detector that, like the thermopile, has a flat wavelength response from the ultraviolet to the extreme infrared. As shown in Figure 5.25(a), it consists essentially of a gas-filled chamber connected by a tubular passage to a flexible diaphragm window whose outer surface is reflecting. Incoming radiation is absorbed on a specially prepared film that is mounted close to the center of the chamber. Expansion of the gas in the cell caused by the increased temperature of the film results in the diaphragm mirror being deflected. Detection of the displacement can be achieved with the optical system shown in Figure 5.25(b). An image of a fine line grid is projected into the diaphragm mirror and is reflected back along the incident path onto a photoelectric detector. Movements of the diaphragm cause the reflected grid image to shift with respect to the grid, causing the intensity of the light measured by the photodetector to change. Such a system is very sensitive to small deflections of the diaphragm. Changes in the photodetector output can be related to the change in the infrared energy falling on the cell by using a source whose temperature is known.

An inherent advantage of the Golay cell is its high signal–noise ratio, which approaches the limit imposed by the mean-square radiation fluctuation between the absorbing membrane and the background to which it is exposed. On the other hand, the Golay cell suffers from poor mechanical stability and a somewhat slow transient response compared to most photon-type detectors.

Recently Fraser [69] has described the use of a Golay cell to measure the transient heat and temperature rise produced in an excised muscle preparation at room temperature. The problem associated with using cooled photovoltaic or photoconductive detectors to measure the small temperature changes is that large artifacts are produced by the temperature gradients that exist between the detector and the source when the muscle moves. The advantage of the Golay cell is that it operates at ambient temperature, so that temperature gradients between the muscle preparation and the cell can be made very small.

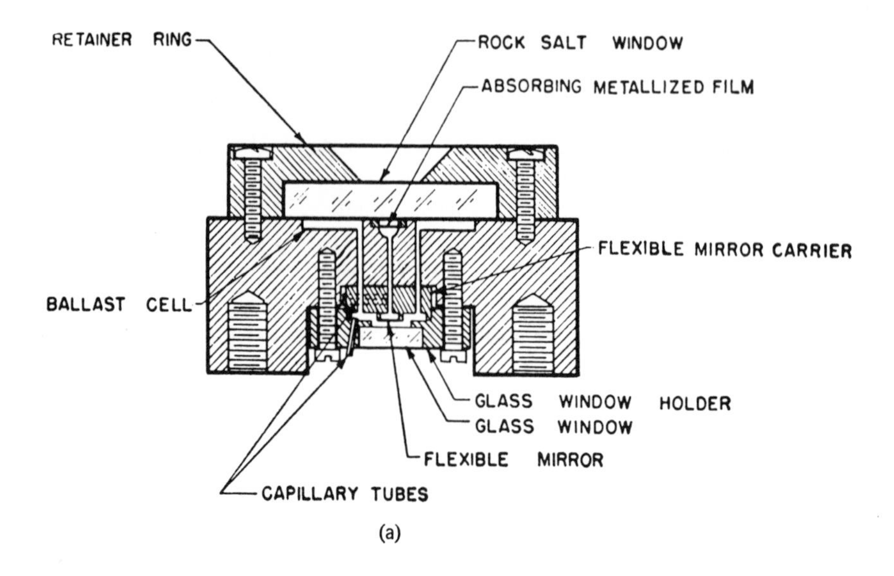

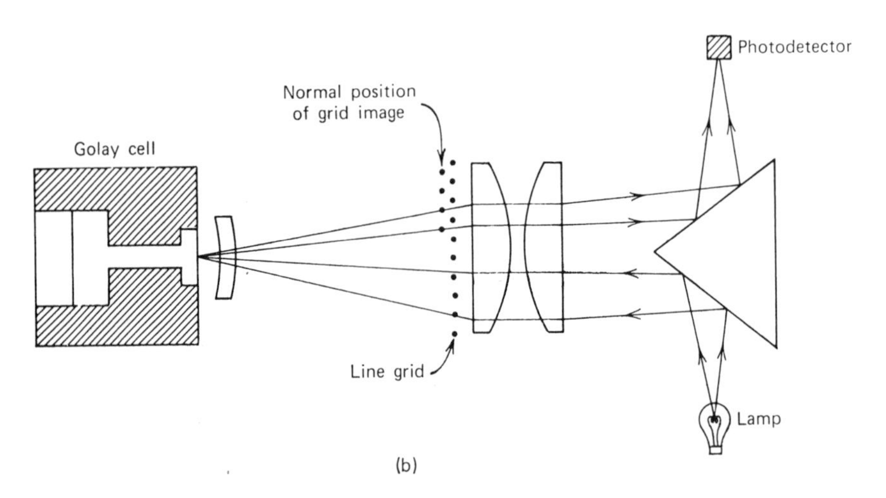

Figure 5.25. Golay-cell radiation detector: (a) details of the cell showing the pneumatic chamber, absorbing film, and diaphragm mirror; (b) details of the optical system for measuring the displacement of the diaphragm mirror (reproduced, with permission, from Golay [68]).

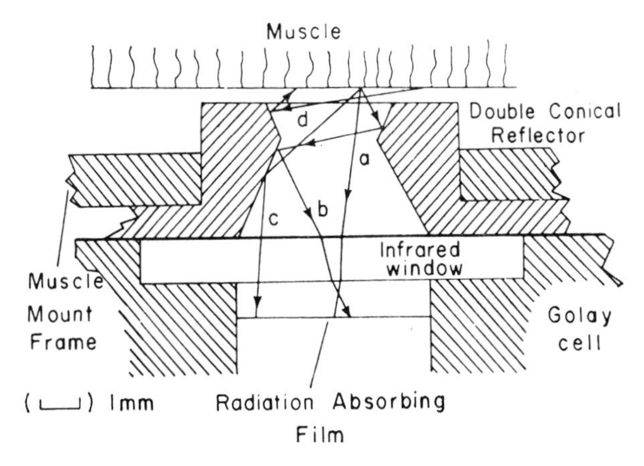

Figure 5.26. Myothermic radiometry: details of the Golay cell used to measure small transient changes in the temperature of muscle (reproduced, with permission, from Fraser [69]).

In the system described by Fraser, the double conical reflector illustrated in Figure 5.26 was used to direct most of the radiation arising from a 3-mm-diameter area of the muscle into the Golay cell. By careful design Fraser was able to achieve a temperature sensitivity of 0.001°C and a transient response of a few milliseconds.

Photon Detectors. Photon detectors rely on the direct interaction of individual photons with the crystal lattice of a semiconductor to create charge carriers that produce either a change in the conductivity (for the photoconductive detector) or result in the generation of a photovoltage (for the photovoltaic detector). Unlike thermal detectors, whose response time is mainly determined by geometrical factors, the response time of photon detectors depends on the carrier lifetimes, which, in turn are governed by such factors as the impurity density, their energy levels, and temperature. As previously noted, photon detectors have a highly selective response and are capable of achieving much higher specific detectivities than the thermal detectors. The reasons for these characteristics will be briefly discussed.

Photoconductive Cells [57, 58]. The energy of a photon can be expressed in terms of the associated wavelength λ by $E_p = 1.24/\lambda$ eV where λ is expressed in microns. Thus, if E_p is sufficiently great (i.e., the wavelength is sufficiently short) for either a hole–electron pair or a single free carrier to be generated, photoconductivity will result. Hole–electron pair production occurs when $E_p \geqslant E_g$, where E_g is the energy band gap of the semiconductor. Photoconductive detectors in which this is the dominant carrier generation mechanism are called *intrinsic* detectors [see Figure 5.27(a)].

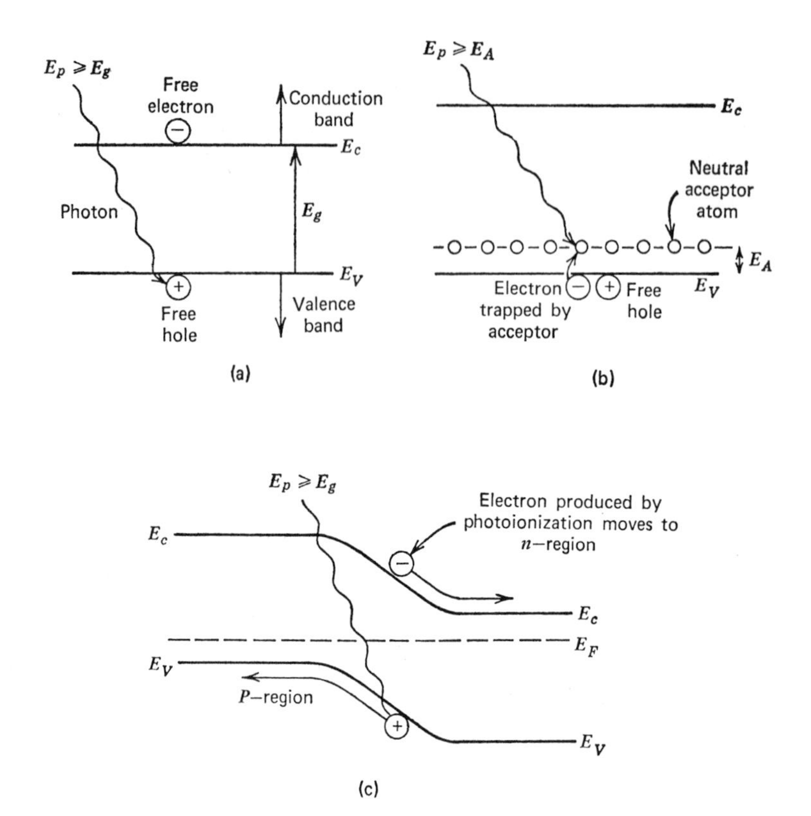

Figure 5.27. Principles of photoconductive and photovoltaic detectors: (a) intrinsic photoconductor, showing the production of a hole–electron pair; (b) extrinsic photoconductor doped with acceptor atoms. Photoionization results in the generation of a free hole: (c) generation of a hole–electron pair in the depletion region of a photovoltaic detector.

For an intrinsic detector to respond to long wavelength radiation it is necessary that the band gap be small. In this regard, indium antimonide is particularly useful [70]: it has a band gap of 0.17 eV at room temperature with a corresponding wavelength limit of 7.3 μm. The increase in band gap with decreasing temperature causes this limit to fall to 5.4 μm at liquid-nitrogen temperatures. Although other semiconductor materials are available with smaller band gaps, it is not possible to achieve a useful response with intrinsic detectors much beyond 10 μm.

Photoconductors designed to respond beyond 10 μm are generally of the *extrinsic* type, having impurities added that introduce energy levels close to either the conduction or valance bands. In such a semiconductor the incident photon causes an electron to be transferred between the impurity energy level and either the conduction or valence band, thereby creating a free carrier. This is illustrated in Figure 5.27(b) for the case of acceptor impurities. For example, zinc (an acceptor) impurities in germanium have an activation energy of 0.029 eV corresponding to a wavelength limit of 43 μm, while for mercury (also an acceptor) in germanium, $E_A = 0.083$ eV and the limit is 15 μm. It is evident from Figure 5.20 that these values correspond closely with the experimentally observed wavelength at which D^* rapidly falls off.

A further general feature of photon detectors to be noted from Figure 5.20 is that the specific detectivities increase with increasing wavelength in approximately the same manner. This is primarily because the energy of a photon decreases inversely with the wavelength, so that if the energy spectrum reaching the detector is constant, there will be more long-wavelength photons incident.

Certain intrinsic photoconductive detectors can be operated at room temperature: however, cooling always increases the detectivity by reducing the noise. With narrow-band photoconductors such as InSb, the intrinsic carrier density at room temperatures is very much larger than that arising from photoexcitation, and as a result, the signal–noise ratio is rather poor. Reducing the temperature greatly reduces the intrinsic carrier density and also has the added advantage of reducing the statistical variations, so that the noise arising from the remaining carriers is small. For extrinsic photoconductors, cooling is required to insure that the impurity atoms are in a neutral state, thereby allowing them to be photoionized. Evidently, the smaller the activation energy of the impurities the lower the temperature required for satisfactory operation. Thus, it will be noted from Figure 5.20, that the long-wavelength detectors require liquid helium rather than liquid-nitrogen temperatures.

Photovoltaic Cells. Photovoltaic detectors consist of a p–n junction located close to the surface of the semiconductor, so that hole–electron pairs created by the incoming radiation will be released either close to or within the junction depletion region. If, as illustrated in Figure 5.27(c), a hole and electron are released in the depletion region, the electric field will cause the two carriers to be swept to opposite sides of the junction, and if the diode is not loaded by the input amplifier, a change in emf will occur. On the other hand, if the diode feeds into a current amplifier, the carriers generated by photoexcitation cause a current to flow. Thus, in contrast to the photoconductive detector, which requires a bias voltage for detecting the conductance change, the photovoltaic cell generates either a current or voltage without any external source (the power delivered is of course supplied by the incoming radiation). With regard to the specific detectivity, it will be noted from Figure

5.20 that there is a small theoretical advantage in using a photovoltaic detector. This advantage arises from the presence of recombination noise in the photoconductive detector, whereas, ideally, recombination of photoexcited carriers in the depletion region of the photovoltaic detector is absent. As a result, it can be shown that the ideal photovoltaic detector has a D^* advantage of $\sqrt{2}$. A further advantage of the photovoltaic cell is that it allows one to design a detector with a small time constant without sacrificing sensitivity.

5.6.4 Radiation Thermometry Systems*

Nonscanning Radiometers. It appears that Hardy [56], in his classic studies of radiation emitted by the human body, was the first to design a radiometer specifically for the measurement of skin temperature [71]. The instrument used a conical blackened cavity with a thermopile placed at the apex, and a galvanometer to read the emf. It was claimed to be accurate to $\pm 0.01°C$. For many years Hardy's radiometer, or an adapted version of it, formed the basic measuring instrument for most investigators interested in biological radiometry. More recently, portable hand-held radiometers [72] specifically designed for biological application have become commercially available. Such instruments are particularly convenient for making contactless measurements of plant leafs, soils, and rocks, as well as for skin-temperature measurements on animals and man. It is perhaps of interest to note that some of the early work on the radiometric detection of breast cancer was done with such an instrument.

In order to illustrate the general features of radiometer design, we shall consider the system illustrated in Figure 5.28. In common with most radiometers, it uses a beam-chopper, which, in this example, consists of a motor-driven fan blade. The incident radiation energy from the object is focused by means of a primary paraboloid mirror and a secondary hyperboloid mirror onto the detector, consisting, perhaps, of a thermistor bolometer or a fast-responding thermopile. After passing through the hole in the primary mirror, the radiation is periodically interrupted by the chopper blade. If the blade is blackened and is at a known temperature, its surface will act as a black-body reference source. Since the detector alternately sees the object and reference source, the amplitude of the ac wave will be related to the difference in temperatures between the object and the blade. It follows from the Stefan–Boltzmann law, Eq. (14), that if the signal produced by the detector is proportional to the total radiation energy, then the amplitude of the ac signal is given by

$$V = K(T^4 - T_0^4),$$

* Ref 49, pp 538–540, contains an annotated list of references through to 1966.

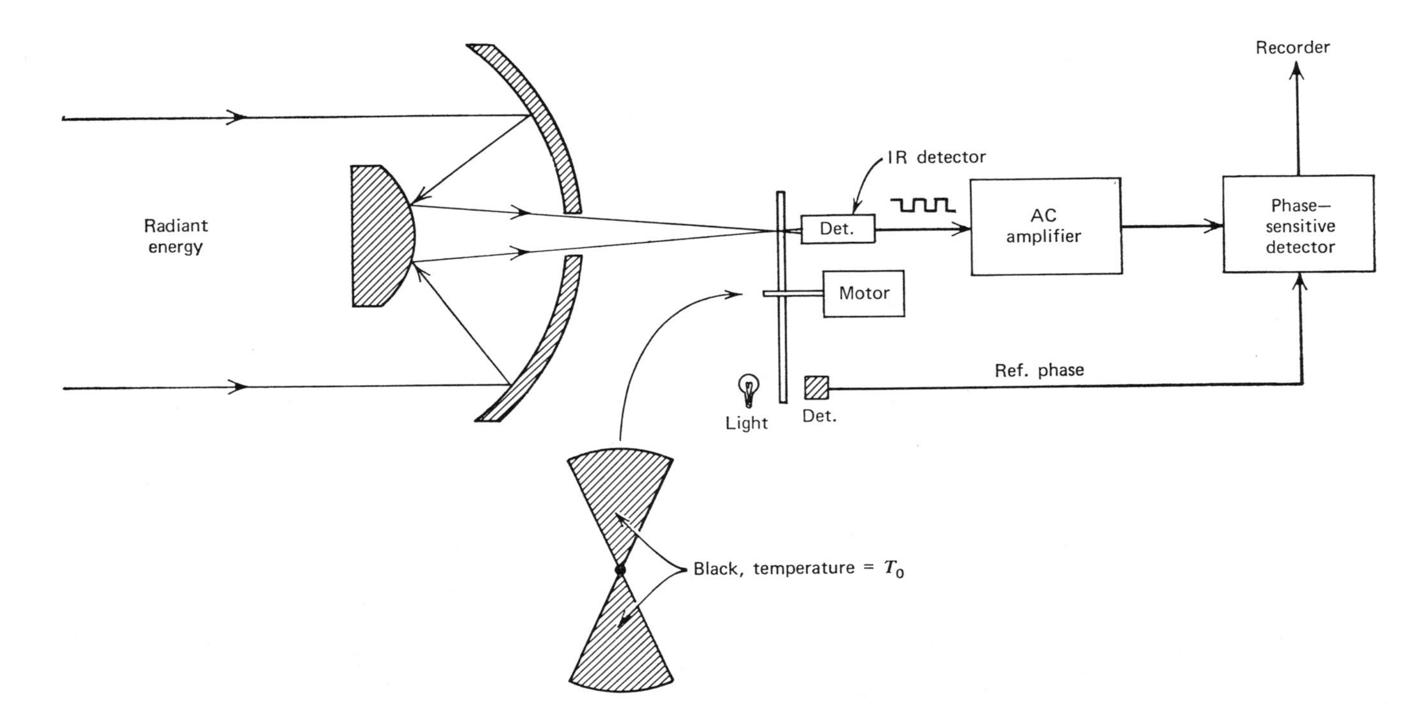

Figure 5.28. Principles of a stationary chopped-beam radiation thermometer.

where K is a constant and the emissivities have been assumed to be unity. Writing $\Delta T = T - T_0$ and expanding as a power series, we find

$$V = K T_0^4 \left\{ \frac{4\,\Delta T}{T_0} + 6\left(\frac{\Delta T}{T_0}\right)^2 + \cdots \right\}.$$

Thus, if ΔT is small, V is proportional to the temperature difference between the source and reference. For $\Delta T = 10°C$ the nonlinearity amounts to about 2% when T_0 is around room temperature.

After amplification by a narrow-band ac amplifier, the detector signal passes to a phase-sensitive demodulator that uses a reference phase signal derived from an optical source–detector arrangement. The resulting dc output for small ΔT is proportional to ΔT, and the constant of proportionality can be found by exposing the detector to a source at a known temperature.

Infrared microscopes can be adapted for spot temperature measurements. Yoder [73] has described the design and performance of such an instrument that uses an objective mirror arrangement similar to that shown in Figure 5.28 and employs a tuning fork as the beam-chopper. The spatial resolution of such a system is limited by the maximum wavelength detected. For a liquid-nitrogen-cooled InSb detector and a 74-power objective with a numerical aperture of 0.65, an 11-μm resolution can be achieved. Callahan [74], for instance, has used a microscope of this type to make nondestructive measurements of the temperature and infrared reflectivity of night-flying moths. Through the addition of an automatic X–Y specimen stage to this system, a region of the object can be scanned and a thermomicrogram produced [73].

Thermography Systems. The earliest infrared imaging system was the evaporograph* developed by Czerny [75] in 1929, based on principles described some 90 years earlier by Herschel [76]. Basically, it consists of a thin supported film blackened on one side to absorb the thermal image focused on it. The other side is exposed to an atmosphere of oil vapor that maintains a thin film of oil on its surface. Heating of this film by the absorbed radiation causes the oil-film thickness to vary, depending on the local radiation intensity. By illuminating the film with white light, interference effects occur, resulting in a visual image. Lawson, one of the pioneers of medical thermography, made use of a commercial version of the evaporograph in the initial phase of his work concerned with the detection of breast cancer [79]. However, its limited temperature and spatial resolution were serious drawbacks, and he abandoned its use in favor of a scanning thermograph.

A second form of direct thermal imaging system based on the properties of liquid crystals discussed earlier in this chapter has been described by

* Some recent work on the evaporograph is contained in Refs. 77 and 78.

Ennulat and Fergason [80]. The system uses a thin mylar membrane (6 μm thick) one side of which is sprayed with an absorbing paint containing carbon granules, the other side being sprayed with a cholesteric liquid-crystal film roughly 10 μm thick. A Cassegrain optical system was used to focus an image onto the blackened side of the film, causing the temperature to rise and thereby producing local changes in the reflecting properties of the liquid-crystal film. By illuminating the film with monochromatic light, regions of differing temperature appeared to an observer as regions of differing intensity. A laboratory version of this system had a temperature resolution of 0.2°C, a limiting spatial resolution of one line pair per millimeter, and the capability of yielding a picture in less than 5 sec.

The first scanning radiometer systems, developed in the mid-1950s, used a thermistor detector whose response time and detectivity was considerably inferior to those currently available. As a result, it was necessary to use a slow scan speed, yielding a complete picture in roughly 15 min. Improvements in the detector signal–noise ratio and more efficient optical design have resulted in greatly reduced scan times: typically, it is possible to achieve a picture with 15,000 elements, having a temperature resolution of 0.2°C, in under 1 sec.

One widely used instrument is the AGA thermovision system whose design and clinical application have been described in papers by Borg [82] and Noller and Melander [83]. As shown in Figure 5.29, the instrument makes use of two motor-driven optical components to scan the surface of the object. An oscillating plane mirror provides the vertical scan at 16 Hz, and an eight-sided silicon transmitting prism driven at 200 rev/sec provides the horizontal scan frequency of 1600 Hz, resulting in 16 pictures per second. Two germanium lenses serve to focus the radiation onto a liquid-nitrogen-cooled InSb detector. The display consists of a CRT that is intensity modulated by the detector signal and is scanned in synchronism with the mechanical scan. A picture is thereby produced whose intensity at any point can be related to the temperature. The system is claimed to have a resolution corresponding to 10,000 picture elements, with a thermal resolution of 0.2°C. However, it should be noted that Macey and Oliver [84] have drawn attention to the fact that at the high scan speeds employed in this instrument, the detector time constant limits the spatial resolution. If the scan passes over a narrow region of higher temperature, the instrument underestimates the temperature rise, because the detector output cannot respond sufficiently fast.

More recently, Watson et al. [85] have described in some detail the design of a system that has a picture time of 1 sec for a 30 cm × 30 cm field. It records 15,000 picture elements per second, covers a 27.8–36.4°C range in 0.2°C steps, has a spatial resolution of 3 mm, a depth of field of ±5 cm, and a stability of 0.2°C. A special feature of this system is the use of a very efficient

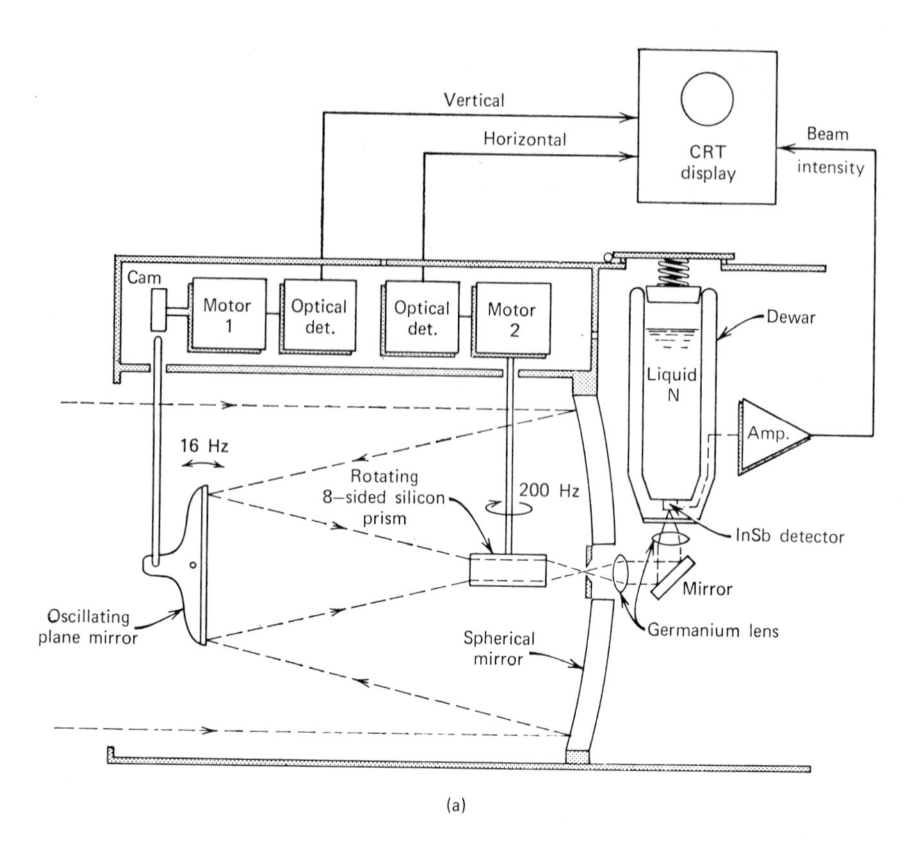

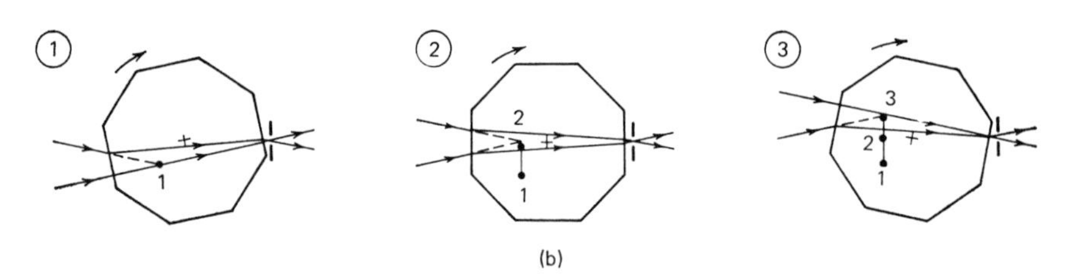

Figure 5.29. Details of a scanning-beam infrared thermograph: (a) block diagram and details of the optical system; (b) eight-sided silicon prism at three different positions, showing how the line scan is achieved (reproduced, with permission, from Borg [82]).

scanning drum incorporating 12 imaging mirrors [86]. With this arrangement a frame time utilization efficiency of 75% is achieved—a figure that is several times greater than that of most previous systems.

Another system that is commercially available has been described by Sundstrom [87]. It uses a six-sided mirror drum rotating at 75 rev/sec for the line scan and a plane mirror tilting four times per second for the frame scan. It is claimed that the system has a spatial resolution corresponding to 25,000 picture elements and that the temperature resolution is 0.1°C. With this system, as with the others described above, it is possible to make color photographs in which regions at the same temperature appear as the same color. This can be achieved by using a number of color filters and successive exposures to the CRT, which is controlled in such a manner that only those regions whose temperatures lie within a certain narrow band appear bright. Since each color filter corresponds to a particular temperature band, a picture results that is isothermally coded.

Nichols and Lamar [88] have described an interesting variation of the thermographic scanner in which the infrared "color" is translated into visible colors. This is achieved by using three detectors that are sensitive to different regions of the spectrum: an uncooled Si cell sensitive from 0.5 to 1.0 μm, an InSb cell cooled to 75°K and sensitive from 3.0 to 5.5 μm, and a mercury-doped Ge cell cooled to liquid-helium temperatures that is sensitive from 8 to 14 μm. Each detector simultaneously looks at the radiation from the scanned region of the object and produces an output dependent on the radiation intensity in the corresponding waveband. By using each detector output to modulate the intensity of a light source and combining the three beams using dichroic mirrors to provide the three primary colors, a color picture is produced in which the color of a particular region depends on the temperature as well as the emissivity and reflectivity of that region.

Finally, brief mention must be made of certain thermal imaging systems that make use of either bolometric or pyroelectric targets in special pick-up tubes of the vidicon type. Such systems offer the possibility of producing thermograms without the necessity for mechanical scanning, thereby eliminating an expensive and somewhat unreliable feature of current thermography systems.

Brissot et al. [89] have described a vidicon tube that uses a thin membrane of an organic polymer coated on one side with a gold-black layer to absorb the infrared radiation. Heating of the membrane causes its resistance to change, and as a result, a charge pattern forms that is sensed by a scanning electron beam.

The development of vidicon tubes that use a pyroelectric target as the sensing element have been described by at least two research groups [90–93]. In one of the systems described [92] the target uses a thin slice ($\sim$50 μm) of triglycine sulphate (TGS), 16 mm in diameter, coated on one side with a thin layer of gold, the other side being exposed to the scanning electron beam. Although the experimental performance was considerably inferior to the mechanically scanned systems described previously and was inadequate for clinical thermography, the performance was adequate to form a recognizable image of a human face. It would seem that with further development, a system of this type may be capable of sufficient improvement to achieve the image quality demanded for clinical work without requiring a cooled target.

REFERENCES

1. Lion, K. S. *Instrumentation in Scientific Research: Electrical Input Transducers.* McGraw-Hill: New York, 1959, Chapter 2.

2. Doebelin, E. O. *Measurement Systems: Application and Design.* McGraw-Hill: New York, 1966, Chapter 8.

3. Norton, H. N. *Handbook of Transducers for Electronic Measuring Systems.* Prentice-Hall: Englewood Cliffs, N.J., 1969, Chapter 14.

4a. Brickwedde, F. G., Ed. "Basic Concepts, Standards and Methods," in C. M. Herzfeld, Ed., *Temperature: Its Measurement and Control in Science and Industry*, Vol. III, pt. 1. Reinhold: New York, 1962–1963.

4b. Dahl, A. I., Ed. "Applied Methods and Instruments," in Herzfeld, Ref. 4a, Vol. III, pt. 2.

4c. Hardy, J. D., Ed. "Biology and Medicine," in Herzfeld, Ref. 4a, Vol. III, pt. 3.

4d. Plumb, H. H., Ed. *Temperature: Its Measurement and Control in Science and Industry*, Vol. IV. Instrument Society of America, Pittsburgh, 1973.

5. Diamond, J. M. "Linearization of Resistance Thermometers and Other Transducers." *Rev. Sci. Instrum.*, **41**, 53–60 (January 1970).

6. van der Wal, C. W., and Struik, L. C. E. "A Direct-Reading Bridge for a Platinum Resistance Thermometer." *J. Sci. Instrum.*, **2**, 143–145 (February 1969).

7. Massey, J. "Electronic Linearization of Temperature Using a Dual Element Sensing Technique." *Rev. Sci. Instrum.*, **43**, 1161–1167 (August 1972).

8. Cooper, M. G., and Lloyd, A. J. P. "Miniature Thin Film Thermometers with Rapid Response." *J. Sci. Instrum.*, **42**, 791–793 (November 1965).

9. Hyde, F. J. *Thermistors.* Iliffe: London, 1971.

10. Scarr, R. W. A., and Setterington, R. A. "Thermistors, Their Theory, Manufacture and Application." *Proc. IEE* (*London*), **107**, pt. B, 395–409 (January 1960).

11. Saburi, O., and Wakino, K. "Processing Techniques and Applications of Positive Temperature Coefficient Thermistors." *IRE Trans. Compon. Parts*, **CP-10**, 53–67 (June 1963).

12. Droms, C. R. "Thermistors for Temperature Measurements," in Ref. 4b, pp. 339–346.

13. Swartzlander, E. E. "Comparison of Temperature Sensors for Apollo Experiment Instrumentation" (Paper 69-665), in *Advances in Instrumentation*, Vol. XXIV, pt. 4. Proc. 24th Ann. ISA Conf., 1969. Instrument Society of America, Pittsburgh, 1969.

14. Prudenziati, M.; Taroni, A.; and Zanarini, G. "Semiconductor Sensors. I. Thermoresistive Devices." *IEEE Trans. Indust. Electron. Control Instrum.*, **IECI-17**, 407–414 (November 1970).

15. Beakley, W. R. "The Design of Thermistor Thermometers with Linear Calibration." *J. Sci. Instrum.*, **28**, 176–179 (June 1951).

16. Bryce, C. H., and Hole, V. H. R. "Measurement and Control by Thermistors." *Indust. Electron.*, **5**, pt. 1, 294–296 (July 1967); pt. 2, 358–363 (August 1967).

17. Trolander, H. W., and Harruff, R. W. "A Wide Range Linear Output Thermistor Sensor for Biological Temperatures." *Digest of Papers*, 6th Int. Conf. Med. Biol. Eng., Tokyo, 1965, pp. 581–582.

18. Priestley, P. T. "A Thermistor Thermometer with Digital Display." *J. Sci. Instrum.*, **40**, 505 (October 1963).

19. Nancollas, G. H., and Hardy, J. A. "A Thermistor Bridge for Use in Calorimetry." *J. Sci. Instrum.*, **45**, 290–292 (April 1967).

20. Guadagni, D. N., Kreith, F., Smyth, C. J., and Bartholomew, B. A. "Contact Probe for Skin Temperature Measurements." *J. Phys. E.*, **5**, 869–876 (September 1972).

21. Krog, J. "Thermistor Hypodermic Needle for Subcutaneous Temperature Measurement." *Rev. Sci. Instrum.*, **27**, 408–409 (June 1956).

22. Dike, P. H. *Thermoelectric Thermometry*, 3rd ed. Leeds and Northrup: Philadephia, 1958.

23. Finch, D. I. "General Principles of Thermoelectric Thermometry," in Ref. 4b, pp. 3–32.

24. Kinzie, P. A. *Thermocouple Temperature Measurement*. Wiley: New York, 1973.

25. Battist, L.; Goldner, F.; and Todreas, N. "Construction of a Fine Wire Thermocouple Capable of Repeated Insertions into and Accurate Positioning Within a Controlled Environmental Chamber." *Med. Biol. Eng.*, **7**, 445–448 (July 1969).

26. Reed, R. P. "Thin Film Sensors of Micron Size and Applications in Biothermology". Ph.D. thesis, Univ. of Texas, 1966; Diss. Abst. 67-3343, Univ. Microfilms Inc., Ann Arbor, Mich., 1967.

27. Stevens, N. B. "Radiation Thermopiles," in R. K. Willardson and A. C. Beer, Eds., *Semiconductors and Semimetals*, vol V. Academic: New York, 1970, Chapter 7.

28. Strong, C. L. "The Amateur Scientist." *Scientific American*, June 1961: see p. 196 where H. Harris is credited with the idea.

29. Barton, L. E. "Measuring Temperature with Diodes and Transistors." *Electronics*, **35**, 38–40 (4 May 1962).

30. McNamara, A. G. "Semiconductor Diodes and Transistors as Electrical Thermometers." *Rev. Sci. Instrum.*, **33**, 330–333 (March 1962).

31. Sclar, N., and Pollock, D. B. "On Diode Thermometers." *Solid State Electron.*, **15**, 473–480 (May 1972).

32. Cohen, B. G.; Snow, W. B.; and Tretola, A. R. "GaAs P-N Junction Diodes for Wide Range Thermometry." *Rev. Sci. Instrum.*, **34**, 1091–1093 (October 1963).

33. Griffiths, C. A., and Hill, D. W. "Some Applications of Microelectronics to Patients." *World Med. Instrum.*, **7**, 8–11 (February 1969).

34. Ganfield, R. A., and Smaha, L. A. "Temperature Measurements in Cats with a Chronically Implanted Sensing Device." *Physiol. Behav.*, **7**, 929–930 (December 1971).

35. Hammond, D. L., and Benjaminson, A. "The Crystal Resonator—A Digital Transducer." *IEEE Spectrum*, **6**, 53–58 (April 1969).

36. Gray, G. W. *Molecular Structure and the Properties of Liquid Crystals.* Academic: London, 1962.

37. Brown, G. H.; Dienes, G. J.; and Labes, M. M., Eds. *Liquid Crystals.* Gordon and Breach: New York, 1966.

38. Brown, G. H.; Doane, J. W.; and Neff, V. D., *A Review of the Structure and Physical Properties of Liquid Crystals.* Chemical Rubber Co.: Cleveland, 1971.

39a. Fergason, J. L. "Liquid Crystals." *Scientific American*, August 1964.

39b. Fergason, J. L. "Liquid Crystals in Nondestructive Testing." *Appl. Optics*, **7**, 1729–1737 (September 1968).

39c. Davis, F. "Liquid Crystals: A New Tool for NDT." *Res. Devel.*, **18**, 24–27 (June 1967).

40. Pick, P. G., and Fabijanic, J. "Cholesteric Liquid Crystals: Ambient Temperature Effects." *Mol. Cryst. Liquid Cryst.*, **15**, 371–376 (January 1972).

41. Woodmansee, W. E. "Aerospace Thermal Mapping Applications of Liquid Crystals." *Appl. Opt.*, **7**, 1721–1727 (September 1968).

42. Crissey, J. T.; Fergason, J. L.; and Bellenhausen, J. L. "Cutaneous Thermography with Liquid Crystals." *J. Invest. Dermatol.*, **45**, 329–333 (November 1965).

43. Selawry, O. S.; Selawry, H. S.; and Holland, J. F. "The Use of Liquid Cholesteric Crystals for Thermographic Measurement of Skin Temperature in Man." *Mol. Cryst.*, **1**, 495–501 (September 1966).

44. Weinstein, B., and Sagi, Z. L. "Disposable Thermometer." U. S. patent 3,631,720, January 1972. Filed October 1969.

45. Sagi, Z., and Weinstein, B. "Temperature Indicator." U.S. patent 3,665,770, May 1972. Filed July 1970.

46. Barnes, R. B. "Diagnostic Thermography." *Appl. Opt.*, **7**, 1673–1685 (September 1968).

47a. Whipple, H. E., Ed. "Thermography and its Clinical Applications." *N.Y. Acad. Sci.*, **121**, art. 1 (1964) (27 papers contained in this issue).

47b. Colloque International de Thermographie Médicale, *J. Radiol. Electrol*, **48** (January–February 1967) (Proc. Strasbourg Conf., 1966; 23 papers).

48. Voss, S. F. C. H. van, and Thomas, P., Eds. *Medical Thermography.* Proc. Boerhaave Course Postgrad. Med. Educ. Karger: Basel, 1969.

49. Hudson, R. D. *Infrared System Engineering.* Wiley: New York, 1969.

50. Kruse, P. W.; McGlauchin, L. D.; and McQuistan, R. B. *Elements of Infrared Technology.* Wiley: New York, 1962.

51. Mitchell, D.; Wyndham, C. H.; Hodgson, T.; and Nabarro, F. R. N. "Measurement of the Total Normal Emissivity of Skin Without the Need for Measuring Skin Temperature." *Phys. Med. Biol.*, **12**, 359–366 (July 1967).

52. Watmough, D. J., and Oliver, R. "Emissivity of Human Skin in Vivo Between 2.0 μ and 5.4 μ Measured at Normal Incidence." *Nature*, 1 June 1968, pp. 885–886.

53. Watmough, D. J., and Oliver, R. "Emissivity of Human Skin in the Waveband Between 2 μ and 6 μ." *Nature*, 10 August 1968, pp. 622–624.

54. Elam, R.; Goodwin, D. W.; and Williams, K. L. "Optical Properties of the Human Epidermis." *Nature*, 8 June 1963, pp. 1001–1002.

55. Derksen, W. L.; Monahan, I. T.; and Lawes, A. J. "Automatic Recording Reflectometer for Measuring Diffuse Reflectance in the Visible and Infrared Regions." *J. Opt. Soc. Am.*, **47**, 995–999 (November 1957).

56. Hardy, J. D., and Muschenheim, C. "The Radiation of Heat from the Human Body. IV. The Emission, Reflection, and Transmission of Infra-Red Radiation by the Human Skin." *J. Clin. Invest.*, **13**, 817–831 (September 1934).

57. Willardson, R. K., and Beer, A. C., Eds. *Semiconductors and Semimetals:* Vol. V, *Infrared Detectors.* Academic: New York, 1970.

58. Putley, E. H. "Solid State Devices for Infra-Red Detection." *J. Sci. Instrum.*, **43**, 857–868 (December 1966).

59. Hicks, C. A., and Mellon, M. R. "Optical Power Measurements Made Easy." *Hewlett-Packard J.*, **22**, 10–16 (July 1971).

60. Putley, J. H. "The Pyroelectric Detector," in Ref. 57, Chapter 6.

61. Cooper, J. "A Fast-Response Pyroelectric Thermal Detector." *J. Sci. Instrum.*, **39**, 467–472 (September 1962).

62. Phelan, R. J.; Mahler, R. J.; and Cook, A. R. "High D^* Pyroelectric Polyvinylfluoride Detectors." *Appl. Phys. Lett.*, **19**, 337–338 (1 November 1971).

63. Cooper, J. " Minimum Detectable Power of a Pyroelectric Thermal Receiver." *Rev. Sci. Instrum.*, **33**, 92–95 (January 1962).

64. Van der Ziel, A. "Pyroelectric Response and D^* of Thin Pyroelectric Films on a Substrate." *J. Appl. Phys.*, **44**, 546–549 (February 1973).

65. Roundy, C. B., and Byer, R. L. "Sensitive $LiTaO_3$ Pyroelectric Detector." *J. Appl. Phys.*, **44**, 929–931 (February 1973).

66. Astheimer, R. W., and Schwarz, F. "Thermal Imaging Using Pyroelectric Detectors." *Appl. Opt.*, **7**, 1687–1695 (September 1968).

67. Golay, M. J. E. "The Theoretical and Practical Sensitivity of the Pneumatic Infra-Red Detector." *Rev. Sci. Instrum.*, **20**, 816–820 (November 1949).

68. Golay, M. J. E. "Bridges Across the Infra-Red Radio Gap." *Proc. IRE*, **40**, 1161–1165 (October 1952).

69. Fraser, A. B. "Myothermic Radiometry." *Rev. Sci. Instrum.*, **42**, 22–26 (January 1971).

70. Kruse, P. W. "Indium Antimonide Photoconductive and Photoelectromagnetic Detectors," in Ref. 57, Chapter 2.

71. Hardy, J. D., and Soderstrom, G. F. "An Improved Apparatus for Measuring Surface and Body Temperature." *Rev. Sci. Instrum.*, **8**, 419–422 (November 1937).

72. Gates, D. M. "Sensing Biological Environments with a Portable Radiation Thermometer." *Appl. Opt.*, **7**, 1803–1809 (September 1968).

73. Yoder, J. R. "Temperature Measurement with an Infrared Microscope." *Appl. Opt.*, **7**, 1791–1796 (September 1968).

74. Callahan, P. S. "Nondestructive Temperature and Radiance Measurements on Night Flying Moths." *Appl. Opt.*, **7**, 1811–1817 (September 1968).

75. Czerny, M. "Über Photographie im Ultraroten." *Z. Phys.*, **53**, 1–12 (1929).

76. Herschel, J. F. W. "On the Chemical Action of the Rays of the Solar Spectrum on Preparations of Silver and Other Substances, Both Metallic and Non-metallic, and on Some Photographic Processes." *Phil. Trans. Roy. Soc.*, **130**, 1–59 (1840).

77. McDaniel, G. W., and Robinson, D. Z. "Thermal Imaging by Means of Evaporograph." *Appl. Opt.*, **1**, 311–324 (May 1962).

78. Sintsov, V. N. "Evaporographic Image Quality." *Appl. Opt.*, **6**, 1851–1854 (November 1967).

79. Lawson, R. N. "Thermography—A New Tool in the Investigation of Breast Lesions." *Can. Serv. Med. J.*, **13**, 517–524 (September 1957).

80. Ennulat, R. D., and Fergason, J. L. "Thermal Radiography Utilizing Liquid Crystals." *Mol. Cryst. Liquid Cryst.*, **13**, 149–164 (May 1971).

81a. Astheimer, R. W., and Wormser, E. M. "Instrument for Thermal Photography." *J. Opt. Soc. Am.*, **49**, 184–187 (February 1959).

81b. Astheimer, R. W., and Wormser, E. M. "High-Speed Infrared Radiometers." *J. Opt. Soc. Am.*, **49**, 179–183 (February 1959).

82. Borg, S.-B. "Thermal Imaging with Real Time Picture Presentations." *Appl. Opt.*, **7**, 1697–1703 (September 1968).

83. Notter, G., and Melander, O. "Thermographische Untersuchung bei Erkrankungen der Brustdrüse." *Fortschr. Rontgenstr.*, **105**, 657–664 (1966).

84. Macey, D. J., and Oliver, R. "Image Resolution in Infrared Thermography." *Phys. Med. Biol.*, **17**, 563–571 (July 1972).

85. Watson, J. L.; Gore, W. G.; Spears, A. B.; and Wolfe, P. A. "A New Scanning Thermometer." *J. Phys. E.*, **4**, 1029–1035 (December 1971).

86. Beach, A. D. "A New Optical System for Quantitative Thermograms." *J. Phys. E.*, **4**, 1025–1028 (December 1971).

87. Sundstrom, E. "Wide-Angle Infrared Camera for Industry and Medicine." *Appl. Opt.*, **7**, 1763–1768 (September 1968).

88. Nichols, L. W., and Lamar, J. "Conversion of Infrared Images to Visible in Colour." *Appl. Opt.*, **7**, 1757–1762 (September 1968).

89. Brissot, J.-J.; Desvignes, F.; and Martres, R. "Organic Semiconductor Bolometric Target for Infrared Imaging Tubes." *IEEE Trans. Electron. Devices*, **ED-20**, 613–620 (July 1973).

90. Le Carvennec, F. "Recherche d'un Dispositif Nouveau de Télévision Thermique," in J. D. McGee, D. McMullen, and E. Kahan, Eds., *Advances in Electronics and Electron Physics*, Vol. XXVIIIA. Academic: New York, 1969, pp. 265–272.

91. Charles, D. R., and Le Carvennec, F. "Infrared Pick-Up Tube with Electronic Scanning and Uncooled Target," in Ref. 90, Vol. XXXIIIA, 1972, pp. 279–284.

92. Holeman, B. R., and Wreathall, W. M., "Thermal Imaging Camera Tubes with Pyroelectric Targets." *J. Phys. D.*, **4**, 1898–1909 (December 1971).

93. Putley, E. H.; Watton, R.; Wreathall, W. M.; and Savage, S. D. "Thermal Imaging with Pyroelectric Television Tubes," in Ref. 91, pp. 285–292.

CHAPTER SIX

Displacement, Motion, and Force Transducers

6.1 DISPLACEMENT

A need for the direct measurement of displacement in biomedical engineering practice is not one that occurs very frequently. More often, it occurs as a means of transducing other physical quantities into electrical signals. Direct measurement of displacement arises, for example, in studying the contractility of isolated muscle, in studying the properties of bone subject to stress, and in the transduction of respiration through changes in the chest volume. Indirectly it occurs in a wide variety of transducers (e.g., diaphragm pressure transducers, force transducers), often as a secondary transducer element, as will be illustrated in this and some of the subsequent chapters.

Before considering the techniques described below as possible solutions to a particular displacement or velocity measurement problem, it is worthwhile to consider whether techniques based on imaging can yield the desired results. Direct visual observation, photographic pictures, as well as X-ray, ultrasound, and other radiation imaging methods form a powerful means for measuring distances, displacements, and velocities. Although consideration of these techniques is outside the scope of this book, it should be noted that computer and other image-processing techniques can be used to obtain remarkable improvements in the resolution. However, it should also be noted that it is generally not possible to obtain an electrical signal proportional to the displacement with these methods; furthermore, the techniques are generally expensive, require the subject to be confined to the machine, and can present radiation-hazard problems.

6.1.1 Potentiometric Resistive Transducers

One of the simplest and most efficient forms of displacement transducer is the resistive potentiometer consisting of a resistance element and a moveable contact (see Refs. 1 and 2 for further details of the design; Ref. 3, Pt. II, gives specifications for commercially available units). As shown in Figure 6.1, the movement can be either translational or rotational. Commercially available units have full-scale ranges from 0.2 to 150 cm for the translational types and from 10° to more than 50 turns for the rotational units. In the past the resistance elements for accurate displacement transducers were nearly always of the wirewound type. However, in recent years major advances have been made in the development of cermet (a conducting ceramic) and conductive plastic resistance elements, resulting in potentiometer transducers that offer specifications which are comparable to, and sometimes even exceed, the best wirewound types.

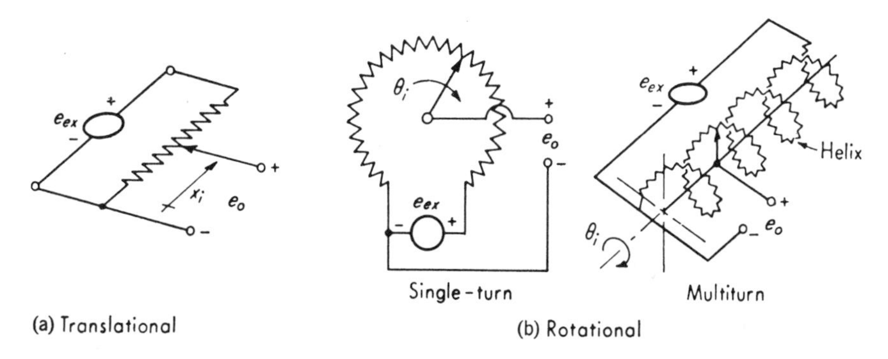

Figure 6.1. Potentiometric displacement transducers. (a) translational; (b) rotational; (from E. O. Doebelin, *Measurement Systems: Application and Design*, © 1966, McGraw-Hill Book Co.; used with permission of McGraw-Hill Book Co., New York).

Although most applications demand a linear relation between displacement (or rotation) and resistance change, for some it is convenient to have a logarithmic, sine, or cosine relation. Both the wirewound and continuous types of elements are made with such relationships, often with an accuracy of better than $\pm 1\%$.

Very small nonlinearities can be achieved with carefully fabricated wirewound potentiometers. For the large-diameter (10 cm) single-turn units, it can be better than $\pm 0.02\%$ of full scale and, for the translational units, $\pm 0.1\%$. Such tight tolerances tend to make these units very expensive;

fortunately, for most biomedical measurements a linearity of $\pm 1\%$ is more than adequate, making the economics rather more palatable.

To make use of the small nonlinearities care must be taken to insure that the load imposed by the voltage-measuring device does not cause distortion. As illustrated in Figure 6.2(a), the nonlinearity from this cause increases as the output load resistance decreases from its ideal value of infinity. A useful figure to remember in connection with the design is that for $R_L > 10\ R$ the maximum loading error is given by

$$\text{Max. error} = \frac{15R}{R_L},\ \%\ \text{of full scale.}$$

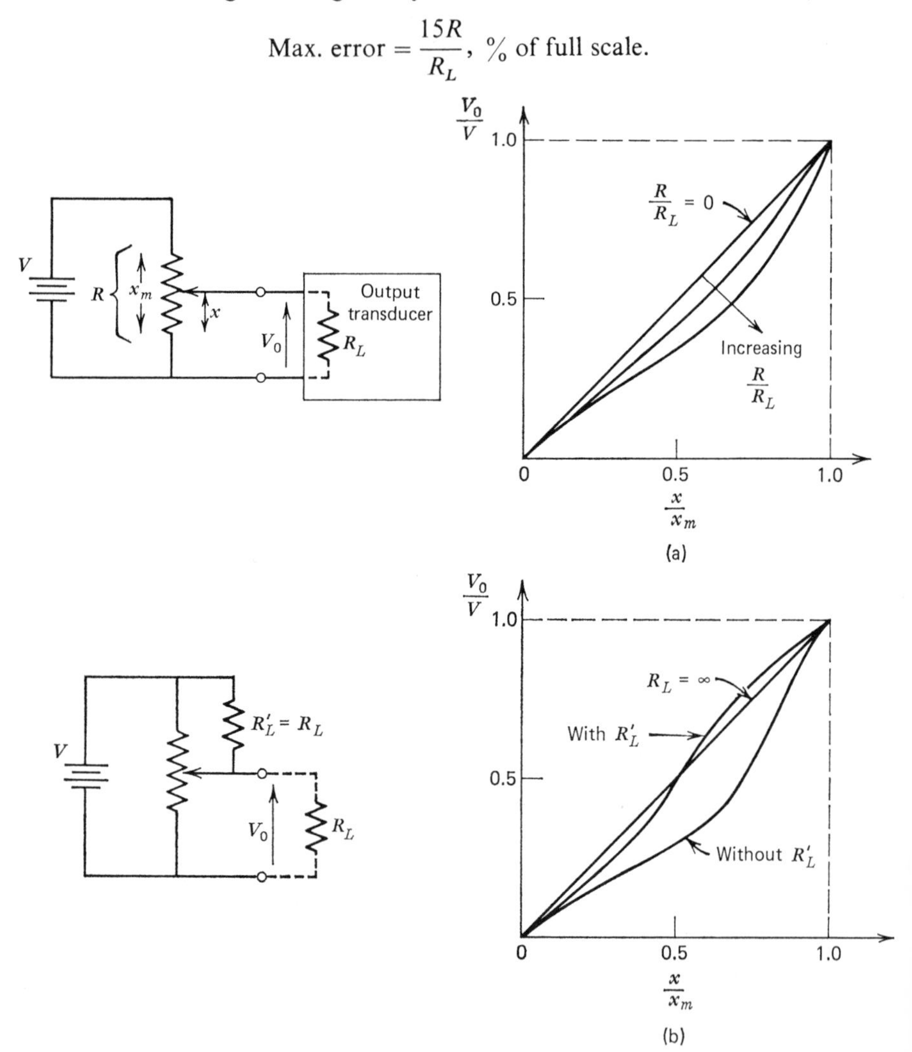

Figure 6.2. Effect of the load resistance on the potentiometer transducer linearity: (a) no compensation; (b) with a nonlinearity-correcting resistance.

By simply shunting the upper arm with R_L, as shown in Figure 6.2(b), this error can be considerably reduced. The effect of the resistance is to reduce the error to zero at $x = 0.5\ x_m$, so that the curve intersects the straight line at three points instead of two.

A further consideration in the design of a displacement transducer concerns the sensitivity or resolution. Wirewound potentiometers are limited in this respect by the minimum wire size that can be properly used. As shown in Figure 6.3, when the wiper moves across the wires it produces small step changes in resistance. Using 500 turns per cm, which is close to the practical limit, the ultimate resolution of a translation potentiometer would be 20 μm. This effect is of course absent in the cermet and conductive-plastic devices.

To be perfect a displacement transducer should have a zero mechanical input impedance. For a rotational transducer, this means that the starting torque, running torque, and moment of inertia of the wiper-arm assembly should be small. With special low-friction designs, the starting torque can be less than 0.3 g-cm, compared to 5–50 g-cm for the more conventional types. For the translation potentiometers, starting forces of less than 30 g can be achieved, although values of around 200 g would be typical of the standard units.

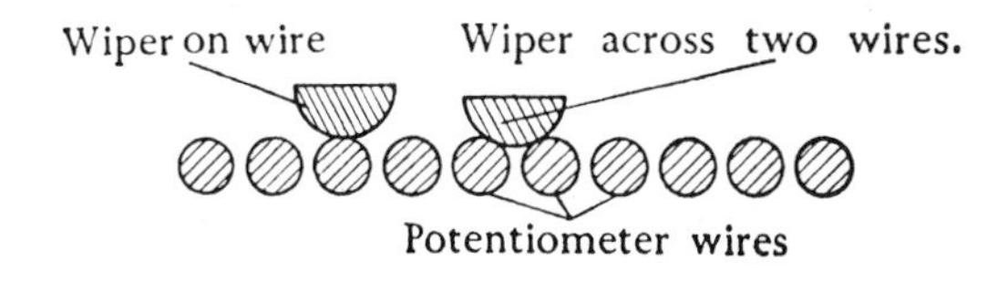

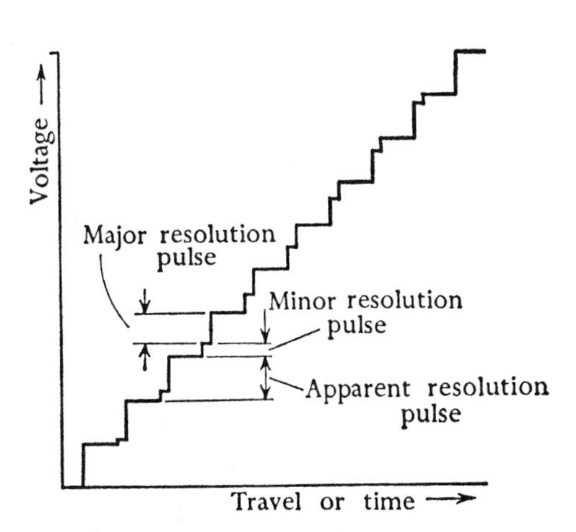

Figure 6.3. Effect of the finite wire diameter on the resolution of a wirewound potentiometer transducer (courtesy of Fairchild Corp., California).

6.1.2 Resistive Strain Gauges

Although the previous section was concerned with the measurement of displacement through potentiometric action without altering the physical properties of the resistance itself, in this section we shall examine methods that involve physical changes in the resistance arising as a direct result of the transducer element being strained by the displacement. Such transducers are called *strain gauges*. (*Strain* is defined as the fractional change in length—that is, strain = $\Delta L/L$. *Stress* is the force per unit area. For simple tensile stress, provided the elastic limit is not exceeded, Young's *modulus* = *stress/strain*—that is, the strain is proportional to the stress.)

Resistive strain gauges for biomedical applications can be divided into two categories: (a) metal and semiconductor gauges and (b) elastic strain gauges. Gauges of the first type are only capable of directly measuring very small (<20 μm) displacements and generally require a fairly large force to actuate them. They find wide application as secondary transducer elements for the measurement of force, pressure, and acceleration. On the other hand, the elastic-type transducers are capable of measuring large displacements, perhaps 50% of their relaxed length, making them particularly suited for measuring both static and dynamic changes associated with limbs, blood vessels, and chambers of the heart.

General Properties of Metal and Semiconductor Gauges. Metal and semiconductor gauges have found extensive application for the measurement of stress in mechanical, civil, and aeronautical engineering, with the result that there is an extensive literature on their theory and practical application [1, 4–7]. The earliest gauges consisted of a thin metal wire arranged so that the majority of its length lay along the direction of maximum strain. Although metal wire gauges are still used, the more recently developed metal-foil gauges, thin-film vacuum-deposited metal gauges, and semiconductor gauges are widely used.

When a wire is stretched, the cross-sectional area is reduced, thereby causing the total wire resistance to increase. In addition, since the lattice structure is altered by the strain, the resistivity of the material may also change, and this, in general, causes the resistance to increase further. Both effects are included in the expression for the strain sensitivity (gauge factor) derived below.

For a wire of cross-sectional area A, resistivity ρ, and length L, the resistance is given by

$$R = \frac{\rho L}{A}. \tag{1}$$

Taking the derivative, the total incremental change in R can be expressed as

$$dR = \frac{\rho}{A}\,dL + \frac{L}{A}\,d\rho - \frac{\rho L}{A^2}\,dA.$$

Dividing this equation by Eq. (1) and assuming that the derivatives can be replaced by the corresponding small, but finite, changes Δ, we find that the fractional resistance change is

$$\frac{\Delta R}{R} = \frac{\Delta L}{L} - \frac{\Delta A}{A} + \frac{\Delta \rho}{\rho}. \tag{2}$$

To find a relation between the change in wire diameter and change in length, use is made of the definition of Poisson's ratio (σ), yielding

$$\frac{\Delta D}{D} \simeq -\sigma\,\frac{\Delta L}{L}. \tag{3}$$

Since $A = \pi D^2/4$, so that $\Delta A/A = 2\Delta D/D$, Eq. (3) can be expressed in the form

$$\frac{\Delta A}{A} = -2\sigma\,\frac{\Delta L}{L}. \tag{4}$$

Substituting Eq. (4) into Eq. (2), we find

$$\frac{\Delta R}{R} = (1 + 2\sigma)\,\frac{\Delta L}{L} + \frac{\Delta \rho}{\rho}. \tag{5}$$

Dimensional effect — Piezoresistive effect

Thus, the change in resistance can be expressed as the sum of two terms: the first arises from simple dimensional changes, and the second is caused by the change in resistivity with strain, commonly called the *piezoresistive effect*.

The *gauge factor*, or strain sensitivity, of a gauge defined by

$$G = \frac{\Delta R/R}{\Delta L/L} = 1 + 2\sigma + \frac{\Delta \rho/\rho}{\Delta L/L} \tag{6}$$

provides a useful means for comparing the performance of various gauge materials. For most metals, Poisson's ratio is approximately 0.3, so that the gauge factor becomes

$$G = 1.6 + \frac{\Delta \rho/\rho}{\Delta L/L}. \tag{7}$$

In practice, as shown in Table 6.1, metals generally have a gauge factor considerably different from 1.6. Although this may be partially caused by

Table 6.1 Properties of Some Metal and Semiconductor Strain-Gauge Materials

Material and composition	Gauge factor	Temp. coeff. Resistivity ($°C^{-1}$-10^{-5})	Coeff. linear expansion ($°C^{-1}$-10^{-5})
Advance / Constantan ($Ni_{45}Cu_{55}$)	2.1	±2.	16.
Isoelastic ($Ni_{36}Cr_8(Mn, Si, Mo)_4Fe_{52}$)	3.52 to 3.6	+17.	0.40
Karma ($Ni_{74}Cr_{20}Fe_3Cu_3$)	2.1	+2.	1.0
Manganin ($Cu_{84}Mn_{12}Ni_4$)	0.3 to 0.47	±2.	
Alloy 479 ($Pt_{92}W_8$)	3.6 to 4.4	+24.	
Nickel	−12. to −20.	670.	1.28
Nichrome V ($Ni_{80}Cr_{20}$)	2.1 to 2.63	10.	1.32
Silicon (p-type)	100 to 170	70 to 700	0.23
Silicon (n-type)	−100 to −140	70 to 700	0.23
Germanium (p-type)	102		0.58
Germanium (n-type)	−150		0.58

the piezoresistive term, it appears [5] that the change in the total wire volume, a factor that was ignored in the derivation of Eq. (6), may be of considerable importance. The much higher gauge factors for single-crystal semiconductors, such as silicon and germanium, arise from their large piezoresistive coefficients, making the second term in Eq. (6) dominant. Although they are roughly 70 times more sensitive, they do suffer from a much higher resistivity temperature coefficient, making it essential that steps be taken in the design to provide temperature compensation.

Unbonded and Bonded Gauges. Depending on their construction, strain gauges can be used in either the bonded or unbonded forms. The unbonded gauge typically consists of a wire 0.002 cm or less in diameter wound between a fixed and movable frame. In the design illustrated in Figure 6.4, there are four sets of identical wires that have been wound under tension so that the movable frame can be displaced by a small amount in either direction without reducing the tension in any of the wires to zero. To measure the change in resistance, the four strain gauges are incorporated into a Wheatstone bridge in the order indicated in the figure. A motion to the left causes the resistance of R_1 and R_4 to increase and R_2 and R_3 to decrease, thereby yielding a bridge output voltage twice that of a two-wire system. A further advantage

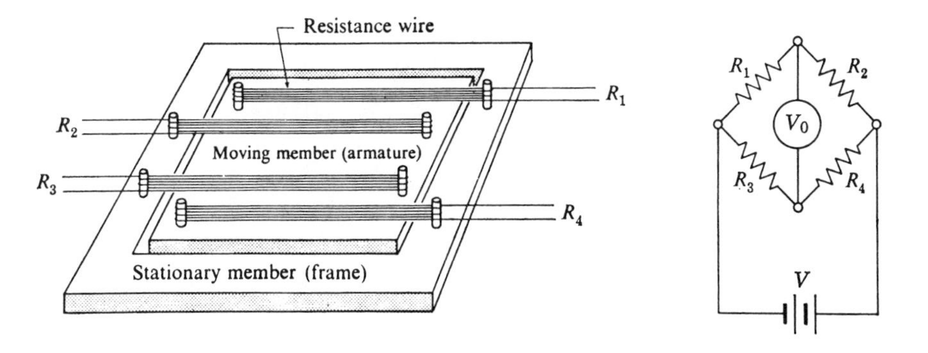

$$\Delta V_0 = V\,\Delta R/R \text{ for } \begin{cases} R_1 = R_4 = R + \Delta R \\ R_2 = R_3 = R - \Delta R \end{cases}$$

Figure 6.4. Temperature-compensated unbonded strain transducer and bridge (reproduced, with permission, from D. Bartholomew, *Electrical Measurements and Instrumentation*, Allyn and Bacon Inc., Boston, 1963).

arising from the balance arrangement is its self-compensating action for any environmental effects. Changes in temperature affect each wire to almost exactly the same extent, thereby leaving the output voltage unchanged. With proper design, the thermal coefficients of both the sensitivity and zero can be less than 0.01 %/°C of full scale.

The maximum fractional change in length that can be permitted with wire gauges is very small; typically it is 5000×10^{-6} ($\equiv$5000 $\mu\varepsilon$, where $\mu\varepsilon$ is a dimensionless quantity called a *microstrain*), giving a 1% change in resistance when the gauge factor is 2.0. A linearity of better than 0.2%, a full-scale displacement of 0.005 cm corresponding to a 30-g force, and a full-scale output voltage of 40 mV (5 V bridge excitation) are typical for an unbonded strain transducer system. Resistance values are usually in the 100–1000 Ω range.

The unbonded strain gauge is very efficient in that force applied to its ends is not shunted by any mechanical members. In spite of its apparent fragility, it is widely used as a secondary transducer element for force, pressure, and acceleration measurement. Many of the earlier blood-pressure transducers used this form of gauge to convert the movement of a pressure diaphragm into an electrical signal.

A second form of strain gauge often used in physiological research is the *bonded* gauge, some examples of which are shown in Figure 6.5. It can consist of metal wire, etched metal foil, vacuum-deposited metal, or a semiconductor bar attached to a suitable backing material. They are designed to

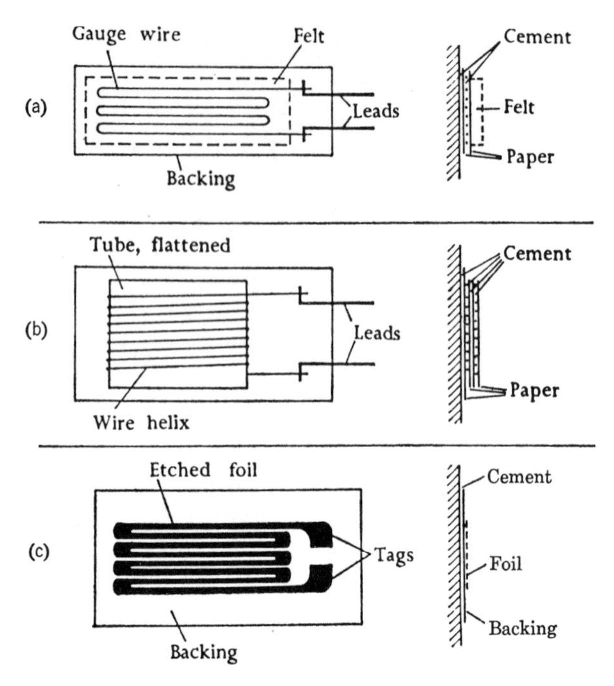

Figure 6.5. Some examples of bonded-wire and foil strain gauges: (a) flat-grid type; (b) Wrap-around type; (c) etched-foil type (reproduced, with permission, from H. K. P. Neubert, *Instrument Transducers*, Clarendon Press, Oxford, 1963).

be cemented to the surface whose strain is to be measured. Once cemented, they effectively become part of the surface, so that ideally any strain that occurs in the surface is transmitted through to the gauge element unchanged. In practice, it is found that the loss of strain transmission becomes more significant as the gauge length decreases. For example, with a 1-cm long gauge with a 0.2-mm bonding-layer thickness, the gauge factor is effectively reduced to 0.98 of its unbonded value. If the gauge length is decreased to 0.1 cm, then for the same bonding layer thickness the loss factor drops to 0.87.

Because the change in resistance with strain is fairly small, the effects of temperature on the design and use of strain gauges assume considerable importance [4]. There are a number of effects that must be accounted for. The first concerns the effect of temperature on the resistivity: for an unstrained wire this results in a fractional resistance change given by

$$\frac{\Delta R}{R} = \alpha \Delta T,$$

where α is the resistivity temperature coefficient. A further factor concerns the effect of thermal expansion both of the gauge itself and the structure to which it is bonded. For a gauge with a coefficient of linear expansion β_G that is bonded to a structure with an expansion coefficient β_S, the fractional change in gauge length for a temperature change of ΔT will be

$$\frac{\Delta L}{L} = (\beta_S - \beta_G)\,\Delta T.$$

Furthermore, it should be noted from Figure 6.6 that the gauge factor G also depends on temperature, and for a small range ΔT, its behavior can be represented by

$$G = G_0(1 + \gamma \Delta T),$$

where γ is the temperature coefficient and G_0 is the gauge factor for $\Delta T = 0$. Thus the fractional resistance change for a strain of $\Delta L/L$, when the temperature changes by ΔT, is given by the sum of the above three effects:

$$\frac{\Delta R}{R} = \frac{\Delta L}{L} G_0(1 + \gamma \Delta T) + \Delta T[G(\beta_S - \beta_G) + \alpha]. \tag{8}$$

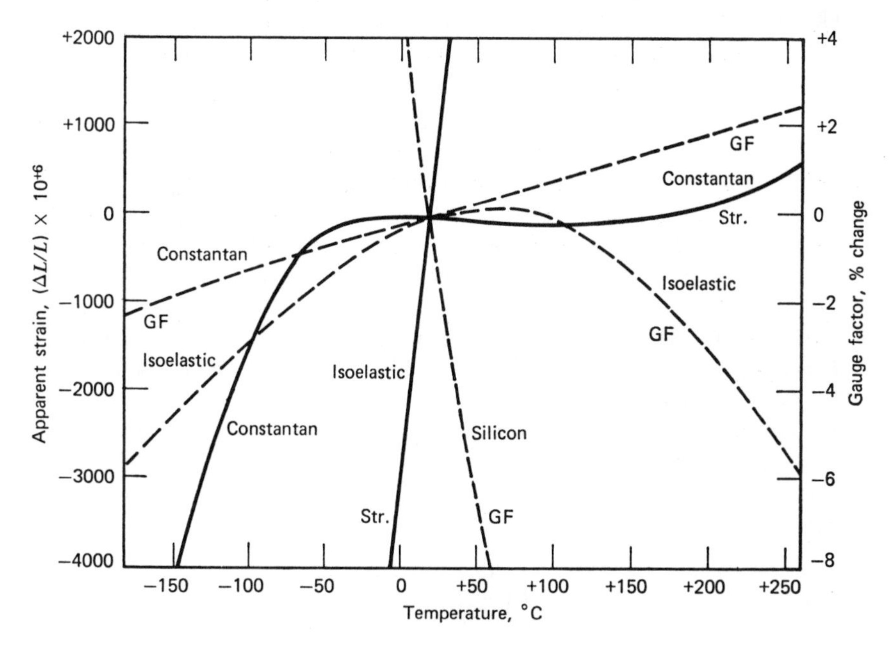

Figure 6.6. Temperature variation of the gauge factor and apparent strain (fractional resistance change divided by the gauge factor) for unbonded silicon, Constantan, and Isoelastic gauges.

It will be noted from the above equation that in the absence of any strain the first term on the right-hand side is zero, so that the second term, without the ΔT, is the zero offset temperature coefficient:

$$\alpha_0 = G(\beta_S - \beta_G) + \alpha. \tag{9}$$

It is evident from Eq. (9) that if the materials can be chosen so that the various terms cancel one another, zero offset temperature compensation can be achieved. Such is possible with certain metal gauges (e.g., Advance gauge on steel) and with n-type silicon gauges. Alternatively, it is possible to use a series-compensating arrangement of two wires having opposing gauge factors (i.e., nickel and constantan) to achieve the same effect.

One of the best ways of achieving temperature compensation is through the use of a 4-gauge balanced Wheatstone bridge arrangement. When this is not possible, using a single gauge paired with a dummy gauge mounted on the same structure in such a way that it is unstressed, compensation for the effects of both expansion and resistivity variation can also be achieved.

Semiconductor Strain Gauges [4–10]. The development of silicon strain gauges around 1960 formed a most significant advance in strain-gauge technology. Not only do they have a much larger gauge factor than metal gauges (see Table 6.1) but their method of construction lends itself to a variety of new applications, some of which will be discussed in this chapter.

Silicon gauges are formed from single-crystal silicon whose orientation and doping are the most important design parameters. As illustrated in Figure 6.7, the gauge factor depends markedly on the resistivity (determined by the doping) and the crystal orientation. It should be noted that the gauge factors for n- and p-type silicon are opposite in sign and that a large gauge factor is attained by using lightly doped material. The orientation-dependence of the piezoresistive strain effect is also illustrated in Figure 6.8, where the gauge factor is plotted on polar coordinates as a function of orientation for a (110) plane p-type silicon slice. Although for most planes a marked orientation-dependence occurs, it should be noted that for (111) p-type silicon the piezoresistive effect is isotropic.

Semiconductor strain gauges are inherently more nonlinear than metal gauges and the nonlinearity increases as the doping decreases. For heavily doped n- and p-type silicon gauges, the gauge characteristics can be expressed by [4]

$$\begin{aligned} \frac{\Delta R}{R} &= 120\frac{\Delta L}{L} + 4000\left(\frac{\Delta L}{L}\right)^2 \quad \left\{\begin{matrix}\text{p-type Si,} \\ \rho = 2 \times 10^{-2}\,\Omega\text{-cm}\end{matrix}\right\} \\ \frac{\Delta R}{R} &= -110\frac{\Delta L}{L} + 10{,}000\left(\frac{\Delta L}{L}\right)^2 \quad \left\{\begin{matrix}\text{n-type Si} \\ \rho = 3.1 \times 10^{-4}\,\Omega\text{-cm}\end{matrix}\right\} \end{aligned} \tag{10}$$

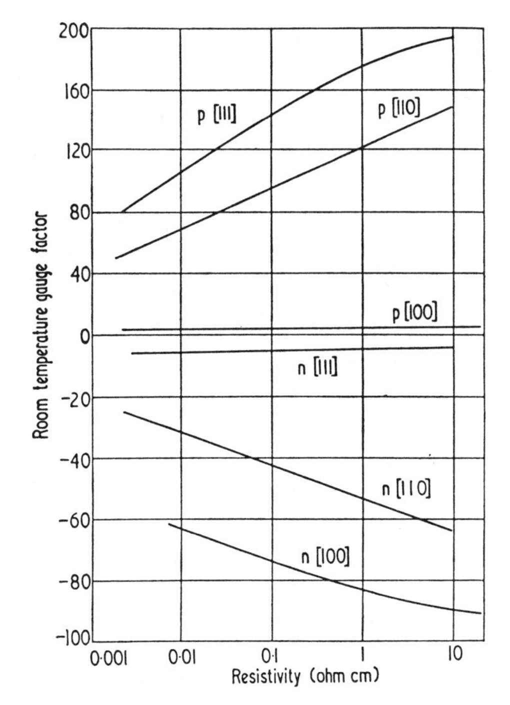

Figure 6.7. Gauge factor of silicon n- and p-type gauges as a function of resistivity for various crystal orientations (reproduced, with permission, from G. R. Higson, *J. Sci. Instr.*, **41**, 405–414, July 1964).

which are plotted in Figure 6.9. The higher nonlinearity of n-type silicon makes it desirable to use p-type in applications where linearity is important. However, the temperature-compensation properties of n-type silicon gauges (it has a negative gauge factor) make it particularly useful when large temperature variations are encountered. A considerable improvement in linearity can be achieved using a 4-gauge arrangement in which two gauges are in compression and two are in tension. Since the squared term in Eq. (10) affects each gauge equally, the output from a standard Wheatstone bridge circuit will be a linear function of the strain.

Temperature generally has a large and highly significant effect on the resistance and gauge factors of silicon gauges. Typically, the gauge factor temperature coefficient is in the range -1×10^{-3} to -4×10^{-3} $(°C)^{-1}$, although for very heavily doped silicon ($\rho \sim 10^{-3}\Omega$-cm) the coefficient can be reduced even further. A similar variation occurs for the resistance temperature coefficient, which becomes close to zero or even negative for very heavy doping.

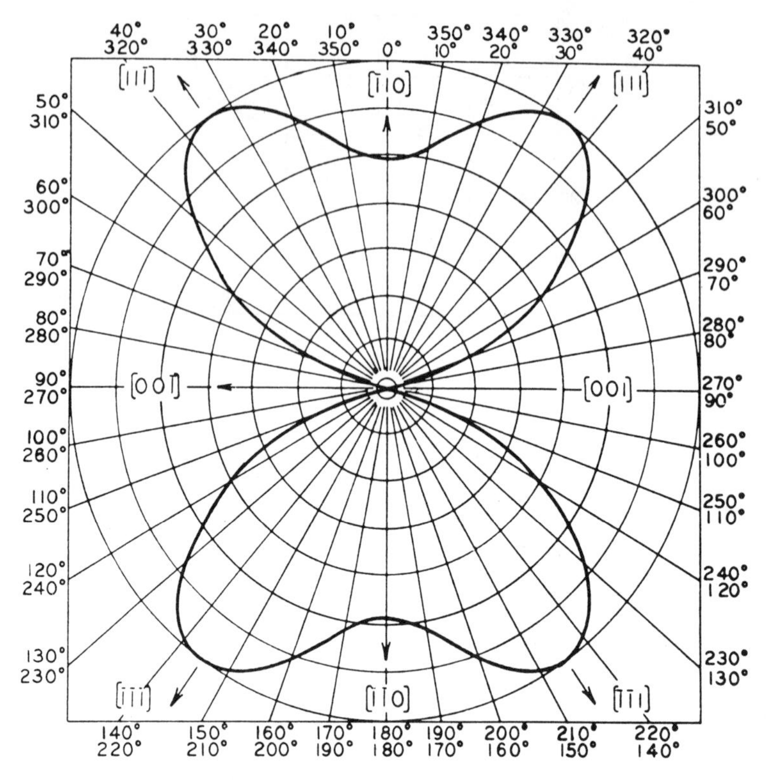

Figure 6.8. Polar graph showing the variation in gauge factor with orientation for a (110) plane of p-type silicon (reproduced, with permission, from N. Zinker, paper 68–503 in *Advances in Test Measurement*, Vol. 5, Instrument Society of America, Pittsburgh, 1968).

Semiconductor gauges can be fabricated by simply cutting or etching a suitably doped single-crystal slice in the appropriate direction. Typically, such a gauge may be 0.001 cm thick, 0.3 cm long, and 0.01 cm wide, with a resistance in the range 100–1000Ω. Alternatively, the gauge may be fabricated [8] by selective diffusion of impurities into a silicon substrate using a SiO_2 mask formed by photolithographic processes. The impurities added convert a portion of the substrate into a region of opposite conductivity type, as illustrated in Figure 6.10(b). With this method of fabrication, gauges with resistance values of greater than 5000 Ω can be made. Much higher impurity concentrations, while retaining a high resistance value, can be achieved through the process of masked ion implantation. Such a method appears to have considerable advantages in fabricating silicon gauges having a nearly temperature-invariant gauge factor and resistance.

Both the uniformly doped bar-type gauge and the diffused gauge are commercially available with backing material to facilitate attachment to a surface. Alternatively, an unbonded-type gauge can be attached directly to a surface, using a suitable epoxy cement.

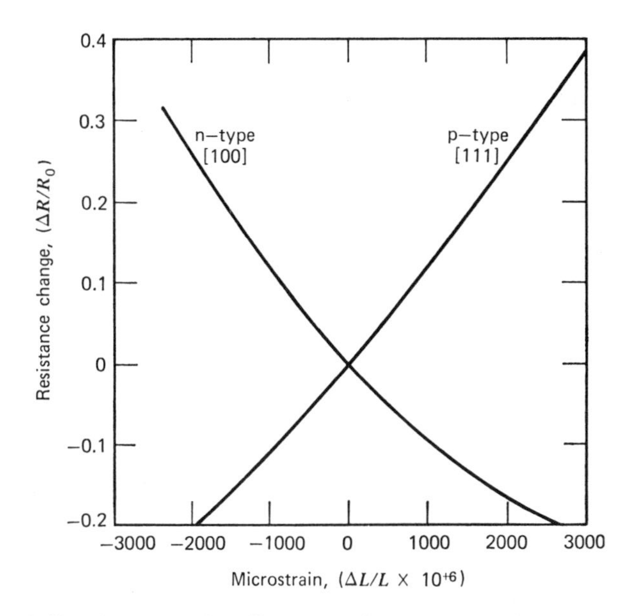

Figure 6.9. Calibration curves for silicon n- and p-type strain gauges (reproduced, with permission, from G. R. Higson, *J. Sci. Instr.*, **41**, 405–414, July 1964).

A most important advantage of the silicon strain gauge is that the method of fabrication enables an integrated-type transducer to be constructed in which the silicon substrate forms the structural member and acts as the primary transducer. For example, as illustrated in Figure 6.10(c), with the gauges diffused directly into the diaphragm, a pressure transducer [4, 11–14] can be fabricated with the thin silicon diaphragm acting as the primary transducer (see Sections 7.2.2 and 7.2.3 for further details of the design). A pressure differential causes the silicon to bend, setting up a radial stress component at the edge that is opposite in sign to the tangential stress component near the center. Using the eight-diffused strain gauge arrangement illustrated in the figure [4, 12] a high sensitivity coupled with good temperature compensation can be achieved.

A second example of an integrated type of system is the force transducer [15] of Figure 6.10(d), in which the gauges are diffused into the silicon

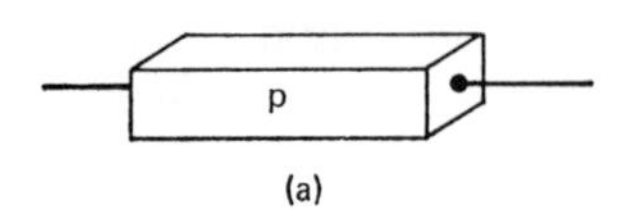

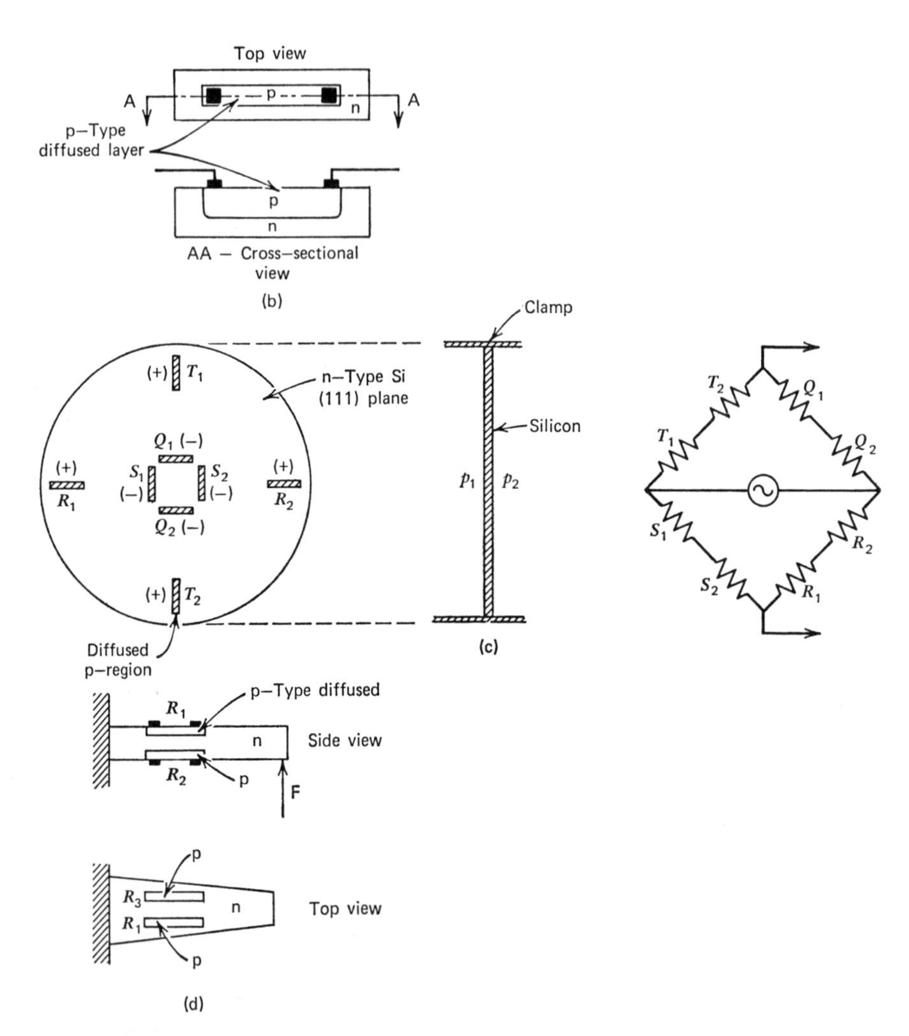

Figure 6.10. Semiconductor strain gauges: (a) unbonded, uniformly doped; (b) diffused p-type gauge; (c) integrated pressure transducer; and (d) integrated cantilever beam force transducer.

cantilever beam. Using four gauges, two in compression and two in tension, a linear temperature compensated output is obtained that is proportional to the applied force.

Elastic Resistance Strain Gauges. Strain gauges that make use of the change in resistance of a conducting fluid contained within an extendable rubber tube have found fairly extensive application for measuring changes in cardiac dimensions [16], changes in major blood vessels [17], as well as for limb (see Section 8.5.3) and chest plethysmography [18, 19]. Although the most popular filling fluid is mercury, various electrolytes such as copper sulfate and ECG electrode paste [20], have also been successfully employed. A commercial version using electrode paste is shown in Figure 6.11.

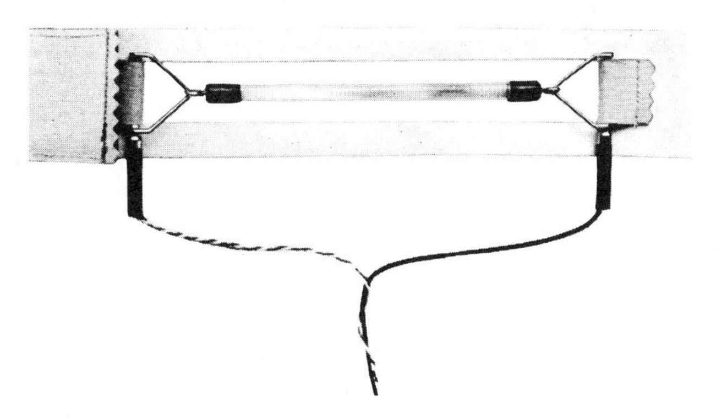

Figure 6.11. Commercial elastic strain gauge, using an electrolyte, for use in respiration monitoring (courtesy Nihon Kohden Kogyo Co., Tokyo).

The modern version of the mercury gauge consists of silicone rubber tubing, typically with a 0.5-mm inside diameter and 2-mm outside diameter, and perhaps 3 cm long, filled with ultrapure mercury. The ends of the tube are sealed with the electrodes, which may consist of amalgamated copper, silver, or platinum. When the tube is stretched, the cross-sectional area decreases, so that the observed resistance increase is the result of changes in both the gauge area and length [19]. Since the volume of the fluid remains constant, it can easily be shown that the fractional change in resistance is given by

$$\frac{\Delta R}{R_0} = 2\frac{\Delta L}{L} + \left(\frac{\Delta L}{L}\right)^2,$$

or, for $\Delta L/L$ small,

$$\frac{\Delta R}{R_0} \simeq \frac{2\Delta L}{L},$$

where $\Delta L/L$ is the strain. For a 10% maximum extension the nonlinearity is less than ±1% of full scale; it increases to ±4% at 30% extension. In practice it is found that apart from an initial nonlinearity usually ascribed to slackness, mercury gauges exhibit the linearity predicted above. It has been found that some long-term creep arising from the properties of the rubber can occur; however, this should not noticeably affect dynamic measurements.

Lawton and Collins [21a] have measured both the static and dynamic response of gauges of the type used by Rushmer [16, 17] for the measurement of aortic and ventricular dimensions during the cardiac cycle. Their results are shown in Figure 6.12. For frequencies up to 10 Hz, both the amplitude and phase characteristics are essentially constant; above this the phase nonlinearity starts to become significant and could be expected to cause significant distortion of frequency components above 30 Hz.

One problem arising with the use of mercury gauges under dynamic conditions that is not evident from the tests of Lawton and Collins, concerns the failure of the gauge to distend fully when measuring the pulsatile variations in a vessel diameter. The mass of the gauge together with its finite mechanical resistance can cause it to dig into the vessel wall as the vessel expands, thereby causing a low reading. Indeed, the indications are that under these circumstances the distension measured may be several times lower than that measured using cineangiography or ultrasonic methods [21b].

A second problem associated with the use of mercury gauges arises from their very small resistance (typically 0.2 Ω/cm of gauge length).* To measure such small resistance values requires considerable care to avoid contact resistance effects and thermoelectric emf's. The latter problem can be circumvented by using ac excitation. This also has the advantage that a narrow-band carrier amplifier can be used and the mercury resistance gauge can be "matched" into the bridge by means of a transformer. The principles of such a bridge [22] are shown in Figure 6.13, where the stepdown transformer effectively transforms the gauge resistance R_G into an equivalent resistance $(N_1/N_2)^2R$ at the primary. Hence, a change of the gauge resistance appears effectively as a much larger change in the bridge arm. For example if $N_1/N_2 = 10$, a change of 0.01 Ω in the gauge resistance appears as a 1.0-Ω effective bridge arm change.

* This problem is avoided in the electrolyte-filled gauge: for example, Waggoner reports that gauges filled with ECG paste have resistances in the range 1–400 kΩ [20].

Finally, some mention should be made of the other practical problems associated with mercury strain gauges. One of these is the difficulty of achieving good long-term mercury contacts; over a period of time, it is often found that the electrodes deteriorate. A second problem that is especially important when the full-scale displacement is small is the gauge temperature coefficient.

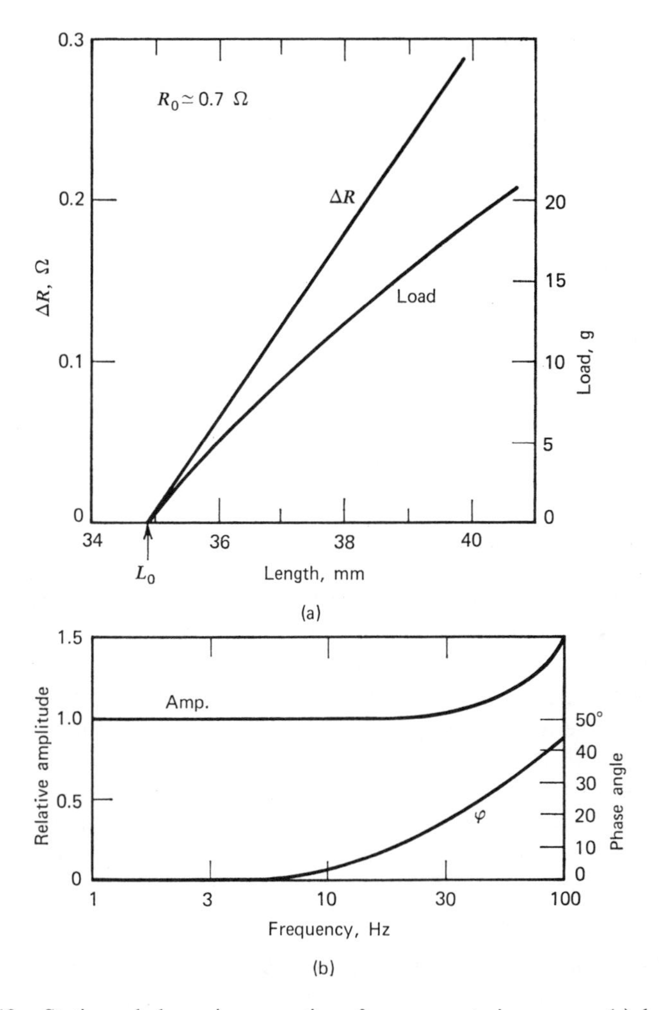

Figure 6.12. Static and dynamic properties of mercury strain gauges: (a) load versus length, and resistance change versus length; (b) amplitude and phase of the resistance change relative to the vibration amplitude, as a function of the vibration frequency (redrawn from R. W. Lawton and G. C. Collins, *J. Appl. Physiol.*, **14**, 465–467, 1959).

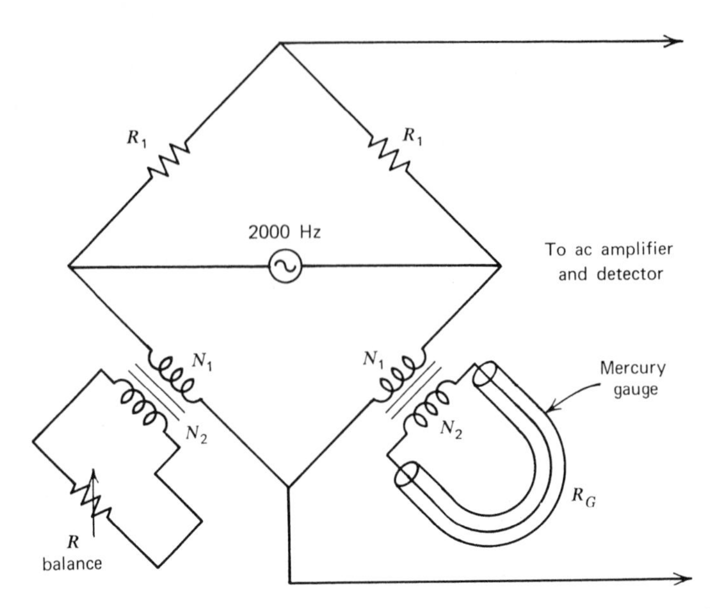

Figure 6.13. Principles of a transformer coupled bridge for use with a mercury strain gauge (adapted from R. W. Elsner, C. J. Eagan, and S. Anderson, *J. Appl. Physiol.*, **14**, 871–872, 1959).

6.1.3 Inductive Displacement Transducers

A wide variety of schemes exist for the measurement of displacement using methods based on the variation of inductance of single coils and the mutual inductance of two coils. Some examples are shown in Figure 6.14. Schemes (a)–(c) are based on the change in inductance of a single coil either through a change in coil geometry or through a change in the properties of the magnetic path. Methods involving two or more coils, such as those illustrated in (d) and (e), make use of a change in mutual coupling resulting either from a relative displacement of the coils or from the movement of a coupling core. While all these principles have found application as useful biomedical transducers, perhaps the most widely used is the differential transformer system that will now be examined in some detail.

Linear Variable Differential Transformer **(*LVDT*).** A prime advantage of the LVDT displacement transducer is its large output for relatively small movements (for a more detailed discussion, see, for example, Ref. 2, pp. 233–242). In essence it consists of three coils: a primary and two identical secondaries as illustrated in Figure 6.15. The moveable core serves to alter the coup-

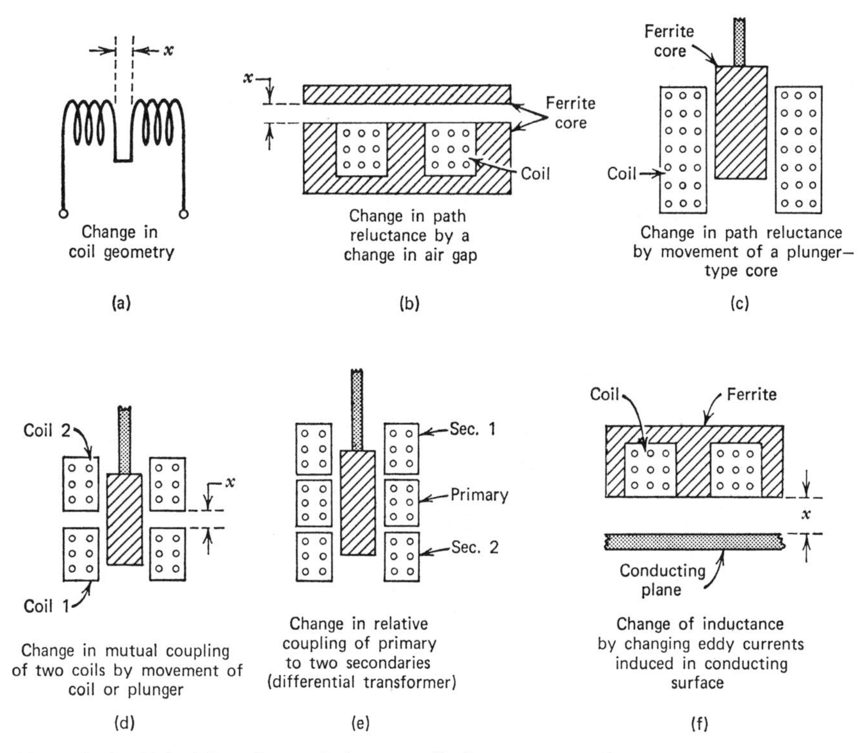

Figure 6.14. Principles of some inductance displacement transducers.

ling between the primary and secondaries: when the core is in the central position the coupling of the two secondary coils to the primary is identical. Thus, if the primary is excited through the application of an ac current, equal voltages will be induced in each secondary. But, since the two secondaries are connected in series opposition, ideally the two induced voltages should exactly cancel, resulting in zero output. When the core is displaced toward secondary 1, the output from 2 decreases and that from 1 increases. If the transformer is ideal, an output signal is obtained that is in phase with the primary voltage; its magnitude being very nearly proportional to the core displacement. A displacement of the core toward secondary 2 results in an output signal 180° out of phase with the primary.

If the primary winding resistance, load resistance, and winding capacitance are finite, the phase angle between the excitation and output voltages may differ from 0° (or 180°). It turns out that for a given load resistance, the phase angle approaches +90° at low frequencies and tends to −90° at high frequencies. Thus, it is possible to choose an exciting frequency so that the

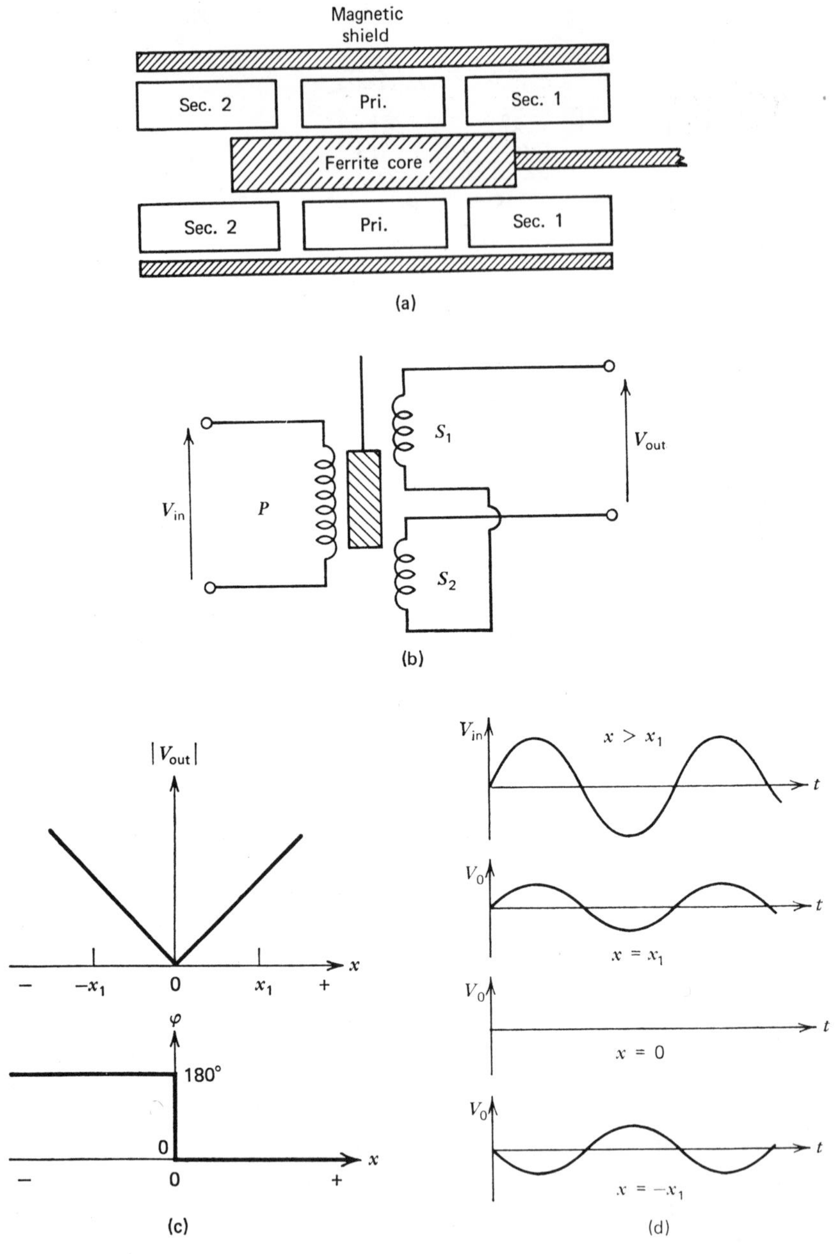

Figure 6.15. Principles of the linear variable differential transformer (LVDT) displacement transducer: (a) construction; (b) circuit diagram; (c) static response; and (d) waveforms for various displacements.

phase angle is 0° on one side of the null position and changes to 180° at the other. Although this can be important for certain carrier systems, more often the relative input–output phase angle is not important as long as it stays constant. What is important is the 180° phase shift that occurs in going through the null. In demodulating the output, it is necessary to preserve this information, since it is the only means of determining the sign of the displacement. One scheme for achieving this is through the use of a phase-sensitive detector such as illustrated in Figure 6.16. Here the demodulation is of the synchronous variety, yielding a positive or negative output according to the direction of the displacement with respect to the null.

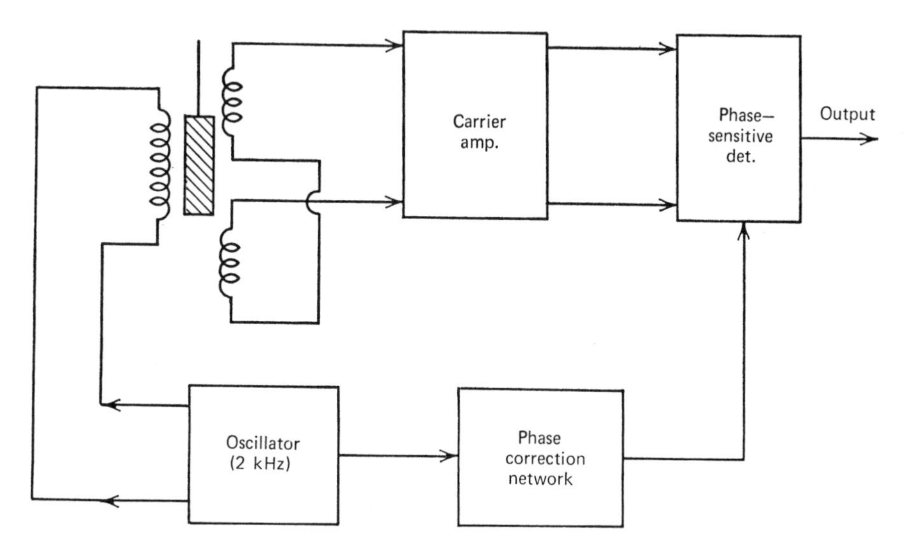

Figure 6.16. Phase-sensitive detection system for an LVDT.

Since the output voltage from an LVDT is proportional to the excitation voltage, it is convenient to specify the sensitivity for 1-V excitation. Commercial devices typically have sensitivities in the range 0.5–2.0 mV/0.001 cm displacement per volt excitation. Although a larger output signal can be obtained through increased excitation amplitude, a limit is imposed by the onset of increased harmonic distortion due to core nonlinearity and thermal effects produced by the core and winding losses. Typically, voltages in the 1–10 V range with excitation frequencies from 50 Hz to 20 kHz, are commonly employed. Although the lower frequencies tend to give lower sensitivities and to limit the dynamic frequency response, for many applications this is not too significant, and the disadvantages are outweighed by the economic advantage of operating at the power-line (60 Hz) frequency.

Full-scale displacements of 0.01–25 cm with a linearity of $\pm 0.25\%$ are available as a standard item from at least one manufacturer. With careful circuit design, 0.1% of full scale can be measured, enabling displacements of less than 0.1 μm to be detected.*

The core weight is less than 0.2 g for the 0.01-cm unit and increases to around 10 g for the 25-cm unit. Since the core has a small radial clearance, no frictional forces need be involved in displacing it, provided the core can be held sufficiently rigidly by the source of motion. The only axial forces that do arise are caused by the core weight and a small emf that tends to

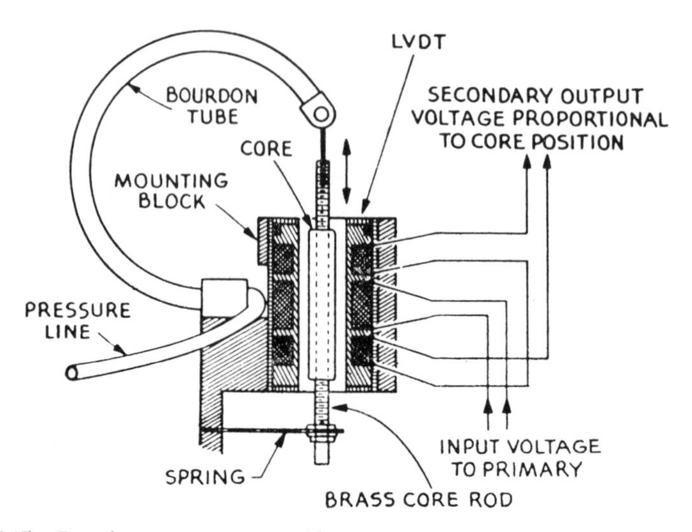

Figure 6.17. Bourdon pressure gauge with an LVDT (reproduced, with permission, from Bulletin AA–1A, Schaevitz Eng , Pennsauken, N.J.).

restore the core to its null position. Also present is a small radially directed electromagnetic force that may necessitate providing an insulating core guide to prevent the core touching the bore.

The LVDT is widely used for displacement, force, and pressure measurements in physiology. In fact, the first catheter-tip blood-pressure tranducer, as described by Wetterer [24] in 1943, used an LVDT to measure the displacement of an elastic diaphragm. The small mass of the core and diaphragm, together with the latter's high stiffness, yielded a resonant frequency

* Much smaller displacements can be detected with LVDT's. Sydenham [23], in his excellent review of microdisplacement transducers, mentions that one commercial LVDT is capable of sensing 1 Å.

of 515 Hz. Figure 6.17 illustrates the use of an LVDT as a secondary transducer to measure the movement of a Bourdon tube and thereby to obtain an electrical signal proportional to the pressure.

Variable Inductance Methods. Systems using a single coil with a displaceable core are generally rather more nonlinear than LVDT-based systems. However, they do have the advantage of enabling a digital output to be readily obtained.

Allard [25] has described an intracardiac transducer that makes use of a single coil with a movable mumetal core to measure the displacement of a diaphragm. As shown in Figure 6.18(a), the system is balanced to achieve temperature compensation, with a dummy core (Plexiglas) on the reference side. An increase in pressure causes the mumetal to be displaced into the coil, thereby increasing its inductance. By incorporating the coil as part of an FM oscillator an output frequency is obtained that is a measure of the displacement. Provided the core movements are small, it turns out that the change in frequency is nearly proportional to the pressure difference between the two diaphragms. Such a system, because of its small mass, has a frequency response that is flat to beyond 1000 Hz.

When positioned in one of the cardiac chambers, it is capable of simultaneously measuring both the pressure waveform and the phonocardiographic sounds. Since the latter signal has a frequency spectrum that normally lies above 50 Hz, the two signals can be separated using the low- and high-pass filters shown in Figure 6.18(b).

A variable inductance transducer system capable of better overall stability and linearity makes use of the balanced coil arrangement [26] illustrated in Figure 6.19. Each coil controls the frequency of a separate oscillator. For zero displacement the oscillator frequencies, f_1 and f_2, differ slightly, so that the mixer delivers an output $f_3 = f_1 - f_2$, which is much less than either f_1 or f_2. When the core is displaced toward L_1 the inductance of L_1 increases and L_2 decreases, causing the oscillator frequencies to change to $f_1 - \Delta f + k(\Delta f)^2$ and $f_2 + \Delta f + k(\Delta f)^2$. Since the mixer and filter take the difference in frequencies, the second-order nonlinearities cancel, yielding a frequency $f_3 - 2\Delta f$. By means of a frequency–voltage converter the change in output frequency ($2\Delta f$) can be converted to an analog output voltage signal. Alternatively, by using a digital counter, the frequency change can be presented in digital form.

The change in coupling between two coils, resulting from a physical displacement from each other, has proved to be an effective means of measuring the dimensional changes of internal organs [27, 28]. If a sinusoidal emf is applied to one coil, the emf induced in the second depends on the excitation frequency and amplitude as well as the geometry, separation, axial align-

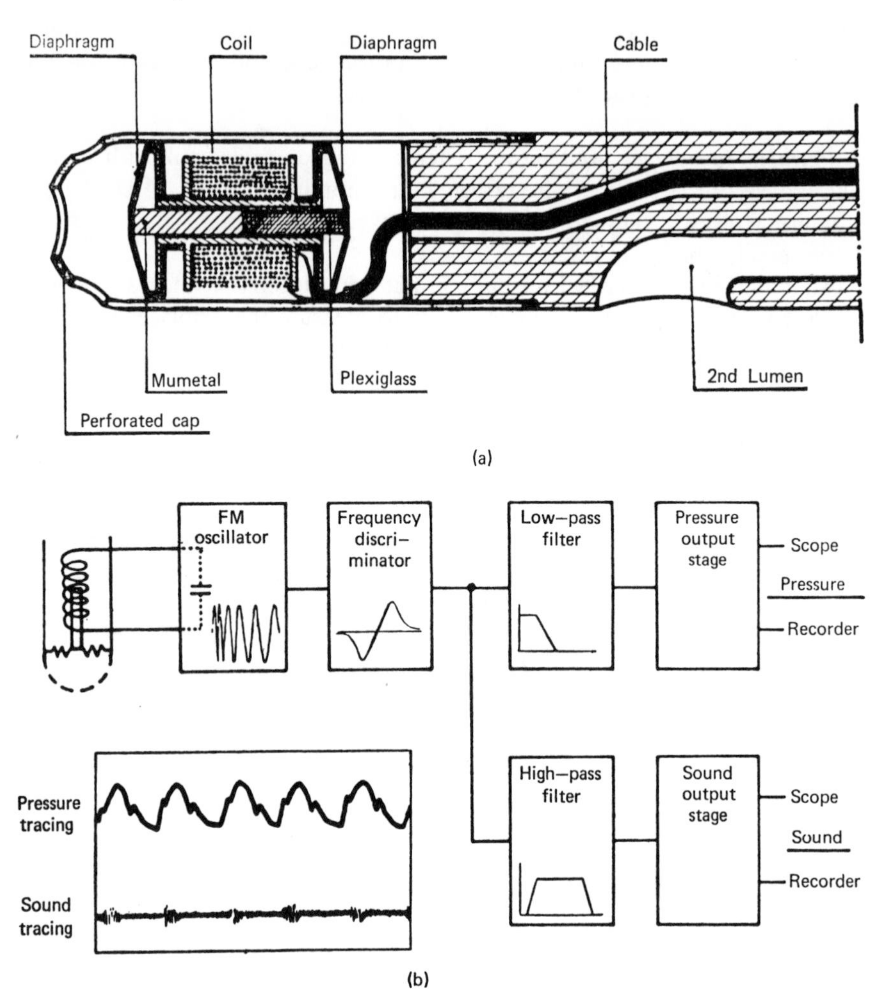

Figure 6.18. The Allard–Laurens micromanometer system: (a) details of the variable inductance pressure transducer; (b) electronic detection system incorporating filters to separate out the pressure and phonocardiographic signals (reproduced, with permission, from E. M. Allard, *IRE Trans. Bio-Med. Electron.*, **BME–9**, 74–77, 1962).

ment, and number of turns on both coils. If the axial alignment and amplitude are held constant, the induced emf is a simple function of the axial coil separation and hence can be used for gauging. Such systems have been successfully used for measuring the dimensional changes of the kidney, vena cava, aorta, and left ventricle of the unanesthetized dog.

Caldwell et al. [27] have recently described a system using the above principle, for measuring dynamic changes in the left-ventricular dimensions.

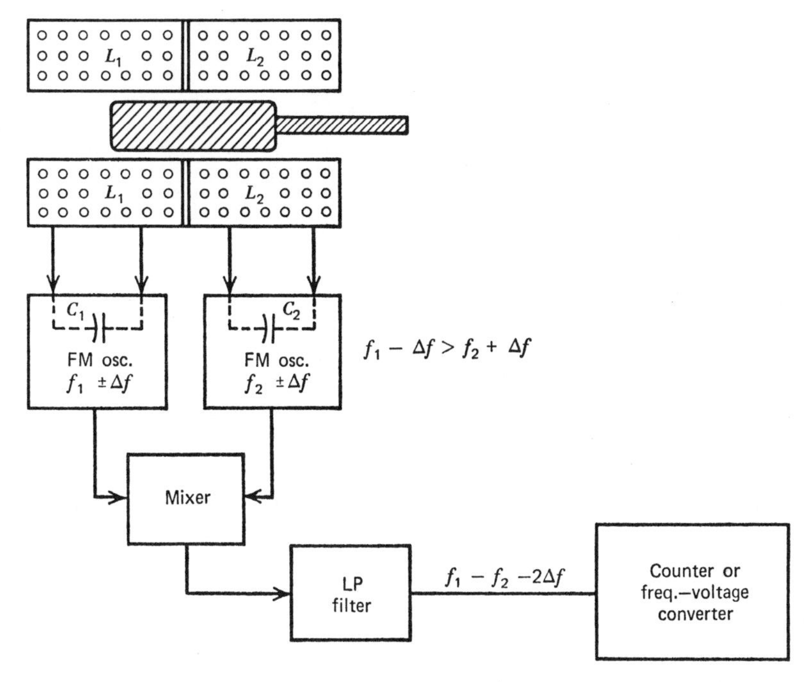

Figure 6.19. Two-coil inductance displacement transducer system.

It used two identical ferrite-cored coils, which were sutured onto opposite walls of the heart. By applying a large ac signal to one of the coils and connecting the other to a high-gain amplifier and demodulator, an output was obtained that varied as the inverse cube of the coil separation (Figure 6.20). To obtain a linear distance-versus-ouput relation they used an analog inverse-cube-root circuit. By this means, they were able to record the dimensional change in a linear manner. Simultaneous measurements on the same organ can be made by using different oscillator frequencies for each coil pair. As shown in Figure 6.21, Caldwell et al. used a narrow-band quartz crystal to control the frequency of each channel by making the coupled coils part of the oscillator feedback loop. Provided the received signal amplitude is above a certain threshold, the amplitude of the primary coil voltage is constant. Misalignment of the coil axes is not too serious: measurements showed that a rotation of one coil by 30° produced an output voltage change equivalent to a 1-mm distance change when the coils were 5 cm apart.

A second example of a two-coil displacement transducer is the respiration monitoring system described by Rolfe [29]. In order to detect the temporary cessation in breathing of premature babies, Rolfe used two ferrite-cored coils, each having a diameter of 1.4 cm and attached symmetrically below

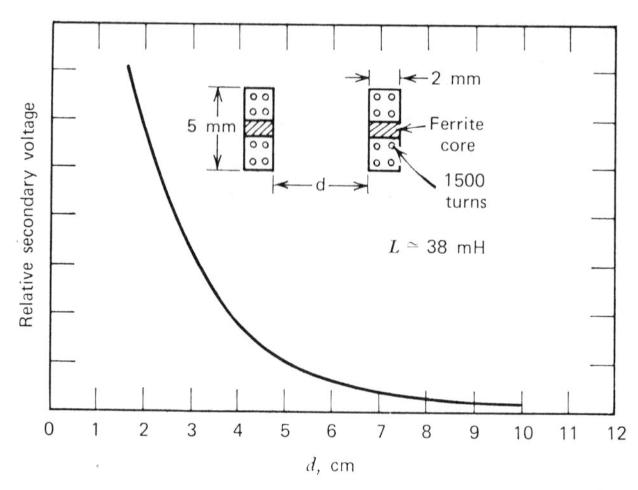

Figure 6.20. Output voltage versus coil separation for a two-coil displacement transducer system designed for measuring changes in cardiac dimensions (adapted from W. M. Caldwell, M. F. Wilson, and R. E. Stealey, *Med. Res. Eng.*, **8**, 11–19, 1969).

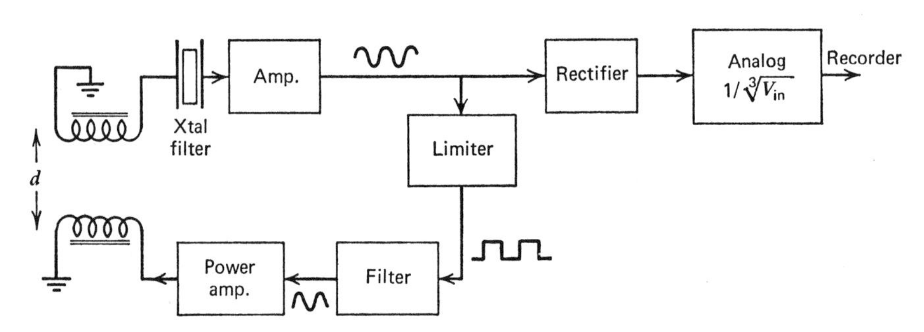

Figure 6.21. Block diagram of a single channel cardiac dimension gauge (adapted from W. M. Caldwell, M. F. Wilson, and R. E. Stealey, *Med. Res. Eng.*, **8**, 11–19, 1969).

the margin of the rib cage. As shown in Figure 6.22, one coil is connected to a 3-kHz oscillator, and the other, to a tuned amplifier–demodulator system. An automatic gain control (agc) with a response time of 30 sec adjusts the signal level so as to compensate for any long-term changes in coil displacement (such as those resulting from body movements) but preserves the respiratory waveform. An additional feature of the agc is that it eliminates the need to adjust the receiver sensitivity every time the coils are attached.

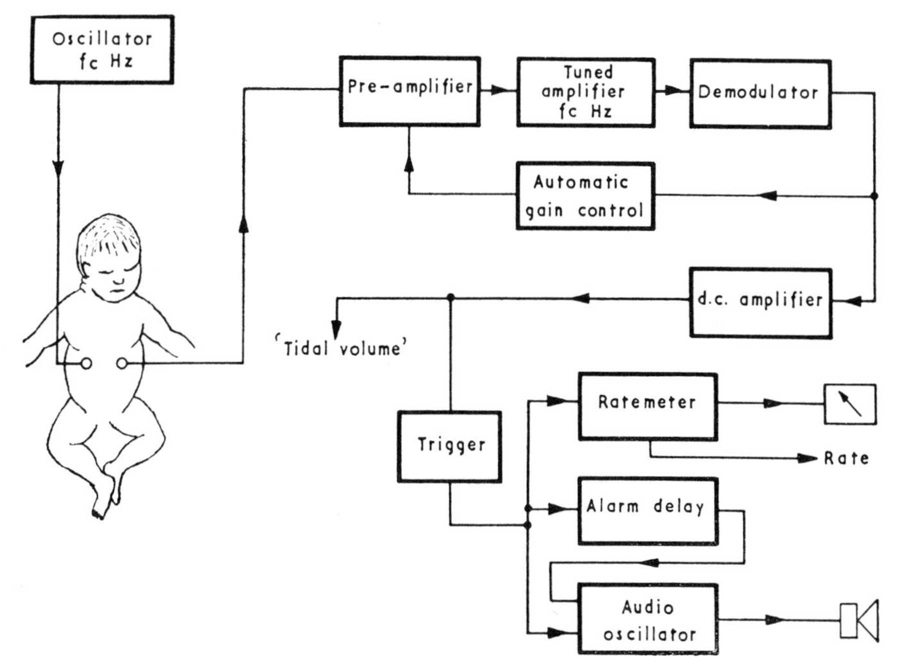

Figure 6.22. Block diagram of a two-coil displacement transducer system for monitoring the respiration in infants (reproduced, with permission, from P. Rolfe, *Bio-Med. Eng.*, **6**, 402–404, 1971).

To circumvent the problems of artifacts arising from nonrespiratory movements causing false alarms, the trigger circuit is activated by the rate of change of the respiratory signal rather than its amplitude. Pulses from the trigger circuit activate the ratemeter and an alarm system. The absence of a pulse from the trigger circuit during a preset time interval causes the audio alarm to be activated signaling that an excessive time interval has elapsed since the last respiratory cycle.

As a final example of two-coil inductance displacement transducers, we shall briefly consider the system described by Kolin and Culp [30] for measuring the internal arterial diameter and its pulsatile fluctuations. The transducer consists of the two coupled loops of wire P and S shown in Figure 6.23, constrained to move with a spring-steel wire loop. The wires are encased in silicone rubber and are sufficiently small for the loop to be introduced into an artery via an F7 catheter. When in place, the loop expands to the inner diameter and follows fluctuations in the arterial diameter. The 400-Hz oscillator connected to loop P induces in S an emf whose amplitude depends

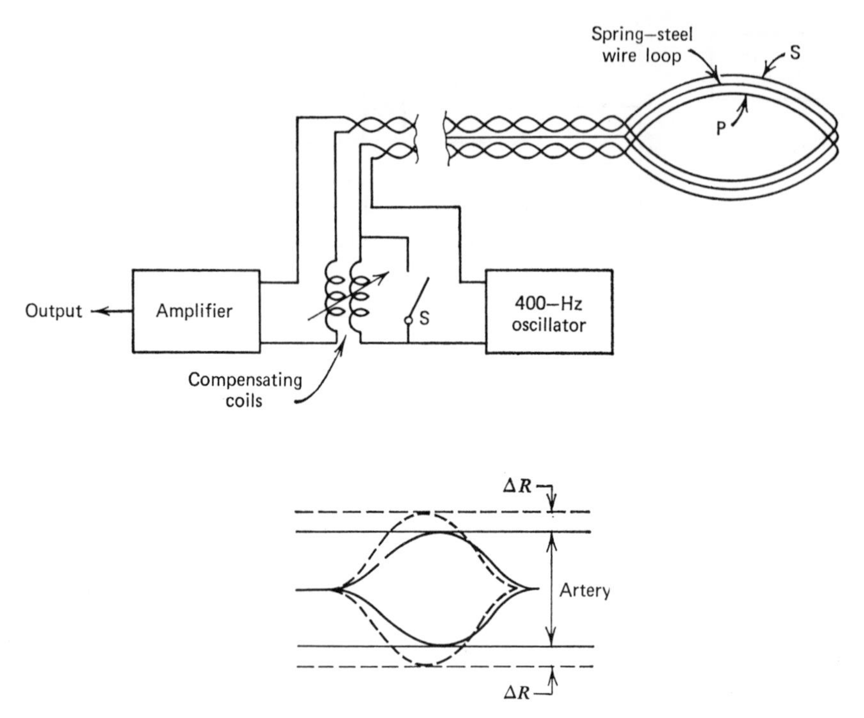

Figure 6.23. Mutual inductance gauge for measuring arterial diameters, according to the design of Kolin and Culp [30].

on the loop area. As the lumen diameter decreases, so the flux generated by P decreases, thereby decreasing the emf induced in S. It is in fact found that the output signal amplitude depends on the log of the arterial diameter over a range from 5 to 15 mm. To measure the arterial diameter, the switch on the compensator coil is closed so that the full secondary amplitude can be measured and then related through a calibration curve to the diameter. Fluctuations in the arterial diameter can be measured by using the compensator coil to null out the steady-state signal, thereby enabling a larger amplifier gain to be used to achieve a higher sensitivity. Kolin and Culp report that variations of 0.01 mm in a 10-mm-diameter lumen can be detected. From the measurements reported it appears that an accuracy of ± 0.3 mm can be achieved.

All the inductance methods described so far entail movement of either a core or a coil, which, even though of very small mass, could under certain circumstances disturb the measured quantity. One inductance scheme that enables a contactless type of measurement to be made is based on the change in eddy currents induced in a conducting surface by a coil [31, pp. 52–56]. If, as shown in Figure 6.14 (f), an excited coil is placed close to a conducting surface, eddy currents will be induced in the surface by the changing magnetic field. These currents flow in a circular manner and in such a direction as to generate a small changing magnetic field opposing the coil's field. As a result the inductance of the coil is reduced from its "free" value, the reduction increasing as the coil approaches the surface. Generally, the inductance versus displacement is quite nonlinear, however, by careful design of coil geometry and use of a two-coil system, it is possible to achieve a linearity of around $\pm 2\%$ of full scale for displacements of 0–0.1 cm. A commercial version* of this system used a 1-MHz excitation frequency, has probes with full-scale ranges of up to 1 cm and is claimed to enable dynamic measurements to be made up to 100 kHz.

6.1.4 Capacitive Displacement Transducers

The dependence of capacitance on plate area, plate separation, and permittivity of the medium between the plates of the capacitor have all been used as a means of converting a displacement to an electrical output. Perhaps the main difficulty with all capacitive transducers is the relatively small change in capacitance with displacement: special circuit techniques are necessary to register these changes accurately and to avoid spurious stray capacitive effects. Nevertheless, they are capable of excellent accuracy and can achieve sensitivities of better than 10^{-12} cm [23]. It is perhaps of interest to note that capacitance microphones make use of the variation of capacitance between a fixed plate and a thin diaphragm displaced by the sound pressure. They are considered to have the best performance characteristics of all microphone types.

Some schemes [31, pp. 66–72; 32] for using the change in capacitance with displacement are illustrated in Figure 6.24. The simplest and most widely used is the parallel plate method shown in (a). It can be shown that if the effects of electric field fringing at the edges can be ignored, the capacitance is given by

$$C = \frac{\varepsilon A}{d} \qquad \text{(in F)}, \tag{11}$$

where A is the area (cm^2), d is the separation (cm), and ε is the absolute permittivity of the medium separating the plates ($\varepsilon = \varepsilon_0 \varepsilon_r = 8.85 \times 10^{-14} \varepsilon_r$ F/cm). The inverse relation between C and d means that the sensitivity increases as

* Kamen Sciences Corp , Colorado Springs, Colorado.

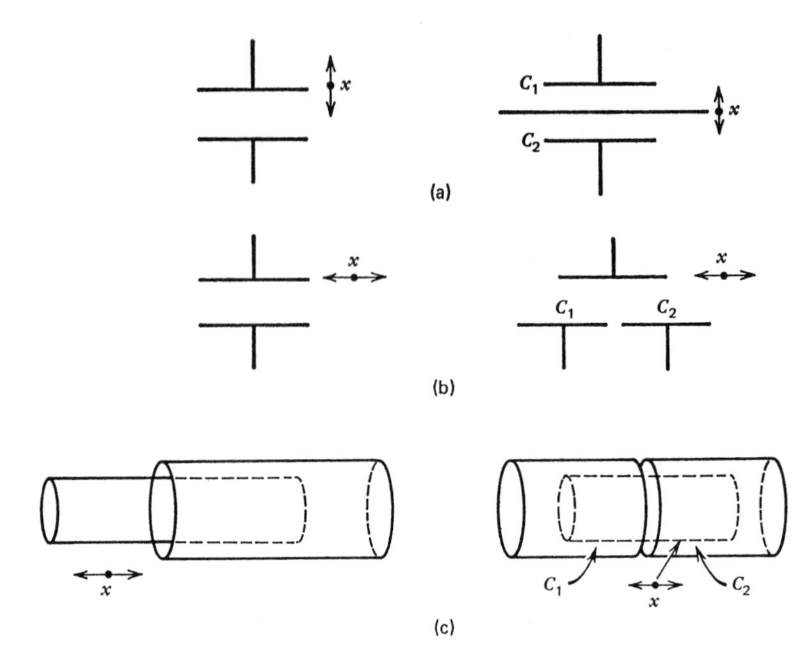

Figure 6.24. Principles of some capacitance displacement transducers.

the plate separation d approaches zero. By differentiating Eq. (11), we find the sensitivity is given by

$$S = \frac{\Delta C}{\Delta d} = -\frac{\varepsilon A}{d^2} \quad \text{(in F/cm)}.$$

Hence, it is desirable to design this capacitor transducer with a small plate separation and a large area. When one plate of the capacitor is a diaphragm, as is the case for a pressure transducer or microphone, it is the fractional change in capacitance ($\Delta C/C$) that is proportional to the pressure. For this case we find from the above two equations

$$S' = \frac{\Delta C}{C\,\Delta d} = \frac{-1}{d} \quad (\text{in cm}^{-1}),$$

which is independent of the plate area but still increases as d approaches zero.

One of the simplest circuits capable of responding proportionally to the displacement of a parallel-plate capacitor transducer is the dc-polarized

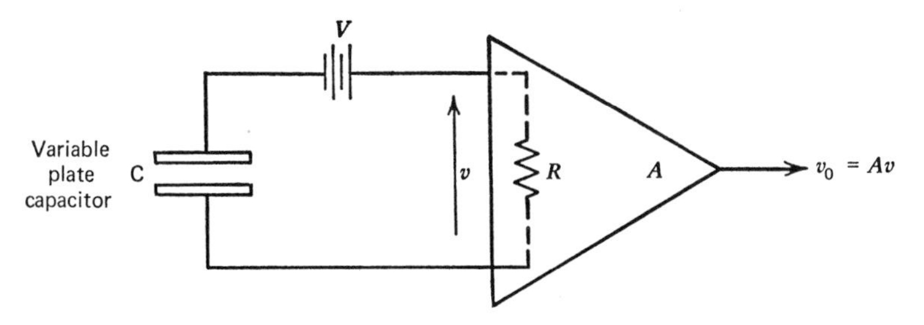

Figure 6.25. DC-polarized capacitance displacement transducer system for measuring dynamic changes.

circuit [1, pp. 278–280; 2, pp. 251–252] shown in Figure 6.25. If the equilibrium plate separation is d, then for a sinusoidal plate displacement amplitude of x_0, it can easily be shown the output voltage v is given by

$$v = \frac{VC_0 R}{d}\left(\frac{j\omega}{1 + j\omega C_0 R}\right) x_0 e^{j\omega t}, \tag{12}$$

where $C_0 = \varepsilon A/d$ and V is the dc-polarization voltage.
If $\omega C_0 R \gg 1$, Eq. (12) reduces to

$$v = \frac{V x_0 \sin \omega t}{d}. \tag{13}$$

If follows from Eqs. (12) and (13) that at higher frequencies the system responds in a proportional manner to displacements, while at lower frequencies the response drops and falls to zero for $\omega = 0$. The lack of a dc response is not important for microphone applications where a low-frequency cutoff of 20 Hz is normally quite adequate, but for measurement of most physiological quantities it is a serious disadvantage.

An ingenious method [2, pp. 253–255] that yields a flat response down to dc and a linear output-versus-displacement characteristic, is shown in Figure 6.26. It uses a parallel-plate capacitor arrangement with a concentric guard ring to eliminate fringing of the electric field at the edges of the inner electrode. By using the transducer as the feedback element of a high-gain operational amplifier the inverse displacement-versus-capacitance relation is turned into a linear output-voltage-versus-displacement relation. If the amplifier gain and input impedance are assumed to be large, the currents through C_x and C_{in} will be given by

$$i_x = j\omega C_x V_0 e^{j\omega t}$$
$$i_{in} = j\omega C_{in} V_{in} e^{j\omega t}.$$

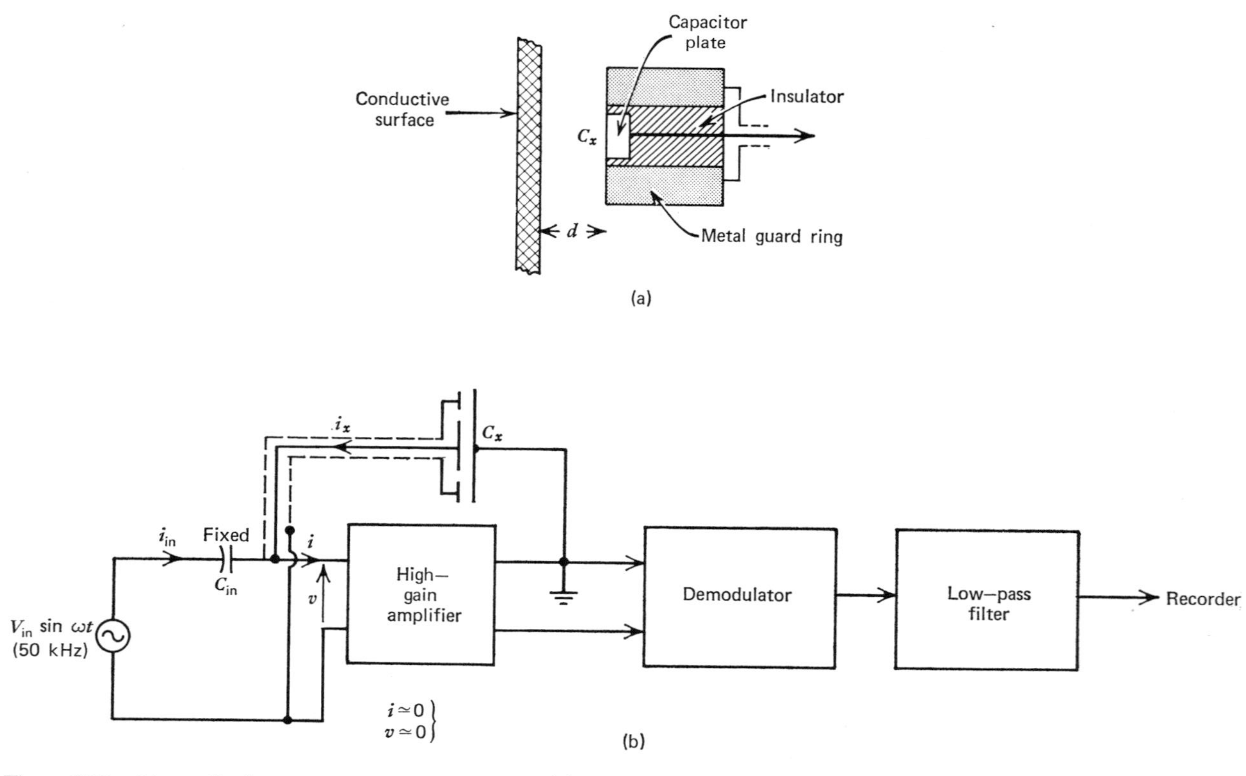

Figure 6.26. Linear displacement measurement system: (a) guarded parallel-plate capacitance transducer; (b) system circuit diagram.

But, since $i_x + i_{in} = 0$, the output voltage for a sine-wave excitation source is

$$V_0 = -\frac{C_{in}}{C_x} V_{in} \sin \omega t,$$

which, by means of Eq. (11), can be expressed in terms of the plate separation d:

$$V_0 = \frac{-C_{in} d V_{in} \sin \omega t}{\varepsilon A}.$$

Hence, the ouput is 180° out of phase with the excitation, is directly proportional to the plate separation d, and is independent of the amplifier gain.

A commercial version of this system* operates at a frequency of 50 kHz, has probes with full-scale displacement ranges from 0.0025 to 2.5 cm, a maximum resolution of around 0.2 μm, and a flat frequency response to 500 Hz. It has been used for measuring the small volume changes from a plethysmograph and for recording apex motion, heart sounds, and vascular pulsations [33–35]. The chief advantage of this method is that it is contactless; however, care must be taken in clinical applications to insure proper patient isolation from the large ac voltages that are often used for the exciting source.

An alternative method of obtaining an indication of the displacement, with an electrode similar to that just described, is to make the capacitor part of an LC oscillator. Through the use of a discriminator, the resulting frequency change can be converted into an equivalent output voltage. In spite of its rather nonlinear input–output characteristics, a number of workers [36] have used this method for recording physiological movements and pulsation. However, a lack of repeatability and the difficulty in properly positioning the transducer make the measurements of dubious value.

Differential capacitor arrangements such as those shown in the second column of Figure 6.24 are more frequently used when accurate measurements are required [37]. The chief advantage of the parallel-plate differential capacitor of Figure 6.24(a) arises from the exact linearity of the fractional difference $(C_1 - C_2)/(C_1 + C_2)$ with displacement. If the equilibrium plate separation is d, then a displacement x in the direction of C_1 results in capacitances

$$C_1 = \frac{\varepsilon A}{d - x}, \qquad C_2 = \frac{\varepsilon A}{d + x}, \tag{14}$$

which can be rearranged in the form

$$\frac{C_1 - C_2}{C_1 + C_2} = \frac{x}{d}.$$

* B731A, vibration meter, Wayne-Kerr Laboratories Ltd., Chessington, England.

Thus, an output voltage proportional to the fractional difference results in a linear displacement characteristic. The bridge circuit of Figure 6.27(a) gives an output of this form. If the bridge is balanced when the displacement is zero ($C_1 = C_2$, $C_3 = C_4$), the output voltage for a displacement x can be shown to be given by

$$v_0 = \frac{V_{in}}{2}\left(\frac{C_1 - C_2}{C_1 + C_2}\right)$$

$$= \frac{V_{in}x}{2d},$$

which is independent of the area and relative permittivity.

An alternative circuit sometimes used with differential capacitor transducers is the transformer ratio-arm bridge shown in Figure 6.27(b). At balance, $C_1 = C_2$ and no current flows into the amplifier. It can be shown that the amplifier input current is directly proportional to the difference $(C_1 - C_2)$, as well as the excitation frequency and amplitude. For a parallel-plate arrangement, we find from Eq. (14)

$$C_1 - C_2 = \frac{2xA\varepsilon}{d^2 + x^2} \qquad \text{(in F)}.$$

Normally the displacement x is small compared to d, so that the denominator is approximately constant, making the capacitance difference proportional to x. Bridges of this type are capable of high accuracy, and sensitivities in the order of 10^{-5} pF. In addition, because of their three-terminal nature, the balance is independent of the shield capacitance, enabling the capacitance transducer to be located remotely from the bridge.

Morgan and Brown [38] have described a somewhat similar transformer ratio-arm–capacitance transducer system capable of excellent performance. They used a differential capacitance transducer consisting of a guarded disc between parallel plates and a precision inductive voltage divider. The voltage divider essentially consisted of the transformer shown in Figure 6.27(b) but with a center tap that was variable over a six decade range. Over 95% of the displacement range the displacement varied linearly with the voltage ratio of the divider, the sensitivity remaining constant to better than 4 parts in 10^5. Displacements of less than 100 Å could be measured, the limit being set by the minimum step size of the voltage divider rather than by the system noise. Moreover, the effects of temperature change were reduced by constructing the transducer from materials having a low coefficient of expansion (e.g., fused quartz or Invar). As a result the sensitivity varied by only 3.5×10^{-6}/°C, over the range 18–90°C. Finally, it should be noted that since the reading was unaffected by changes in dielectric constant, the transducer could be used either submerged in liquids or exposed to variable-humidity air.

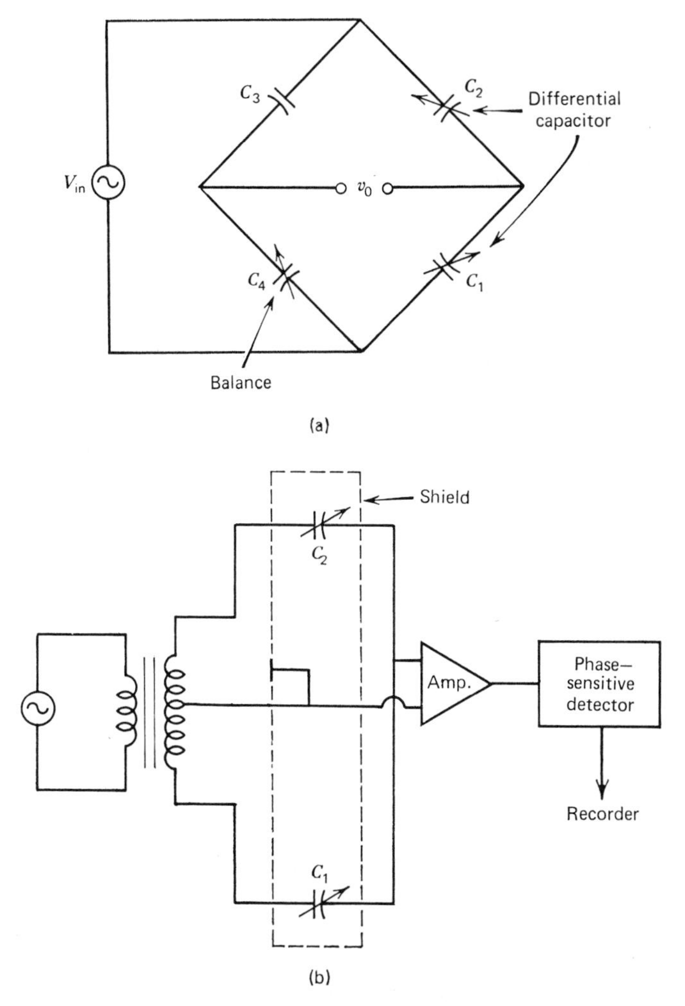

Figure 6.27. Bridge circuits for differential capacitance transducers. (a) conventional bridge yielding an output proportional to the fractional change in total capacitance; (b) transformer ratio-arm bridge.

6.1.5 Ultrasonic Methods

Static and dynamic dimensional measurements can be made either by finding the time taken for a pulse of ultrasound to move between two transducers attached to opposite sides of the organ or vessel to be measured [39–41] or by measuring the difference in the echo reflection times from opposite vessel walls using a transducer or transducers placed on just one side [42–46]. Examples of both methods will be discussed.

If, as shown in Figure 6.28(a), a short pulse of ultrasound is transmitted from one transducer, a received pulse will occur at the second transducer after a time $\tau = d/c$. Provided the velocity c of ultrasound in the medium is known and remains constant as the dimensions change, a measurement of the transit time enables the distance d to be obtained. In point of fact the received signal waveform is rather more complex: multiple reflections at the interfaces within the measured volume and simple reflections from the sides cause ultrasound signals to arrive after the directly transmitted pulse. Thus, all that the "receiver" system is required to do is to measure the time interval from the beginning of the transmitted pulse to the beginning of the first pulse that arrives at the receiver transducer, and to produce a proportional output voltage.

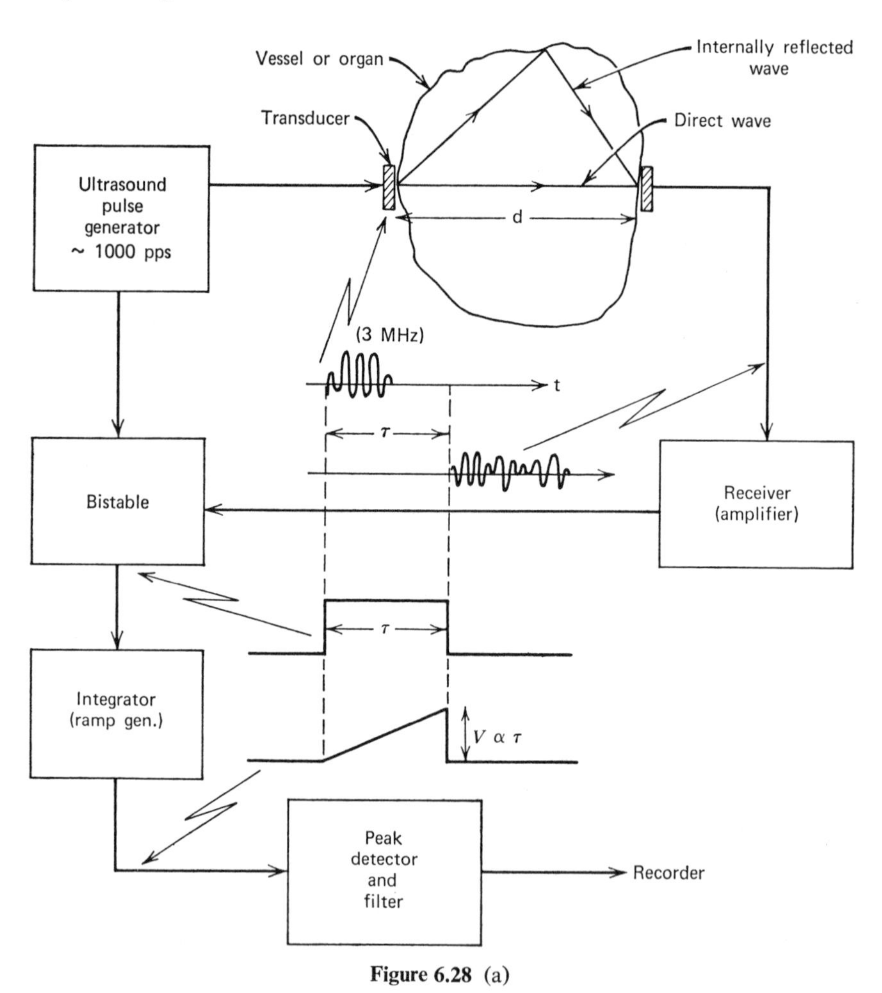

Figure 6.28 (a)

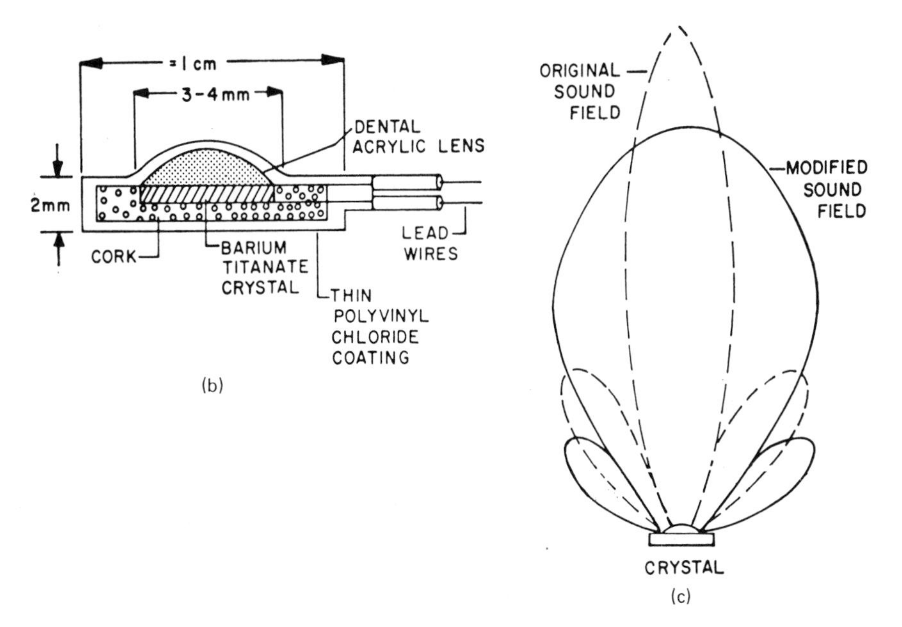

Figure 6.28. Sonomicrometer. (a) Block diagram showing the ultrasound pulse generator and receiver, together with a circuit for converting the delay τ into a proportional output voltage V; (b) barium titanate piezoelectric transducer; (c) radiation pattern of transducer with and without the acrylic lens (from "Sonocardiometer" by D. W. Baker, pp. 31–34 in *Methods in Medical Research*, Vol. 11, R. F. Rushmer (ed.): copyright © 1966 by Year Book Medical Publishers Inc.; used by permission).

The accuracy of this method is limited by the "rise-time" of the sinusoidal burst of ultrasound and the dispersion of the pulse as it travels to the receiver. With a 3-MHz frequency the rise-time can be less than 0.5 μs; for $c = 1.5 \times 10^5$ cm/sec, this corresponds to a distance of 0.075 cm. By increasing the frequency to 20 MHz, the resolution improves to 0.01 cm; however, the greatly increased attenuation at this frequency causes difficulties with the signal–noise ratio, especially when the path length is long. The dynamic frequency response of the system is determined by the pulse repetition frequency. For physiological measurements a flat frequency response to 50 Hz is sufficient, so that a pulse repetition frequency of 1000 Hz, some 20 times greater than the highest frequency component of interest, is more than adequate.

As pointed out by Baker [39] axial alignment of the two transducers presents a serious problem especially when the dimensional changes are large and are not of a simple translational type. To partially overcome this,

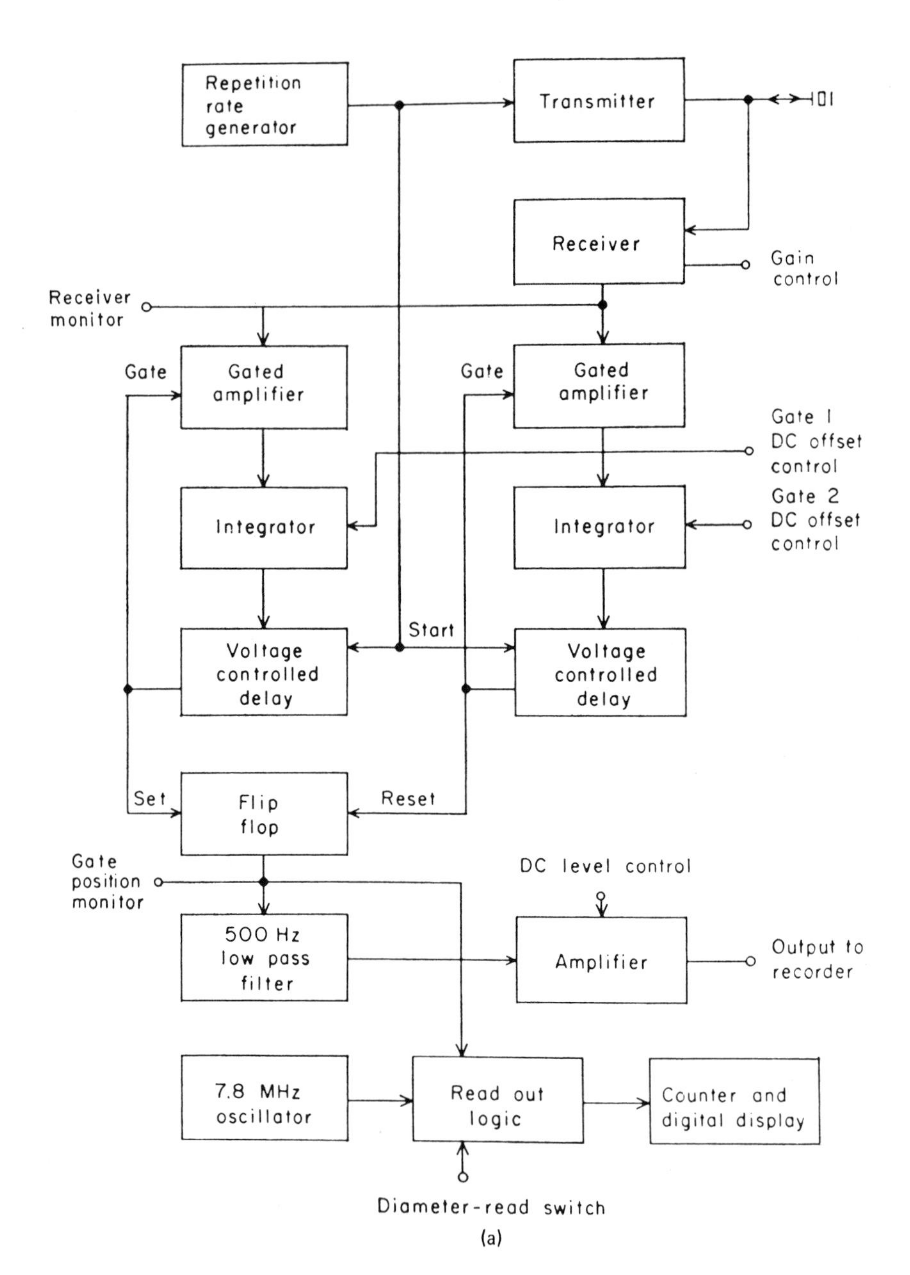

Repetition rate generator
Transmitter
Receiver
Gain control
Receiver monitor
Gate
Gated amplifier
Gate
Gated amplifier
Gate 1 DC offset control
Integrator
Integrator
Gate 2 DC offset control
Start
Voltage controlled delay
Voltage controlled delay
Set
Flip flop
Reset
Gate position monitor
DC level control
500 Hz low pass filter
Amplifier
Output to recorder
7.8 MHz oscillator
Read out logic
Counter and digital display
Diameter-read switch

(a)

Figure 6.29

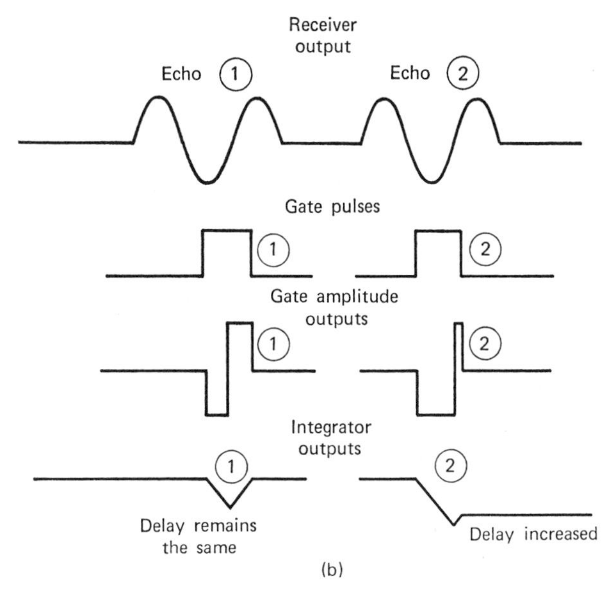

Figure 6.29. Ultrasonic phase-lock system for measuring arterial diameters: (a) block diagram; (b) waveforms associated with the phase-lock subsystem (reproduced, with permission, from D. E. Hokanson, D. J. Mozersky, D. S. Sumner, and D. E. Strandness, *J. Appl. Physiol.*, **32**, 728–733, 1972).

lenses made of a dental acrylic are attached to the barium titanate piezoelectric crystals so as to broaden the radiation pattern [see Figure 6.28(b) and (c)]. Even so, the problem is not entirely eliminated and considerable care must be taken to attach the transducers so that they remain reasonably well aligned during movements.

An implanted telemetered gauge of this type has recently been described by Lee and Sandler [41] for measuring the left ventricular dimensions of unrestrained dogs. By incorporating an RF-actuated switch to turn the transmitter on or off at will they conserve battery power, enabling intermittent measurements to be made over long periods of time.

A sophisticated single transducer system developed by Hokanson et al. [45] for in vivo measurement of arterial diameters and their pulsatile changes makes use of two phase-locked feedback loops to track the echoes from each arterial wall. Although arterial diameter changes can be measured using standard echo techniques [42, 44], problems arise with the large amplitude variations that occur as the artery moves with respect to the transducer. The new system overcomes this problem and, furthermore, automatically follows the echoes from each wall, thereby enabling a signal to be derived whose amplitude is proportional to the instantaneous diameter.

In the block diagram of Figure 6.29(a) it will be noted that each phase-locked loop consists of a gated amplifier, integrator, and voltage-controlled delay (VCD). The echo signal from each wall is gated by a narrow VCD pulse in such a way that the amplifier output is proportional to the phase difference between the gate and the echo [see Figure 6.29(b)]. As the gate moves with respect to the echo, an error signal is produced whose magnitude and sign depends on the phase difference. The integral of the error signal controls the VCD in such a way that the next echo signal will be perfectly aligned with the gate pulse if the echo remains stationary. A flip-flop is set and reset by the gate pulses from each VCD, thereby producing a pulse whose duration is proportional to the arterial diameter. By passing these pulses through a low-pass filter, an output is produced in the form of an analog voltage signal. Alternatively, a digital output can be produced by gating a 7.8-MHz oscillator into a digital counter. Although, the accuracy of arterial diameter measurements is limited to ~0.2 mm by the wavelength of the 4-MHz transmitted pulse, diameter changes of 0.002 mm (2 μm) corresponding to a phase difference of about 2° can be resolved. Furthermore, the fairly high pulse repetition frequency of 7 kHz enables a frequency response of 0–75 Hz to be achieved.

Finally, some mention should be made of the method used by Barnes and Thurstone [46] for extracting moving-target information from ultrasound echoes. In order to determine whether an echo corresponds to a moving interface, the received waveform is stored in an ultrasonic analog delay line and is subtracted from the waveform produced by the succeeding transmitted pulse. This results in echoes arising from stationary interfaces being canceled out, while those from moving interfaces remain. By displaying the subtracted signal waveform using z-modulation of a CRT, a display that shows the time variation of moving interfaces can be obtained. Clinical measurements are reported by Barnes and Thurstone [46] showing clearly defined pictures of the positional variation of the anterior leaflet of the mitral valve, the ball and cage of a mitral prosthesis, and the pulsatile behavior of a branch of the femoral artery.

6.2 VELOCITY AND ACCELERATION TRANSDUCERS

6.2.1 Differentiation and Integration Methods

In principle it is possible to determine the instantaneous velocity and acceleration by electronically differentiating the output from a displacement transducer. As shown in Figure 6.30(a), the first derivative gives the velocity and the second gives the acceleration. Generally, only the first derivative

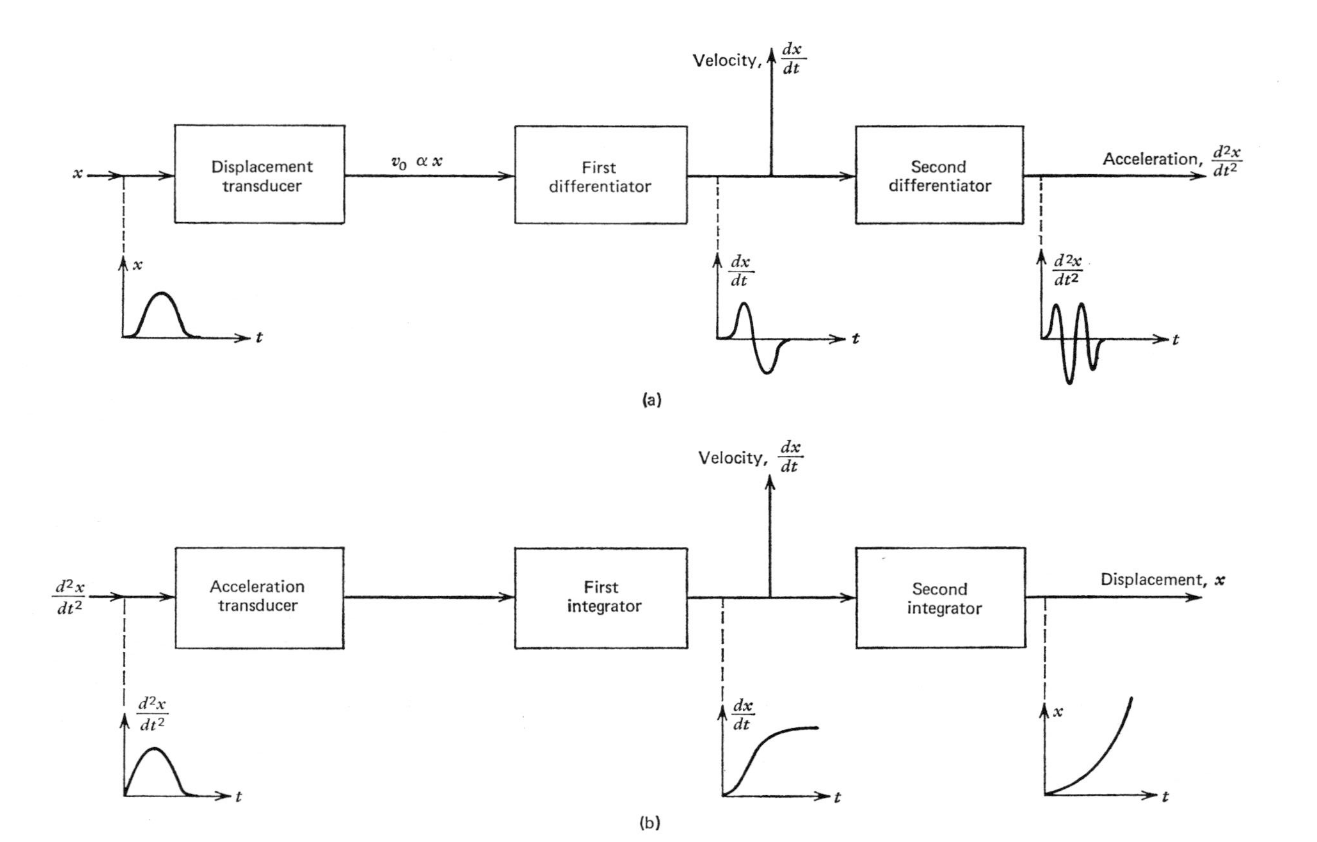

Figure 6.30. (a) Velocity and acceleration obtained by differentiating the output from a displacement transducer; (b) velocity and displacement obtained by integrating the output from an acceleration transducer (after Lion [31]).

can be obtained with a reasonable degree of accuracy: small nonlinearities, measurement errors, and noise in the signal get accentuated by the differentiation process, resulting in large errors when a second derivative is attempted.

The inverse of this process, illustrated in Figure 6.30(b), enables the velocity and displacement to be determined from the acceleration [47, 48]. Integration of the acceleration gives the velocity, and a further integration yields the displacement. Since integration involves a smoothing out of random variations, this method can yield instantaneous velocity and displacement signals that are relatively free from any high-frequency noise present in the original acceleration signal. However, it should be noted that dc drift in the integrator can be troublesome if the signals are nonperiodic or if the period is very long. One example of this technique is that described by Lim et al. [47], who used two miniature accelerometers attached to opposite walls of the heart to determine the wall velocities and, through the use of a difference circuit, the relative dimensional changes.

6.2.2 Doppler Systems

When electromagnetic or ultrasonic radiation is reflected or emitted from an object moving relative to an observer, the observed radiation undergoes an apparent frequency change, generally referred to as the *Doppler shift*. Provided the wave velocity is large compared to the object's velocity, this shift is proportional to the velocity of the object, so that a measurement of the frequency change enables the velocity to be deduced in a very simple manner.

Many examples of the application of this technique can be cited. One concerns the determination of the velocity of a star relative to the earth by comparing the spectrum of radiation emitted from that star to that expected from a stationary one. The change in wavelength of a well-recognized spectral line enables the velocity to be found. Radio waves are also widely used to determine velocities. For example, part of an airplane's navigation system might well include a Doppler ground speed indicator, consisting of a microwave transmitter and receiver on the plane to measure the frequency shift of the radiation reflected from the earth.

Ultrasonic radiation penetrates biological media reasonably well and, as a result, enables Doppler-shift determination of velocities to be made without surgical intervention. An example of the application is the Doppler blood flowmeter, described in Chapter 8, which measures the axial blood-flow velocity without requiring penetration of the vessel wall. A second example is the use of ultrasound to measure ventricular and mitral-valve velocities [49–51]. One of the major problems associated with this type of measurement arises from reflections produced by all moving and stationary interfaces in the

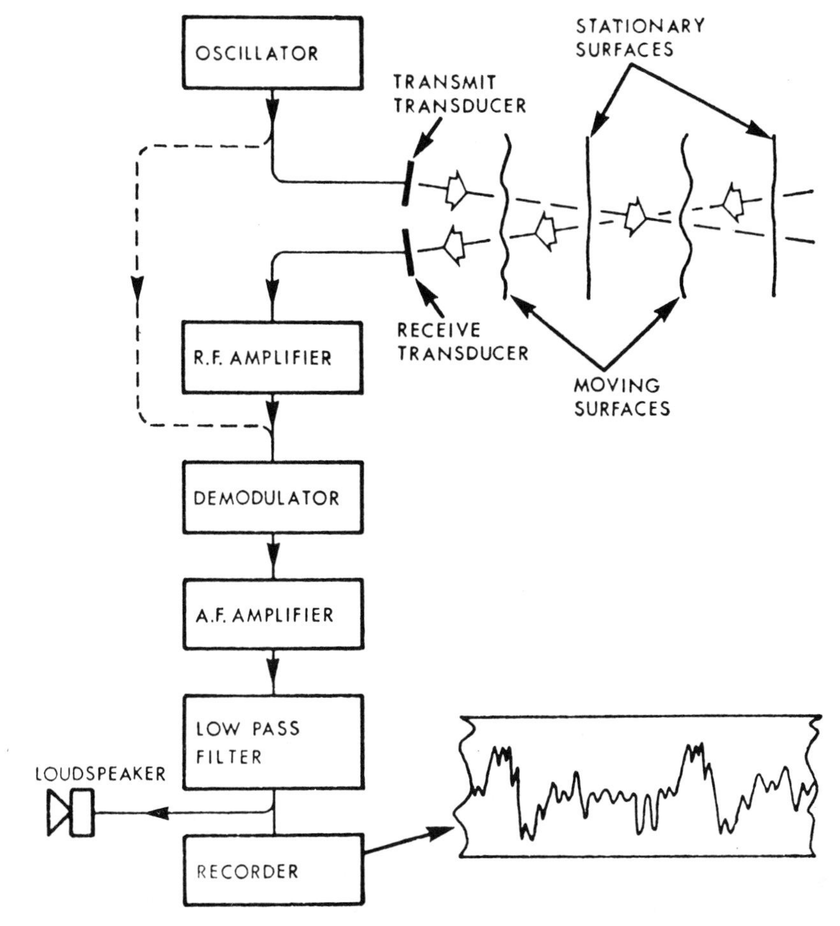

Figure 6.31. A continuous-wave ultrasound Doppler system (reproduced, with permission, from P. N. T. Wells, *Med. Biolog. Eng.*, **7**, 641–652, Nov. 1969).

beam path. As a result, for the continuous-wave Doppler system shown in Figure 6.31, the Doppler signal is a complex combination of signals from each moving interface, making the determination of the velocity of an individual structure very difficult.

Extraction of the wanted Doppler signal can be achieved by use of the range-gated system illustrated in Figure 6.32 [50, 51]. Ultrasound pulses of short duration are generated by the transducer when excited by the oscillator–gate arrangement. The transmitted pulse is partially reflected at each interface

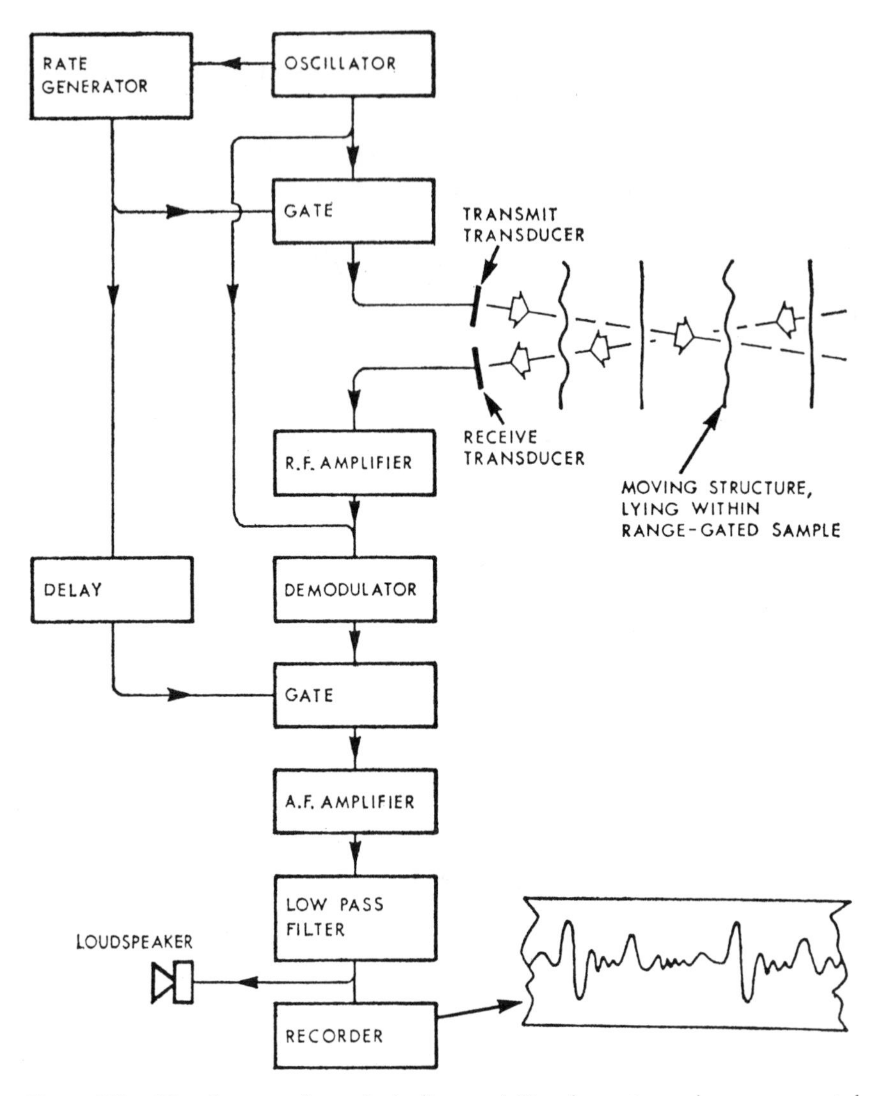

Figure 6.32. The elements of a pulsed ultrasound Doppler system using a range-gated receiver to eliminate the signals arising from unwanted structures (reproduced, with permission, from P. N. T. Wells, *Med. Biolog. Eng.*, 7, 641–652, Nov. 1969).

and, if the interface is moving, suffers a frequency change. Since structures at various depths give rise to reflected pulses that arrive at the receiver transducer after differing time intervals, it is possible to separate out the required signal. The scheme for achieving this consists of a gate activated by a delayed pulse that allows the demodulated receiver output to pass into the AF amplifier for the precise time interval corresponding to the depth range of the interface.

6.2.3 Methods Based on the Mössbauer Effect

A further method of considerable practical importance for measuring very small velocities is based on the discovery by Mössbauer in 1957 that recoilless emission and resonant absorption of γ-rays can occur when both the emitter and absorber nuclei are "embedded" in a suitable lattice. As will be seen, the Mössbauer effect makes possible some very sophisticated measurements on the vibration characteristics of certain parts of the auditory system. But before presenting this, it seems desirable to discuss briefly the physical principles involved and to indicate the manner in which the effect can be observed [52–54].

The nucleus of an atom possesses a certain set of possible energy levels that define the transitions that may occur when the nucleus is excited or when it de-excites. When an excited nucleus, which is free to move, emits a γ-ray photon, it is found that the energy of the photon is less than the energy difference of the two nuclear states. The reason is simply that in order to conserve momentum, the nucleus must acquire translational energy; that is, the nucleus recoils on emitting the γ-ray. Thus, if E_0 is the difference in the nuclear states, then the photon will have an energy of $E_0 - R$, where the recoil energy R is equal to $E_0{}^2/2mc^2$, m is the nuclear mass and c is the velocity of light. Similarly, in the process of γ-ray absorption, the nucleus acquires a translational energy of R. This implies that a γ-ray must have an energy of $E_0 + R$ in order for the probability of absorption to be a maximum. These two processes are illustrated in Figure 6.33(a), where the natural emission and absorption line widths are shown broadened by thermal movement Doppler shifts associated with the recoil. It will be noted that the fairly large energy difference means that γ-rays emitted cannot be reabsorbed by a nucleus of the same type.

To make the emission and absorption lines coincide, it is necessary to eliminate the recoil energy. This can be achieved by embedding the emitter and absorber nuclei in a solid so that they are tightly coupled to the crystal lattice and the crystal as a whole forms the recoil mass. That the recoil energy is inversely proportional to the recoil mass effectively means that the recoil energy is eliminated. As shown in Figure 6.33(b), an appreciable fraction of the γ-rays are emitted in a recoilless manner, and as a result, resonant absorption can be observed. Furthermore, the absence of recoil effectively eliminates the Doppler broadening, and the line widths approach their natural values (e.g., $\Delta E/E \approx 10^{-13}$).

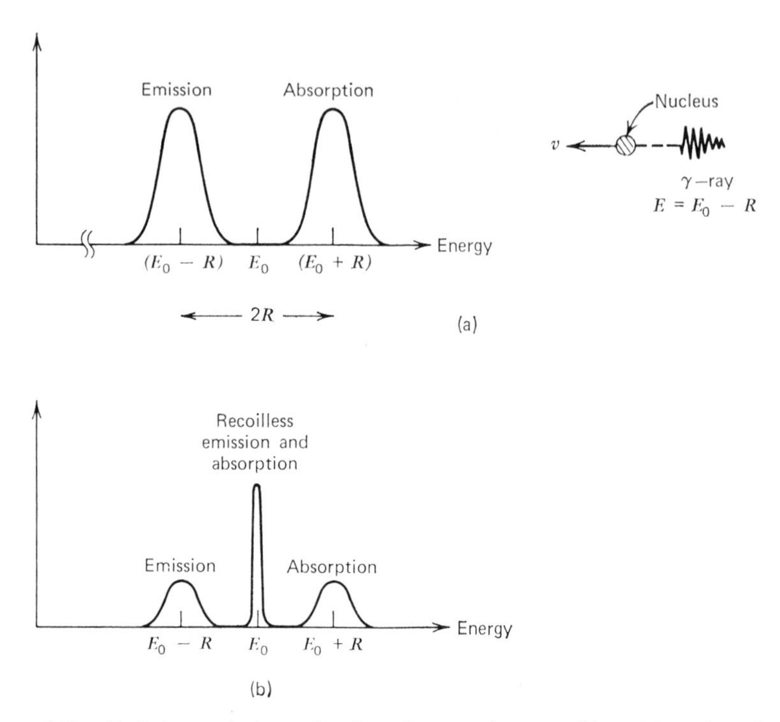

Figure 6.33. Emission and absorption lines for a nuclear transition. (a) nucleus free to recoil; (b) nucleus embedded in a solid matrix.

A frequently used Mössbauer source consists of the isotope $^{57}_{27}Co$, which can be plated by electrochemical deposition onto a stainless-steel substrate. As illustrated in Figure 6.34, ^{57}Co decays with a 270-day half-life to an excited form of ^{57}Fe, by electron capture. Subsequent decay to the ground state can occur either through direct emission of a γ-ray or through an intermediate state with the emission of two γ-rays, one having an energy of 122 keV and the other being the Mössbauer 14.4-keV γ-photon. The natural line width of the 14.4 keV radiation is 4.6×10^{-9} eV, and it is found that approximately 70% of these γ-rays are emitted in a recoilless manner at room temperature. This endows ^{57}Fe with one of the largest Mössbauer effects.

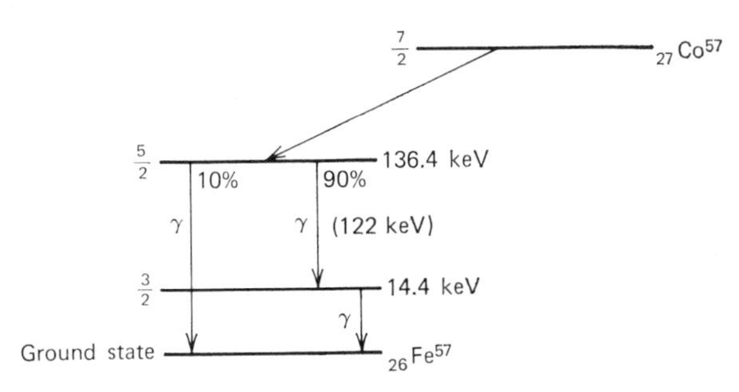

Figure 6.34. Approximate decay scheme for the Mössbauer source, ^{57}Co.

The very narrow Mössbauer line widths implies that very small velocities of the source with respect to the absorber can produce Doppler shifts that result in measurable changes in the number of γ-rays transmitted through an absorber. In fact, as shown in Figure 6.35, this provides the simplest method for obtaining the line shape. By measuring the number of γ-rays transmitted for a fixed period of time for various source velocities, a velocity-versus-count-rate graph can be obtained, which can, if required, be used to obtain the line shape.

To measure an unknown velocity using the Mössbauer effect, a Mössbauer source can be attached to the moving object and a measurement made of the γ-ray absorption by a fixed absorber. The velocity can then be found

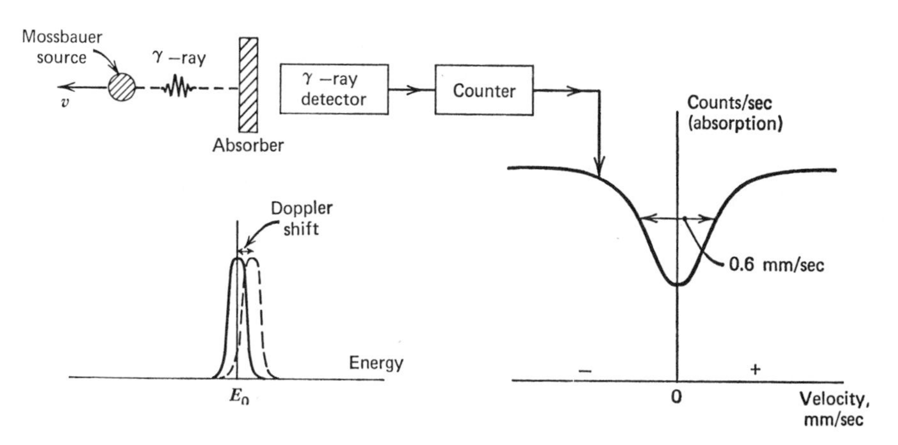

Figure 6.35. Mössbauer effect experiment to measure the shape of the resonance absorption line by using the Doppler effect.

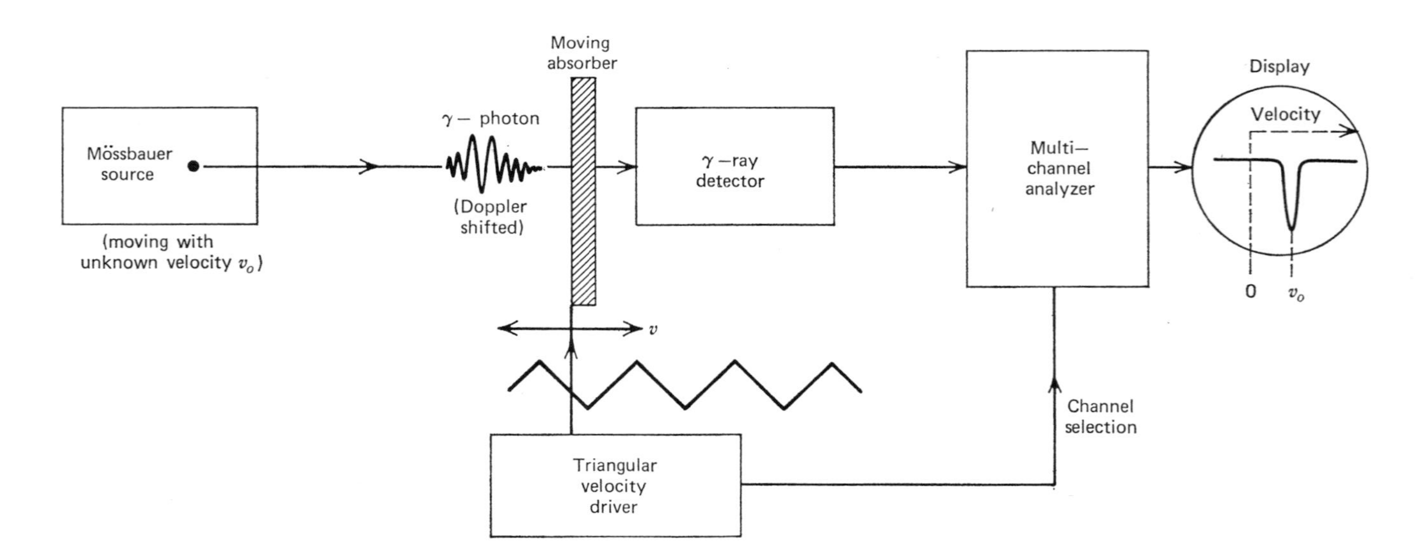

Figure 6.36. Method for measuring an unknown velocity using the Mössbauer effect, and a "kicksorter" as a multiscaler.

from a calibration curve. Velocities in the range 0.01–1 mm/sec can be determined in this way [54]. A somewhat better scheme is illustrated in Figure 6.36. Here, the absorber is subject to a triangular velocity profile and a multichannel analyzer is used as a multiscaler. Each address of the analyzer corresponds to a small incremental velocity range, so that the content of the analyzer is the resonance absorption curve shifted by an amount that is linearly related to the source velocity. In this way the nonlinear characteristic of the absorption curve can be avoided and a linear display of velocity would be obtained.

The sensitivity of the Mössbauer method depends on the source-absorber characteristics, the source strength, and the time interval over which the measurement is made. By measuring over long time intervals so as to achieve a high statistical accuracy, displacement amplitudes (integral of the velocity) of less than 1 Å can be measured [55].

An important example of the Mössbauer technique in physiological investigations is the measurement of the vibration characteristics of certain parts of the auditory system. For example, Gilad et al. [56] have reported measurements of the umbo and the incudostapedial joint of the guinea-pig ear in vivo. In addition, Johnstone and Boyle [57] and Rhode [58] have used this method to measure the vibration of the basilar membrane of the cochlea.

Movements associated with auditory excitation by an external source are very small: even under very intense stimulation movements of less than 1 μm occur. Typically the displacements are in the order of 100 Å. Threshold amplitudes for the basilar membrane, corresponding to the minimum discernable sound level, are believed to be in the order of 0.01 Å for frequencies in the kilohertz range.

Rhode [58], in his experiments on the movement of the basilar membrane, used a ^{57}Co source measuring about 50 × 50 μm^2 and weighing 0.2 μg attached to the basilar membrane. With a ^{57}Fe absorber and a γ-ray detection system feeding an on-line computer, the velocity of the membrane was determined for various excitation amplitudes and frequencies. Both the velocity amplitude and the phase of the vibration relative to the excitation could be determined. In addition, by integration, the displacement amplitudes were found.

6.2.4 Electromagnetic Methods

A number of electromagnetic schemes exist for obtaining an output voltage directly proportional to a linear translational or angular rotational velocity. These mostly make use of the fact that the voltage induced across a conductor moving through a uniform magnetic field is directly proportional to its velocity. One commercial translational velocity transducer, illustrated in Figure 6.37, uses a permanent magnet movable core inside a long coil consisting of two halves that are wound in opposite directions. The transducer output voltage reverses sign with the velocity direction, has a linearity of about 1%, and a sensitivity in the range 0.04–0.3 V/(cm) (sec). Transducers with full-scale stroke lengths of 1–25 cm are available, and these enable velocities from zero frequency (a constant velocity) up to the limit imposed by inertial effects of the core mass to be measured.

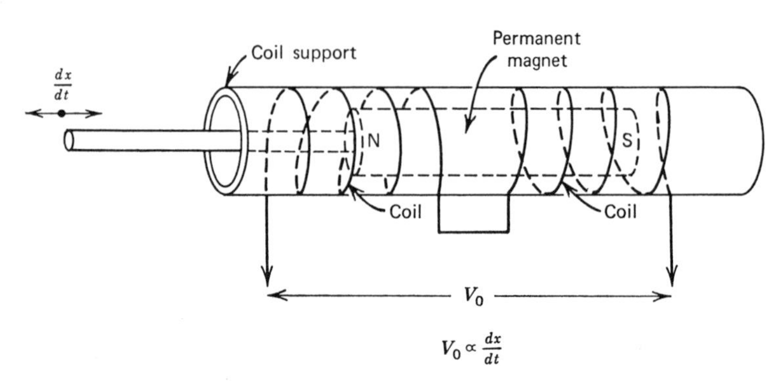

Figure 6.37. Moving-magnet type of translational velocity transducer.

On the other hand, the seismic type of velocity transducer illustrated in Figure 6.38 can only measure velocities of a vibrationary nature; that is, it has a low-frequency cutoff. The system shown is similar to that of Figure 6.37, except that it contains a seismic mass (the permanent magnet) suspended "loosely" by two springs. It has a second-order transfer function with a resonant frequency that is often in the range 5–20 Hz. Above the resonant frequency the frequency response is flat; below it the output falls off, becoming zero for a constant velocity (zero frequency).

Perhaps the simplest way of understanding its operation is to consider what happens to the seismic mass as the vibration frequency is raised from zero to some high value. At zero and low frequencies the force exerted by the spring will be sufficient to cause the seismic mass to move with a velocity approximately equal to that of the surrounding coil. At frequencies above the natural frequency the force exerted by the springs will not be sufficient to cause significant movement of the seismic mass; that is, the coil moves relative to the mass with a velocity equal to the absolute vibratory velocity. As a result, an emf is generated in the coil with an instantaneous value proportional to the instantaneous vibratory velocity.

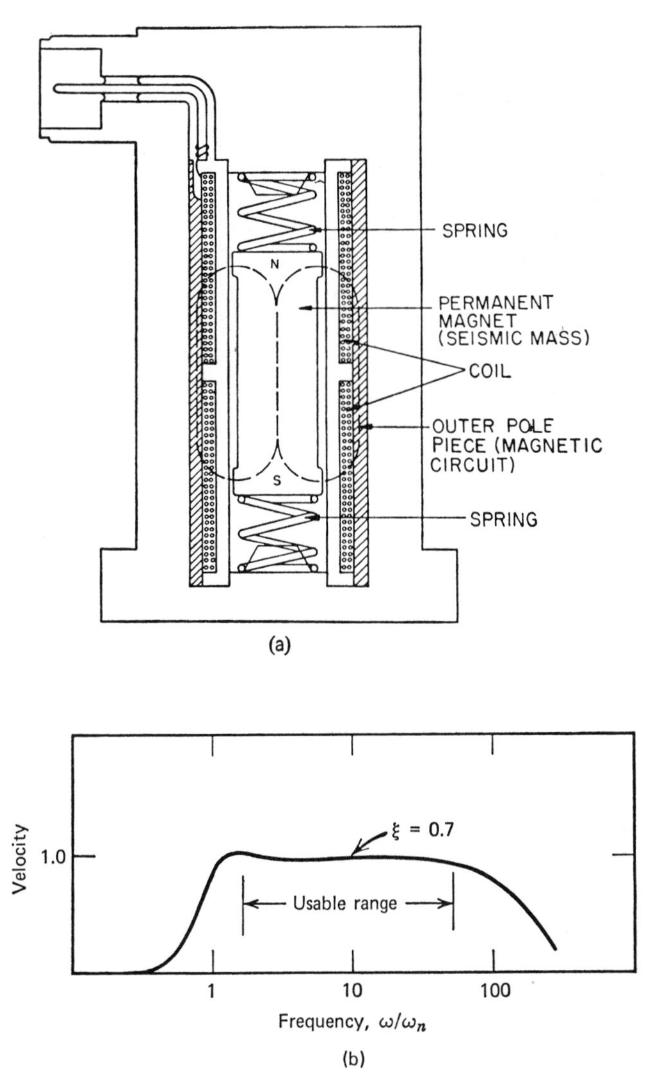

Figure 6.38. Seismic-mass type of velocity transducer: (a) physical structure; (b) approximate frequency response when the damping factor is 0.7 (reproduced by permission of Bell and Howell, Calif., from Consolidated Electrodynamics Bulletin #1322, 1964).

6.2.5 Acceleration Transducers

Acceleration transducers are extensively used in industrial work for general measurement of motion. Basically they all make use of Newton's law $F = Ma$, by measuring the force required to accelerate a known mass M. The force is usually measured in one of two ways: by measuring the strain in the spring element that supports the seismic mass and by using a piezoelectric element to measure the force directly. A third, much more complex method consists of using a balance force whose magnitude is controlled by a displacement transducer connected to the mass. If the feedback to the balance force generator results in zero displacement, the balance and acceleration forces will be equal. Hence, if the balance force generator is linear, the input to it will be directly proportional to the acceleration.

In the unbonded wire gauge system shown in Figure 6.39(a) the seismic mass is supported at both ends by spring elements that also support the strain-gauge windings. When the acceleration is toward the upper winding, the top spring moves downward causing the upper winding to relax and the bottom winding to increase in tension. Such a system is sensitive to the absolute component of acceleration in the direction of the axis and has a response that is flat from a frequency of somewhat less than the resonant frequency down to dc. The second-order properties of this system make it essential to provide the correct degree of damping. Sometimes this is achieved by immersing the system in a viscous fluid (e.g., silicone oil). The larger the seismic mass the greater will be the force exerted on the strain gauges and hence the greater will be the sensitivity. On the other hand, a large seismic mass means that the system resonant frequency will be lower and the loading imposed on the platform whose acceleration is being measured will be greater.

One of the simplest forms of accelerometer consists of a cantilever beam with a mass attached to the free end, as in Figure 6.39(b). If the cantilever is silicon, the gauges can be incorporated in an integrated form; if metal is used, gauges can be bonded to the cantilever. Proper damping can be achieved by immersing the system in an appropriate oil. One example of such an arrangement is that described by Daniker [59a], consisting of a semiconductor gauge bonded to a beryllium–bronze spring cantilever, with a seismic mass attached to its end. Damping was provided by oil contained within the 0.6-ml package. The gauge was sufficiently small and light to enable it to be used for the radiotelemetric recording of the motor activity of a rat.

Compared to the unbonded gauge accelerometer, the bonded cantilever type is less sensitive, since only a portion of the force produced by the accelerated mass is transmitted to the gauge. However, as demonstrated by

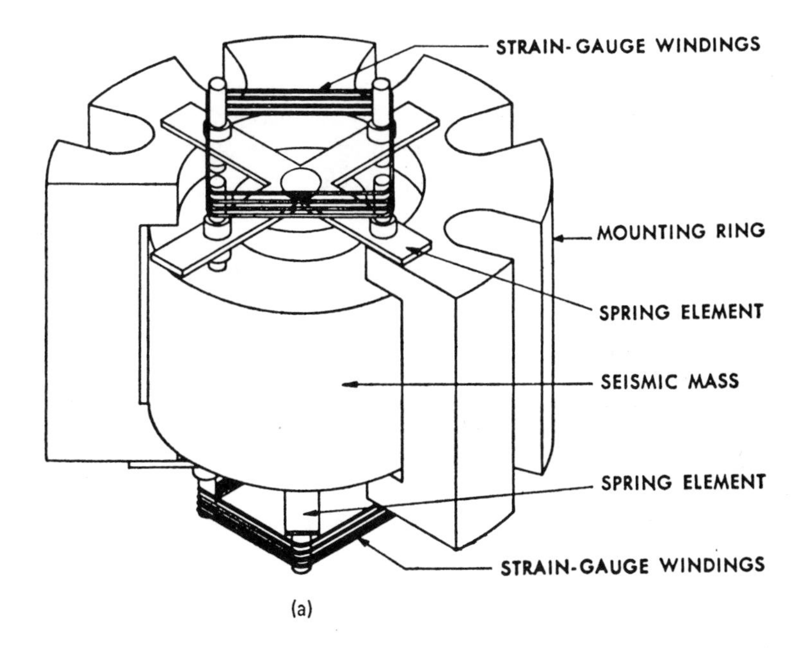

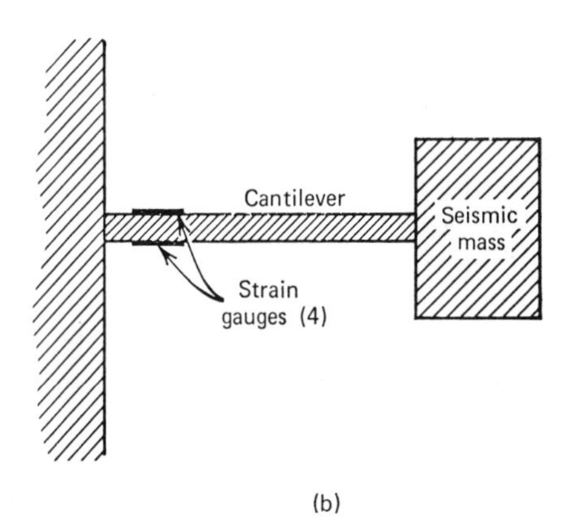

Figure 6.39. Seismic-mass accelerometers (a) unbounded strain gauge type; (b) cantilever-type with bonded strain gauges (reproduced by permission of Bell and Howell, Calif., from Consolidated Electrodynamics Bulletin #1322, 1964).

the above example, their rather simpler structure enables a lighter and more compact transducer to be fabricated.

A second important class of accelerometer is that using the piezoelectric effect to transduce the force produced by the acceleration directly into a charge or voltage. The next subsection discusses the piezoelectric effect and shows how it can be used for force and acceleration measurements.

6.3 PIEZOELECTRIC ACCELERATION AND FORCE TRANSDUCERS

6.3.1. Piezoelectric Effect

Certain crystals and ceramics when mechanically strained in particular directions become electrically polarized and this can be detected by evaporating metal electrodes onto opposite faces, so that the change in charge manifests itself as a potential difference. It is found that the effect is reversible; that is, the application of an emf between the plates results in a strain. Substances that possess this property are called *piezoelectric* and the effect they exhibit is called the *piezoelectric effect* [1, pp. 302–362].

Fundamentally the piezoelectric effect arises from an asymmetrical charge distribution in the material structure. A deformation of the lattice results in a relative displacement of these internal charges, causing the substance to exhibit a change in the surface charge. Piezoelectric materials are of two kinds: naturally occurring materials, such as quartz, and synthetic materials, such as barium titanate ceramic and lead zirconate titanate ceramic [59b]. The latter materials must be artificially polarized during fabrication in order to exhibit piezoelectric properties. Important advantages of the ceramics are that they can be fabricated to any desired shape, they have large piezoelectric coefficients, and they are mechanically very stable.

Some of the basic deformation modes for piezoelectric materials are shown in Figure 6.40. Not all of these result in the development of a surface charge: for example, quartz has no volume or shear piezoelectric effect but possesses a good thickness and length effect. It is the thickness mode that will be considered in the discussion that follows. In this mode the strain resulting from an applied force is very small—typically less than 1 μm. As a result the mechanical input impedance is very large, making the device a nearly ideal force transducer. In physiological terms, a piezoelectric transducer behaves isometrically.

Piezoelectric materials generally possess a linear relation between the change in induced surface charge ΔQ and the change in applied force ΔF. Thus, we can write

$$\Delta Q = D\,\Delta F, \tag{15}$$

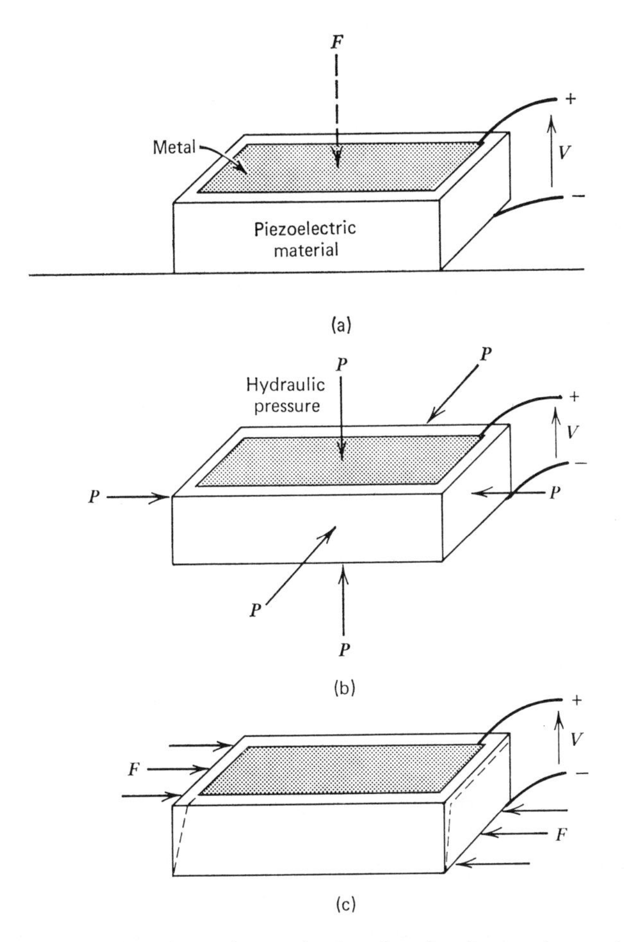

Figure 6.40. Some basic deformation modes for piezoelectric transducers: (a) thickness-expansion mode: (b) volume-expansion mode; and (c) thickness-shear mode.

where D is a constant for the material that expresses its charge sensitivity. Values of this constant, together with some of the other important parameters, are shown in Table 6.2. The change in potential between the plates can be calculated very simply by assuming that the arrangement behaves like a parallel-plate capacitor of capacitance C given by

$$C = \frac{\varepsilon_r \varepsilon_0 A}{d} \qquad \text{(in F)},$$

Table 6.2 Properties of Some Piezoelectric Materials[a]

Material	D-coefft., C/N[b]	Relative dielectric constant	Young's modulus, N/m^2	Max. safe stress, N/m^2	Resistivity, Ω-m
Multiply by	10^{-12}	1	10^9	10^6	10^9
Quartz	2.3	4.5	80	98	>1000
Barium titanate ceramic[c]	140	1200	110	80	>100
Lead zirconate titanate[c]	105	1600	55	—	>30
Lead niobate[c]	200	1500	88	20	>100

[a] Values taken from an extensive table given by Neubert [1].
[b] Values given are for the thickness expansion mode (see Figure 6.40).
[c] Properties vary considerably according to exact composition and fabrication.

where A is the area (cm^2), d is the plate separation (cm) and ε_r is the relative permittivity (dielectric constant). Since $\Delta V = \Delta Q/C$, it follows that Eq. (15) can be written as

$$\Delta V = \frac{D\,\Delta F}{\varepsilon_r\,\varepsilon_0\,A/d} \qquad \text{(in V)},$$

where D is expressed in coulombs per newton and F is in newtons. To obtain a feel for the magnitudes involved, we consider a barium titanate transducer of 1-cm^2 area and 1-mm thickness subjected to the force from a 1-g weight. Using the values of D and ε_r from Table 6.2, we find that $C \simeq 1000$ pF and $\Delta V \simeq 1.4$ mV.

Table 6.2 shows that piezoelectric materials have a high, but finite, resistivity. As a result, the charge generated by a change in applied force slowly leaks away, causing the potential difference to reduced eventually to zero. Effectively this means that piezoelectric transducers lack a dc response: only forces that vary in time are capable of yielding an output. At medium and low frequencies the circuit model of piezoelectric transducers consists of the parallel CR circuit shown in Figure 6.41, together with a charge source that delivers charge proportional to the applied force. The attachment of a voltage amplifier of input resistance R_{in} and input capacitance C_{in} effectively degrades the transducer characteristics. The effect of C_{in} is to decrease the

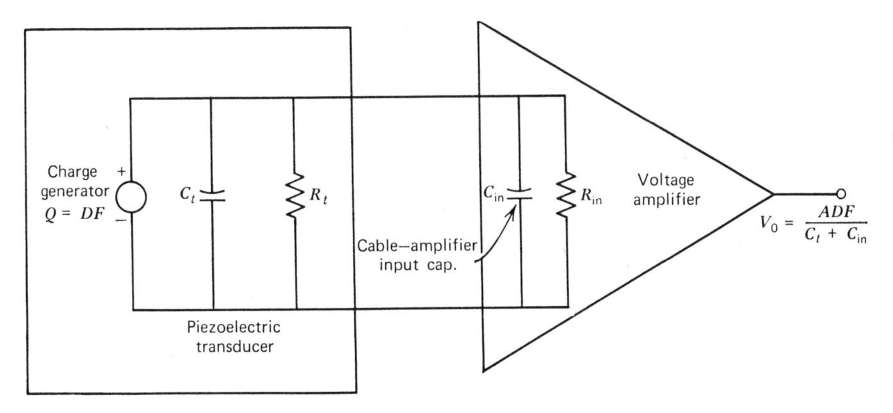

Figure 6.41. Medium- and low-frequency circuit model of a piezoelectric transducer connected to a voltage amplifier. The transducer capacitance and leakage resistance are represented by C_t and R_t.

force to voltage sensitivity by causing the charge generated to be developed across a larger capacitance ($C_{in} + C_t$). The increased charge leakage due to R_{in} becomes important at low frequencies, causing charge to be lost and thereby decreasing the output voltage. It can be shown that the low-frequency response is determined by

$$f_c = \frac{1}{2\pi CR},$$

where

$$C = C_{in} + C_t$$

$$R = \frac{R_{in} R_t}{R_{in} + R_t}$$

and f_c is the frequency at which the magnitude of the input–output transfer function is reduced to 0.707 of its mid-frequency value. Usually, $R_{in} \ll R_t$ so that the input resistance of the amplifier determines the low-frequency response. For $R_{in} = 10\ \text{M}\Omega$ and $C = 1000$ pF, $f_c = 17$ Hz: by increasing R_{in} to $1000\ \text{M}\Omega$ (a figure that can be readily achieved with modern amplifiers), the low-frequency response is reduced to 0.17 Hz.

A charge amplifier that converts the transducer charge into a proportional output voltage in the manner shown in Figure 6.42 offers several important advantages over a voltage amplifier system [2]. In the first place, its very large input capacitance makes the sensitivity of such a system essentially independent of both the transducer and connecting-cable capacitance.

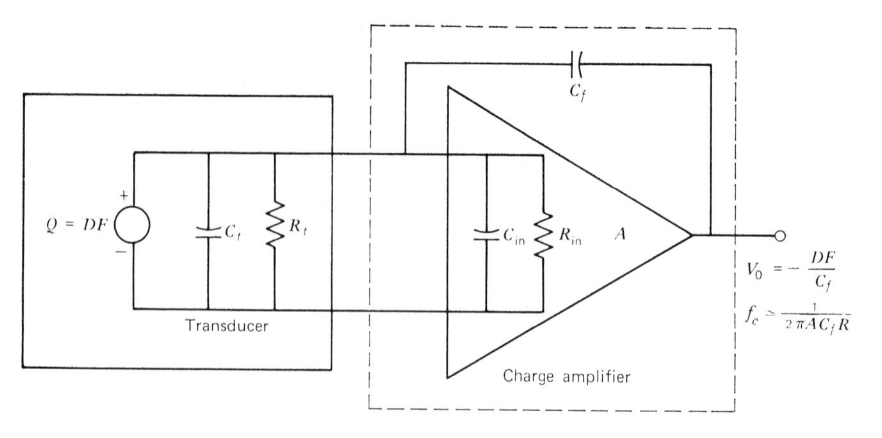

Figure 6.42. Model of a piezoelectric transducer connected to a charge amplier.

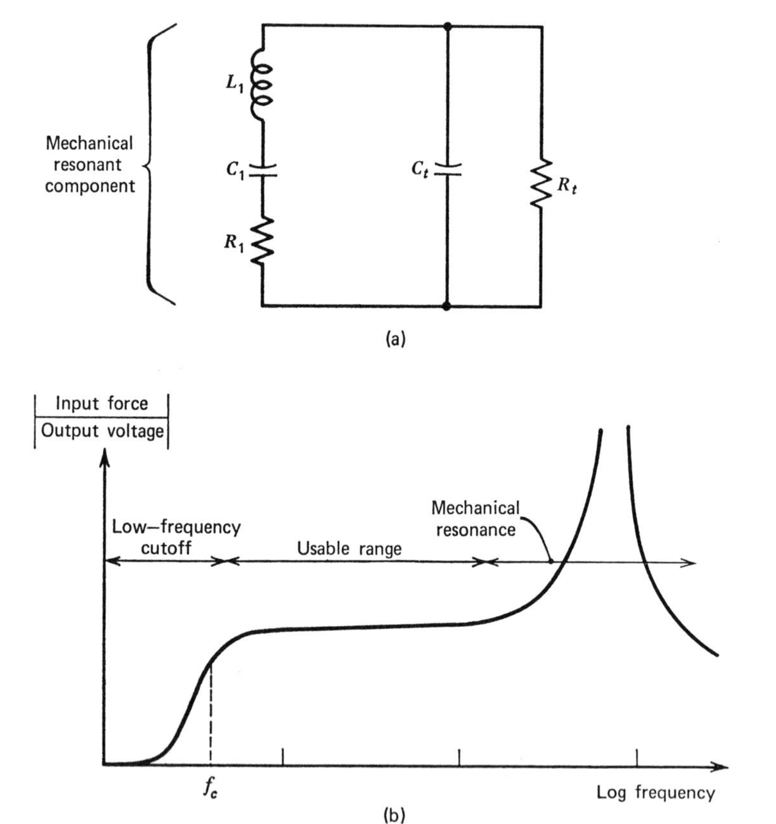

Figure 6.43. Circuit model of a piezoelectric transducer that includes high-frequency mechanical resonance effects: (a) circuit model; (b) frequency response.

Secondly, since the voltage developed across the input is greatly reduced, the effect of the amplifier input resistance and transducer loss resistance on charge leakage becomes very small. Finally, it should be noted that if the gain of the operational amplifier is large, the feedback capacitance C_f is the only element that affects the charge sensitivity.

At frequencies approaching the mechanical resonant frequency of the piezoelectric slice, the circuit model becomes more complex. As shown in Figure 6.43 this effect can be accounted for by the addition of a series RLC circuit, the elements of which are determined by mechanical parameters. Piezoelectric devices designed especially to act as a frequency-determining element (e.g., quartz-crystal filters) have a very sharp mechanical resonance. It is the sharpness of this phenomenon that makes possible the very accurate control of frequency that is characteristic of crystal-controlled oscillators.

6.3.2 Piezoelectric Transducers

The low cost, simplicity, and relatively large output voltages generated by piezoelectric materials make them a particularly effective means of transducing a variety of physiological phenomena. Crystal microphones of special design are quite often used for measuring and recording heart sounds (phonocardiography). The properties desired for this application are a flat frequency response from 20 to 1000 Hz; a directional sensitivity, so that breathing sounds, room noise, and the like are suppressed; and finally, a negligible loading effect on the chest wall. Microphones for this application are either air-coupled or direct-coupled. In the air-coupled system the cardiac sounds are transmitted through the chest wall to an air space that serves as a coupling medium to a piezoelectric element. Alternatively, direct contact between a movable plunger and the chest wall can be employed. All sounds, as well as low-frequency vibratory noises, are then transmitted to the plunger, whose displacement is measured by the piezoelectric element. Although this arrangement has a high efficiency and good room-noise rejection, its loading effect on the chest wall can be a cause for concern in achieving standardized results.

A variety of catheter-tip piezoelectric sensors suitable for localized pickup of sounds from within the chambers of the heart (intracardiac phonocardiography) have been described by Busser [60]. Consisting of a hollow cylinder of barium titanate ceramic mounted at the catheter tip, they can be made sufficiently small to enable them to be introduced directly into the left heart via a No. 17 thin-walled needle. The somewhat larger and more sturdy single- and double-lumen versions are introduced via a peripheral vein or artery.

The use of piezoelectric crystals for detecting the sounds associated with the occlusive cuff method of measuring systolic and diastolic pressure (Korotkoff sounds) has been reported by a number of investigators. The cuff pressures at which these sounds appear and disappear as the pressure is reduced correspond to the systolic and diastolic pressures, respectively. Automatic cuff inflation and deflation, together with a Korotkoff sound transducer, a signal processor, and threshold detector, form the basis of several automatic blood-pressure measurement systems designed for patient monitoring (see Section 7.2.1.).

The much larger piezoelectric effect in ferroelectric ceramic materials (compared to quartz) makes them the preferred material for use in accelerometers. Such a transducer, as shown in Figure 6.44, basically consists of a seismic mass attached to one face of the piezoelectric material. Sometimes the system is preloaded by a spring attached to the top surface so as to operate the piezoelectric element in a more linear portion of its characteristics.

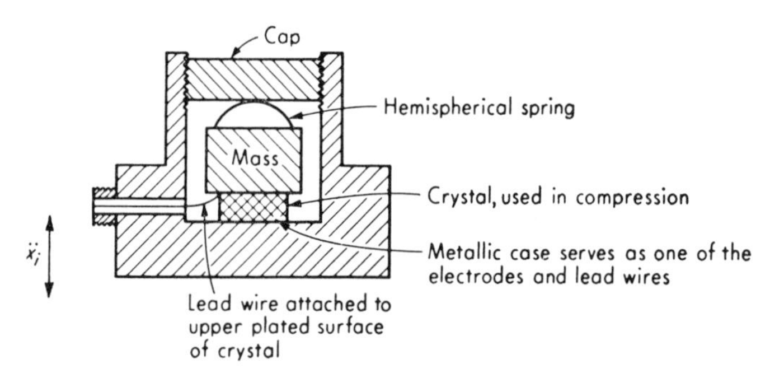

Figure 6.44. Piezoelectric accelerometer construction (from E. O. Doebelin, *Measurement Systems; Application and Design*, © 1966, McGraw-Hill Book Co.; used with permission of McGraw-Hill Book Co., New York).

Miniature forms of this system typically yield outputs of around 50 mV per g of acceleration and have resonant frequencies of 50 kHz. Somewhat higher sensitivities can be achieved with a loaded piezoelectric cantilever-bar arrangement, although the resonant frequency may be much lower. Accelerometers of this type are available in a miniature form, weighing less than 30 g and having sensitivities sufficient to enable accelerations of 0.0001 cm/sec^2 to be detected. They have been used as direct-contact phonocardiography transducers, with the advantage that their small weight creates a very small chest-wall-loading effect. Other applications include the measurement of tremors and the measurement of the motility of small animals.

6.4 FORCE TRANSDUCERS

Force is not a fundamental quantity but is defined through the equation $F = Ma$. As a result it depends on two quantities: mass, which is a fundamental quantity; and acceleration, which is derived from two other fundamental quantities, length and time. In the MKS system of units the unit of force is the newton: it is the force required to accelerate a mass of 1 kg by 1 m/sec^2. Since the earth's gravitational acceleration is essentially constant with time and varies in a known manner with location and height, it provides an excellent means whereby known masses can be used to create an accurately calculable force. The static calibration of force transducers is usually carried out in this way.

The various means by which forces can be measured can be categorized as follows [2, p. 333]:

a. By balancing the unknown force against the gravitational force of a standard mass

b. By measuring the acceleration of a known mass to which the force is applied

c. By balancing the force against an electromagnetically developed force

d. By converting the force to a fluid pressure and measuring that pressure

e. By measuring the strain produced in an elastic member by the unknown force.

Methods a–d, examples of which are given in Figure 6.45, are rarely employed for physiological measurements. On the other hand, a wide variety of schemes based on method e have been used, especially for studies of muscle activity. Because of the importance of elastic force transducers, we shall devote the remaining portion of this section to a discussion of their properties and application.

The properties of muscle are usually studied under one of three conditions. *Isometric* conditions occur when the muscle is constrained to a constant length and the force generated by various forms of stimuli is studied. *Isotonic* conditions occur when a constant force is applied and studies are made on the change in length. In the case of certain muscles it is convenient to define a third condition—namely, the *auxotonic*, in which neither length nor force stays constant. Auxotonic-contraction measurement conditions occur, for example, when a force transducer is placed in series with the myocardium such that it measures the force generated circumferentially around the heart without affecting significantly the natural changes in length during contraction or relaxation. The measured force is that generated by the heart in contracting against its outflow resistance. Since both the force and circumferential length vary, this condition can be classified as neither isotonic nor isometric.

Measurement of isolated muscle under isometric conditions can be made by attaching one end of the muscle to a force transducer and the other end to a fixed frame of reference. Isometric conditions are achieved if the maxi-

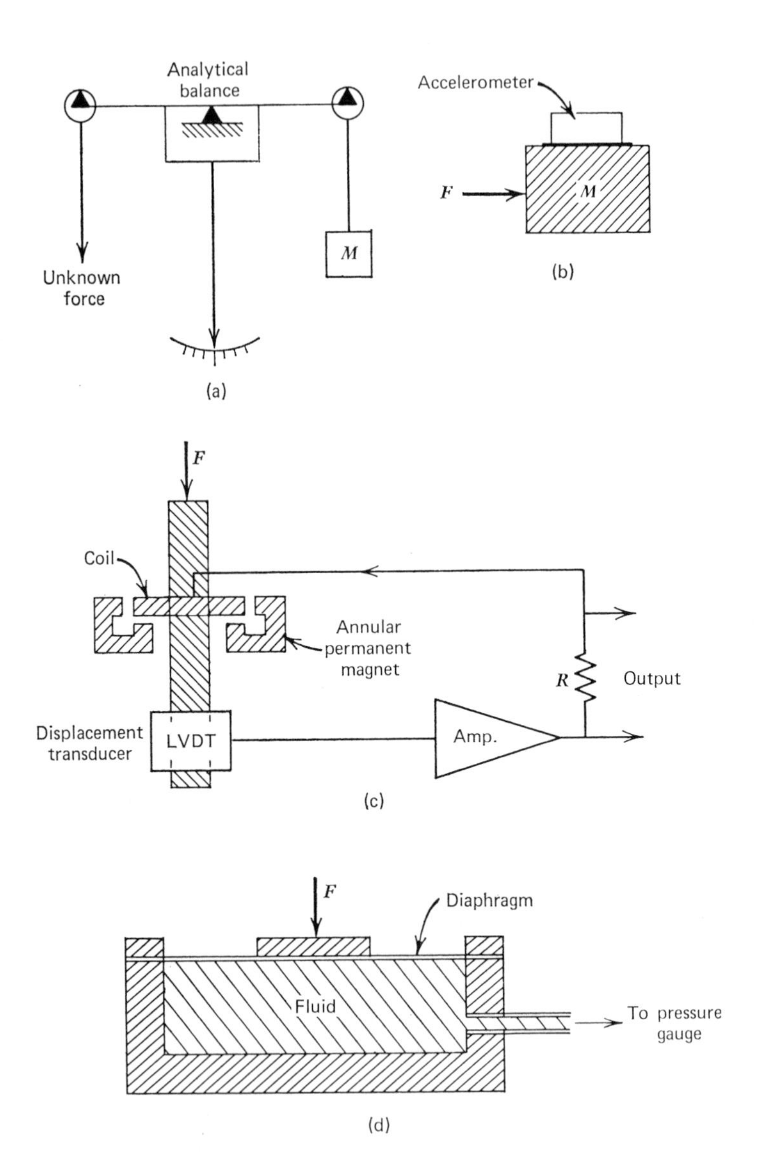

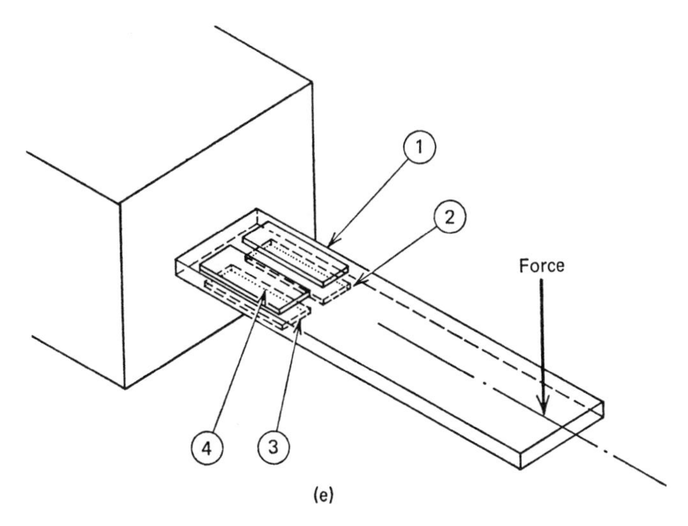

Figure 6.45. Methods for force measurement: (a) balance; (b) accelerometer; (c) electromagnetic force balance; (d) force-to-fluid-pressure transducer; (e) elastic-member deflection.

mum displacement of the transducer is sufficiently small for it to have no significant effect on the force produced.

Any sensitive displacement transducer can be readily changed to an isometric force transducer by simply adding an appropriate elastic restoring member (e.g., a spring). One commonly used system consists of a cantilever arm with strain gauges, as shown in Figure 6.46. For the most sensitive range (0–20 g) the restoring force of the cantilever is sufficient. By the addition of various spring pairs the stiffness can be increased, enabling forces of up to 1 kg to be measured. An accuracy of $\pm 2\%$ of full scale is claimed for this system.

A much higher accuracy can be achieved with the universal transducer and adaptors shown in Figure 6.47. The transducer, consisting of an unbonded strain gauge bridge, can be attached to a variety of adaptors to enable pressure, force, and displacement to be measured with a combined hysteresis and nonlinearity error equal to $\pm 0.25\%$ of full scale.

Measurement of the in vivo properties of the myocardial wall is of great importance in the study of cardiac physiology. Of the wide variety of methods devised for measuring the myocardial force, thickness and shear, the majority make use of bonded foil or wire strain gauges. One of the earliest and most widely used is the Walton strain gauge arch [61], consisting of a wire strain gauge mounted on beryllium–copper, as illustrated in Figure 6.48(a). In

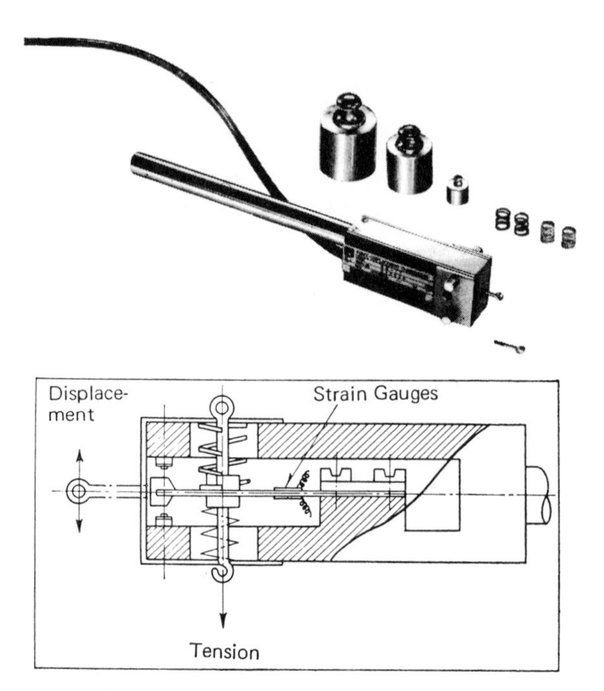

Figure 6.46. Cantilever-beam force (or displacement) transducer using bonded strain gauges (courtesy, Nihon Kohden Kogyo Co., Tokyo, Japan).

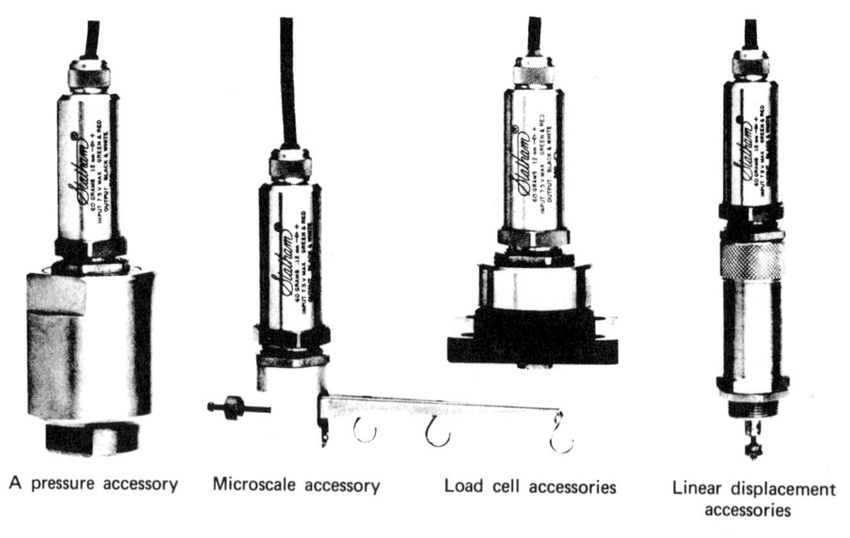

Figure 6.47. Universal transducing cell and adaptors (courtesy, Statham Industries Inc., Oxenard, Calif.).

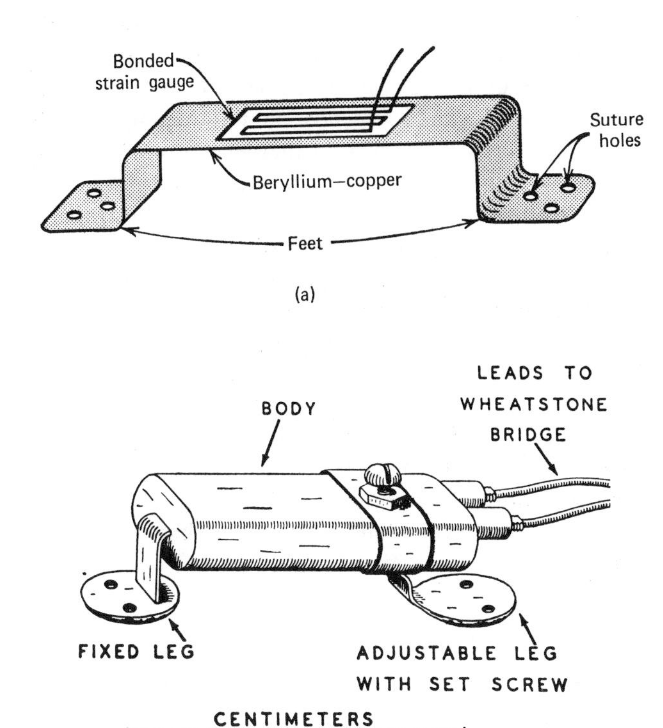

Figure 6.48. Walton-type strain gauge: (a) General principles; (b) encapsulated gauge suitable for long-term measurements (reproduced, with permission, from M. de V. Cotten and E. Bay, *Am. J. Physiol.* **187**, 122–134, 1956).

practice, it is convenient to be able to adjust the distance between the feet of the arch after their attachment by sutures to the myocardium. Stretching the region between the feet by up to 60% is sometimes necessary in order to avoid artifacts associated with large changes in cardiac size. The encapsulated gauge of Figure 6.48(b) has this facility.

Careful measurements of the static and dynamic properties of the Walton gauge [62] have shown that the static response is fairly linear and the frequency response is flat to 45 Hz with a linear phase shift of 1°/Hz. However, because of the unbalanced strain-gauge arrangement, this form of arch is significantly affected by temperature. A more recent and compact version [63] using balanced gauges is reported to decrease the temperature-dependence by more than an order of magnitude.

The Walton type of gauge measures the force developed in the muscle segment contained between the feet, under essentially isometric conditions. Unfortunately, the use of sutures for attachment to the myocardium is far from ideal. The measured force depends on how deeply and tightly the sutures are made [64], in part the result of the shear forces in the myocardial wall. To overcome this disadvantage, Feigl et al. [65] have developed an adjustable isometric transducer with two sets of pins, as illustrated in Figure 6.49(a). Both sets of pins are thrust right through the heart wall to provide essentially complete coupling of the myocardial force to the two flexure plates. A pair of strain gauges bonded to one plate enables the deflection to be measured. Since the deflection is proportional to the force between the sets of pins, an output is obtained that is linearly related to the force. Feigl et al. [65] report that for loads of up to 1 kg the system nonlinearity and hysteresis is less than $\pm 1\%$ of full scale. Further, they find that the frequency response is flat to more than 30 Hz, enabling the dynamic forces of myocardial contraction to be faithfully reproduced.

An auxotonic force transducer of similar design is shown in Figure 6.49(b). Again, the two sets of pins enable the myocardial force to be properly trans-

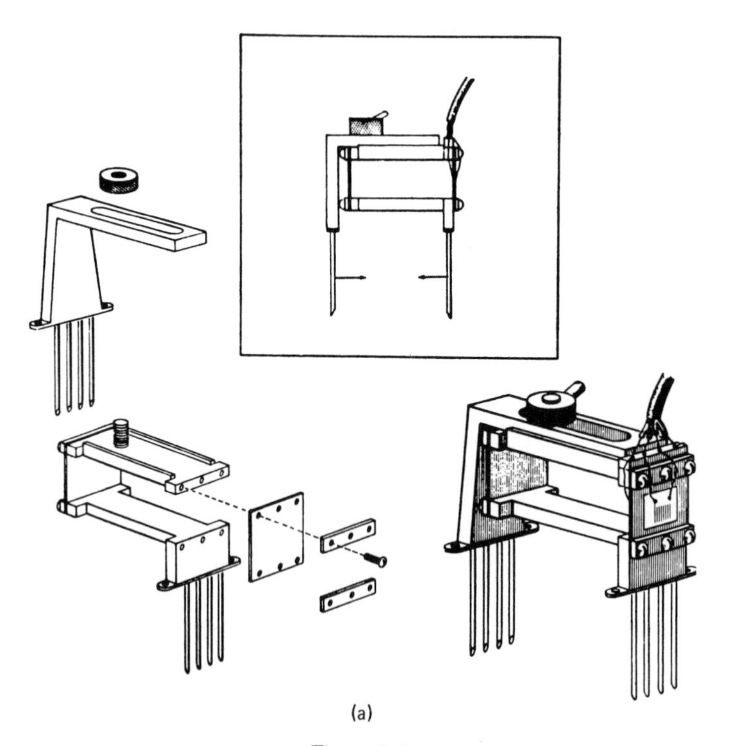

(a)

Figure 6.49

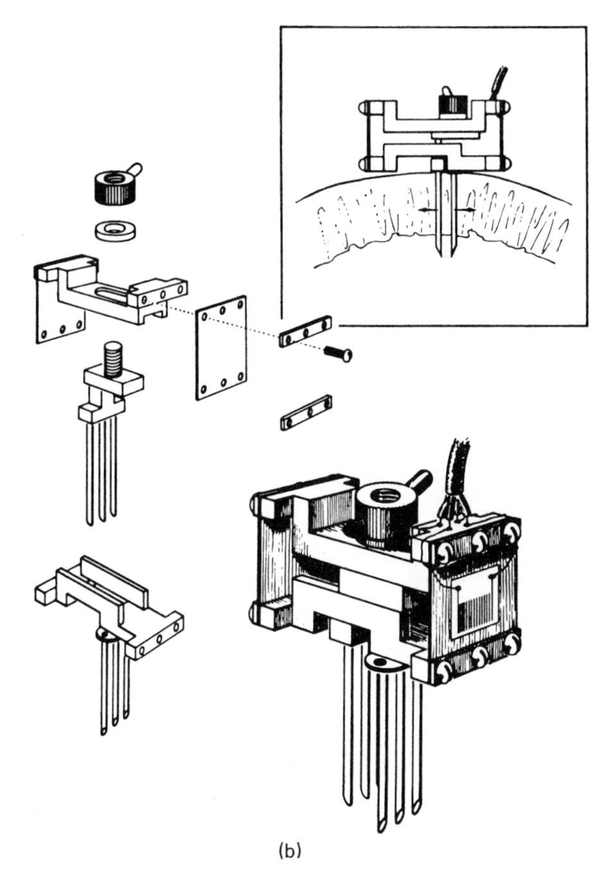

Figure 6.49. Adjustable cardiac force transducers (a) isometric type: (b) auxotonic type (reproduced, with permission, from E. O. Feigl, G. A. Simon, and D. L. Fry, *J. Appl. Physiol.*, **23**, 597–600, 1967).

mitted to the flexure plates. After insertion into the myocardium, the pins are moved closer together to compress the segment between. This maneuver prevents the segment from exerting any contractile force on the pins, thereby enabling only the circumferentially outward-directed force to be measured. Since the two sets of pins are close together, the transducer is essentially in series with the muscle and has no significant effect on its contractile properties. Recordings from both the isometric and auxotonic tranducers are shown in Figure 6.50.

Two further strain-gauge tranducers are shown in Figure 6.51. The first, a myocardial shear transducer [66], consists of a pivoted shaft, *A*, contained

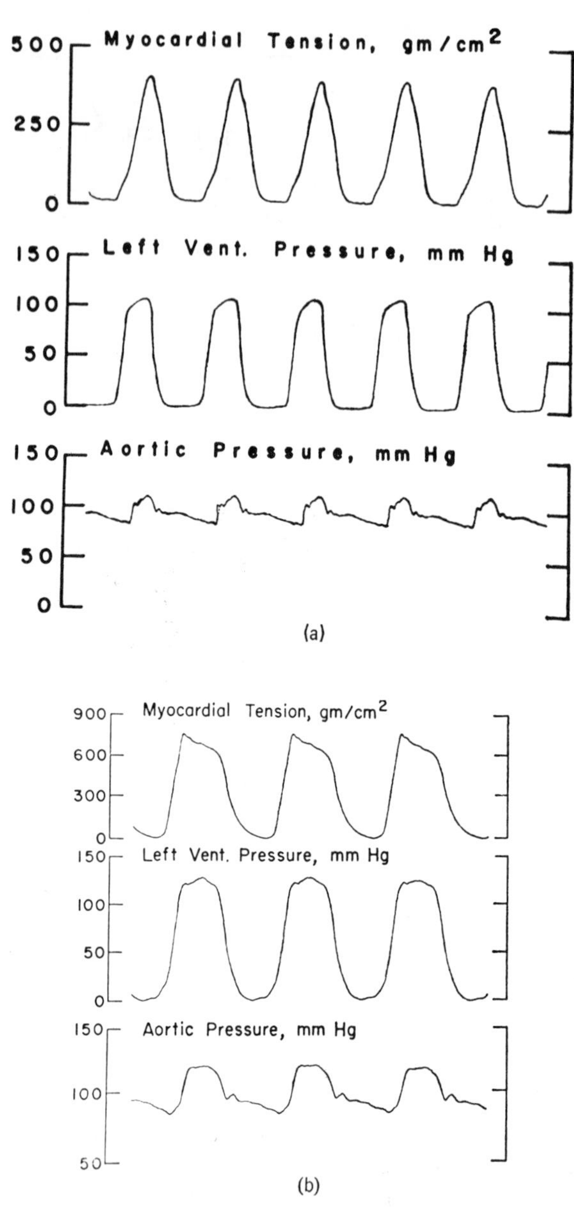

Figure 6.50. Recording from the left ventricle of a dog: (a) isometric stress; (b) auxotonic stress (reproduced, with permission, from E. O. Feigl, G. A. Simon, and D. L. Fry, *J. Appl. Physiol.*, **23**, 597–600, 1967).

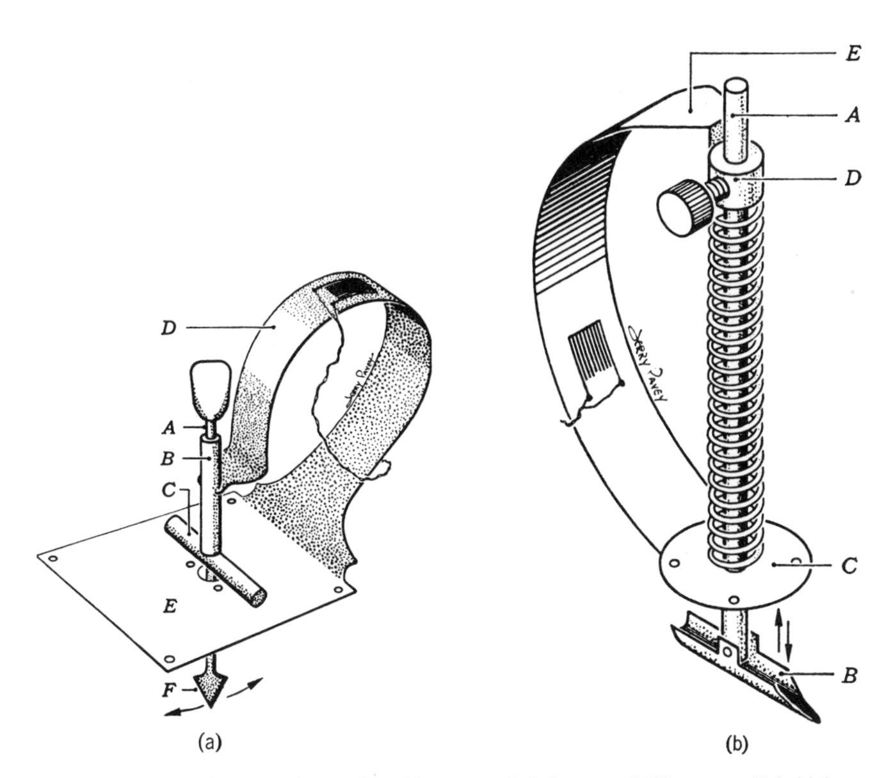

Figure 6.51. Cardiac transducers for: (a) myocardial shear, and (b) myocardial thickness (reproduced by permission of the American Heart Association Inc., from E. O. Feigl and D. L. Fry, "Intramural Myocardial Shear During the Cardiac Cycle" and "Myocardial Mural Thickness During the Cardiac Cycle," *Circ. Res.*, **14**, 536–545, June 1964).

in a sleeve, *B*, which is free to rotate in a single plane about the axis of *C*. The blade, *F*, is thrust into the mycardium such that it creates a slit perpendicular to the axis *C*. By rotating the blade through 90°, the blade edges become hooked into the myocardium and the slit enables the shaft to freely rotate about the axis *C*. For small angular rotations the strain-gauge output is proportional to the angle between the surface plane and shaft, thereby enabling the shear angle to be recorded from various depths. The myocardial thickness transducer* [67] of Figure 6.51(b) contains a harpoonlike endpiece, which is thrust right through the wall. A spring maintains contact between the base plate, *C*, and the harpoon, so that changes of thickness cause the

* An improved thickness gauge, using two-coil variable coupling, has more recently been described by McHale et al. [68].

elastic member, E, to flex. Both transducers have linear static characteristics and a flat frequency response to more than 30 Hz.

In studies of the biomechanics of locomotion and in certain areas of muscle physiology there is frequently a need to know the tension generated by a muscle in a freely moving animal. The problem is one of devising an implantable transducer that will respond directly to tension in the muscle tendon but will not interfere with the normal use of the muscle. For example, configurations that required the tendon to be cut or shortened appreciably would in most cases be quite unacceptable. An ingenious device* to fulfil these requirements has been developed by Salmons [69] as part of an implantable system for stimulating and telemetering tension from skeletal muscles. The transducer, as illustrated in Figure 6.52, operates in the following way.

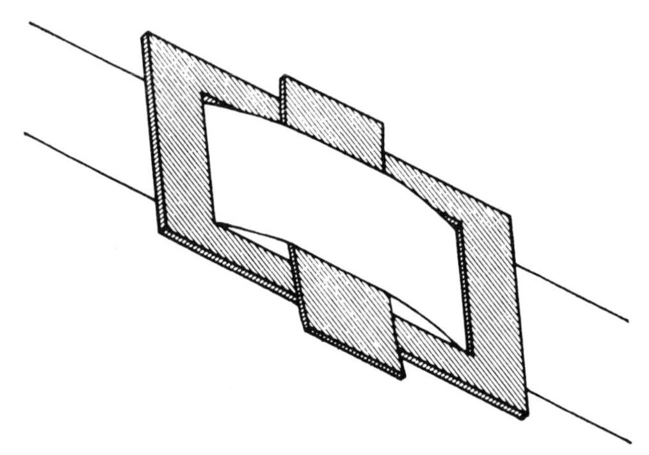

Figure 6.52. Principle of the "buckle" transducer for measuring the tension generated by a muscle (reproduced by permission of Dr. S. Salmons, University of Birmingham, England).

A loop of tendon is drawn through a small rectangular frame and secured in position by a narrow cross-piece, or beam: an arrangement that has the appearance of a buckle. The tension in the muscle tendon sets up a corresponding strain in the beam that is detected by a semiconductor strain gauge bonded to its surface. The characteristic of the device is basically linear; however, departures from linearity occur because of the small changes in the geometry of the device that accompany increasing tension, and because of non-linearities in the characteristic of the semiconductor strain gauge

* The author is indebted to Dr. Salmons for providing a drawing and description of this transducer,

itself. It is possible to introduce a calculated amount of nonlinearity into the characteristic by making the frame, as well as the beam, compliant; this has the advantage of protecting the gauge from excessive strain while at the same time providing high sensitivity at low levels of tension. However, in most cases the advantages of this nonlinear approach will be more than offset by the difficulty of maintaining a reliable calibration. Suitable materials for the beam and frame are titanium and beryllium–copper; the latter should be gold-plated in order to insure compatibility with the body environment.

REFERENCES

1. Neubert, H. K. P. *Instrument Transducers.* Clarendon: Oxford, 1963.

2. Doebelin, E. O. *Measurement Systems: Application and Design.* McGraw-Hill: New York, 1966.

3. Harvey, G. F., Ed. *ISA Transducer Compendium*, Pts. 1–3. Instrument Society of America: Pittsburgh, 1969–1972.

4. Neubert, H. K. P. *Strain Gauge: Kinds and Uses.* Macmillan: London, 1968.

5. Higson, G. R. "Recent Advances in Strain Gauges." *J. Sci. Instr.*, **41**, 405–414 (July 1964).

6. Dean, M., Ed. *Semiconductor and Conventional Strain Gauges.* Academic: New York, 1962.

7. Perry, C. C., and Lissner, H. R. *The Strain Gauge Primer.* McGraw-Hill: New York, 1955.

8a. Geyling, F. T., and Forst, J. J., "Semiconductor Strain Transducers." *Bell Syst. Tech. J.*, **39**, 705–731 (May 1960).

8b. Tufte, O. N., and Stelzer, E. L. "Piezoresistive Properties of Silicon Diffused Layers." *J. Appl. Phys.*, **34**, 313–318 (February 1963).

9a. Moore, R. M. "Semiconductor Gages Make Sense in Most Transducer Applications." *Electronics*, 18 March 1968, pp. 109–116.

9b. Geyling, F. T., and Forst, J. J. "Semiconductor Strain Transducers." *Bell Syst. Tech. J.*, **39**, 705–731 (May 1960).

10. Taroni, A.; Prudenzaiati, M.; and Zanarini, G. "Semiconductor Sensors: II. Piezoresistive Devices." *IEEE Trans. Industrial Electron. Control Instr.*, **IECI-17**, 415–421 (November 1970).

11. Tufte, O. N.; Chapman, P. W.; and Long, D. "Silicon Diffused-Element Piezoresistive Diaphragms." *J. Appl. Phys.*, **33**, 3322–3327 (November 1962).

12. Zinker, N. "Diffused Silicon Diaphragm Pressure Transducers" (Paper 68-503), in *Advances in Test Measurement*, Vol. V. 1968 ISA Conference Proceedings. Instrument Society of America: Pittsburgh, 1968, pp. 1–6.

13. Peake, E. R.; Zias, A. R.; and Egan, J. V. "Solid-State Digital Pressure Transducer." *IEEE Trans. Electron Devices*, **ED-16**, 870–876 (October 1969).

14. Gieles, A. C. M. "Subminiature Silicon Pressure Transducer." Digest of Technical Papers, 1969, Int. Solid-State Circuits Conference, pp. 108–109.

15. Fulkerson, D. E. "A Silicon Integrated Circuit Force Sensor." *IEEE Trans. Electron Devices*, **ED-16**, 867–870 (October 1969).

16. Rushmer, R. F. "Pressure Circumference Relations in the Left Ventricle." *Am. J. Physiol.*, **186**, 115–121 (July 1956).

17. Rushmer, R. F. "Pressure-Circumference Relations in the Aorta." *Am. J. Physiol.*, **183**, 545–549 (December 1955).

18. Brakkee, A. J. M., and Vendrik, A. J. H. "Strain-Gauge Plethysmography; Theoretical and Practical Notes on a New Design." *J. Appl. Physiol.*, **21**, 701–704 (March 1966).

19. Sigdell, J. "A Critical Review of the Theory of the Mercury Strain-Gauge Plethysmograph." *Med. Biol. Eng.*, **7**, 365–371 (July 1969).

20. Waggoner, W. C. "High-Impedance Elastic Force Gauge." *Am. J. Med. Electron.*, **4**, 175–177 (October–December 1965).

21a. Lawton, R. W., and Collins, C. C. "Calibration of an Aortic Circumference Gauge." *J. Appl. Physiol.*, **14**, 465–467 (May 1959).

21b. Gonza, E. R.; Marble, A. E.; Shaw, A. J.; and Winter, D. A. "Mechanical Properties of the Ascending Thoracic Aorta of Man." *Cardiovasc. Res.*, **7**, 261–265 (March 1973).

22. Elsner, R. W.; Eagan, C. J.; and Andersen, S. "Impedance Matching Circuit for the Mercury Strain Gauge." *J. Appl. Physiol.*, **14**, 871–872 (September 1959).

23. Sydenham, P. H. "Microdisplacement Transducers." *J. Phys. E*, **5**, 721–733 (August 1972).

24. Wetterer, E. "Eine neue manometrische Sonde mit elektrischer Transmission." *Z. Biol.*, **101**, 332–350 (August 1943).

25. Allard, E. M. "Sound and Pressure Signals Obtained from a Single Intracardiac Transducer." *IRE Trans. Bio-Med. Electron.*, **BME-9**, 74–77 (April 1962).

26. Allard, E. M. "Transducteur de Pression à Modulation Différentielle de Fréquence," in F. H. Bostem, Ed., *Medical Electronics*. Proc. 5th Int. Conf. on Med. Electron. Univ. of Liège, 1965, pp. 198–208.

27. Caldwell, W. M.; Wilson, M. F.; and Stealey, R. E. "A Multichannel Cardiac Dimension Gauge." *Med. Res. Eng.*, **8**, 11–19 (October–November 1969).

28. van Citters, R. L. "Mutual Inductance Transducers," in R. F. Rushmer, Ed., *Methods in Medical Research*, Vol. XI. Year Book: Chicago, 1966, pp. 26–30.

29. Rolfe, P. "A Magnetometer Respiration Monitor for Use with Premature Babies." *Bio-Med. Eng.*, **6**, 402–404 (September 1971).

30. Kolin, A., and Culp, G. W. "A Intra-Arterial Induction Gauge." *IEEE Trans. Bio-Med. Eng.*, **BME-18**, 110–114 (March 1971).

31. Lion, K. S. *Instrumentation in Scientific Research: Electrical Input Transducers*. McGraw-Hill: New York, 1959.

32. Wolfendale, P. C. F. "Capacitance Displacement Transducers With High Accuracy and Resolution." *J. Sci. Instrum.*, **1**, 817–818 (August 1968).

33. Podolak, E.; Kinn, J. B.; and Westura, E. E. "Biomedical Applications of a Commercial Capacitance Transducer." *IEEE Trans. Bio-Med. Eng.*, **BME-16**, 40–44 (January 1969).

34. Weaver, J. P. A., and Evans, A. "A Plethysmograph with an Air Capacitance Recording System." *J. Appl. Physiol.*, **23**, 591–592 (October 1967).

35. Aronow, S.; Currens, J. H.; and Cosman, B. J. "A Capacitance Method for Recording Vascular Pulsations," in F. H. Bostem, Ed., *Medical Electronics.* Proc. 5th Int. Conf. on Med. Electron. Univ. of Liège, 1965, pp. 213–220.

36. Groom, D.; Medina, L. H.; and Sihvonen, Y. T. "The Proximity Transducer." *Am. J. Med. Electron.*, **3**, 261–265 (October–December 1964).

37. Schofield, J. W. "A Linear Capacitance Micrometer." *J. Phys. E*, **5**, 822–825 (August 1972).

38. Morgan, V. T., and Brown, D. E. "A Differential-Capacitance Transducer for Measuring Small Displacements." *J. Phys. E*, **2**, 793–795 (September 1969).

39. Baker, D. W. "Sonocardiometer," in R. F. Rushmer, Ed., *Methods in Medical Research*, Vol. XI. Year Book: Chicago, 1966, pp. 31–34.

40. Stegall, H. F.; Kardon, M. B.; Stone, H. L.; and Bishop, V. S. "A Portable, Simple Sonomicrometer." *J. Appl. Physiol.*, **23**, 289–293 (August 1967).

41. Lee, R. D., and Sandler, H. "Miniature Implantable Sonomicrometer System." *J. Appl. Physiol.*, **28**, 110–112 (January 1970).

42a. Arndt, J. O.; Klauske, J.; and Mersch, F. "The Diameter of the Intact Carotid Artery in Man and its Change with Pulse Pressure." *Pflüg. Arch.*, **301**, 230–240 (1968).

42b. Arndt, J. O. "Über die Mechanik der Intakten A Carotis Communis des Menschen unter verschiedenen Kreislaufbedingungen." *Arch. Kreislaufforsch.*, **59**, 153–197 (1969).

43a. McLeod, F. D. "The Pulsed Doppler Flow Probe as a Diameter Gage." Digest, 9th Int. Conf. Med. Biol. Eng., Melbourne, 1971, p. 277.

43b. Franklin, D.; Kemper, W. S.; Patrick, T.; and McKown, D. "In Vivo Measurement of Regional Myocardial Segment Dimensions in Chronic Animal Preparations." Digest, Vol. I. 10th Int. Conf. Med. Biol. Eng., Dresden, 1973, p. 19.

44. Hokanson, D. E.; Strandness, D. E.; and Miller, C. W. "A Echo-Tracking System for Recording Arterial-Wall Motion." *IEEE Trans. Sonics Ultrasonics*, **SU-17**, 130–132 (July 1970).

45. Hokanson, D. E.; Mozersky, D. J.; Sumner, D. S.; and Strandness, E. "A Phase-Locked Echo Tracking System for Recording Arterial Diameter Changes in Vivo." *J. Appl. Physiol.*, **32**, 728–733 (May 1972).

46. Barnes, R. W., and Thurstone, F. L., "An Ultrasound Moving Target Indicator System for Diagnostic Use." *IEEE Trans. Bio-Med. Eng.*, **BME-18**, 4–8 (January 1971).

47. Lim, R. S.; Fryer, T. C.; Lineberger, R. N.; and Sandler, H. "Real Time Computer Measurement of Heart Dimensions from Implanted Accelerometers." Proc. 20th Ann. Conf. on Eng. in Med. and Biol., Vol. IX, 1967.

48. Meldrum, S. J., and Watson, B. W. "Tremor Recording in Parkinson's Disease." *Phys. Med. Biol.*, **15**, 249–254 (April 1970).

49. Yoshitoshi, Y.; Machii, K.; Sekiguchi, H.; Mishina, Y.; Ohta, S.; Hanaoka, Y.; Kohashi, Y.; Shimizu, S.; and Kuno H. "Doppler Measurements of Mitral Valve and Ventricle Wall Velocities." *Ultrasonics*, **4**, 27–28 (1966).

50. Wells, P. T. N. *Physical Principles of Ultrasonic Diagnosis.* Academic: London, 1969.

51. Wells, P. T. N. "A Range Gated Ultrasonic Doppler System." *Med. Biol. Eng.*, **7**, 641–652 (November 1969).

52. Frauenfelder, H. *The Mössbauer Effect.* Benjamin: New York, 1962.

53. Wertheim, G. K. *Mössbauer Effect: Principles and Applications.* Academic: New York, 1964.

54. Lackner, H. G. "The Mössbauer Effect and its Application to Measuring Technology," in G. G. Mannella, Ed., *Aerospace Measurement Techniques.* NASA publication, NASA SP-132, 1967, pp. 1–27.

55. Hillman, P.; Schechter, H.; and Rubinstein, M. "Application of the Mössbauer Technique to the Measurement of Small Vibrations of the Ear." *Rev. Mod. Phys.*, **36**, 360 (Abstract) (January 1964).

56. Gilad, P.; Shtrikman, S.; Hillman, P.; Rubinstein, M.; and Eviatar, A. "Application of the Mössbauer Method to Ear Vibrations." *J. Acc. Soc. Am.*, **41**, 1232–1236 (May 1967).

57. Johnstone, B. M., and Boyle, A. J. F. "Basilar Membrane Vibration Examined with the Mössbauer Technique." *Science*, 20 October 1967 pp 389–390.

58. Rhode, W. S. "Observations of the Vibration of the Basilar Membrane in Squirrel Monkeys Using the Mössbauer Technique." *J. Acc. Soc. Am.*, **49**, 1218–1231 (April 1971).

59a. Daniker, M. H. "Miniature Accelerometer for Radiotelemetric Recording of Motor Activity in the Rat." Digest, Vol. II, 10th Int. Conf. Med. Biol. Eng., Dresden, 1973, p. 61.

59b. Jaffe, B.; Cook, W. R.; and Jaffe, H. *Piezoelectric Ceramics.* Academic: New York, 1971.

60. Busser, J. H. "Phonocatheter," in O. Glasser, Ed., *Medical Physics.* Vol. III. Year Book: Chicago, 1960, pp. 445–450.

61. Boniface, K. J.; Brodie, O. J.; and Walton, R. P. "Resistance Strain Gauge Arches for Direct Measurement of Heart Contractile Force in Animals." *Proc. Soc. Exp. Biol. Med.*, **84**, 263–266 (November 1953).

62. Shimosato, S.; Herpfer, G. E.; and Etsten, B. E. "Static and Dynamic Performance of Walton Strain-Gauge Arches." *J. Appl. Physiol.*, **21**, 1892–1896 (November 1966).

63. Sutfin, D. C., and Lefer, A. M. "A Modified Strain Gage Arch for Measurement of Heart Contractile Force." *Med. Electron. Biol. Eng.*, **1**, 371–376 (August 1963).

64. Cotten, M. deV., and Bay, E. "Direct Measurement of Changes in Cardiac Contractile Force: Relationships of Such Measurements to Stroke Work, Isometric Pressure Gradient and Other Parameters of Cardiac Functions." *Am. J. Physiol.*, **187**, 122–134 (October 1956).

65. Feigl, E. O.; Simon, G. A.; and Fry, D. L. "Auxotonic and Isometric Cardiac Force Transducers." *J. Appl. Physiol.*, **23**, 597–600 (October 1967).

66. Feigl, E. O., and Fry, D. L. "Intramural Myocardial Shear During the Cardiac Cycle." *Circ. Res.*, **14**, 536–540 (June 1964).

67. Feigl, E. O., and Fry, D. L. "Myocardial Mural Thickness During the Cardiac Cycle." *Circ. Res.*, **14**, 541–545 (June 1964).

68. McHale, P. A.; Haliasos, C. A.; and Greenfield, J. C. "An Improved Transducer to Measure Left Ventricular Wall Thickness in Open-Chest Dogs." *J. Appl. Physiol.*, **32**, 257–258 (February 1972).

69. Salmons, S. "Implantable Devices for Simulating and Telemetering Tension from Skeletal Muscles." Proc. 8th Int. Conf. on Med. and Biol. Eng., 1969.

CHAPTER SEVEN

Pressure Transducers

Accurate measurement of pressure is of basic importance for many diagnostic, surgical, and patient-care procedures, and, furthermore, provides information essential for the control and interpretation of many types of physiological research experiments. In diagnostic work, the measurement of arterial, venous, intraocular, and intracranial pressures often form a vital part of certain investigative procedures. During surgery, the intermittent or continuous monitoring of systolic and diastolic pressure is of particular importance, since it can provide the surgeon or anesthetist with an early warning of a potentially irreversible situation. Furthermore, in assessing intravenous blood and fluid needs and in preventing cardiac overloading in patients receiving blood transfusions, the monitoring of central venous pressure (CVP) can also be valuable [1, 2]. The much smaller values of pressure encountered in CVP monitoring make rather more stringent demands on the measurement system than arterial monitoring.

Modern physiological research can impose exacting demands on the design of suitable pressure transduction systems. The higher heart rate and smaller vessels of most experimental animals requires smaller transducers capable of better high-frequency performance than are necessary in most clinical applications. Devices suitable for long-term implantation and transducers for measuring dynamic pressures in micron-size vessels are two particular examples of rather exacting requirements: both of these are discussed in detail in the last two sections of this chapter.

7.1 FUNDAMENTALS

7.1.1 Some Definitions

Before discussing the various methods of pressure transduction it is perhaps worthwhile to review briefly certain fundamental aspects of pressure. Pressure is *defined* as the force exerted per unit area. In the cgs system the unit of pressure is the *bar*, which by definition is equal to one dyne per square centimeter. Physiological pressures are usually expressed in millimeters of mercury, though, particularly for venous pressures, centimeters or millimeters of water are often used. A generally accepted unit of pressure is the *torr*, which is very nearly equal to the pressure produced by 1 mm of mercury; however, it is only rarely used by physiologists.

It should be noted that for the "standard" gravitational acceleration of 981 cm/sec^2 the hydrostatic pressure produced by 1 mmHg at 0°C is 1330 dynes/cm^2. Thus, assuming that the density of mercury is 13.6 gm/cm^3, the density of whole blood is 1.055 gm/cm^3 and the density of physiological saline is 1.04 gm/cm^3, we find that

$$1 \text{ mmHg} = 1 \text{ torr} = 12.9 \text{ mm blood} = 13.1 \text{ mm saline} = 1330 \text{ dynes/cm}^2.$$

The absolute pressure is measured with respect to a perfect vacuum: atmospheric pressures are measured in this way. Since physiological pressures are normally expressed relative to the atmospheric pressure existing at the time of measurement, they are pressure differences and are sometimes referred to as *gauge* pressures. Because normal atmospheric pressure changes have only a second-order effect on most physiological pressures, it normally is unnecessary to specify the absolute atmospheric pressure at which the measurement was conducted. However, for certain types of pressure transducer, atmospheric pressure variations can have a major effect on the apparent physiological pressure. Sealed pressure transducers are of this type: they measure the pressure difference between the sealed inner chamber and the external pressure. For long-term measurements, atmospheric pressure changes can result in very significant errors unless the reading is properly corrected. For example, a 20-mmHg atmospheric pressure change will result in a large error for arterial blood-pressure measurements and a quite unacceptable error in CVP measurements. By establishing a "zero" pressure reading at the beginning of the experiment, all subsequent measurements can be properly corrected by noting the atmospheric pressure variation throughout the experiment. A further point to note in regard to sealed-chamber transducers is that temperature variations affect the reference pressure and may also have to be corrected for.

7.1.2 Sources of Error

Only in the absence of flow is the pressure at a point the same in all directions. With flow present, the pressure sensed by a transducer varies according to the direction of the sensing element with respect to the flow. This variation is caused by the kinetic energy of the medium.

Bernoulli's equation [3] states that the total fluid energy per unit volume is given by

$$E = P_s + \zeta gh + \tfrac{1}{2}\zeta v^2 \qquad \text{(in dynes/cm}^2 \text{ or ergs/cm}^3\text{)},$$

where P_s is the static pressure (dynes/cm^2), ζ is the density (gm/cm^3), g is the acceleration of gravity (981 cm/sec^2), h is the fluid height above an arbitrary reference level (cm), and v is the fluid velocity (cm/sec). The first term is the static pressure or the pressure energy: it is the energy required to move 1 cm^3 of the fluid against the pressure without imparting any velocity to it. The second term is the gravitational potential energy, and the third term is the kinetic energy of the fluid. In the absence of any energy dissipative effects E remains constant. Thus, if $\zeta gh = 0$, a change of $\Delta(\frac{1}{2}\zeta v^2)$ in the kinetic energy causes the pressure to change by

$$\Delta P_s = -\Delta(\tfrac{1}{2}\zeta v^2).$$

In the case of the catheter-coupled manometer system shown in Figure 7.1(a), with the catheter tip facing upstream, the total indicated pressure will be the static pressure plus the kinetic energy pressure of nearly $\frac{1}{2}\zeta v^2$ (the fluid is essentially stopped by the catheter). When the catheter tip is facing downstream, as shown in Figure 7.1(b), the indicated pressure will be less than P_s by approximately $\frac{1}{2}\zeta v^2$. Only when the end is parallel to the flow, as in Figure 7.1(c), will the measured pressure be equal to the static pressure.

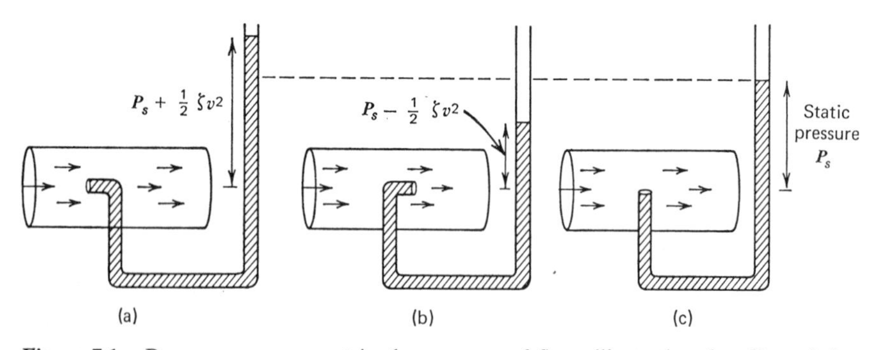

Figure 7.1. Pressure measurement in the presence of flow, illustrating the effect of the fluid kinetic energy on the apparent pressure.

To illustrate the significance of the transducer placement in measuring the static pressure, we consider a measurement of the human aortic blood pressure [3]. Since the peak flow velocity at the center of the descending aorta is roughly 150 cm/sec, the kinetic energy pressure at the center will be $\frac{1}{2} \times 1.05 \times 150^2 = 1.17 \times 10^4$ dynes/cm^2. Converting to millimeters of mercury by dividing by 1330, we find that the kinetic energy pressure is 9 mmHg. From this, it follows that the orientation of the hydraulic coupling tube can significantly affect the measured aortic pressure. Under laminar flow conditions, this error does of course decrease when the tip is moved to the wall where the average flow velocity is less. As shown in Table 7.1, even larger errors can occur for the venae cavae and pulmonary artery [3]. Measurements by O'Rourke [4] of the kinetic energy pressure in the ascending aorta and pulmonary artery of dogs have confirmed these results.

For the smaller vessels, the flow velocity is sufficiently small for the kinetic energy pressure to be negligible. However, an additional source of error then

Table 7.1[a] **Amount and Relative Importance of the Kinetic Energy Pressure in Different Parts of the Circulatory System**[b]

	Resting cardiac output				Cardiac output increased 3 times		
Vessel	Velocity (cm/sec)	Kinetic energy (mmHg)	Pressure (mmHg)	Kinetic energy as % of total	Kinetic energy (mmHg)	Pressure (mmHg)	Kinetic energy as % of total
Aorta, systolic	100	4	120	3%	36	180	*17%*
Mean	30	0.4	100	0.4%	3.8	140	2.6%
Arteries, systolic	30	0.35	110	0.3%	3.8	120	3%
Mean	10	0.04	95	Neg.[c]		100	Neg.
Capillaries	0.1	0.000004	25	Neg.	Neg.	25	Neg.
Venae cavae and atria	30	0.35	2	*12%*	3.2	3	*52%*
Pulmonary artery, systolic	90	3	20	*13%*	27	25	*52%*
Mean	25	0.23	12	2%	2.1	14	*13%*

[a] Used with permission, from A. C. Burton, *Physiology and Biophysics of the Circulation*, 2nd ed., copyright © 1972, Year Book Medical Publishers, Inc., Chicago.

[b] The cases where kinetic energy should not be neglected—that is, where it is more than 5% of the total fluid energy—are indicated by italic figures. When an artery is narrowed by disease processes, the kinetic energy becomes very important.

[c] Neg. = Negligible.

becomes more significant. If the pressure measurement is made using a catheter whose diameter is comparable to the vessel diameter, the flow pattern and pressure can be seriously affected. Constriction of the vessel by the catheter increases the flow velocity in the constricted region, causing a decreased static pressure at the downstream end. At the upstream end the reduction in flow causes the static pressure to be increased. It is evident that the insertion of a long catheter along the vessel whose pressure is to be measured should be avoided: preferably it should be inserted through a small branch in the vicinity of the measuring point. If the insertion of a catheter along the vessel cannot be avoided then, to achieve an accuracy of $\pm 10\%$, the catheter diameter should be less than one-tenth of the vessel diameter.

7.1.3 Techniques and Dynamic Requirements

Methods for the measurement of pressure in an organism can be divided into two categories: indirect (noninvasive) methods; and direct (invasive) methods. The absence of surgical procedures makes the indirect methods the most attractive from a clinical point of view. However, they suffer from various restrictions, not the least of which is the difficulty in measuring the pressure waveshape. Direct methods require either the introduction of a pressure-sensing element into the fluid or coupling of the fluid via a catheter or hollow needle to an external transducer. Both schemes require the puncture of the vessel and contact of a foreign material with the fluid. This by itself introduces a number of problems; nevertheless, fairly accurate dynamic pressure measurements can be made with this method if certain precautions are taken.

Most physiological pressures are dynamic, consisting of a mean pressure and a periodic component whose fundamental period is equal to the period of the cardiac or respiratory systems. The mean pressure can be expressed as

$$\bar{P} = \frac{1}{T}\int_0^T P(t)\,dt,$$

which is represented graphically in Figure 7.2.

A simple hydraulically coupled mercury manometer measures the mean pressure: the mass of mercury reduces the system frequency response to a sufficiently low value so that periodic changes are effectively "damped out." A similar effect can be produced using a low-pass filter to eliminate the fundamental and harmonics from the output of a transducer measuring the instantaneous pressure.

Accurate recording of the dynamic pressure requires that the measuring and recording system be capable of handling a sufficient number of harmonics of the fundamental frequency without significant phase or amplitude distortion. For the clinical recording of blood pressure close to or within the heart

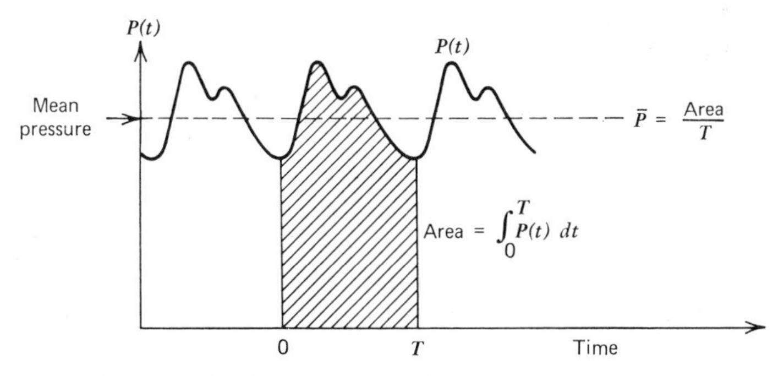

Figure 7.2. Graphical interpretation of the mean pressure.

vessels, it appears that the inclusion of 10 harmonics is sufficient [5]. If the heart rate is 120/min, this implies that the system frequency response should be flat to 20 Hz. In experimental investigations of cardiovascular dynamics this may well be inadequate. For example, Noble et al. [6] have clearly demonstrated for dogs that the ascending aortic pressure waveform measured close to the aortic valve contains harmonics whose amplitudes are greater than 5% of the fundamental up to about the twentieth harmonic. It thus appears that a flat response to 50 Hz is desirable for the research-type measuring system.

7.2 INDIRECT MEASUREMENT TECHNIQUES

7.2.1 Occlusive Cuff Methods

For routine clinical measurements of blood pressure the sphygmomanometric technique is the most familiar. It makes use of an occlusive cuff applied to the arm and positioned over the brachial artery. In the normal measurement sequence the cuff is first inflated to well beyond the systolic pressure, thereby collapsing the brachial artery and cutting off all blood flow. As illustrated in Figure 7.3, the cuff is then allowed to deflate slowly and the cuff pressures at which pulsatile flow just begins (systolic pressure) and at which it becomes continuous (diastolic pressure) are noted. If it is assumed that the cuff pressure is transmitted to the artery without attenuation, then the two cuff pressures recorded will correspond to the true systolic and diastolic pressures, respectively.

Several methods have been used to determine the state of flow in the artery and thus enable the systolic and diastolic pressures to be found [5]. The most

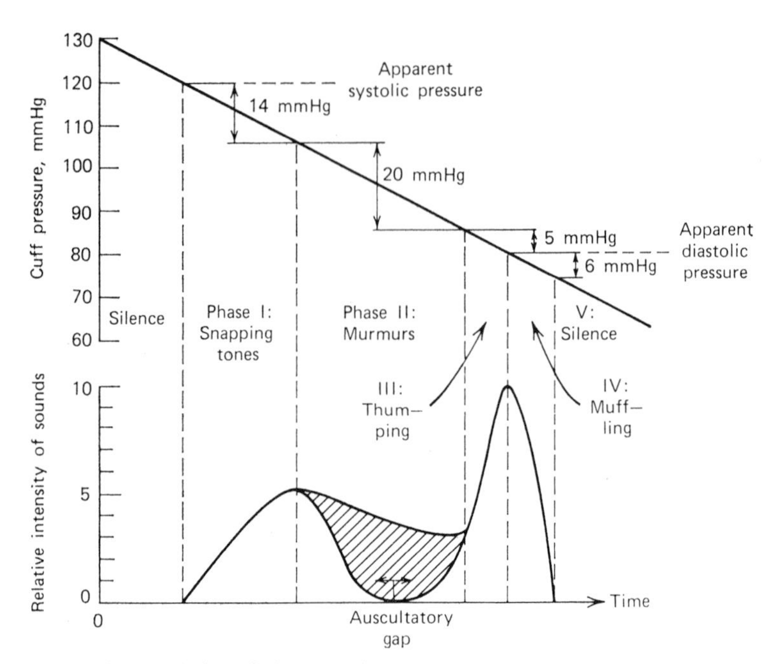

Figure 7.3. Characteristics of the auscultatory method of measuring the systolic and diastolic pressures (used with permission, from L. A. Geddes, *Direct and Indirect Measurement of Blood Pressure*, copyright © 1970, Year Book Medical Publishers Inc., Chicago).

widely used scheme is based on the change in character of the sounds produced by the pulsatile flow through the constriction. The Korotkoff sounds, named after their discoverer, can be detected by a stethoscope or a piezoelectric transducer placed over the artery. As shown in Figure 7.3, the character and intensity of the sounds vary as the cuff pressure is reduced. It is generally accepted that if the beginning of phase I and the beginning of phase IV are used as the criteria for the systolic and diastolic pressures, respectively, the cuff pressure at which these points occur will be a measure of the true (directly measured) pressures. Geddes [5] suggests that if the measurement is taken carefully, with due regard to the cuff size in relation to the arm diameter and the rate of deflation of the cuff, the apparent systolic pressure will, on the average, be 5 mmHg below the true systolic pressure and the apparent diastolic pressure will, on the average, be 8 mmHg above the true diastolic pressure.

Automatic Indirect Techniques. Automatic methods for the measurement and recording of systolic and diastolic pressures can be particularly valuable for patient monitoring, for mass screening, and for eliminating the variability between operators that occurs with manual methods. The earliest attempts to achieve automatic measurements date from the early 1900s, when a number of systems were described for automatically following either the systolic or diastolic pressure variations by means of an arm cuff whose pressure was adjusted to follow the variations.* These systems required the cuff to remain inflated thereby causing eventual patient discomfort; but they lacked what is an essential ingredient of an automatic system, namely automatic cuff inflation and deflation.

The first automatic systems were those described by Weiss [7] and Gilson et al. [8] in 1941, which included programmable cuff inflation and deflation, a means of measuring and recording the cuff pressure, and a small microphone for detecting the Korotkoff sounds.† In the Weiss instrument the sounds were superimposed on the cuff pressure and recorded on a single channel, whereas Gilson et al. used two separate recording channels. Thus, both systems required subsequent interpretation of the recording to determine the systolic and diastolic pressures.

Improvements to these Korotkoff detecting systems, some of which incorporated a means for displaying and storing the measured pressures, have been reported by various authors [10–19].‡ Systems using a pulse pressure detector distal to the occlusion cuff instead of the more usual Korotkoff sound detector have been described by Smyth [22] and Flanagan and Hull [23]. In the latter system, the double compartment brachial cuff illustrated in Figure 7.4 was used. The proximal compartment enables the blood flow to be occluded, while the distal compartment acts as a pulse volume detector that, when the brachial pulse is allowed to be transmitted, produces a puff of air that cools the self-heated thermistor detector. In essence, this system of detecting is the same as that reported by Lange [24] in 1943 for his recording sphygmotonograph that followed either the systolic or diastolic pressures. However, the system described by Flanagan and Hull was designed only for measuring the systolic pressure.

A double-cuff system in which the diastolic pressure is determined by the time taken for the pressure pulse to travel between the two cuffs has been

* See references given by Slocum [8b].

† Reference 10 gives a brief but useful historical review of automatic systems. It should be noted that semiautomatic portable systems incorporating magnetic tape to record the Korotkoff sounds and the cuff pressure but that require the patient to inflate the cuff periodically have been developed [9]. Such systems are particularly valuable, since they enable a patient's blood pressure to be recorded over a considerable period of time during normal daily activities.

‡ Crul [20] has reviewed and compared a number of automatic systems that were commercially available prior to 1962 A more recent account of commercial systems is contained in reference 21.

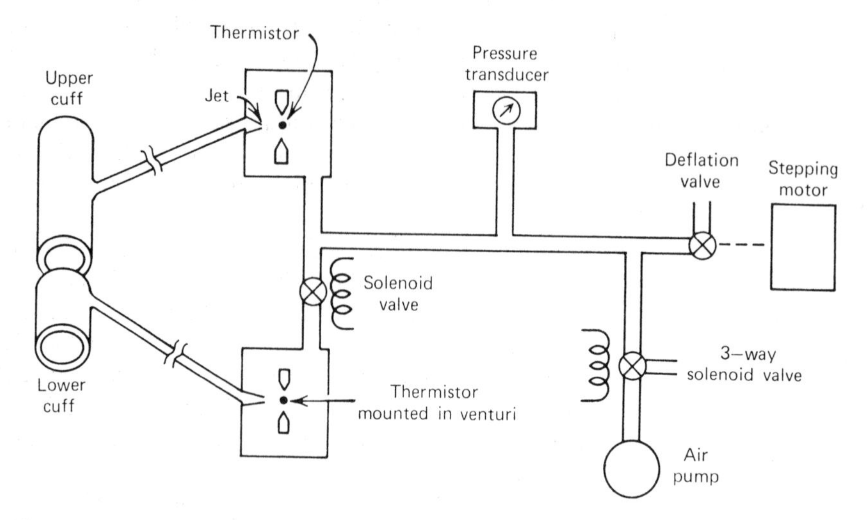

Figure 7.4. Pneumatic system for a double-cuff automatic systolic-pressure measurement instrument. A self-heated thermistor is used to detect the onset of pulses from the lower cuff. A discriminator circuit using inputs derived from both thermistors enables artifacts to be ignored (adapted from G. J. Flanagan and C. J. Hull, *British J. Anaesth.*, **40**, 292–298, 1968).

described by de Dobbeleer [25–27] and also by de Temmerman [28, 29].* The velocity with which a pulse wave travels down a partially occluded artery depends on the degree of occlusion. When a cuff is inflated to near the systolic pressure, the velocity will be small; if the cuff pressure is close to diastolic, the velocity will be comparatively large. The pneumatic detection system described by de Dobbeleer and illustrated in Figure 7.5, contains two self-heated thermistor detectors. If both the upper and lower cuffs are inflated to beyond the systolic pressure and are allowed to deflate slowly, the lower cuff will show no pressure fluctuations and therefore cause no cooling of the two thermistors until the systolic pressure is reached. The onset of air puffs to the thermistors signals that the systolic pressure has been reached. For this condition the pulse wave velocity between the two cuffs is relatively small, so that the air puffs from the upper and lower cuffs arrive out of phase, causing pulsatile cooling of the thermistors. As the cuff pressure approaches diastolic, the air puffs at the lower thermistor arrive nearly in phase. Thus, if the upper cuff jet is arranged to cross the lower one, as the diastolic pressure is reached air puffs from the lower cuff are blown away from the thermistor,

* See also Gruen [30] and, for a clear description, pp. 81–83 in reference 31.

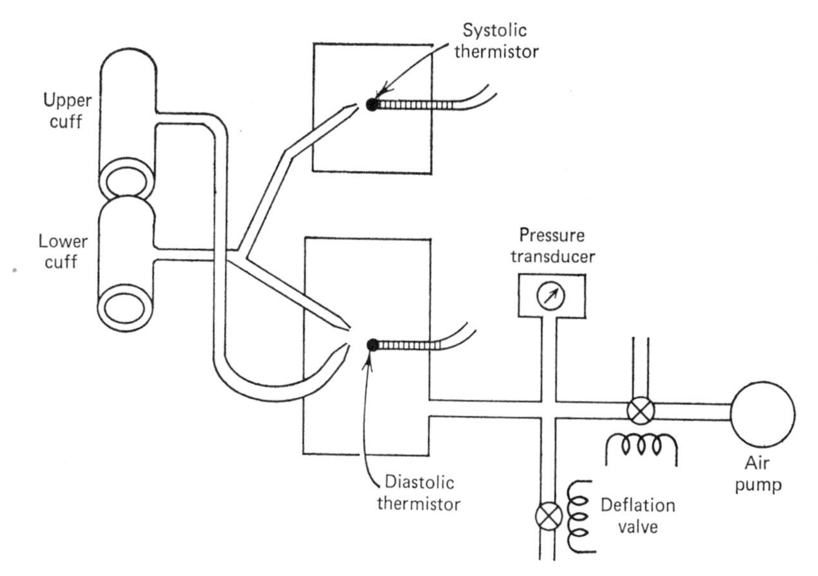

Figure 7.5. Pneumatic circuit for a phase shift automatic systolic- and diastolic-pressure measurement system (adapted from G. D. P. de Dobbeleer, *World Med. Electron. Instr.*, **3**, 122–126, July 1965).

causing its temperature to remain fairly steady. The point at which this occurs is used to signal the diastolic pressure.

Several systems have also been described and made commercially available for automatically determining the systolic pressure using a finger cuff [20, 32, 33]. The advantages of a finger cuff over an arm cuff are that it can be inflated for long periods of time without patient discomfort and that intermittent inflation and deflation of a finger cuff causes less disturbance to a sleeping patient and causes less apprehension in the conscious patient. In the system developed by Green [32], the pressure in a finger cuff was automatically adjusted to follow the systolic pressure. He used a piezoelectric crystal to detect the presence or absence of pulsations and thereby control the cuff pressure. Green claimed that with this system continuous systolic pressure recordings could be made for periods of up to four hours. Ball et al. [33] used a double finger cuff with an inflation–deflation cycle. The distal cuff produced pulses that were transmitted via a tube to an optical detection type of pressure transducer.

The beat-to-beat variation in the systolic and diastolic pressures can be a significant source of apparent error with the sphygmomanometric technique, which, by its nature, measures the pressures associated with a single beat and not the mean value. Armitage et al. [34, 35], in a survey of 722 men, found a large standard deviation for both the systolic and diastolic pressures with repeat measurements on the same occasion as well as for measurements taken on different occasions. Tursky et al. [36] quote the results of direct arterial measurements on 5 subjects for 50 successive beats. They found that the systolic pressure had a range of 6–18% of the mean systolic value depending on the subject and a range of 8–27% for the diastolic pressure. With such large ranges it is hardly surprising to find considerable scatter in the correlation between the direct and indirect measurements based on conventional sphygmomanometric methods [37, 38]. To overcome this problem Tursky et al. [36] have developed an indirect measurement system for automatically measuring the *median* systolic and diastolic pressures.

The block diagram of their system, shown in Figure 7.6, includes a brachial cuff with a pneumatic pressure control, a Korotkoff sound transducer, and electrodes for detecting the ECG signal. A coincidence detector that senses the presence of Korotkoff sounds within a period of 300 msec from the occurrence of the ECG R-wave reduces the effect of external and body-movement noise and also serves to insure that the presence or absence of Korotkoff sounds will be detected once every cardiac cycle [19, 39]. The system operates by periodically inflating the cuff to a pressure at which it is held for a fixed number of beats (perhaps 50), counting the number of coincidences that occur, and then

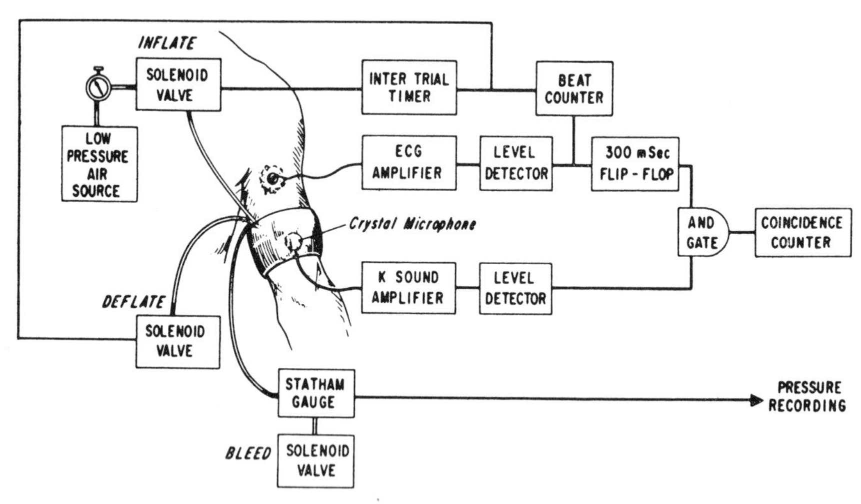

Figure 7.6. Block diagram of an automatic system for measuring the median systolic and diastolic pressures with a constant cuff pressure (reproduced, with permission, from B. Tursky, D. Shapiro, and G. E. Schwartz, *IEEE Trans. Biomed. Eng.*, **BME-19**, 271–276, 1972).

deflating the cuff to restore normal circulation. The number of coincidences is expressed as a percentage of the total number of beats during the particular inflation In measuring the systolic pressure, if the percentage of coincidences lies between 25% and 75%, the cuff pressure is assumed to be at the median systolic pressure; if the percentage is greater than 75%, the cuff pressure is too low and during the next inflation the pressure is increased by 2 mmHg: Similarly, if the coincidence percentage is less than 25%, the cuff pressure is too high and for the next trial the pressure is lowered by 2 mmHg. Thus, the system searches out the median systolic pressure by a trial-and-error process and attempts to arrive at a cuff pressure where the number of coincidences is close to 50%. A similar search process is initiated for arriving at the diastolic pressure.

With this system the median pressures could be arrived at to an accuracy of ± 2 mmHg. Comparison of the median systolic pressure measured in this way with the median pressure determined intra-arterially on a single patient indicated excellent agreement for five separate trials. As pointed out by the authors, the system could be particularly useful for mass screening when it is only necessary to determine whether the pressures lie outside a particular predefined range. Under such circumstances the cuff pressure can be set to one of the limit values, and depending on whether the coincidence percentage is greater or less than 50%, the individual can be immediately classified.

Methods Using Ultrasound. While the basic ausculatory method is simple, requires a minimum of equipment, and is sufficiently accurate for most purposes, it does suffer from the disadvantage that it fails to give both the systolic and diastolic pressures for hypotensive patients and infants. In addition, in a noisy environment or when there is significant patient movement, it becomes difficult to distinguish accurately the beginning of the two Korotkoff sound phases.

Of the methods that have been proposed for overcoming these difficulties, the use of ultrasound is particularly attractive [40–45].* In the system described by Stegall et al. [42], Doppler ultrasound is used to determine the state of closure of an artery beneath the cuff. As illustrated in Figure 7.7, two piezoelectric crystals are attached to the bottom of the arm cuff. One crystal, connected to an 8-MHz oscillator, generates ultrasound that is reflected off the vessel walls. The other crystal, connected to a narrow-band amplifier, detects the reflected signal. If the vessel wall is moving, the reflected signal will be Doppler-shifted in frequency by an amount proportional to the instantaneous wall velocity. Opening of the artery generates a fairly high frequency signal ($\Delta f \approx$ 200–500 Hz), while closing generates a low-frequency

* A fully automatic system using ultrasound for the detection of the systolic and diastolic pressures is manufactured by Hoffman-La Roche Inc., New Jersey.

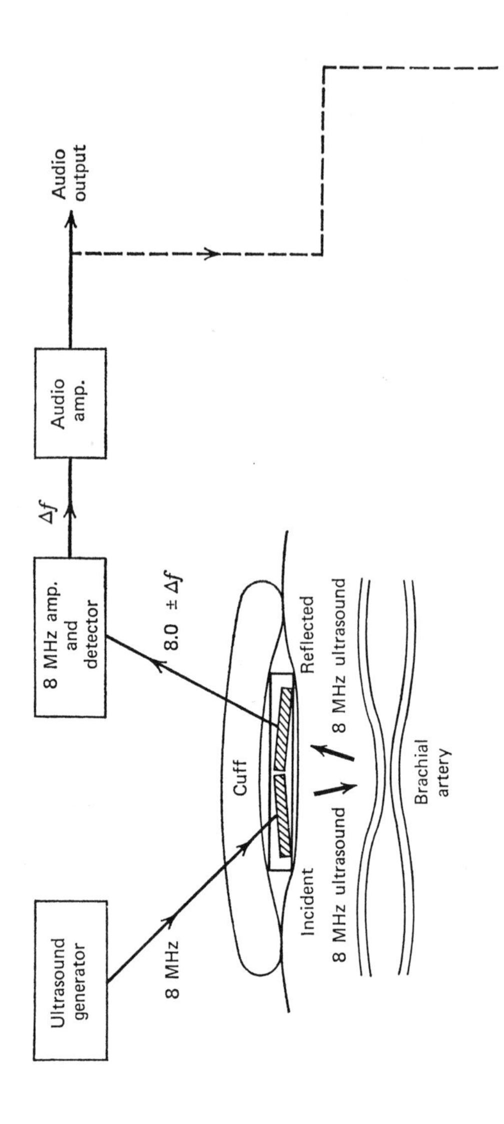
Ultrasound generator
8 MHz
8 MHz amp. and detector
8.0 ± Δf
Δf
Audio amp.
Audio output
Cuff
Incident
8 MHz ultrasound
Reflected
8 MHz ultrasound
Brachial artery

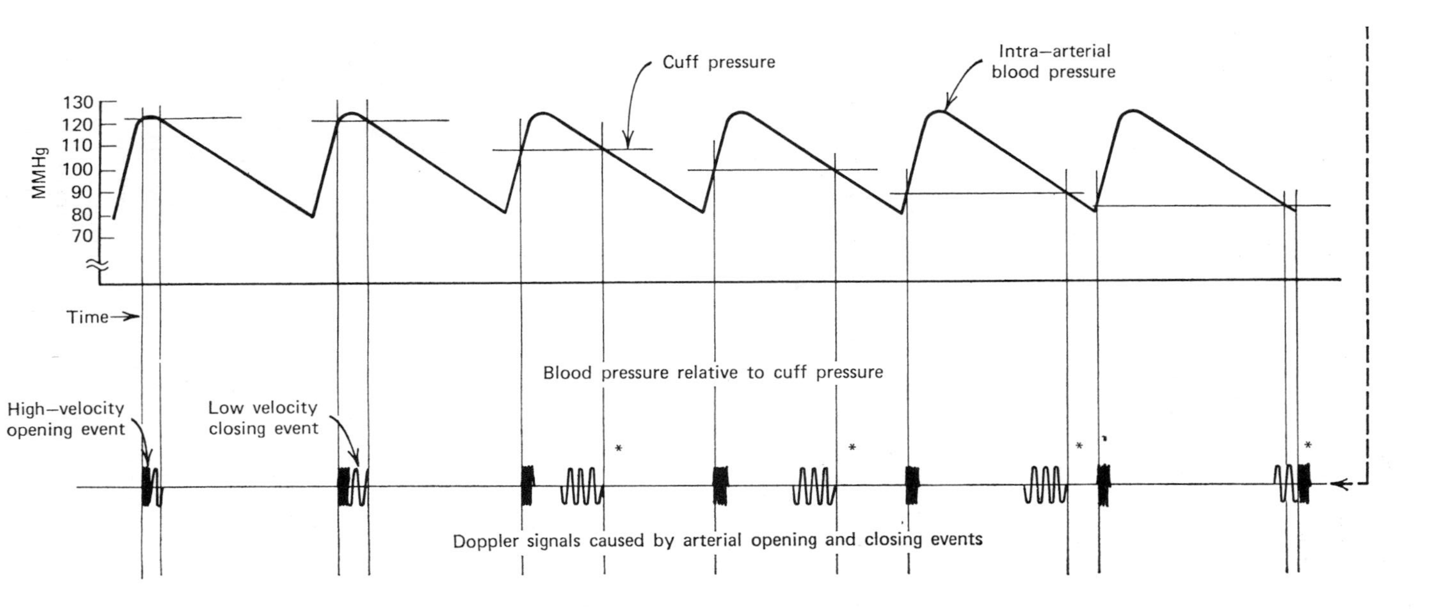

* Note approach of closing event to successive opening event as cuff pressure decreases.

Figure 7.7. Principle of the indirect blood-pressure measurement system using the ultrasonic Doppler effect. When the cuff pressure lies between the systolic and diastolic pressures, the artery opens and closes once every cardiac cycle (adapted from Stegall et al. [42] and, Ware and Laenger [40]).

signal ($\Delta f \approx$ 30–100 Hz). Essentially no Doppler shift occurs when the artery is open throughout the cardiac cycle. Thus, as the cuff is deflated, the systolic pressure is signaled by the start of a high-frequency audio signal. Further deflation causes the time separation between the high- and low-frequency signals first to increase and then to decrease. Merging of the two signals is accompanied by a definite change in the audible character of the signal and is used to indicate the diastolic pressure.

With this method Stegall et al. [42] report that on a series of 10 normotensive subjects the error compared to direct measurement for both the systolic and diastolic pressures was less than 2.5 mmHg. Further, they report successful measurements of both the systolic and diastolic pressures on 8 infants and 8 patients in clinical shock: neither of these two groups gave detectable Korotkoff sounds.

Improvements, such as the use of a multiple transducer arrangement to make the cuff placement less critical [44], have enabled the Doppler detection method to be automated, allowing systolic and diastolic pressures to be displayed on a semicontinuous basis. It is perhaps of interest to note that the Doppler method makes possible the reconstruction and display of the complete pressure waveform [5: pp. 127–128]. It is evident from Figure 7.7 that the time separation between two adjacent Doppler pulses is equal to the time between the two equal pressure points. From a complete set of such points, using the ECG R-wave as a reference and knowing the cuff pressure for each point, the complete pressure waveform can be reconstructed graphically or, using some electronic processing, displayed on an oscilloscope.

7.2.2 Force Balance Methods

A second class of noninvasive pressure measurement corresponds to that commonly used in measuring intraocular (IO) pressure (tonometry). Although tonometers have been used for many years, most of the early methods suffered from a variety of operational defects, as well as serious inaccuracies [46]. To overcome these problems, Mackay and Marg [47] used a coplanar guard ring, similar to that previously reported by Smyth [48] for the measurement of intra-amniotic pressures. By this means they developed an instrument that accurately measured IO pressures with a minimum of inconvenience.

As shown in Figure 7.8, the Mackay–Marg tonometer consists of a flat probe containing a force transducer. The surface of the force transducer is coplanar with the fixed outer annular ring of the probe. When the probe is applied, the corneal surface first contacts the transducer surface, causing the force to increase as the probe is advanced. The cornea is increasingly flattened as the probe is further advanced, until the flattened region covers just the force transducer area. At this point, the measured force is a maximum,

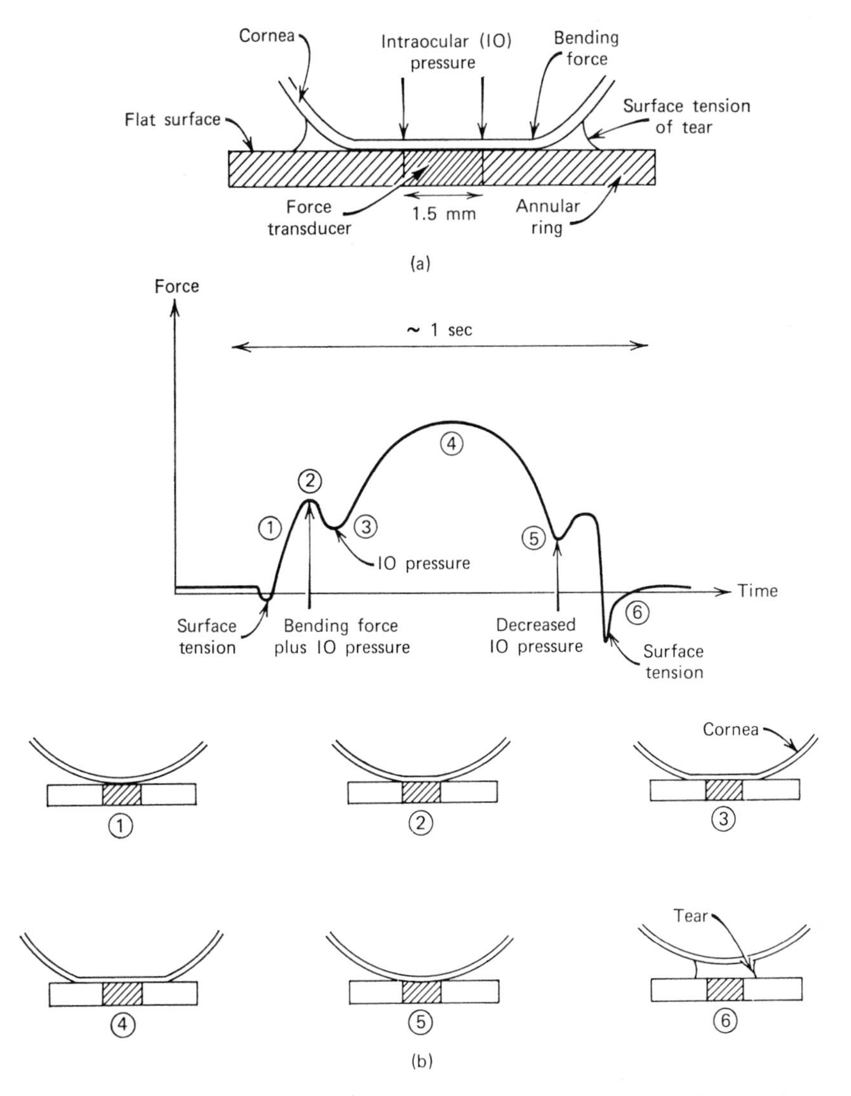

Figure 7.8. Principles of the Mackay–Marg tonometer: (a) details of the forces acting on the cornea when flattened by a plane surface; (b) the force transducer output as a function of time when the probe is slowly applied to and removed from the cornea (adapted from Mackay [46]).

since both the IO fluid pressure force and the force required to bend the cornea will be measured by the transducer. As the probe is further advanced toward the cornea, the bending force is transferred to the fixed outer ring, causing the indicated force to reach a minimum. At this point the force registered by the transducer is equal to the product of the IO pressure and the force transducer area. In essence the fixed annular ring acts as a guard ring, to prevent the bending force from affecting the measurement. As the probe is further advanced the indicated force again increases owing to the increase in IO pressure caused by the probe displacement. Gradual removal of the probe results essentially in a reversal of the force waveshape. However, the second dip may be less than the first, because of a temporary loss of IO fluid.

For accurate registration of the true IO pressure it is essential that the force transducer be near ideal. Any movement of the transducer surface with respect to the annular ring causes bending forces to affect the reading. Mackay [46] has described several types of force transducer that meet the requirements: a displacement transducer with electromagnetic force feedback to maintain the displacement close to zero [see Figure 6.45(c)]; a linear-variable differential transformer (see Figure 6.15) having a displacement of 200 Å/mmHg; and a piezoelectric transducer (see Section 6.3). Since a dc response is not required, the piezoelectric quartz transducer [49] in view of its high stiffness and simplicity, is particularly attractive. When used in combination with a high input impedance amplifier its low-frequency response can be made sufficiently small that for the second or so required for the measurement the baseline remains steady.

Although the force balance method of indirect pressure measurement can be readily applied to tonometry, there are other applications that should be considered. One of these is the measurement of intracranial pressures of infants for the early detection of hydrocephalitis. The incomplete closure of the fetal skull, especially the anterior fontanelle, enables the intracranial pressure to be determined with this method.

For measuring the intracranial pressure through the dura (a membrane between the skull and brain) in experimental animals, Schellini et al. [50] have developed a guard-ring coplanar structure that uses two piezoresistive elements for determining the force on the central disk. A more recent version developed by the same group [51] incorporates a means of accurately controlling the penetration depth. Furthermore, it uses a miniature diaphragm-type sealed pressure transducer as the central planar sensing element.

One further application of the force balance method of indirect measurement is that described by Smyth [48] for determining the intra-amniotic pressure (the amnion is a membrane enclosing a fetus). For this purpose Smyth developed a guard-ring transducer that he claims enables reasonably accurate pressure measurements to be made through the abdominal wall and even through light clothing.

7.3 DIRECT HYDRAULICALLY COUPLED SYSTEMS

Direct methods of measuring pressure entail the introduction of either the transducer or part of the transducer system into the region of interest. The fluid filled catheter coupled to an external membrane-type pressure transducer is one of the simplest means of directly recording the pulsatile pressure and is one that is widely used in clinical and research practice. Ideally the catheter fluid serves to transmit—in an undistorted manner, one hopes—the pressure at the catheter tip to the external transducer, but as will be seen, certain errors can arise, especially in a poorly designed system.

For nonpulsatile pressures or for measuring the mean pressure, the significant sources of error are the kinetic-energy artifact previously discussed, the change in pressure caused by the introduction of the catheter [52], and the uncertainty in knowing the height of the catheter tip in relation to the transducer. Although for arterial measurements this latter error source is not normally troublesome, for venous pressures (e.g., CVP's), small variations in height can cause significant problems.

In making pulsatile pressure measurements some sources of error, in addition to those mentioned above, must be considered. One of these concerns an effect arising from the reflection of the pressure wave from the tip of the catheter or from the point at which the vessel is occluded. Such effects have been studied both experimentally and theoretically by Kanai et al. [53] and are present for both the catheter-tip and hydraulically coupled measuring systems. An additional source of error, present only in the hydraulically coupled system, concerns the possible distortion introduced by the wave-transmission properties of the catheter–transducer arrangement. This will now be considered in detail.

7.3.1 System Properties

As indicated in Figure 7.9(a) the transfer function of a catheter–transducer system is governed by a number of parameters, some of which may be unfamiliar to the reader. A catheter of length L_c and inner diameter D_c will not of course be perfectly rigid and will possess some elastic properties. A measure of the elasticity is the catheter compliance per unit length. By definition, it is the change in the internal volume per unit length per unit pressure change. In the cgs system, the units for the compliance C_c are cm^4 per dyne. The volume displacement coefficient V_c, for the catheter is a more frequently used quantity. When expressed in cubic millimeters per 100 mmHg, it is related to C_c by

$$V_c = 1.33 \times 10^8 C_c L_c \qquad (\text{in mm}^3/100\ \text{mmHg}).$$

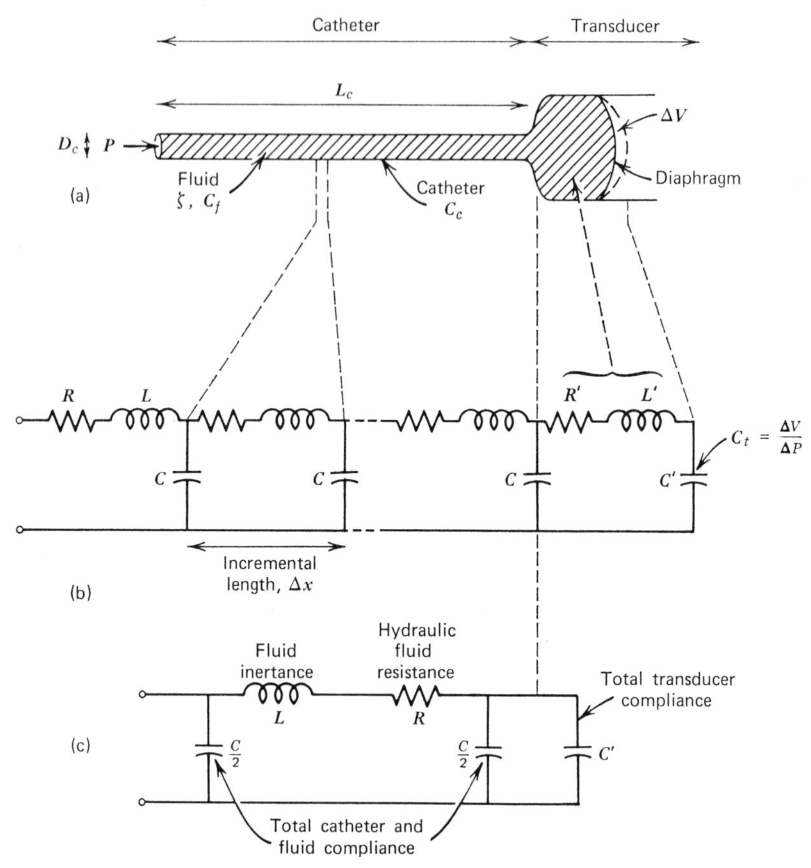

Figure 7.9. The hydraulically coupled catheter–transducer system: (a) physical model; (b) fairly exact electrical transmission line analog; and (c) simplified electrical analog.

Since the catheter fluid is also compressible, the total catheter compliance per unit length will be the sum of C_c and fluid compliance per unit length C_f. To determine the value of C_f, it should be noted that it can be expressed in terms of the fluid compressibility K_f [$(1/V)(dV/dP)$, in cm^2/dyne] by

$$C_f = \frac{\pi D_c^2 K_f}{4} \qquad \text{(in cm}^4\text{/dyne).}$$

Thus, the volume displacement coefficient of the fluid can be written as

$$V_f = 1.33 \times 10^8 \frac{\pi D_c^2 K_f L_c}{4} \qquad \text{(in mm}^3\text{/100 mmHg).}$$

Finally, we note that the transducer terminating the catheter will have a total compliance C_t (cm^5/dyne) and a corresponding volume displacement coefficient V_t given by

$$V_t = 1.33 \times 10^8 \, C_t \qquad (\text{in mm}^3/100\,\text{mmHg}).$$

If the catheter were perfectly stiff and the fluid were incompressible, an increase in the pressure P at the catheter tip would cause fluid to flow down the catheter into the transducer and displace the diaphragm by an amount such that the volume displaced was exactly equal to the volume of fluid flowing into the tip. Since the mass of moving fluid possesses inertia, the diaphragm behaves like a spring and the viscous resistance to flow behaves like a damper, it can be expected that the system will behave somewhat like the second-order systems described in Section 2.2.

When the nonzero compliances of the fluid and catheter are properly accounted for, the system analysis becomes much more complicated [54–57]. It can be shown that under these circumstances the system behaves like the electrical transmission line shown in Figure 7.9(b). It is found that, just as with an electrical transmission line, improper termination of the catheter by the transducer can cause a pressure wave reflection phenomenon [58], which manifests itself as a form of transient distortion. A further property of transmission lines is that they can be characterized by a certain cutoff frequency, above which the amplitude response drops rapidly.

It is fortunate that for most practical purposes the catheter–transducer system can be represented by the simplified model shown in Figure 7.9(c). Here the catheter and fluid compliances are represented by the sum of two capacitances, $C/2$. The moving mass of fluid possesses a certain inertia (fluid inertance) represented by the inductance L, and the viscosity of the fluid, which tends to resist any flow, by the resistance R. The transducer itself can be represented by the capacitance C', corresponding to the compliance, if the velocity of fluid in the transducer housing is sufficiently small compared to the catheter, so that its inertance and resistance can be ignored (L', $R' \approx 0$).

From the analog circuit model of Figure 7.9(c) the transfer function of the catheter–transducer system can be deduced. A sinusoidal voltage generator when applied to the input (equivalent to a sinusoidal pressure generator at the catheter tip) generates an output voltage across C', corresponding to the transducer output. It is a simple matter to calculate the input–output relationship in terms of the circuit elements and frequency. We find that the transfer function is that of a simple second-order system and is determined by the elements L, R, and $(C/2 + C')$. Note that the capacitance $C/2$ on the left-hand side does not affect the transfer function, since it simply shunts the input voltage source without affecting the voltage applied to the network. Thus, the transfer function is that of a simple series resonant circuit, the amplitude and phase characteristics of which are the same as given in Figure 2.13 and the transient response of which is the same as that of Figure 2.15.

As discussed in Section 2.2 a simple second-order system can be characterized by the natural (resonant) frequency f_n $(= \omega_n/2\pi)$, and the damping coefficient ξ. It can be shown that for the catheter–transducer system, they are given by [5]

$$\xi = \frac{1.35 \times 10^{-3}\eta}{D_c{}^3}\sqrt{\frac{L_c V_e}{\zeta}}, \tag{1}$$

$$f_n = \frac{1.4 \times 10^3 D_c}{\sqrt{V_e L_c \zeta}}, \tag{2}$$

where

η = viscosity of the fluid (poise),
L_c = catheter length (cm),
D_c = catheter diameter (cm),
V_e = effective volume displacement coefficient of the system $= V_t + (V_c + V_f)/2$ (mm^3/100 mmHg),
ζ = density of fluid (gm/cm^3).

It should be noted from Eq. (1) that the damping coefficient depends on the inverse cube of the catheter diameter and is proportional to the fluid viscosity. Since the viscosity of water is temperature-dependent (~2.5%/°C at 25°C) and changes greatly with small amounts of blood, it is a somewhat fruitless task to attempt to set the damping coefficient very accurately. Nevertheless, it is desirable that the coefficient be close to 0.7 (see Figure 2.15).

The graphical information contained in Figure 7.10 shows the variation of the natural frequency with the effective volume displacement coefficient for two catheter (or hypodermic tube) diameters and various catheter lengths [60]. The volume displacement coefficient of the water contained in a catheter of given diameter and length sets an upper bound to the natural frequency that can be attained. This upper bound is given in the graph by the frequency at which the line, for a given catheter, terminates. The corresponding value of V_e is one-half of that for the water in the catheter. It therefore follows that no advantage is gained toward achieving a better frequency response by using a transducer whose V_t is much less than this value of V_e. It also is evident from the graph that a short, stiff, large-diameter catheter combined with a transducer having a small volume displacement coefficient are necessary ingredients for a high natural frequency.

Figure 7.11 shows the length of catheter (or hypodermic tubing) necessary to make the damping coefficient 0.7. It should be noted that to achieve this optimum and a frequency response of 50 Hz or greater, a small-diameter catheter is necessary. Even with a F3.5 catheter having an inner diameter

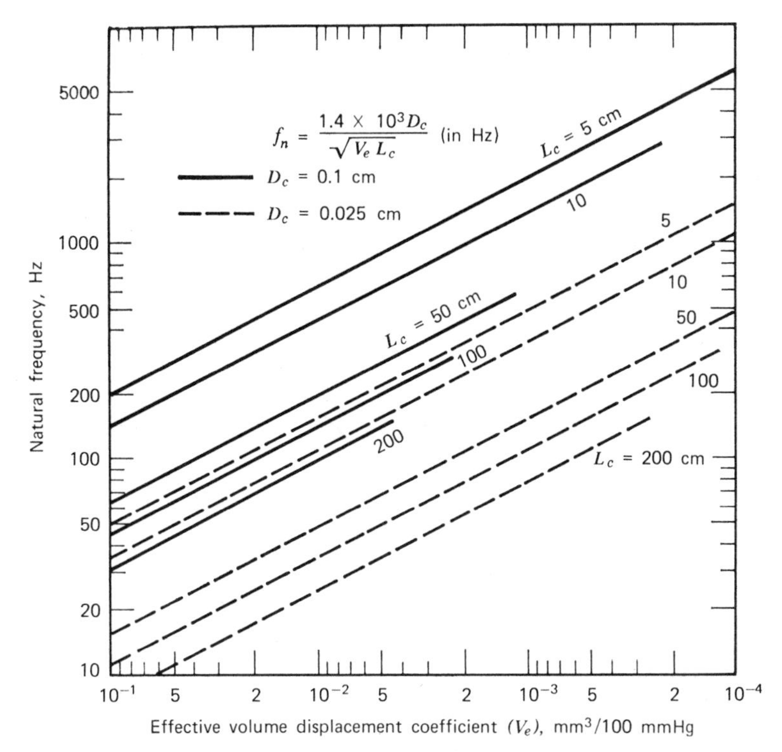

Figure 7.10. Natural frequency of a catheter–transducer system, as computed from Eq. (2), for two inner diameters, various catheter lengths, and $\zeta = 1.0$ gm/cm^3.

of 0.4 mm, the best that can be achieved with optimum damping is 17 Hz. In point of fact most catheter–transducer systems operate in an underdamped condition.

Optimum system damping can be achieved through the use of (1) a viscous fluid such as oil, in the catheter, (2) a series or parallel hydraulic damping system [20, 61, 62], or (3) a compensating electrical network [57, 63]. Method 1 is of little practical use, since catheters must be flushed to keep them patent. The series damping method [20, 61, 62] simply consists of a very narrow tube in series with the catheter between the catheter and transducer. Parallel damping can be achieved by using a distensible plastic tube in series with a throttle resistance to shunt the connection between the catheter and transducer [20, 61].

Figure 7.12 illustrates the improved frequency response that can be achieved with parallel damping. The phase response is essentially linear, giving a

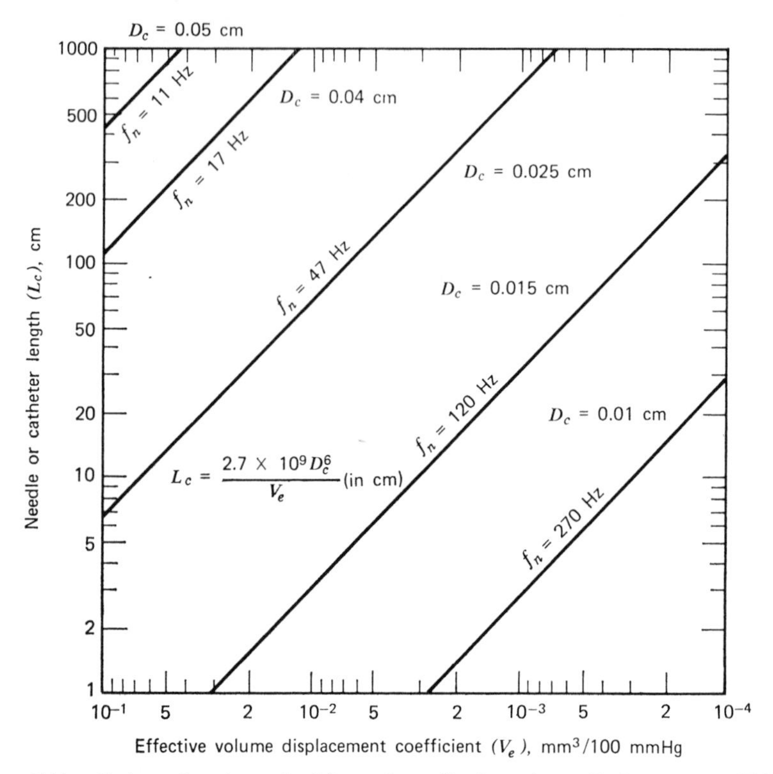

Figure 7.11. Catheter length required for a given effective volume displacement coefficient to achieve optimum damping ($\xi = 0.7$).

constant signal delay, whereas with series damping this is not the case and significant signal distortion can result.

An electrical method for achieving optimum system damping has been described by Noble [63]. Through the use of an amplifier containing a compensation network of appropriate design, he was able to achieve a total system response that was nearly optimally damped. His results, with and without the compensating amplifier, are shown in Figure 7.13.

The presence of small air bubbles in the catheter and transducer increases the effective volume displacement coefficient, thereby increasing the damping and decreasing the natural frequency [64]. To eliminate such bubbles is a problem, since, even with repeated flushing of the system, small air bubbles remain. One method to achieve an air-free system is to boil the catheter–transducer system in water [61]. Another is to fill and flush the system with boiled water to which some alcohol and a wetting agent have been added [5].

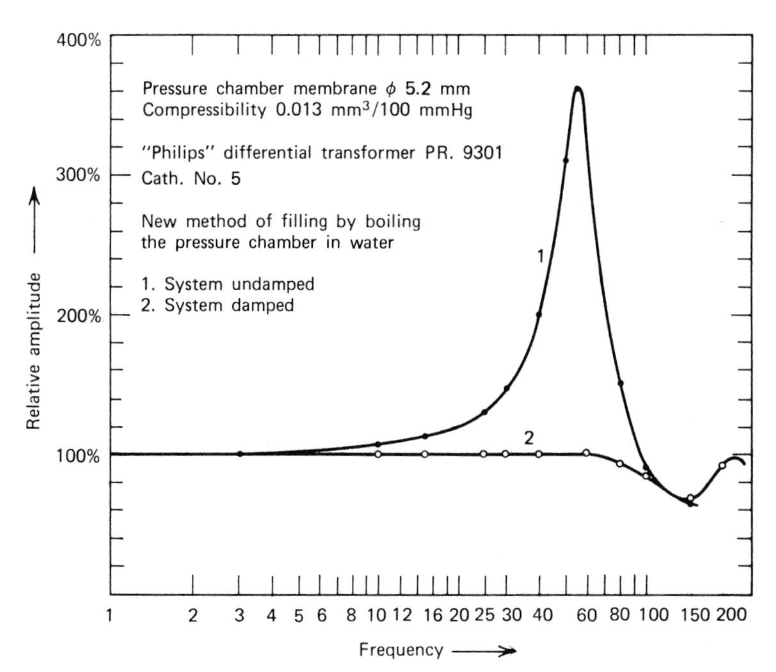

Figure 7.12. Measured frequency-response characteristics of a catheter–transducer system with and without parallel damping (reproduced, with permission, from J. F. Crul, *Acta Anaesth. Scand.*, suppl. 11, **6**, 135–169, 1962).

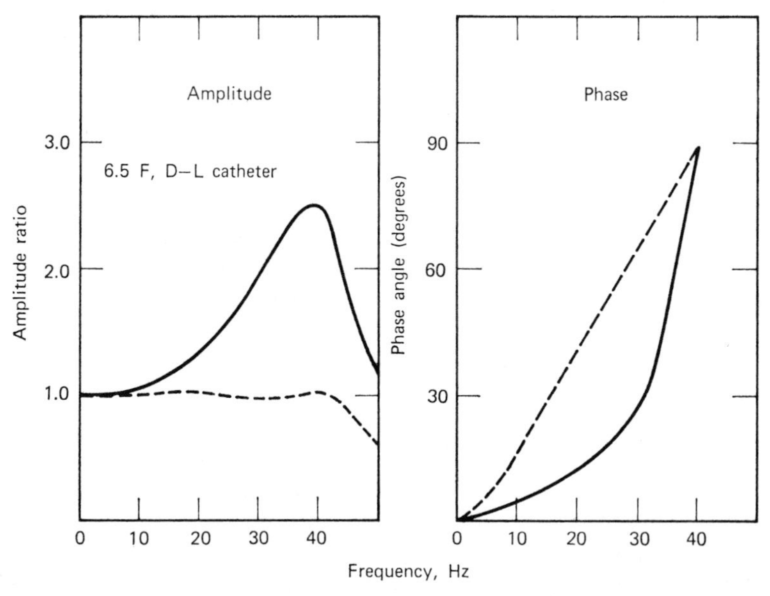

Figure 7.13. Electrically compensated catheter–transducer response curves: solid lines, uncompensated; broken lines, compensated; transducer, Statham P-23Db (reproduced, with permission, from F. W. Noble and G. O. Barnett, *Med. Electron. Biolog. Eng.*, **1**, 537–545, 1963).

A second important point to consider in making accurate pulsatile measurements is the artifact created by acceleration of the catheter when placed, for example, in one of the cardiac chambers. Acceleration of the fluid within the catheter causes a force to be generated that produces an equivalent pressure change [64, 65].

The simple resonant circuit model described above becomes inadequate when one tries to extend the frequency response to a region where cardiovascular sounds can be properly recorded. Under these circumstances, the distributed nature of the system must be included so that wave transmission and reflection phenomena can be properly accounted for. In 1949 Hansen [54] proposed that the frequency response could be greatly enhanced by placing a constriction at the catheter tip so that pressure waves reflected from the transducer could be fully absorbed. From a practical viewpoint, the position of the proposed constriction is unfortunate, since tip blockage through thrombus formation would be a problem. Recently, Latimer [59] has described an arrangement that achieves the same result using two identical catheters: one inserted in the subject and the other, a dummy filled with saline and with its tip blocked off. The two catheters each have a small constriction at the transducer ends and are connected to a common transducer. Such an arrangement properly absorbs all reflected waves. Latimer reports that over a frequency range up to 500 Hz the phase response of this system is linear (giving zero phase distortion) and that the amplitude response varies as the log of the frequency with a deviation of no more than 1 dB. Compensation for the signal attenuation is achieved electronically to yield a flat frequency response for the overall system.

Measurement of the frequency-response characteristics of the catheter–transducer system can be accomplished through the use of a sinusoidal pressure generator. Alternatively, by using a "step" source of pressure, the transient response can be measured, enabling the frequency and phase response to be derived. Several sinusoidal pressure generators have been described in the literature [66, 67]. A highly sophisticated system employing feedback control has recently been described by Foreman and Hutchison [67]. It is capable of generating sinusoidal pressures of constant amplitude with less that 3% harmonic distortion over the range 20–20,000 Hz.

7.3.2 Properties of Elastic-Type Transducers

Most pressure transducers are of the primary–secondary type: a primary transducer to convert hydraulic pressure to displacement and a secondary transducer to produce an electrical output proportional to the displacement. Commonly used forms of the primary transducer have an elastic member of the Bourdon tube, diaphragm, or bellows varieties illustrated in Figure 7.14.

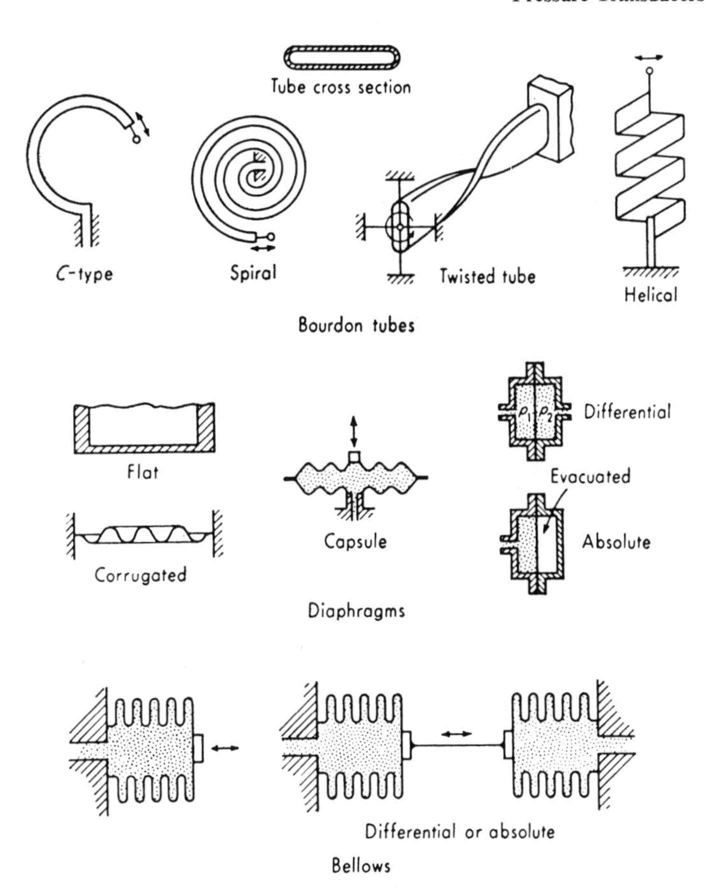

Figure 7.14. Various forms of elastic pressure transducers (from E. O. Doebelin, *Measurement Systems: Application and Design*, © 1966, McGraw-Hill Book Co.; used with permission of McGraw-Hill Book Co., New York).

In the Bourdon tube, a pressure difference between the inside and outside causes the tube, whose cross section is a flattened circle, to approach a more circular form. In doing so, the free end is translated in the direction shown in the figure. Motion of the free end can be transduced in a number of ways: it can cause a pointer to be rotated, leading directly to a visual output; it can actuate an LVDT as discussed in Section 6.1.3 (see Figure 6.15); or, it can cause the light to a photoelectric cell to be partially interrupted [5, p. 27]. Although simple and reliable, Bourdon-type pressure transducers have a large volume displacement coefficient (~ 2 mm^3/100 mmHg is typical) and are therefore unsuitable for dynamic pressure transduction using hydraulic pressure coupling via a narrow tube.

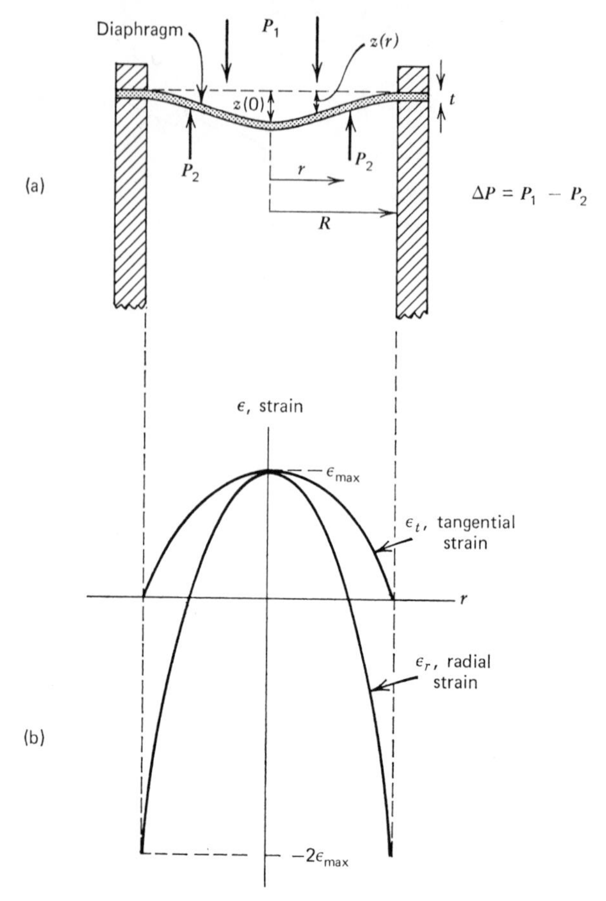

Figure 7.15. Mechanical properties of a thin circular diaphragm: (a) displacement; (b) radial and tangential strain components.

Since diaphragms of the flat or corrugated types are commonly used for accurate pressure transduction, it is worthwhile to consider briefly their theory of operation.

The simplest form consists of a thin circular plate that is rigidly clamped at its edge. As illustrated in Figure 7.15(a), a pressure differential causes the plate to be displaced by an amount that depends on the distance from the center. It can be shown that the displacement at a distance r from the center c(r) is given by [68]

$$z(r) = \frac{3(1 - \mu^2)(R^2 - r^2)^2 \, \Delta P}{16Et^3[1 + (z(r)/t)^2/2]} \qquad \text{(in cm)}, \tag{3}$$

where

t = diaphragm thickness (cm),
R = diaphragm radius (cm),
E = Young's modulus (dynes/cm^2),
μ = Poisson's ratio,
ΔP = pressure difference (dynes/cm^2).

It will be noted from Eq. (3) that the displacement depends nonlinarly on ΔP; however, if the maximum displacement is small compared to the diaphragm thickness [$z(0) \leqslant t/4$], the nonlinearity will be small and the maximum displacement can be written as

$$z(0) = \frac{3(1-\mu^2)R^4\,\Delta P}{16Et^3} \qquad \text{(in cm)}. \tag{4}$$

The dependence of the displacement on the fourth power of the radius makes it very desirable that the diaphragm not be too small. It should also be noted that a thin diaphragm is also desirable, to achieve a high sensitivity; however, its minimum value is set by the maximum overpressure that the transducer must withstand without exceeding its yield point.

Also of interest is the natural frequency of the diaphragm vibrating in a vacuum. In point of fact there exist an infinite number of natural frequencies, the lowest of which is given by

$$f_n = \frac{2.56t}{\pi R^2}\sqrt{\frac{gE}{3\,\delta(1-\mu^2)}} \tag{5}$$

where

g = acceleration of gravity (cm/sec^2),
δ = specific weight of the diaphragm material (dynes/cm^3).

It is evident from Eq. (5) that a high natural frequency requires a small-diameter, thick diaphragm—the opposite of that for the best sensitivity. However, for most practical designs f_n is greater than 1000 Hz, so that for physiological-type measurements no real problem arises.

Finally, we turn to the stress and strain distribution in the diaphragm. The stress produced by the pressure differential can be divided into a radial component σ_r and a tangential component σ_t whose values are given by [68]

$$\sigma_r = \frac{3\,\Delta P}{8t^2}[(1+\mu)R^2 - (3+\mu)r^2] \qquad \text{(in dynes/cm}^2\text{)} \tag{6}$$

$$\sigma_t = \frac{3\,\Delta P}{8t^2}[(1+\mu)R^2 - (1+3\mu)r^2] \qquad \text{(in dynes/cm}^2\text{)}. \tag{7}$$

To obtain expressions for the strain components, we note that the diaphragm is in a state of biaxial stress with both σ_t and σ_r contributing to the radial and tangential strain at any point, according to

$$\varepsilon_r = \frac{\sigma_r - \mu\sigma_t}{E}$$
$$\varepsilon_t = \frac{\sigma_t - \mu\sigma_r}{E} \tag{8}$$

Substituting Eqs. (6) and (7) into Eq. (8), we find that the two strain components can be expressed as

$$\varepsilon_r = \frac{3\,\Delta P(1 - \mu^2)}{8t^2E}\,[R^2 - 3r^2] \tag{9}$$

$$\varepsilon_t = \frac{3\,\Delta P(1 - \mu^2)}{8t^2E}\,[R^2 - r^2], \tag{10}$$

which are plotted in Figure 7.15(b).

7.3.3 Diaphragm-Displacement Pressure Transducers

The diaphragm displacement of a hydraulically coupled pressure transducer can be converted into an electrical signal through the use of an unbonded strain gauge, a bonded strain gauge, a thin-film-deposited strain gauge, a silicon diaphragm with integrated gauges, an LVDT, a variable inductance, or a variable capacitance. All these methods of transduction were described in Section 6.1. Of the above, the unbonded wire strain-gauge arrangement, because of its high sensitivity and stability, has been frequently used. Figure 7.16(b) illustrates its use with a diaphragm that is partially corrugated. One

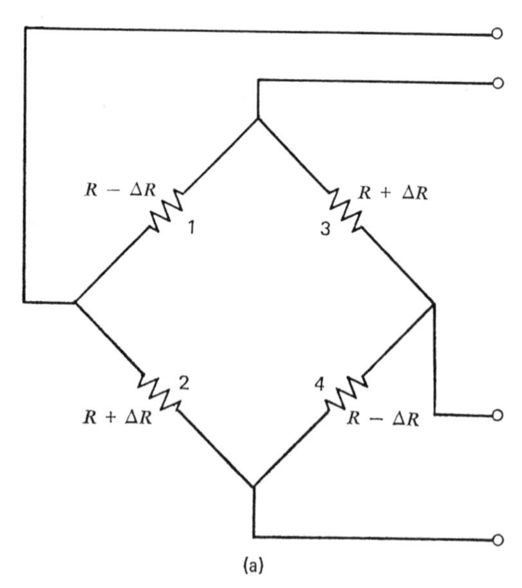

(a)

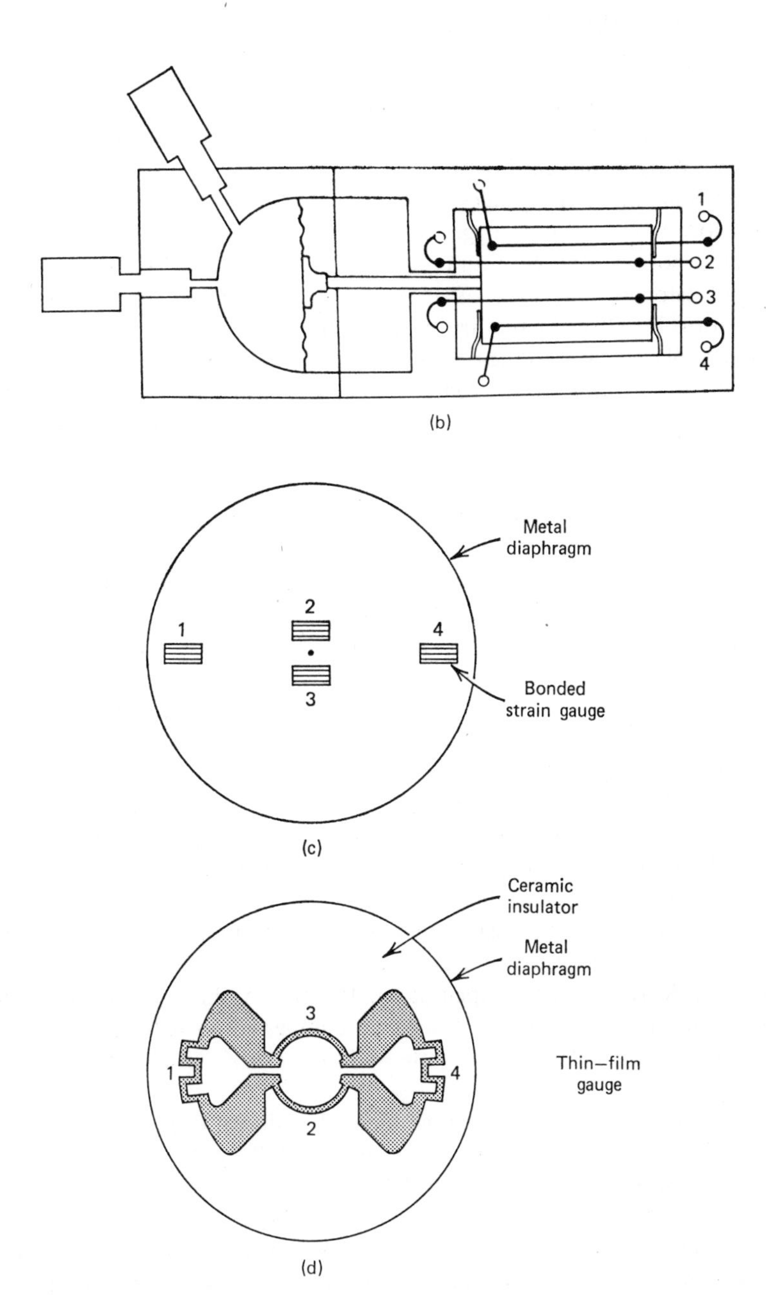

Figure 7.16. Various strain-gauge pressure transducers: (a) Wheatstone-bridge arrangement of strain gauges; (b) Unbonded strain-gauge pressure transducer; (c) bonded strain-gauge placement on a metal diaphragm; and (d) thin-film vacuum-deposited strain gauge on a metal diaphragm.

feature of this type of system is that if the stiffness of the center portion of the diaphragm is less than that of the strain-gauge assembly, pretty well all of the force produced by the pressure differential will be transmitted to the strain gauges, thereby yielding a high sensitivity.

Direct bonding of the gauges to the diaphragm does, of course, lead to a much more compact and rugged transducer. As shown in Figure 7.15(b), there exist both compressive and tensile strain in the diaphragm, enabling a full Wheatstone-bridge type of arrangement to be used with its inherent temperature stability. In the arrangement illustrated in Figure 7.16(c), two gauges are placed close to the edge to measure the radial compressive strain; the other two are close to the center to measure the tangential tensive strain. A similar gauge arrangement is used with vacuum-deposited thin-film metal gauges. As shown in Figure 7.16(d), the metal diaphragm is coated with a vacuum-deposited insulating film on top of which lie the thin-film gauges arranged in a bridge configuration. The narrow regions of metal form the gauges; the wider regions serve to interconnect them.

The use of single-crystal silicon as the diaphragm material has significant advantages in achieving miniaturized transducers. As discussed in Section 6.1.2, strain gauges can be formed by diffusing the appropriate impurity into the diaphragm using standard integrated circuit techniques [69–72]. The gauges are simply narrow regions of different conductivity type to the diaphragm, organized in such a manner as to make best use of the high piezoresistive coefficient of silicon. Transducers with diaphragms of around 20 μm thickness and a few millimeters in diameter have very high natural frequencies ($\sim$100 kHz), and because they use single-crystal high-purity silicon, excellent mechanical stability is possible. A further advantage of this transducer form arises from the much higher gauge factor of silicon. Offsetting these advantages is the much greater temperature sensitivity of silicon gauges, necessitating careful design and good control of the diffusions to achieve a reasonable degree of self-compensation. In spite of this, such gauges often require some form of external resistance compensation network to correct for the effects of temperature on the gauge sensitivity and the zero offset [69, 73].

As shown in Figure 6.7 the gauge factor for silicon decreases by roughly 0.25%/°C, causing the transducer sensitivity to fall by the same amount. In addition, it should be noted from Table 6.1 that the resistance of silicon gauges increases with temperature by an amount that depends on the doping. Thus, if, as shown in Figure 7.17, the Wheatstone-bridge strain-gauge configuration is fed from a voltage source, the transducer sensitivity falls with increasing temperature, because of the decreased gauge factor; however, the resistance change only affects the bridge current and thus has only a second-order effect on the bridge sensitivity. On the other hand, if the bridge

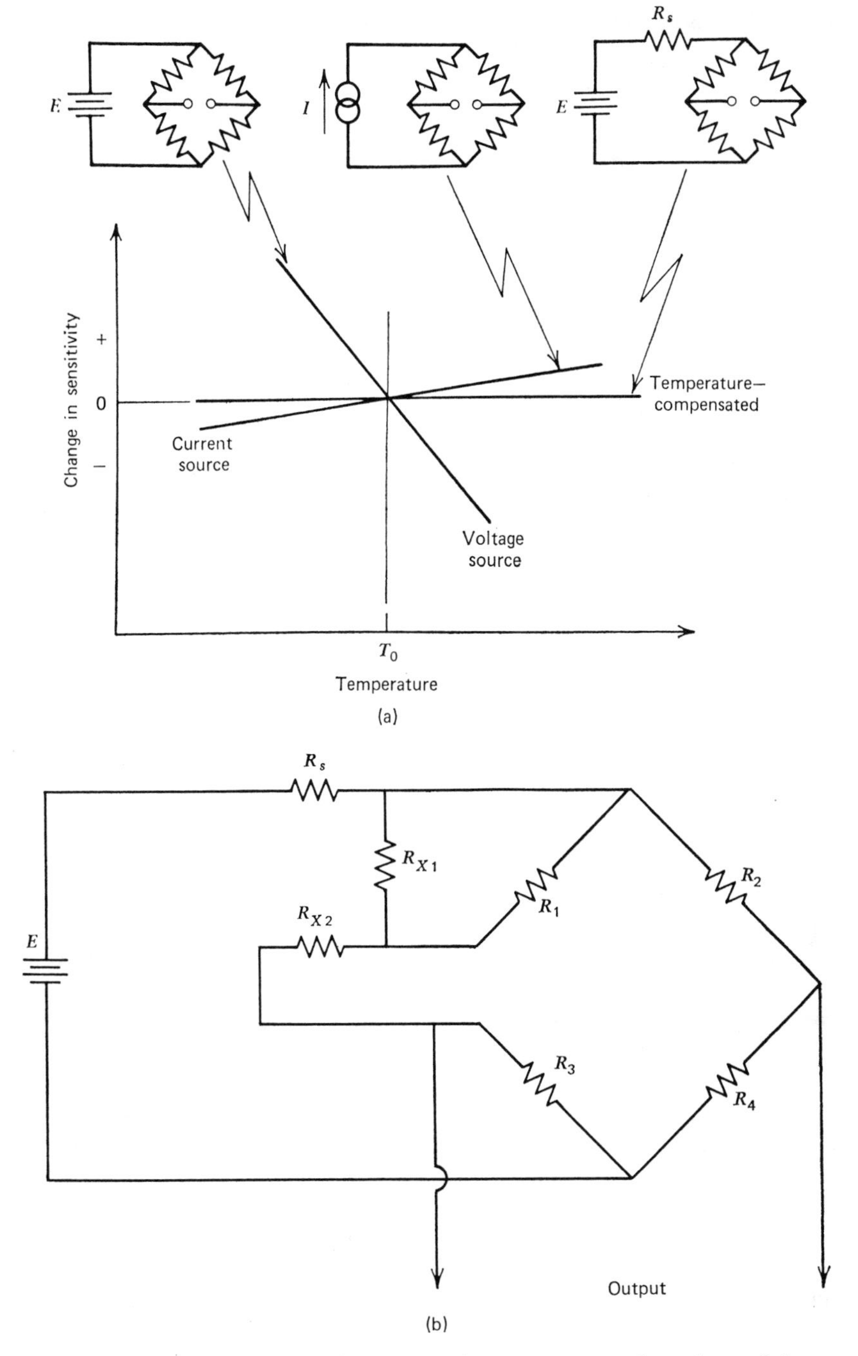

Figure 7.17. Bridge compensation networks: (a) the temperature dependence of the sensitivity of a strain gauge bridge when excited with sources of different resistance; (b) inclusion of zero-drift compensation network.

Table 7.2 Properties of Some Commercial Pressure Transducers

Transducer type	Nominal pressure range, mmHg	Max. pressure, mmHg	Sensitivity, $\mu V/(V)$ (mmHg)	Nonlinearity and hysteresis, %F.S.D.	Zero temp. coefficient, mmHg/°C	Volume displacement, mm^3/100 mmHg	Remarks
Statham							
P23Db	0/+750	1500	5	±0.5		0.04	
P23Dd	0/+750	1500	5	±0.5		0.02	Unbonded wire gauges (P23Dd–SP37)
P23De	0/+750	1500	10	±0.5		0.04	
P23Gb	0/+750	1500	2	±0.5		0.01	
SP37	0/+300	900	5	±0.5		0.001	
SF4	−30/+300	500	1	2.0		0.001	Cylindrical diaphragm, unbonded
Bell and Howell							
CM0109	0/+400	>4000	5	±0.5	0.3	0.04	Unbonded wire gauges
Hewlett–Packard							
1280B	−40/+400	750	40	1.0	0.4	0.04	
1280C	−40/+400	750	40	1.0	0.15	0.04	
Birtcher							
462	−100/+300	>3000	10	±1.0	2.0		Silicon-diaphragm diffused gauges
Electrometric							
MS-5	0/+300	>5000	10	0.5	0.2	0.5×10^{-4}	Silicon-diaphragm diffused gauges

is fed from a constant-current source, the increased gauge resistance at higher temperatures causes the bridge sensitivity to rise and perhaps overcompensate for the decreased gauge sensitivity. To obtain just the correct degree of compensation, the bridge can be fed from a voltage source with an appropriately chosen value of resistance in series. Thus, the arms of the bridge see a supply that is intermediate between a voltage and a current source, resulting in fairly complete compensation for the sensitivity dependence on temperature over a wide temperature range.

A rather more serious temperature drift problem arises from thermal expansion of the diaphragm and transducer assembly. This manifests itself as a change in the electrical zero. Compensation for these effects can be achieved by using an external shunt resistance R_{X1} across one of the strain gauges, together with a series resistance R_{X2} to restore the electrical zero. The complete circuit, designed to compensate for both forms of temperature drift, is shown in Figure 7.17(b).

At this point it is worthwhile to consider the properties of some commercial transducers especially those designed for physiological pressure measurement using hydraulic coupling.* Table 7.2 compares some of the significant electrical and hydraulic properties. It does not provide comparative information on the safety aspect: the guaranteed maximum leakage current from the transducer bridge to the fluid and the effect of possible diaphragm rupture on this hazard must of course be considered when hospital use is contemplated.

7.4 CATHETER-TIP TRANSDUCERS

The prime advantage of the catheter-tip pressure transducer is that it measures the pressure at the point at which it occurs rather than having to rely on the transmission of the pressure through a hydraulic coupling line to an external transducer. In spite of the near-ideal performance of modern pressure transducers, the hydraulically coupled system is fundamentally limited in frequency response by the compressibility of water. Although such systems can be designed to cover the frequency range associated with the blood-pressure waveform, it is difficult to achieve a sufficiently large frequency response to cover the spectrum associated with cardiovascular sounds. Furthermore, hydraulically coupled systems suffer from acceleration artifacts associated with the rapid movement of the catheter when positioned in the heart.

* Reference 74 contains a comprehensive listing of commercial pressure transducers designed mainly for nonphysiological measurements. Reference 70 contains a useful comparison of semiconductor strain-gauge pressure transducers, some of which are designed for physiological application.

7.4.1 Electrical Transduction Methods

It is of interest to note that the first electrical blood pressure transducer was of the catheter-tip variety. In 1898 Grunbaum described an electrolytic transducer mounted at the end of a catheter. It consisted of two closely spaced electrodes mounted within a small electrolyte-filled cylindrical capsule [5, p. 23]. One electrode was attached to a rubber-membrane window; the other was fixed so that a pressure change altered the electrode spacing, thereby changing the interelectrode resistance. The advantages of a catheter-tip transducer were recognized by a number of subsequent investigators, several of whom made significant improvements to Grunbaum's design. A more recent development of the electrolytic pressure transducer principle is that described by Wiederhielm et al. [75] in 1964. In order to measure the pressure in very small vessels, they used a micropipette filled with $2M$ saline. When the tip was inserted in a blood vessel the position of the blood–saline interface in the tapered tip was found to affect the electrical resistance. By maintaining the resistance constant through the use of pressure feedback, a signal was obtained that was proportional to the pressure at the tip. Details of this technique and some recent improvements are presented in Section 7.6.

Through the years various forms of catheter-tip transducers have been developed. Often these systems yielded excellent results in the hands of the inventor but were unsuited for manufacture, because of the great skill required for their fabrication and their fragile nature.

The first catheter-tip transducer to become generally available was the Allard–Laurens [76] transducer described in Section 6.1.3 and illustrated in Figure 6.18.* As previously discussed, it uses an inductive-type displacement transducer mounted at the end of a 8F double-lumen catheter. It has a frequency response that is flat to beyond 1000 Hz and a sensitivity sufficient to measure cardiovascular sounds. The second lumen can be used either for withdrawing blood samples or for checking the electrical zero. This latter operation can be performed with the catheter in place, using a hydraulically coupled transducer to provide an independent measurement of the mean pressure, whose value can be compared to that derived from the catheter-tip transducer.

The first strain-gauge catheter-tip transducer to become commercially available† is based on a design described by Warnick and Drake [77] in 1958. As shown in Figure 7.18, it consists of a thin, hollow metal cylinder, that can be strained by a pressure differential between the inside and outside. The unbonded strain-gauge wire around it consists of four elements: two of the

* Telco Corp., Paris.
† Model SF-1, Statham Instruments Inc., Oxnard, Calif.

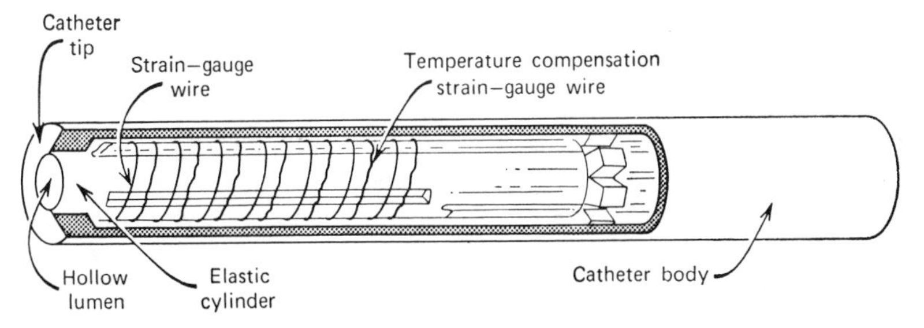

Figure 7.18. Sectioned view of a catheter tip transducer using a cylindrical elastic member and unbonded strain gauges (courtesy, Statham Instruments, Oxnard, Calif.).

wires are loosely wound to provide temperature compensation, and the other two are tightly wound on spacers to measure the strain in the cylinder. This method of transduction requires the presence of a lumen in the catheter to permit fluid flow into the cylinder. It has the advantage of enabling the zero to be checked and blood samples to be withdrawn. In addition, the lumen enables a small steady infusion of saline to be carried out without affecting the process of measurement. The prime disadvantages of this transducer are the absence of a stable zero, a low sensitivity* and the relatively fragile construction. To overcome the zero-drift problem, an external pressure transducer, hydraulically coupled through the catheter-tip pressure-transducer lumen, is often used.

The development of silicon piezoresistive strain gauges led shortly to their application in catheter-tip pressure sensors. The first reported gauge of this type used silicon cantilever bars to sense the movement of a metal diaphragm [78]. Subsequently, Angelakos [79] disclosed the development of a silicon-diaphragm gauge mounted at the end of an F7 catheter. More recently, Samaun et al. [72b] have described in detail a method of fabricating catheter-tip gauges using silicon disks etched to a thickness of less than 10 μm and selectively diffused in the usual manner to form a piezoresistive bridge. The smallest sensor, when mounted at the tip of a catheter, has an outside diameter of 0.9 mm, which is small enough to be inserted into the bore of an F9 catheter. The authors point out that the gauge itself has a temperature coefficient of 5 mmHg/°C, largely the result of the stresses introduced during mounting the diaphragm and the coefficients of expansion of the various materials. To compensate for this large effect, a temperature-dependent signal is derived by feeding the bridge from a current source and measuring

* Specifications for this device are: catheter size, F6.5; pressure range, −30 to +300 mmHg; sensitivity, 1 μV/Volt/mmHg; frequency response, flat to greater than 800 Hz.

the changes in voltage across the driving points. This voltage, which depends on the temperature and is independent of the pressure, is used to compensate for the drift through the use of analog circuits.

Although catheter-tip silicon-diaphragm gauges became commercially available, it is apparent that certain problems arose with their use. One of these is the difficulty of properly sealing the diaphragm to the tip; another is the danger of the diaphragm being accidentally cracked and being inserted in this state in a patient, thereby exposing the patient to a shock hazard. As a result, a metal diaphragm with diffused silicon-chip gauges attached, has been preferred by at least one manufacturer. Gauges of this form have been made significantly reduced in size from prior commercial catheter-tip gauges. A similar reduction has been achieved with a metal-diaphragm thin-film strain gauge* mounted at the end of a F5 catheter (1.67 mm o.d.).

A pressure sensor of somewhat different construction, mounted at the tip of an F5 teflon catheter, has been described by Millar and Baker [80a]. It uses a silicone-rubber diaphragm coupled to two unbonded silicon strain gauges arranged in a push-pull manner, yielding a sensitivity of 100 μV/(mm)(volt) excitation. This high sensitivity, a thermal stability of ± 0.15 mmHg/°C, and excellent long-term stability appear to make this a very attractive probe.

Catheter-tip gauges of small size have also been developed using a metal diaphragm and employing the capacitance change to determine the displacement. Coon and Sandler [80b] have described a series of gauges having outside diameters ranging from 2.25 to 1.0 mm. They report a linearity of 1% from 0–200 mmHg, a resolution of 1 mmHg, and a temperature sensitivity of 0.3 mmHg/°C. However, such gauges demand a great deal of high-accuracy machining and, as a result, can be expected to be very costly to produce. Comparable sizes are possible using the fiber-optics sensor described in the next subsection, at a rather lower cost.

7.4.2 Optical Transducers

The idea of measuring the displacement of a diaphragm by optical means is not a new one. In fact one of the earliest methods used for the high-frequency recording of intravascular pressures was by means of a hydraulically coupled diaphragm system in which the diaphragm displacement was measured by means of an optical lever. More recently, with the perfection of fiber optics for transmitting and receiving light [81], it has been possible to fabricate catheter-tip pressure transducers whose diaphragm displacement is optically measured [82–84].

As illustrated in Figure 7.19, the diaphragm displacement is determined by

* Model P866, Statham Instruments Inc., Oxnard, Calif.

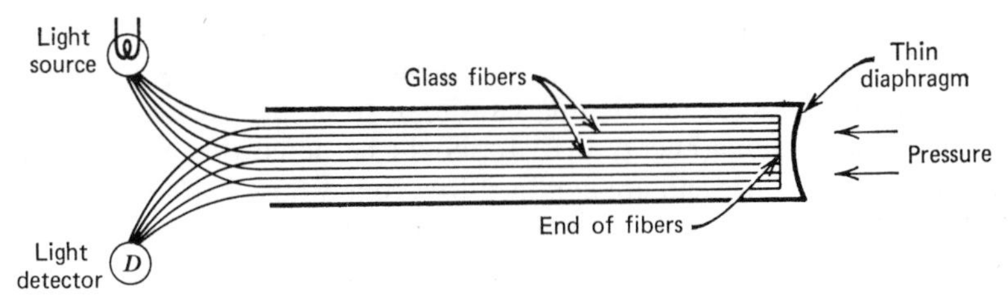

Figure 7.19. Principles of a fiber optic pressure transducer.

means of two bundles of coated glass fibers. The first bundle serves to transmit light from a source to the tip; the second serves to detect the amount of light reflected from the diaphragm inner surface. The amount of light received by the detector bundle depends on the diaphragm displacement. By proper design it is possible to arrange for the reflected intensity to be nearly proportional to the pressure differential across the diaphragm if the pressure range is fairly small.

The way in which a coated fiber transmits incident light is illustrated in Figure 7.20. The fiber core consists of a high refractive index glass ($n_1 \simeq 1.7$) having a diameter in the range 2–100 μm. It is covered by a low refractive index glass ($n_2 \simeq 1.5$) having a thickness of perhaps 0.5 μm, which serves to (1) reduce light losses that occur at each reflection, (2) essentially eliminate the cross-coupling of light between adjacent fibers, and (3) act as a matrix whereby bundles of fibers can be fused together. As shown in the figure, the angle of incidence of ray R_1 at the glass–glass interface is less than the critical

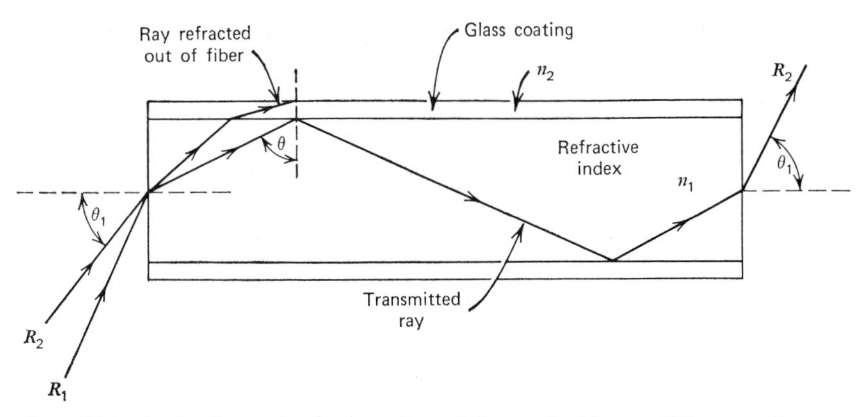

Figure 7.20. Refraction and reflection of two light rays incident at different angles on a coated glass fiber.

angle $\theta_c = \sin^{-1}(n_2/n_1)$, causing it to be refracted out. On the other hand, ray R_2 is incident at an angle greater than the critical angle, causing it to suffer total internal reflection. All subsequent encounters of this ray in the fiber will also be at angles greater than θ_c causing it to be propagated down the fiber with only minimal energy loss. It should be noted that the light rays emerging from the fiber end are confined to a cone whose half-angle is equal to the half angle of the cone containing those incident rays that are transmitted.

In the fiber-optics pressure transducer, the illuminated fibers are uniformly mixed with the detector fibers. Thus, to study the reflection of light at the diaphragm, we can look at the ray diagram for two adjacent fibers as shown in Figure 7.21. It will be noted that the light intensity emerging from (1) and reflected into (2) is less when the reflecting surface is closer to the fiber surface. If the equilibrium position of the diaphragm is properly chosen and its displacement is fairly small, it turns out that the received light intensity is approximately proportional to the displacement.

If the air space between the diaphragm and end of the fiber optics is sealed, the transducer will measure absolute pressure changes. Furthermore, because of thermal expansion of the trapped air, it will be rather more sensitive to temperature changes. To avoid this problem a small capillary could be introduced running parallel to the fiber bundles, to vent the space to atmospheric pressure.

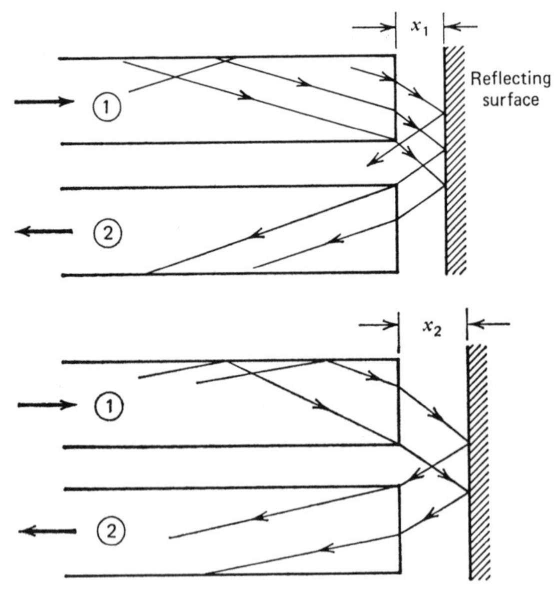

Figure 7.21. Effect of a change of the reflecting surface position on the light transmission between two adjacent fibers.

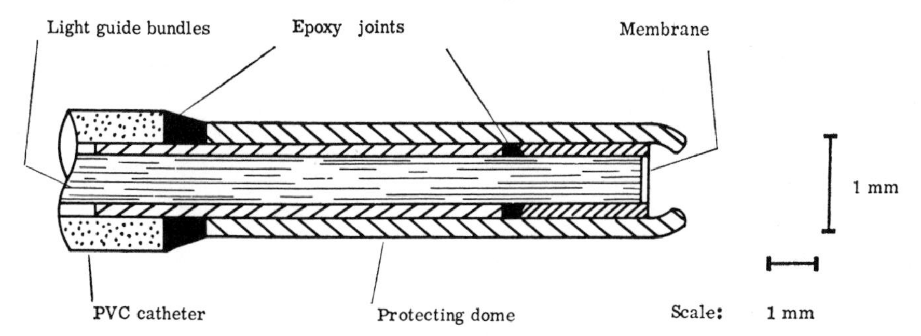

Figure 7.22. Constructional details of a fiber optic pressure transducer (reproduced, with permission, from L. H. Lindstrom, *IEEE Trans. Bio-Medical Eng.*, **BME-17**, 207–219, 1970).

The transducer described by Lindstrom [83], which is illustrated in Figure 7.22, uses a sealed air space between the 6-μm-thick beryllium–copper diaphragm and the fiber optics. The performance claimed by Lindstrom for a prototype version of this transducer is as follows: catheter diameter, 1.5 mm (F4.5); pressure range, -50 to $+200$ mmHg; linearity, 2.5% of full scale; zero stability, 2.5 mmHg/h; resolution, 1 mmHg; frequency response, dc to >15 kHz. Lindstrom also reported the testing of a transducer having an outer diameter of 0.85 mm.

Ramirez et al. [84] have described a somewhat similar system using a 12-μm-thick, 1-mm-diameter polyester diaphragm and having an atmospheric pressure vent tube. Significant baseline shifts were observed with this system—possibly because of pressure deformation of the plastic diaphragm. As a result, it was necessary to use a second lumen to record the mean pressure.

The main advantages of the fiber-optics catheter-tip pressure transducer are its small size and the absence of any ac or dc voltages within the catheter. This latter feature makes it inherently safer than the other systems. Offsetting these advantages is its more complex construction, which adversely affects its cost and reliability.

7.5 IMPLANTABLE PRESSURE TRANSDUCERS

A wide variety of miniature pressure transducers have been developed for long-term implantation studies in animals. Konigsberg [73, 85] has described a family of metal diaphragm transducers* using either individual silicon

* Konigsberg Instruments, Pasadena, Calif.

strain-gauge elements or an integrated silicon chip. These devices, illustrated in Figure 7.23, are fabricated from titanium with either a nickel or titanium diaphragm of 15-μm thickness. Either individual silicon gauges (for the larger transducers) or a single chip of silicon containing four diffused gauges are bonded to the diaphragm. Since the unit is sealed at atmospheric pressure, it measures the absolute pressure changes.

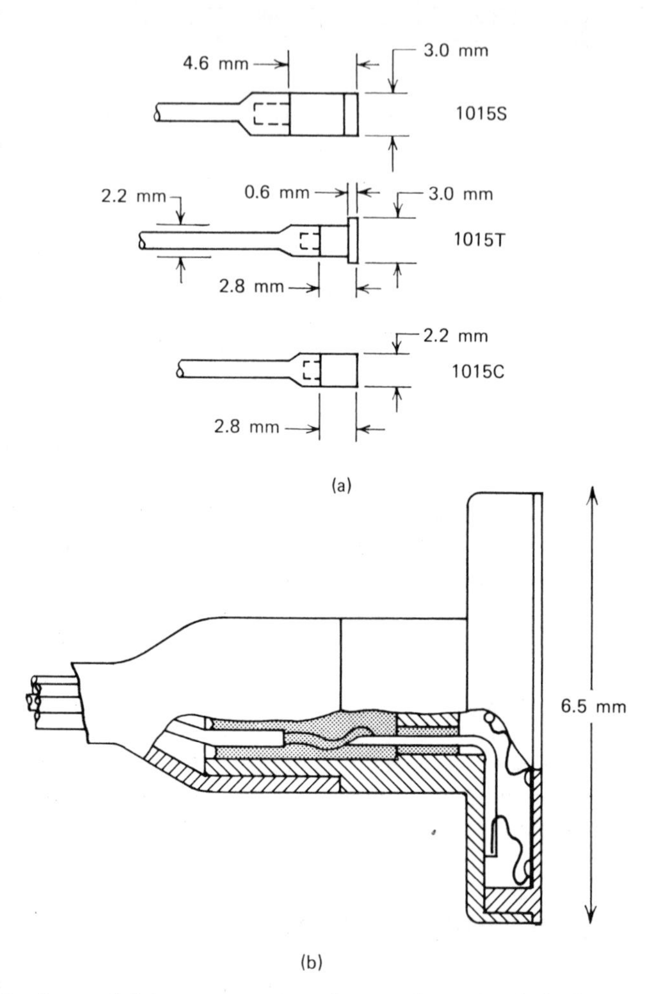

Figure 7.23. Some miniature pressure transducers using a metal diaphragm and silicon strain gauges: (a) dimensions of various types; (b) cross-sectional view of a somewhat larger version showing the construction (reproduced, with permission, from E. Konigsberg and R. H. Russell, *Biomedical Sciences Instrumentation*, Vol. 3, 1967 and Vol. 4, 1968, Instrument Society of America).

Sandler et al. [86] and other workers [87–89] have used this type of transducer to telemeter ventricular and arterial pressures from freely roaming animals over periods ranging up to six months. Sandler et al. point out that the gauge sensitivity can be checked in vivo by subjecting the animal to known atmospheric pressure changes, using a pressure chamber and recording the changes in the transducer output. However, zero drift, resulting perhaps from changes in the reference pressure caused by adsorption or desorption of gas, is a serious problem. When long-term changes in the baseline are important, it is necessary to check the zero by catheterization.

Several other forms of strain-gauge pressure transducers suitable for implantation have been developed. Some use stainless-steel diaphragms with either metal foil or silicon strain gauges,* while others use a silicon diaphragm with an integrated gauge.†

An additional semiconductor-type pressure sensor, based on the effect of local stress applied to the emitter of a silicon n-p-n transistor, has undergone extensive development.‡ As illustrated in Figure 7.24, a pressure differential causes a point stress to be applied to the emitter, resulting in a substantial change in the common-emitter current gain. Douglas [90] has used this device in a passive (no internal power source) transponder designed to measure cerebrospinal fluid pressure.

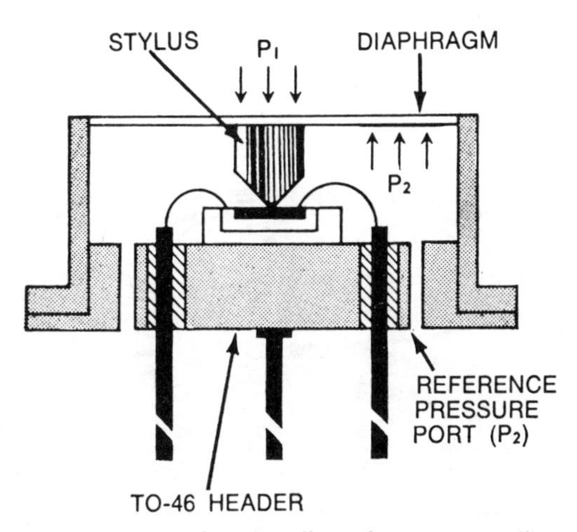

Figure 7.24. Pressure transducer using the effect of stress on a silicon n-p-n transistor (reproduced, with permission of Stow Laboratories Inc., Hudson, Mass.).

* Sensotec Div. of Comtel Corp., Columbus, Ohio.
† Kulite Semiconductor Products, Inc., Ridgefield, N. J.
‡ Pitran, Stow Laboratories, Inc., Hudson, Mass.

Many of the early implantable pressure sensors, designed as part of an active or passive endoradiosonde, made use of inductive-type displacement transducers of the form shown in Figure 6.14(b) and (c). The core of the inductor is coupled to the diaphragm, so that a change in pressure changes the inductance. By making the inductor part of an oscillator circuit, an FM output is obtained. Jacobson [91] has reviewed many of these systems.

A more recent version of the passive type of pressure endoradiosonde is shown in Figure 7.25. It consists of an air-filled pillbox having two flexible diaphragms [92, 93]. Between the diaphragms and coupled to them are two

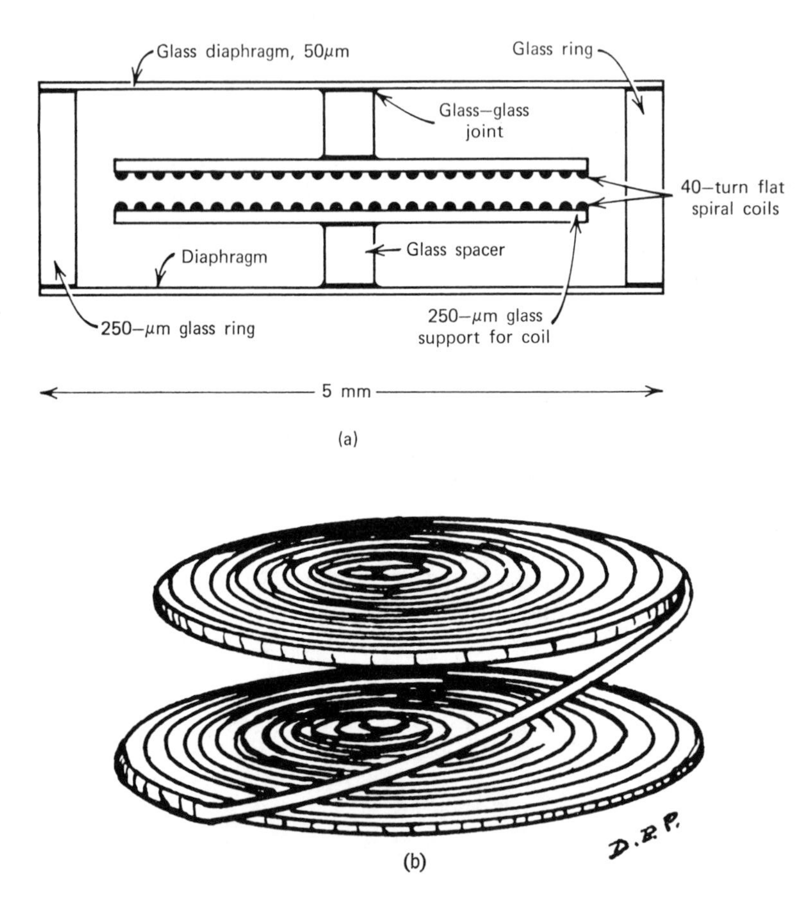

Figure 7.25. Details of a 5-mm-diameter glass pressure transensor designed for long-term implantation: (a) cross-sectional view; (b) details of the two spiral coils: a change in coil separation changes the resonant frequeney (reproduced, with permission, from C. C. Collins, *J. Biomedical Systems*, **1**, 23–39, 1970).

spiral coils forming a high-Q resonant circuit. When the diaphragms are displaced, the relative spacing of the coils changes, causing their mutual inductance and stray capacitance to change. By coupling into the capsule RF energy of the appropriate frequency the change in resonant frequency, and hence the pressure, can be determined. In the earlier versions Collins used a polyester diaphragm stretched over a thin-walled glass tube. The more recent versions using an all-glass construction have superior long-term stability and are therefore better suited for implantation extending over many months. Collins and others [93] have used miniature versions of this capsule for studying IO, intracranial, and other body pressures.

7.6 MICROPRESSURE TRANSDUCTION

Attempts to measure the pressure in capillaries date back to the late 1800s. Roy and Brown [94] in 1880 were the first to report measurements on a frog's capillary pressure using a distensible membrane forced against the tissue with a known pressure. By observing the state of flow through the capillary with a microscope, they interpreted the capillary pressure as that membrane pressure for which flow just ceased. Naturally, this and similar measurements of an indirect nature were subject to considerable criticism. Landis [95] in 1926 was one of the first to report a direct determination of pressure in microvessels. His system consisted of a glass micropipette with a tip diameter in the range 4–8 μm, filled with a suitable dye, and hydraulically coupled to a device for the application of a defined pressure. To measure the systolic and diastolic pressures, the tip of the micropipette was inserted into the vessel and the pressure in the pipette was increased until a point was reached at which a spurt of dye from the tip flowed into the vessel. This was interpreted to be the diastolic pressure. As the pressure in the pipette was further increased, a point was reached at which the flow of dye into the vessel was continuous over the cardiac cycle: this was believed to indicate the systolic pressure.

A more accurate method used by Landis to measure the mean pressure in a capillary consisted of inserting the micropipette tip into a collateral of the capillary. The mean pressure in the occluded collateral was measured by adjusting the pressure in the micropipette until the dye–blood interface oscillated about a stationary mean point. These techniques have, over the intervening years, been used by a number of workers: more recently, for example, Wirz [96] used it to determine the intratubular pressures in the rat kidney, using a micropipette with a tip diameter of around 15 μm.

Measurement of the pulsatile pressure waveform in vessels down to a diameter of 50 μm can be satisfactorily made with a micropipette hydraulically coupled to a pressure transducer [97–99]. It is, however, necessary that the volume displacement coefficient of the transducer system be small and that the tip diameter be sufficiently large to insure an adequate frequency response. Wunderlich and Schnermann [99] used an integrated silicon pressure transducer to investigate the response time of the system with glass micropipettes whose tip diameters ranged from 6 to 15 μm. They concluded that for rats (HR ~ 300/min), tip diameters of greater than 15 μm were necessary to avoid serious waveform distortion. A similar conclusion was also reached by Intaglietta et al. [100] using a transducer with a somewhat larger displacement coefficient [101, 102].

To achieve an adequate frequency response using micropipettes with tip diameters in the 1-μm range requires the use of a null-balance feedback

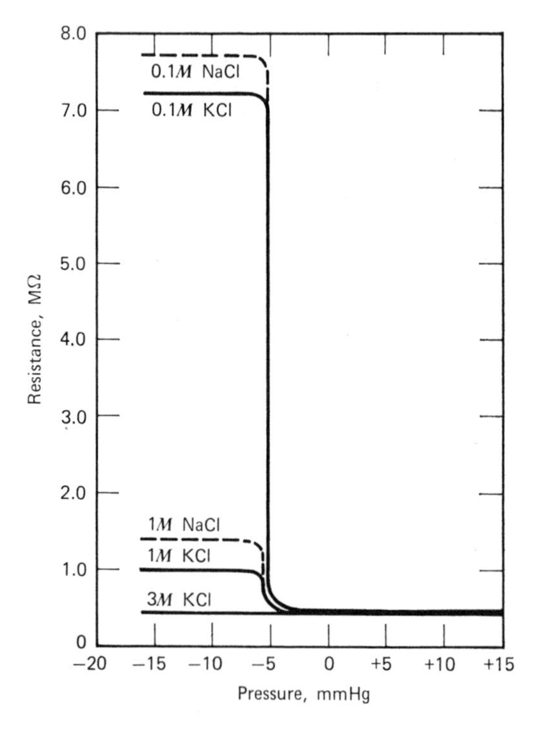

Figure 7.26. Resistance of a microcapillary filled with 3M KCl when subjected to various pressures. The tip was immersed in either NaCl or KCl having the concentration indicated on the curve. Measurements were made with an initial positive pressure that was then reduced slowly to a negative value as the resistance values were read. These results differ from those of Figure 10.29, which were taken after steady-state conditions had occurred (reproduced, with permission, from H. Fein, *J. Appl. Physiol.*, **32**, 560–564, April 1972).

system. The first system of this type was described by Wiederhielm et al. [75] in 1964 and was used for measuring pressures in the microcirculatory system of the frog's mesentery. The system makes use of the fact that a change in the electrical conductivity of the medium in the tip of a microelectrode produces a very marked change in the micropipette resistance. The micropipette is filled with a solution (2*M* NaCl) whose conductivity is considerably different from blood plasma, thereby insuring that a large resistance change occurs as the plasma enters the tip. This is illustrated in Figure 7.26, where the change in resistance is plotted as a function of the pressure. It will be noted that a very sharp increase in the resistance occurs at −4.5 mmHg, which corresponds to a pressure gradient at the tip of approximately 0 (4.5 mmHg corresponds to the fluid height in the micropipette). Wiederhielm et al. [75] used the signal obtained from the change in resistance to actuate a servo-system that generated a counter pressure tending to restore the NaCl–plasma interface to its original position. Thus, by measuring the counter pressure with a conventional pressure transducer, the pressure at the micropipette tip was determined. The authors report that the frequency response is essentially flat from dc to 20 Hz.

Improvements to the above method have been reported by Intaglietta et al. [100, 103] and Fein [104]. The system described by Intaglietta et al. [100] and subsequently improved [101] for use with 1-μm pipettes, is illustrated in Figure 7.27. The resistance-measuring circuit essentially consists of a Wheatstone bridge driven from a 500-Hz oscillator. To neutralize the electrode capacitance, and thus avoid the problem of a reactive component in the bridge, a negative input capacitance preamplifier is used (see Section 10.3.2 for a discussion of negative input capacitance amplifiers and the electrical properties of glass microelectrodes). The amplified bridge signal is passed into an active filter with corner (6 dB) frequencies of 940 and 220 Hz and thence onto a phase-sensitive detector. The dc output from the detector via a power amplifier actuates an electromagnetically driven (bellows) pump that is hydraulically coupled to the micropipette and a suitable pressure transducer. With this system* Intaglietta and Tompkins [103] report pressure measurements on vessels down to an 11-μm diameter using micropipettes with inside diameters in the 0.5–1 μm range. Furthermore, they report that the frequency response, measured under in vitro conditions, is around 25 Hz.

More recently, Fox and Wiederhielm [105] have described the characteristics of a feedback measurement system using glass micropipettes with tip diameters of less than 1 μm. They report that the micropipettes of less than 0.1-μm diameter behave quite differently from those of larger diameter. In particular, they have a smaller fractional resistance change with pressure and they are

* Commercially available from: Instrumentation for Physiology and Medicine, San Diego, California.

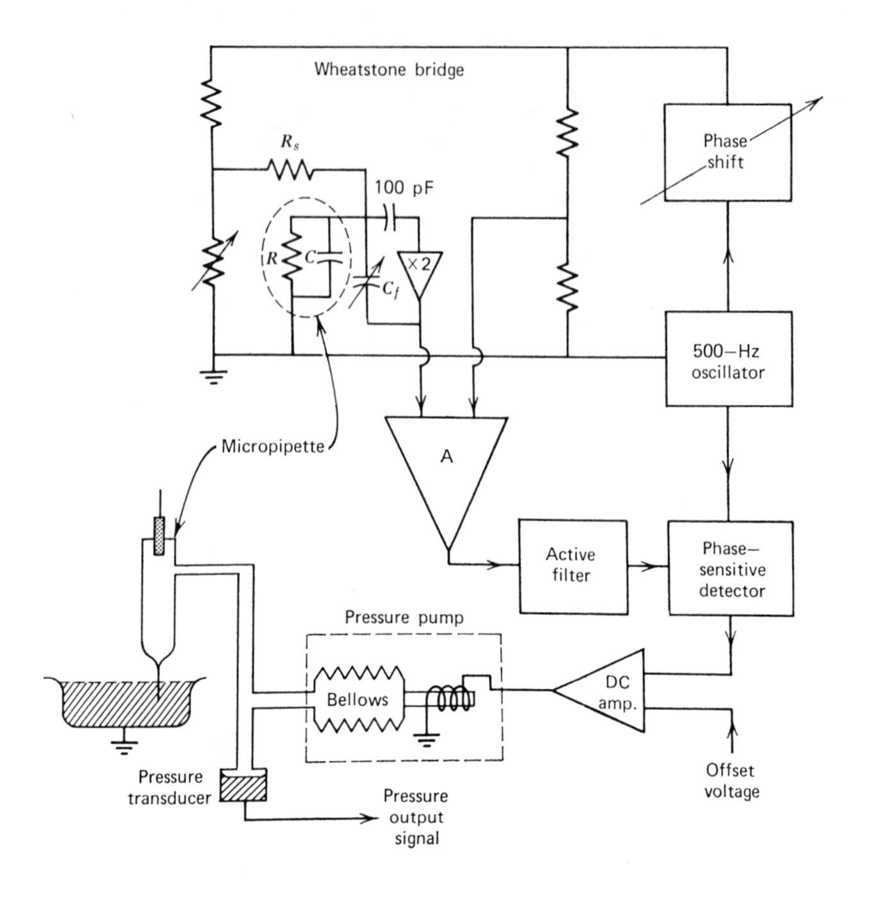

Figure 7.27. Block diagram of a micropressure null-type measurement system (adapted from Intaglietta, Pawala, and Tompkins, [100, 103].

more sensitive to resistivity and temperature changes in the external solution. Furthermore, they are sensitive to local contact potentials and are more susceptible to becoming plugged. In spite of these problems, they do enable pressure measurements to be made in very small diameter vessels with a minimum of disturbance and pass readily even through the toughest of tissue. It appears that the frequency response obtainable with such small electrodes is quite adequate for the faithful recording of dynamic changes under normal physiological conditions.

REFERENCES

1. Longerbeam, J. K.; Vannix, R.; Wagner, W.; and Joergenson, E. "Central Venous Pressure Monitoring. A Useful Guide to Fluid Therapy During Shock and Other Forms of Cardiovascular Stress." *Am. J. Surg.*, **110**, 220–230 (August 1965).
2. Brisman, R.; Parks, L. C.; and Benson, D. W. "Pitfalls in the Clinical Use of Central Venous Pressure." *Arch. Surg.*, **95**, 902–907 (December 1967); see also *Brit. Med. J.*, **1**, 246–247 (30 January 1971).
3. Burton, A. C. *Physiology and Biophysics of the Circulation*, 2nd ed. Year Book: Chicago, 1972.
4. O'Rourke, M. F. "Impact Pressure, Lateral Pressure and Impedance in the Proximal Aorta and Pulmonary Artery." *J. Appl. Physiol.*, **25**, 533–541 (November 1968).
5. Geddes, L. A. *The Direct and Indirect Measurement of Blood Pressure*. Year Book: Chicago, 1970.
6. Noble, M. I. M.; Gabe, I. T.; Trenchard, D.; and Guz, A. "Blood Pressure and Flow in the Ascending Aorta of Conscious Dogs." *Cardiovasc. Res.*, **1**, 9–20 (January 1967).
7. Weiss, H. "An Automatic Blood Pressure Recording Apparatus." *J. Lab. Clin. Med.*, **26**, 1351–1358 (May 1941).

8a. Gilson, W. E.; Goldberg, H.; and Slocum, H. C. "An Automatic Device for Periodically Determining Both Systolic and Diastolic Pressure in Man." *Science*, 22 August 1941, p. 194.

8b. Slocum, H. C. "An Apparatus for the Automatic Recording of Diastolic and Systolic Blood Pressure in Clinical Practice." *Anesthesiology*, **3**, 141–145 (March 1942).

9a. Hinman, A. T.; Engel, B. T.; and Bickford, A. "Portable Blood Pressure Recorder. Accuracy and Preliminary Use in Evaluating Intradaily Variations in Pressure." *Am. Heart J.*, **63**, 663–668 (May 1962).

9b. Wallis, A. T.; Meek, A. P.; and Simpson, F. O. "Portable Indirect Blood Pressure Recorder." Digest of the 9th Int. Conf. Med. Biol. Eng., Melbourne, 1971, p. 44.

10. Lywood, D. W. "Blood Pressure," in P. H. Venables and I. Martin, Eds. *Manual of Psychophysiological Methods*. North Holland: Amsterdam, 1967.
11. Rose, J. C.; Gilford, S. R.; Broida, H. P.; Soler, A.; Partenope, E. A.; and Freis, E. D. "Clinical and Investigative Applications of a New Instrument for Continuous Recording of Blood Pressure and Heart Rate." *New Eng. J. Med.*, **249**, 615–617 (8 October 1953).
12. Gilford, S. R., and Broida, H. P. "Physiological Monitor for Anesthesia." *Electronics*, October 1955, pp. 130–134.

13. Simpson, D. C. "A Clinical Blood Pressure Recorder." *Anaesthesia*, **11**, 89–96 (January 1956).

14. Wilmowsky, H. J. "Über die selbsttätiger laufende Messung von Blutdruck-Grössen mit Hilfe einer Regeleinrichtung." *Regelungstechnik*, **7**, 427–433 (1959).

15. Roy, R., and Weiss, M. "Automatic Blood Pressure Indicator." *IRE Trans. Bio-Med. Electron.*, **BME-9**, 244–246 (October 1962).

16. Follett, D. H.; Freundlich, H. F.; Shaw, D. B.; and Davies, D. H. "An Apparatus for Automatic Recording of Systolic and Diastolic Blood Pressure." *Lancet*, **1**, 808–809 (13 April 1963).

17. Ware, R. W., and Kahn, A. R. "Automatic Indirect Blood Pressure Determination in Flight." *J. Appl. Physiol.*, **18**, 210–214 (January 1963).

18. Steinberg, B. L., and London, S. B. "Automatic Blood Pressure Monitoring During Surgical Anaesthesia." *Anesthesiology*, **27**, 861–863 (November–December 1966).

19. Canzoneri, J.; Geddes, L. A.; Vallbona, C.; and Viscusi, R. L. "An Electronic System for the Detection of Indirect Systolic and Diastolic Blood Pressure" in R. D. Allison, Ed., *Biomedical Sciences Instrumentation*, Vol. IV. Plenum: New York, 1968, pp. 65–70.

20. Crul, J. F. "Measurement of Arterial Pressure." *Acta Anaesth. Scand.*, **6**, Supp. 11, 135–169 (1962).

21. Rochmis, P. G., Ed. Proc. 2nd Annual Conf. on Automated Indirect Blood Pressure. Roche Medical Electronics Division, Hoffman-La Roche Inc., New Jersey, May 1969.

22. Smyth, C. N. "Electrical Techniques in Medicine." *Trans. Soc. Instr. Tech.*, **6**, 87–90 (1954).

23. Flanagan, G. J., and Hull, C. J. "A Blood Pressure Recorder." *Br. J. Anaesth.*, **40**, 292–298 (April 1968).

24. Lange, K. "A Recording Sphygmotonograph: A Machine for the Continuous Recording of Systolic and Diastolic Arterial Pressure in Man." *Am. Int. Med.*, **18**, 367–383 (March 1943).

25. de Dobbeleer, G. "Procédé Nouveau de Mesure de la Tension Artérielle Maxima et Minima." *Acta Anaesthesiol. Belg.*, **14**, 21–36 (June 1963).

26. de Dobbeleer, G. D. P. "Measurement of the Systolic and Diastolic Blood Pressure by Means of Phase Shift," F. H. Bostem, Ed., *Medical Electronics.* Proc. 5th Int. Conf. Med. Electron. Univ. of Liège, 1965, pp. 229–250.

27. de Dobbeleer, G. D. P. "Measurement of Systolic and Diastolic Blood Pressure by Means of Phase Shift." *World Med. Electron. Inst.*, **3**, 122–126 (July 1965).

28. de Temmerman, P. "Le Sphygmotensiomèter Electronique UTEC." *Acta Anaesthesiol. Belg.* **14**, 11–20 (June 1963).

29. de Temmerman, P. "L'Haemotonographe: Appareil de Monitoring Circulatoire." *Acta Anaesthesiol. Belg.* **14**, 37–46 (June 1963).

30. Gruen, W. "An Assessment of Present Automatic Methods of Indirect Blood Pressure Measurements." *Ann. N.Y. Acad. Sci.*, **147**, Art. 3, 109–126 (February 1968).

31. Hill, D. W. *Electronic Techniques in Anaesthesia and Surgery*, 2nd ed., Butterworths: London, 1973.

32. Green, J. H. "Blood-Pressure Follower for Continuous Blood Pressure Recording in Man." *J. Physiol.*, **130**, 37P–38P (November 1955).

33. Ball, G. R.; Pallet, J.; and Shillingford, J. P. "An Automatic Finger Blood Pressure Recorder." *Lancet*, **2**, 1178–1180 (25 November 1961).

34. Armitage, P., and Rose, G. A. "The Variability of Measurements of Casual Blood Pressure: I. A Laboratory Study." *Clin. Sci.*, **30**, 325–335 (April 1966).

35. Armitage, P.; Fox, W.; Rose, G. A.; and Tinker, C. M. "The Variability of Measurements of Casual Blood Pressure: II. Survey Experience." *Clin. Sci.*, **30**, 337–344 (April 1966).

36. Tursky, B.; Shapiro, D.; and Schwartz, G. E. "Automated Constant Cuff-Pressure System to Measure Average Systolic and Diastolic Blood Pressure in Man." *IEEE Trans. Bio-Med. Eng.*, **BME-19**, 271–276 (July 1972).

37. Van Bergen, F. H.; Weatherhead, D. S.; Treloar, A. B.; Dobkin, A. B.; and Buckley, J. J. "Comparison of Direct and Indirect Methods of Measuring Arterial Blood Pressure." *Circulation*, **10**, 481–490, Oct. 1954.

38. Raftery, E. B., and Ward, A. P. "The Indirect Method of Recording Blood Pressure." *Cardiovasc. Res.*, **2**, 210–218 (April 1968).

39. Geddes, L. A.; Hoff, H. E.; Vallbona, C.; Harrison, G.; Spencer, W. A.; and Canzoneri, J. "Numerical Indication of Indirect Systolic and Diastolic Blood Pressures, Heart and Respiratory Rate." *Anesthesiology*, **25**, 861–866 (November–December 1964).

40. Ware, R. W., and Laenger, C. J. "Indirect Blood Pressure Measurement by Doppler Ultrasonic Kinetoarteriography." Proc. 20th Ann. Conf. Eng. in Med. and Biol., Vol. IX, paper 27.3, 1967.

41. Ware, R. W.; Kemmerer, W. T.; and Salomon, H. "The Doppler Ultrasonic Arterial Wall Motion Detector Method of Indirect Blood Pressure Measurement" in Ref. 21, pp. 41–47.

42. Stegall, H. F.; Kardon, M. B.; and Kemmerer, W. T. "Indirect Measurement of Arterial Blood Pressure by Ultrasonic Sphygmomanometry." *J. Appl. Physiol.*, **25**, 793–798 (December 1968).

43. Salomon, H., and Snyder, P. "Indirect Blood Pressure by Ultrasonic Detection of Arterial Wall Motion." Proc. 21st Ann. Conf. Eng. in Med. and Biol., Vol. X, paper 1.2, 1968.

44. Ziedonis, J. G., and Mount, B. "Ultrasonic Transducer Design." Proc. 21st Ann. Conf. Eng. in Med. and Biol., Vol. X, paper 1.3, 1968.

45. Kazamias, T. M.; Gander, M. P.; Franklin, D. L.; and Ross, J. "Blood Pressure Measurement with Doppler Ultrasonic Flowmeter." *J. Appl. Physiol.*, **30**, 585–588 (April 1971).

46. Mackay, R. S. "The Application of Physical Transducer to Intracavity Measurement, with Special Application to Tonometry." *Med. Electron. and Biol. Eng.*, **2**, 3–17 (March 1964).

47. Mackay, R. S., and Marg, E. "Fast Automatic Ocular Pressure Measurement Based on an Exact Theory." *IRE Trans. Med. Electron.*, **ME-7**, 61–67 (1960).

48. Smyth, C. N. "The Guard-Ring Tocodynamometer: Absolute Measurement of Intra-amniotic Pressure by a New Instrument." *J. Obs. Gynaec.*, **64**, 59–66 (1957).

49. Mackay, R. S.; Marg, E.; and Oechsli, R. "A Quartz Crystal Tonometer." *IRE Trans. Bio-Med. Electron.*, **BME-9**, 174 (April 1962).

50. Schettini, A.; McKay, R.; Majors, R.; Mahig, J.; and Nevis, A. H. "Experimental Approach for Monitoring Surface Brain Pressure." *J. Neurosurg.*, **34**, 38–47 (January 1971).

51. Majors, R.; Schettini, A.; Mahig, J.; and Nevis, A. H. "Intracranial Pressures Measured with the Coplanar Pressure Transducer." *Med. Biol. Eng.*, **10**, 724–733 (November 1972).

52. Kanai, H., and Iizuka, M. "Problems in the Measurement of Blood Pressure by Catheter Insertion." Proc. 8th Int. Conf. Med. Biol. Eng., Paper 33-12, July 1969.

53. Kani, H.; Iizuka, M.; and Sakamoto, K. "One of the Problems in the Measurement of Blood Pressure by Catheter-Insertion: Wave Reflection at the Tip of the Catheter." *Med. Biol. Eng.*, **8**, 483–496 (September 1970).

54. Hansen, A. T. "Pressure Measurement in the Human Organism." *Acta Physiol. Scand.*, **19**, Suppl. 68, 1–227 (1949).

55. Hansen, A. T. "The Theory for Elastic Liquid-Containing Membrane Manometers: Special Part." *Acta Physiol. Scand.*, **19**, 333–343 (1950).

56. Hansen, A. T., and Warberg, E. "A Theory for Elastic Liquid-Containing Membrane Manometers: General Part." *Acta Physiol. Scand.*, **19**, 306–332 (1950).

57. Fry, D. L. "Physiologic Recording by Modern Instruments with Particular Reference to Pressure Recording." *Physiol. Rev.*, **40**, 753–788 (October 1960).

58a. Latimer, K. E. "The Transmission of Sound Waves in Liquid-Filled Catheter Tubes Used for Intravascular Blood-Pressure Recording." *Med. Biol. Eng.*, **6**, 29–40 (January 1968).

58b. Latimer, K. E., and Latimer, R. D. "Measurements of Pressure-Wave Transmission in Liquid-Filled Tubes Used for Intravascular Blood-Pressure Recording." *Med. Biol. Eng.*, **7**, 143–167 (March 1969).

59a. Latimer, K. E. "A Simple Method of Extending the Frequency Spectrum of Catheter–Manometer Blood Pressure Recording Systems." Digest, 10th Int. Conf. Med. Biol. Eng., Dresden, 1973, p. 127.

59b. Latimer, K. E. "Extending the Frequency Spectrum of Electromanometry Systems into Audio Frequencies." *Biblig. Cardiol.* (in press).

60. Shirer, H. W. "Blood Pressure Measuring Methods." *IRE Trans. Bio-Med. Electron.*, **BME-9**, 116–125 (April 1962).

61. Vierhout, R. R. "Indirect and Direct Blood Pressure Measurements," in F. H. Bostem, Ed., *Medical Electronics.* Proc. 5th Int. Conf. Med. Electron. Univ. of Liège, 1965, pp. 151–165.

62. Sutterer, W. F., and Wood, E. H. "Strain-Gauge Manometers: Application to Recording of Intravascular and Intracardiac Pressures," pp. 641–651. in O. Glasser, Ed., *Medical Physics*, Vol. III. Year Book: Chicago, 1960.

63. Noble, F. W., and Barnett, G. O. "An Electric Circuit for Improving the Dynamic Response of the Conventional Cardiac Catheter System." *Med. Electron. Biolog. Eng.*, **1**, 537–543 (December 1963).

64. Piemme, T. E. "Pressure Measurement: Electrical Pressure Transducers." *Prog. Cardiovasc. Dis.*, **5**, 574–594 (May 1963).

65. Fry, D. L.; Noble, F. W.; and Mallow, A. J. "An Evaluation of Modern Pressure Recording Systems." *Circ. Res.*, **5**, 40–46 (January 1967).

66. Stegall, H. F. "A Simple Inexpensive Sinusoidal Pressure Generator." *J. Appl. Physiol.*, **22**, 591–592 (March 1967).

67. Foreman, J. E. K., and Hutchison, K. J. "Generation of Sinusoidal Fluid Pressures of Relatively High Frequency." *J. Appl. Physiol.*, **29**, 511–516 (October 1970).

68. Timoshenko, S., and Woinowsky-Krieger, S. *Theory of Plates and Shells.* McGraw-Hill: New York, 1959.

69. Zinker, N. "Diffused Silicon Diaphragm Pressure Transducers" (Paper 68-503), in *Advances in Test Measurement*, Vol. V. 1968 ISA Conference Proceedings. Instrument Society of America: Pittsburgh, 1968, pp. 1–6.

70. Taroni, A.; Prudenzaiati, M.; and Zanarini, G. "Semiconductor Sensors: II—Piezoresistive Devices." *IEEE Trans. Industrial Electron. Control Instr.*, **IECI-17**, 415–421 (November 1970).

71. Peake, E. R.; Zias, A. R.; and Egan, J. V. "Solid-State Digital Pressure Transducer." *IEEE Trans. Electron Devices*, **ED-16**, 870–876 (October 1969).

72a. Gieles, A. C. M. "Subminiature Silicon Pressure Transducer." Digest of Technical Papers, 1969 Int. Solid-State Circuits Conference, pp. 108–109.

72b. Samaun; Wise, K. D.; and Angell, J. B. "An IC Piezoresistive Pressure Sensor for Biomedical Instrumentation." *IEEE Trans. Bio-Med. Eng.*, **BME-20**, 101–109 (March 1973).

73. Konigsberg, E. "A Pressure Transducer for Chronic Intravascular Implantation," J. Poyer, J. Herrick, and T. B. Weber, Eds., *Biomedical Sciences Instrumentation*, Vol. III. Plenum: New York, 1967, pp. 259–268.

74. Harvey, G. F., Ed. *ISA Transducer Compendium*, 2nd ed., Pt I. Instrument Society of America: Pittsburgh, 1969.

75. Wiederhielm, C. A.; Woodbury, J. W.; Kirk, S.; and Rushmer, R. F. "Pulsatile Pressures in the Microcirculation of the Frog's Mesentery." *Am. J. Physiol.*, **207**, 173–176 (January 1964).

76. Allard, E. M. "Sound and Pressure Signals Obtained from a Single Intracardiac Transducer." *IRE Trans. Bio-Med. Electron.*, **BME-9**, 74–77 (April 1962).

77. Warnick, A., and Drake, E. H. "A New Intra-Cardiac Pressure Measuring System for Infants and Adults." *IRE Nat. Conv. Record*, Pt. 9, 68–73 (1958).

78. Traite, M.; Welkowitz, W.; and Downs, R. "Intracardiac Catheter Tip Piezoresistive Pressure Gauge." *Rev. Sci. Instrum.*, **31**, 987–991 (September 1960).

79. Angelakos, E. T. "Semiconductor Pressure Microtransducers for Measuring Velocity and Acceleration of Intraventricular Pressures." *Am. J. Med. Electron.*, **3**, 266–270 (October–December 1964).

80a. Millar, H. D., and Baker, L. E. "A Stable Ultraminiature Catheter-Tip Pressure Transducer." *Med. Biol. Eng.*, **11**, 86–89 (January 1973).

80b. Coon, G. W., and Sandler, H. "Ultra-Miniature Manometer Tipped Cardiac Catheter" (Paper 22.2). Proc. 20th Ann. Conf. Eng. Med. Biol., Vol. IX, 1967.

81. Kapany, N. S. *Fiber Optics: Principles and Applications.* Academic: New York, 1967.

82. Clarc, F. J.; Schmidt, E. M.; and De La Croix, R. F. "Fiber Optic Blood Pressure Catheter with Frequency Response from DC into the Audio Range." *Proc. 1965 Nat. Electron. Conf.*, **21**, 213–216 (1965).

83. Lindstrom, L. H. "Miniaturized Pressure Transducer Intended for Intravascular Use." *IEEE Trans. Bio-Med. Eng.*, **BME-17**, 207–219 (July 1970).

84. Ramirez, A.; Hood, W. B.; Polanyi, M.; Wagner, R.; Yankopoulos, N. A.; and Abelman, W. H. "Registration of Intravascular Pressure and Sound by Fiberoptic Catheter." *J. Appl. Physiol.*, **26**, 679–683 (May 1969).

85. Konigsberg, E., and Russell, R. H. "A Battery Operated Miniature Pressure Transducer Amplifier System," in R. D. Allison, Ed., *Biomedical Sciences Instrumentation*, Vol. IV. Plenum: New York, 1968.

86. Sandler, H.; Fryer, T. B.; and Datnow, B. "Single-Channel Pressure Telemetry Unit." *J. Appl. Physiol.*, **26**, 235–238 (February 1969).

87. Van Citters, R. L., and Franklin, D. L. "Telemetry of Blood Pressure in Free-Ranging Animals Via an Intravascular Gauge." *J. Appl. Physiol.*, **21**, 1633–1636 (September 1966).

88. Bicker, A. A.; Lupo, F. J.; and Bergofsky, E. H. "On the Sensitivity Calibration of Implanted Pressure Transducers." *IEEE Trans. Bio-Med. Eng.*, **BME-17,** 353 (October 1970).

89. Casadei, F. W.; Gerold, M.; and Baldinger, E. "Implantable Blood Pressure Telemetry System." *IEEE Trans. Bio-Med. Eng.*, **BME-19**, 334–341 (September 1972).

90. Douglas, D. W. "A Chronic Epidural Intracranial Pressure Monitor." Proc. 21st Ann. Conf. Eng. Med. Biol., Vol. X, paper 38.5, 1968.

91. Jacobson, B. "Endoradiosonde Techniques—A Survey." *Med. Electron. Biol. Eng.*, **1**, 165–180 (April–June 1963).

92. Collins, C. C. "Miniature Passive Pressure Transensor for Implanting in the Eye." *IEEE Trans. Bio-Med. Eng.*, **BME-14**, 74–83 (April 1967).

93. Collins, C. C. "Biomedical Transensors: A Review." *J. Biomed. Syst.*, **1**, 23–39 (1970).

94. Roy, C. S., and Brown, J. G., "The Blood-Pressure and its Variations in the Arterioles, Capillaries and Small Veins." *J. Physiol.*, **2**, 323–359 (1880).

95. Landis, E. M. "The Capillary Pressure in Frog Mesentery as Determined by Micro-Injection Methods." *Am. J. Physiol.*, **75**, 548–570 (February 1926).

96. Wirz, H. "Druckmessung in Kapillaren und Tubuli der Niere durch Micropunktion," *Helv. Physiol. Acta*, **13**, 42–49 (1955).

97. Rappaport, M. B.; Bloch, E. H.; and Irwin, J. W. "A Manometer for Measuring Dynamic Pressures in the Microvascular System." *J. Appl. Physiol.*, **14**, 651–655 (July 1959).

98. Levasseur, J. E.; Funk, F. C.; and Patterson, J. L. "Physiological Pressure Transducer for Microhemocirculatory Studies." *J. Appl. Physiol.*, **27**, 422–425 (September 1969).

99. Wunderlich, P., and Schnermann, J. "Continuous Recording of Hydrostatic Pressure in Renal Tubules and Blood Capillaries by Use of a New Pressure Transducer." *Pflüg. Arch.*, **313**, 89–94 (1969).

100. Intaglietta, M.; Pawala, R. F.; and Tompkins, W. R. "Pressure Measurements in the Mammalian Microvasculature." *Microvasc. Res.*, **2**, 212–220 (April 1970).

101. Intaglietta, M. "Pressure Measurements in the Microcirculation with Active and Passive Transducers." *Microvasc. Res.*, **5**, 317–323 (May 1973).

102. Intaglietta, M. "The Measurement of Pressure and Flow in the Microcirculation." *Microvasc. Res.*, **5**, 357–361 (May 1973).

103. Intaglietta, M., and Tompkins, W. R. "Micropressure Measurement with 1 μ and Smaller Cannulae." *Microvasc. Res.*, **3**, 211–214 (April 1971).

104. Fein, H. "Microdimensional Pressure Measurements in Electrolytes." *J. Appl. Physiol.*, **32**, 560–564 (April 1972).

105. Fox, J. R., and Wiederhielm, C. A., "Characteristics of the Servo-Controlled Micropipet Pressure System." *Microvasc. Res.*, **5**, 324–335 (May 1973).

CHAPTER EIGHT

Flow-Measurement Transducers

Like the measurement of pressure, the measurement of flow is of fundamental importance in many areas of physiological research and forms an essential part of certain clinical investigative techniques. Although blood flow measurement is perhaps the most obvious of applications, it should be realized that several other flow processes associated with living organisms are also of considerable significance. For example, in the study of respiratory function the measurement of gas flow rates is of diagnostic importance. Another example is the measurement of the time variation of the urine outflow in relation to the bladder pressure and urethral EMG data. Such measurements can yield important information, leading to a better understanding of urethral physiology.

A great variety of flow-measurement techniques exist, all of which have certain advantages and disadvantages. In choosing the most suitable method for a particular experiment, two important steps must be taken [1]. The first is to define clearly, in a realistic manner, the experimental requirements. The second is to survey possible techniques and to choose that which most closely fits the requirements. In this regard catalog-type surveys of flow measurement techniques, such as that published by Fry and Ross [2], and up-to-date collected papers, such as those edited by Roberts [3], are particularly valuable.

This chapter does not attempt to survey all possible flow transduction techniques; rather, attention is focused on well-established methods for phasic blood flow or velocity measurements. A somewhat brief discussion of mean flow measurement methods using noninvasive techniques can be found in the latter sections of this chapter.

8.1 ELECTROMAGNETIC METHODS

Currently, the electromagnetic flowmeter is regarded as the standard method for the measurement of pulsatile blood flow in intact vessels. The prime reasons for this are as follows:

1. The method measures volumetric flow rate, with a sensitivity that is independent of the flow velocity profile.
2. Extensive research into the pitfalls of the method have been carried out since its first application to blood flow measurement in 1936. Through an improved understanding of the details, electromagnetic flowmeters can now be designed to yield accuracies of $\pm 5\%$ on the larger vessels.
3. The method can be applied to a wide range of vessel sizes, ranging from the largest vessel in man down to vessels as small as 1 mm in diameter.

8.1.1 Theory

When a conductor is moved through a magnetic field so as to cut the flux lines, an emf is generated, the value of which at any given instant is proportional to the velocity at that time. If, as illustrated in Figure 8.1, the conductor is a fluid moving with a uniform velocity v, then the emf generated across the diameter EE' for a uniform magnetic flux density B is given by

$$V = \frac{2aBv}{100} \qquad (\text{in } \mu V),$$

where B is in gauss, the radius a is in centimeters, and the velocity v is in centimeters per second.

By solving Maxwell's equations, it can be shown that for the case where the fluid velocity is nonuniform within the cross-sectional area but remains symmetrical about the tube axis (axisymmetrical), the emf generated is the same as that given above but with v replaced by the average flow velocity $\bar{v}$. Hence [4],

$$V = \frac{2aB\bar{v}}{100}, \tag{1}$$

where

$$\bar{v} = \frac{1}{\pi a^2} \int_0^a 2\pi v r \, dr$$

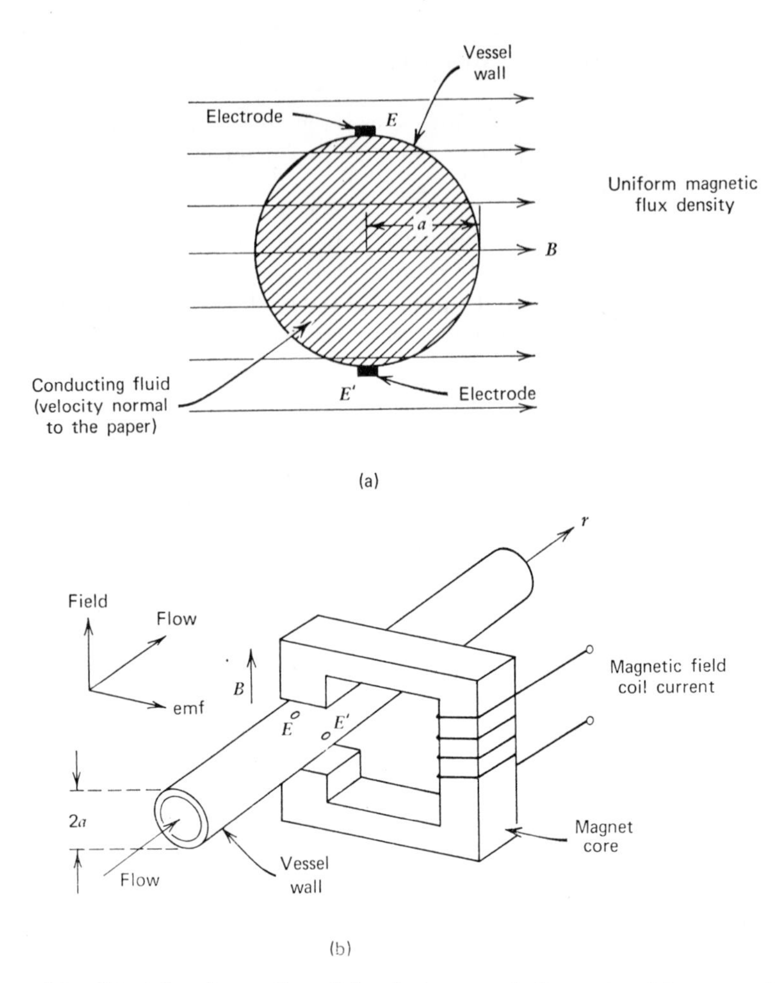

Figure 8.1. Principles of operation of the electromagnetic flowmeter: (a) cross-sectional view showing the magnetic flux in relation to the electrodes; (b) three-dimensional view.

is the average velocity for any axisymmetric flow profile. Equation (1) can be expressed in terms of the volumetric flow rate Q (in cm^3/sec) by putting $\bar{v} = Q/\pi a^2$, yielding

$$V = \frac{QB}{50\pi a}. \tag{2}$$

This equation expresses the important potential advantage of the electromagnetic flow-measurement technique—namely, that the flow emf is independent of the flow profile. For a given vessel diameter and flux density, it depends only on the instantaneous volumetric flow rate.

To illustrate the magnitudes of the quantities involved, we consider two examples. The first concerns the peak flow emf obtained from a flow transducer on the aorta of a dog. Typically, $a = 0.8$ cm and $Q_{max} = 200$ cm^3/sec; assuming $B = 300$ G, we find from Eq. (2) that $V \simeq 500$ μV, a value that can be easily measured. The second example concerns the average flow emf from the left circumflex coronary artery of a dog. Here, $a = 0.15$ cm and $Q_{av} = 0.9$ cm^3/sec; and assuming the same flux density as before, we find that $V \simeq 12$ μV. If a signal–noise voltage ratio of 40 : 1 is demanded in the phasic flow record, then the RMS noise should be less than 0.3 μV over the required bandwidth (30 Hz). With careful design, this can be realized in practice.

Circulating Currents. The generation of emf's within the fluid itself can, in general, be expected to produce circulating electric currents. The only condition for which they are absent occurs when the velocity is constant (corresponding closely to the turbulent flow condition). For this particular case, each elementary cross section of the fluid across the diameter EE' [Figure 8.1(a)] generates the same emf. Hence, as shown in Figure 8.2(a), the electric field is constant and no currents flow [5]. If, however, a velocity distribution exists, regions of higher velocity will generate greater incremental emf's, resulting in a nonuniform electric field, and the presence of circulating currents, such as those illustrated in Figure 8.2(b). It turns out that the emf lost in driving these circulating currents is exactly compensated for by the increased emf's generated by the higher velocity regions, thereby yielding a flow emf that is independent of the velocity profile [6] and the fluid conductivity.

Effect of the Vessel Wall and Hematocrit. In order to discuss the effect of the vessel wall and the presence of any conducting fluid surrounding the electrodes, it is useful to define the flowmeter sensitivity S by

$$S = \frac{100V}{2aB\bar{v}}, \tag{3}$$

where V is expressed in microvolts. By comparing Eq. (3) with Eq. (1) it can be seen that the deviation of S from unity expresses how close the performance is to the ideal.

The cuff-type flow probe, which fits around the vessel and makes electrical contact to the blood via the vessel wall, is subject to sensitivity changes from several causes. One of these arises when the vessel wall conductivity σ_2 is different from the fluid conductivity σ_1. For the dog aorta it has been found that the vessel wall conductivity is less than that of blood by a factor of

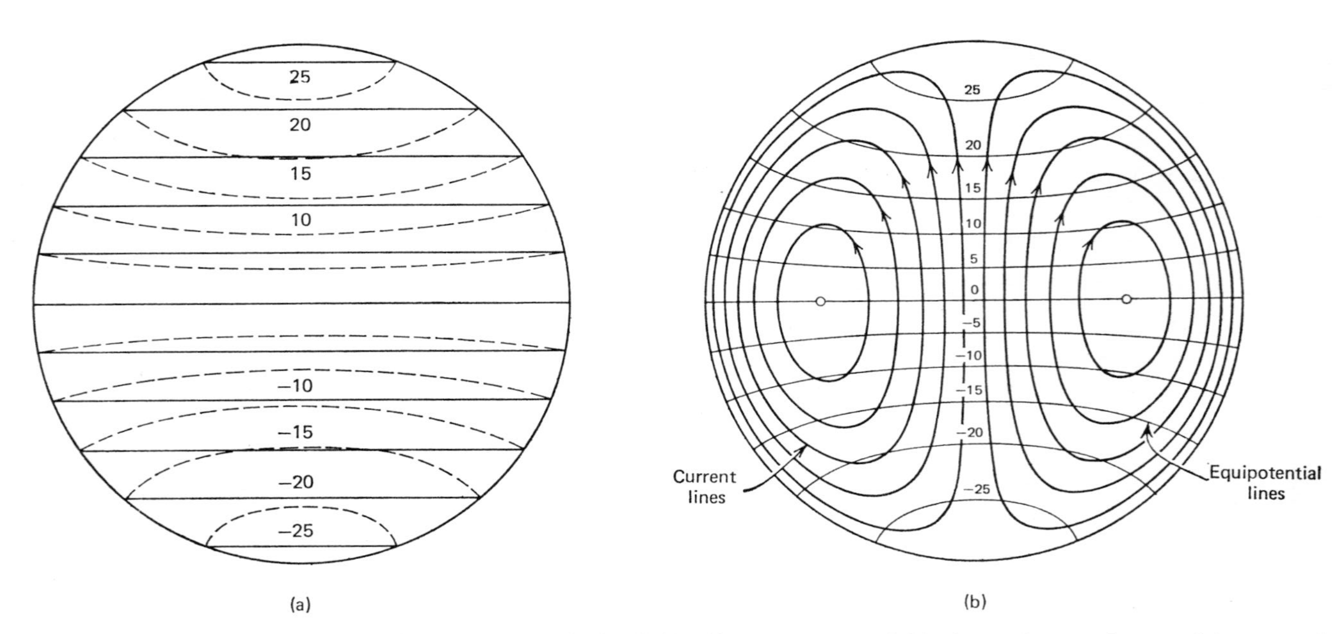

Figure 8.2. Equipotential and current flow lines in a conducting fluid subject to a magnetic field. The numbers are the potentials expressed in arbitrary units: (a) equipotential lines for a uniform velocity (solid lines) compared to those for a laminar velocity profile (broken lines); (b) equipotential and current flow lines for a laminar profile (reproduced, with permission, from B. Thurlemann, *Helv. Phys. Acta*, **14**, 383–419 [1941]).

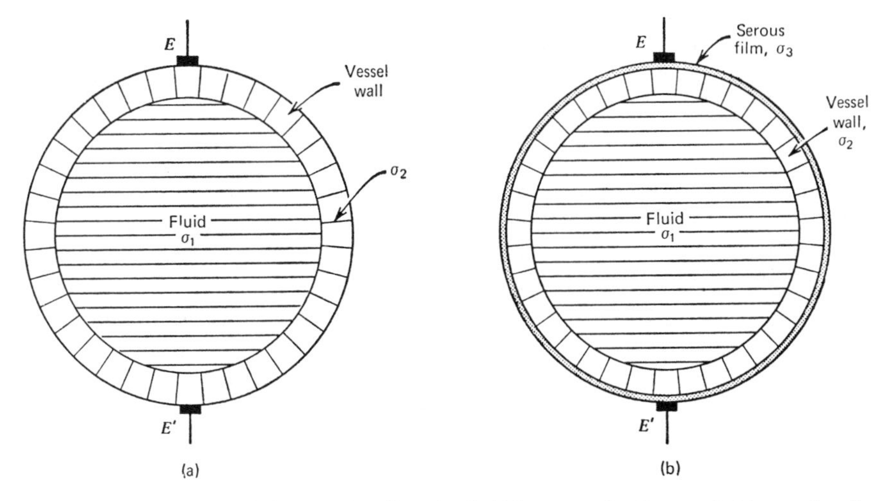

Figure 8.3. Influence of the vessel wall and a fluid layer on the flow emf: (a) vessel wall alone; (b) combined effect of the vessel wall and a film of serous fluid.

approximately 2 [7]. The situation illustrated in Figure 8.3(a) has been investigated theoretically by Gessner [8] and others [9]. Wyatt [10], using the theory of Gessner, has shown that the sensitivity of a given flow transducer is *increased* when $\sigma_2 < \sigma_1$ (a situation that is valid for the aorta of a dog) and is decreased when $\sigma_2 > \sigma_1$. Experimental confirmation of these results has been presented by Ferguson and Landahl [7], who find that typically the change in sensitivity is less than 15%.

A second possible source of sensitivity change is the presence of a serous film of fluid between the vessel wall and the flow transducer sleeve [see Figure 8.3(b)]. Since the conductivity of this fluid layer is greater than that of the vessel wall, the net effect is to decrease the sensitivity through a shunting of the flow emf [7, 10]. Thus, the effect of the vessel wall plus that of the fluid layer may be to increase, decrease, or leave unchanged the sensitivity, depending on the thicknesses and conductivities of the various regions involved. With regard to the serous film it should also be noted that if the length of the insulating flow probe sleeve (along the flow direction) is small and the probe and vessel are submerged in saline, the sensitivity can be very significantly reduced by the shunting effect of the surrounding saline [11]. To eliminate error from this cause, it is necessary that the cuff length be greater than the vessel diameter by a factor of at least 2 [7].

A related effect is the experimentally observed variation of the flow probe sensitivity with hematocrit. A number of workers have reported quite large changes of sensitivity [7, 12, 13]—for example, a 30% reduction in sensitivity when a change is made from plasma or normal saline to 45% hematocrit blood. Others [14] have indicated that such changes are small ($< -5\%$) for a similar range and that the effects can generally be ignored in most applications.

Dennis and Wyatt [15] in a careful study of hematocrit effects have pointed out that this confusion arises because the conductivity of blood varies with hematocrit and no distinction is generally made between measurements made with and without the blood vessel. It appears that where large changes were observed, the effect was primarily caused by variations in the blood-conductivity–wall-conductivity ratio: as the hematocrit increases, so the blood conductivity decreases, causing a net reduction in the sensitivity [7]. There does appear to be a much smaller effect (a few percent), which perhaps arises from the nonuniformity and anisotropy of the blood conductivity due to the unique flow behavior of red blood cells [15]. Such phenomena have been investigated theoretically by Baker [16] and Bevir [17], with results that are in reasonable agreement with the experimental observations of Dennis and Wyatt.

Field Inhomogeneity and Nonaxisymmetric Flow. To understand the influence of a nonaxisymmetric flow profile on the transducer sensitivity, it is helpful to consider the relative contributions made by each element of cross-sectional area to the total induced emf. The function that expresses this is the weighting function $W(x, y)$, introduced by Shercliff [4, 19].* If the walls are nonconducting and the magnetic field is uniform across the circular flow cross section, it can be shown that the flowmeter sensitivity can be expressed as

$$S = \frac{\iint v(x, y) W(x, y)\, dx\, dy}{\iint v(x, y)\, dx\, dy},$$

where

$$W(x, y) = \frac{a^4 + a^2(x^2 - y^2)}{a^4 + 2a^2(x^2 - y^2) + x^2 + y^2} \tag{4}$$

is the weighting function and $v(x, y)$ is the flow velocity at a point (x, y). It will be noted from Eq. (4) that $W(x, y)$ weights the velocity in the integrand and therefore determines the relative contributions of $v(x, y)$ to the sensitivity. The graph of Eq. (4), shown in Figure 8.4(a), immediately indicates the influence of the flow velocity in the various regions. It shows that $W \geqslant 0.5$ and that W increases to infinity as the electrodes are approached. This last point suggests that an asymmetrical flow could have a major influence on the

* In a three-dimensional approach to electromagnetic flowmeter theory Bevir [18] has extended the scalar weight function concept by introducing a weight *vector*.

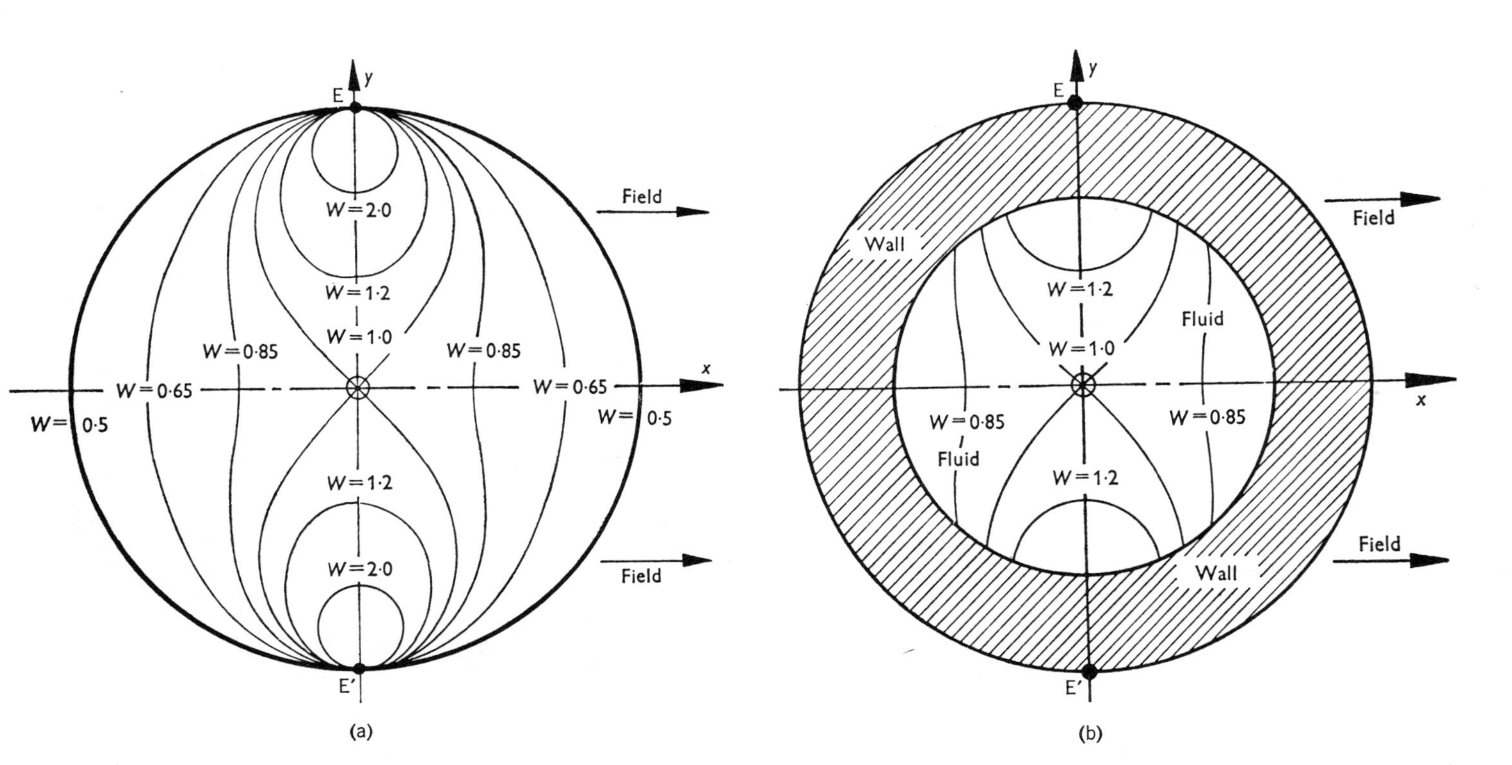

Figure 8.4. The weighting function, representing the relative flow contributions to the total induced emf across the electrodes EE': (a) electrodes in direct contact with the fluid; (b) effect of the vessel wall having a conductivity equal to that of the fluid (reproduced, with permission, from J. A. Shercliff, "*The Theory of Electromagnetic Flow-Measurement*," Cambridge University Press, Cambridge, 1962).

sensitivity if the flow velocity close to one of the electrodes is appreciable. But, in practice, since the electrodes are separated from the flow by a conducting wall, the situation is not so serious. As shown in Figure 8.4(b), for a wall whose conductivity is the same as the fluid and whose thickness is half the inner radius, the singularities are avoided and the W variation throughout the area is greatly reduced. Nevertheless some variation still exists and this, as demonstrated by Goldman et al. [20], results in an effect that requires consideration when measurements are made close to a sharp bend or arterial junction.

The problem of designing a flow probe to achieve a weight function that is constant throughout the vessel cross section, thereby making the response independent of the flow profile, is a difficult one. One approach [21] is to use strip electrodes that partially surround the vessel, rather than the usual point contact electrodes. But, as pointed out by Wyatt [22], such an arrangement suffers from the disadvantage of requiring an intimate electrical contact to the vessel wall over a large area, so that in practice, imperfections may result in significant sensitivity variations. An alternative approach is to use a nonuniform magnetic field to compensate for the W variations. Such an approach has been used by Rummel and Ketelsen [23] for an industrial flowmeter. In this design the magnetic field varies in a three-dimensional manner in such a way that the flux close to the electrodes is less than that elsewhere.

For the more conventional probe, it is necessary to consider the question of how uniform the magnetic field should be and over what length of the flow axis it should extend. It has been shown that the effect of field nonuniformity is to make the flow emf dependent on the flow profile, even when the profile is axisymmetric [19, 24]. In point of fact, even for gross field nonuniformities, the effect is fairly small. It would seem desirable that the field should be uniform across the tube to $\pm 10\%$ and that the field should extend along the flow axis a minimum distance of one diameter [7, 25]. The field nonuniformity may significantly change the transducer sensitivity from that expected with a uniform field; however, this can be accounted for in the probe calibration factor.

8.1.2 Field Excitation Methods

DC Excitation. The first form of electromagnetic blood flowmeter used a dc field produced by an electromagnet together with nonpolarizable Zn–$ZnSO_4$ electrodes in contact with the artery [26]. There are several reasons why dc excitation is not a practical proposition for accurate blood flow measurements. The first and most important is that even with so-called nonpolarizable electrodes, there is always a small, but finite, electrode imbalance that is subject to unpredictable changes. Effectively this introduces a noise emf in series with the flow emf, and the two cannot be separated. A second reason arises from the presence of other biological signals such as the

ECG and EMG, whose amplitudes may be considerably greater than the flow signal. Coupling of these signals to the flow electrodes can occur, especially when the transducer probe is close to the heart, and can result in severe interference with the flow signal. A third cause of difficulties is the noise and drift properties of the flow signal amplifier. For small flow rates, the dc stability of such an amplifier must be in the fractional microvolt range. Not only is this fairly difficult to achieve but also, unless the signal is chopped at the input, the amplifier must operate in a region where $1/f$ noise is dominant. Generally, for low-signal noise-free amplification, it is desirable to use the amplifier in a frequency region where the $1/f$ noise is small (i.e., at higher frequencies).

AC Excitation. All the above mentioned problems can be avoided if ac excitation is used. However, as will be seen, ac excitation introduces a number of additional problems that require solutions.

An ac field results in an ac flow signal, the frequency of which, for sinusoidal excitation, is centered about the excitation frequency. Thus, if the maximum frequency of practical interest in the flow signal is f_x and the excitation frequency is f_e, the information bandwidth will be from $f_e - f_x$ to $f_e + f_x$. It is evident that the lower sideband frequency should be significantly greater than any interfering signal frequencies, such as may result from ECG and "mains" pickup. The upper limit on the choice of the excitation frequency is governed by the "transformer emf," whose amplitude increases as the frequency rises. For these reasons the choice usually lies in the range 200–1000 Hz, the higher frequency being chosen either for multiplexed systems or when the flowmeter is to be used with animals having a high heart rate (e.g., rats) [27].

The primary difficulty arising from ac excitation is the transformer emf. The electrode leads and the conducting path through the blood between the two electrodes form an electrical circuit that inevitably cuts some of the magnetic flux lines. As a result, the time variation of the flux density will induce into this conducting loop an emf whose amplitude is proportional to the product of the rate of flux change and the number of lines cut. This emf can be several orders of magnitude greater than the flow signal.

Some of the more commonly used magnet current waveforms (proportional to the magnetic flux density) are illustrated in Figure 8.5. The sine-wave system, described first by Kolin [28] in 1938, was introduced to circumvent the various problems arising with dc system. Although the sine-wave system enabled major improvements to be made to the technique of electromagnetic phasic flow measurement, it did suffer from a somewhat unstable baseline, necessitating fairly frequent occlusion of the vessel to check the zero. In an attempt to overcome this problem, Denison et al. [29, 30] introduced the square-wave system in 1955. However, this was also

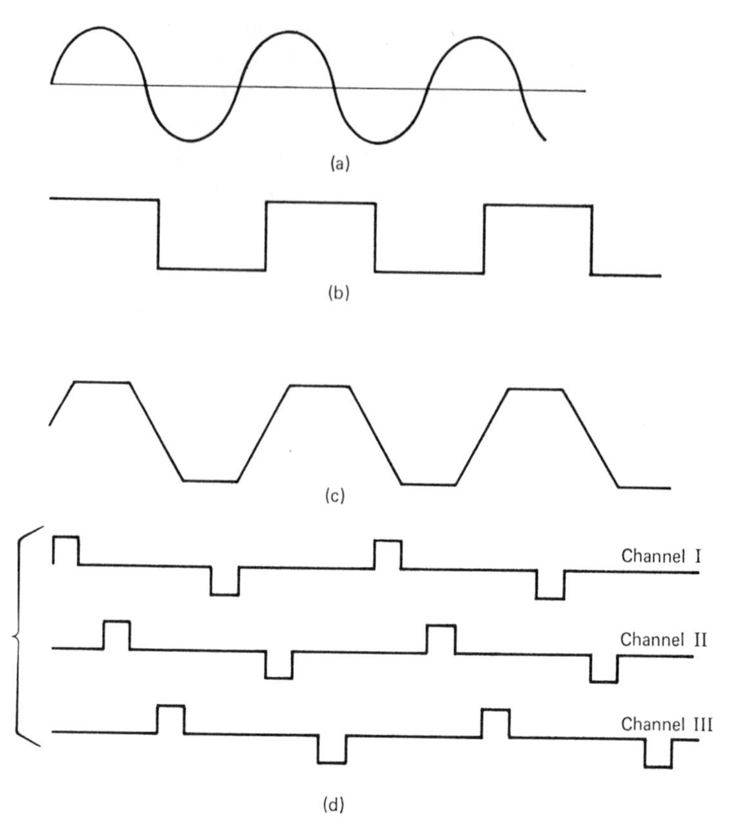

Figure 8.5. Some forms of the magnet excitation current: (a) sine wave; (b) square wave; (c) trapezoidal wave; and (d) multiplex pulse system.

found to suffer from certain baseline stability problems, especially for small flows. This was partially because of the large transformer emf's generated during the rapid changes in magnet current. In an effort to reduce this effect, Yanof et al. [31] modified the square-wave system by incorporating a means of controlling the transition rate to yield the trapezoidal current waveform shown in Figure 8.5(c).

An inherent advantage of the square-wave system is that it can be readily extended for multiplexed operation of several adjacent transducer probes. Since, as shown in Figure 8.5(d), the transducers are activated one at a time, flow-head magnetic interaction is avoided. A somewhat lower signal–noise ratio is an inherent penalty incurred by reducing the time for which the flow signal is measured. However, this can be partially offset by increasing the magnet current: the shorter time for which the current is applied enables a larger current to be used for the same maximum probe heat dissipation.

8.1.3 The Transformer EMF

As mentioned earlier, the transformer emf is the most serious by-product of the ac excitation method. Not only does it introduce a large unwanted emf into the electrode detection circuit, but it is also the cause of a number of other, more subtle side effects that result in baseline errors [32]. Careful positioning of the electrode leads enables the transformer emf to be greatly reduced, although not eliminated. For example, a transformer emf of less than 10 μV can be achieved when the magnet excitation is sinusoidal.

Since induced currents occur in any conductive loop that cuts the flux, currents will flow in the fluid, vessel wall, and any exterior fluid. Furthermore, as illustrated in Figure 8.6(a), the presence of the highly conductive metal electrodes causes the induced currents in the vessel wall to flow through the electrode. Such a current changes the state of polarization at the metal–electrolyte interface and generates a signal that cannot be distinguished from

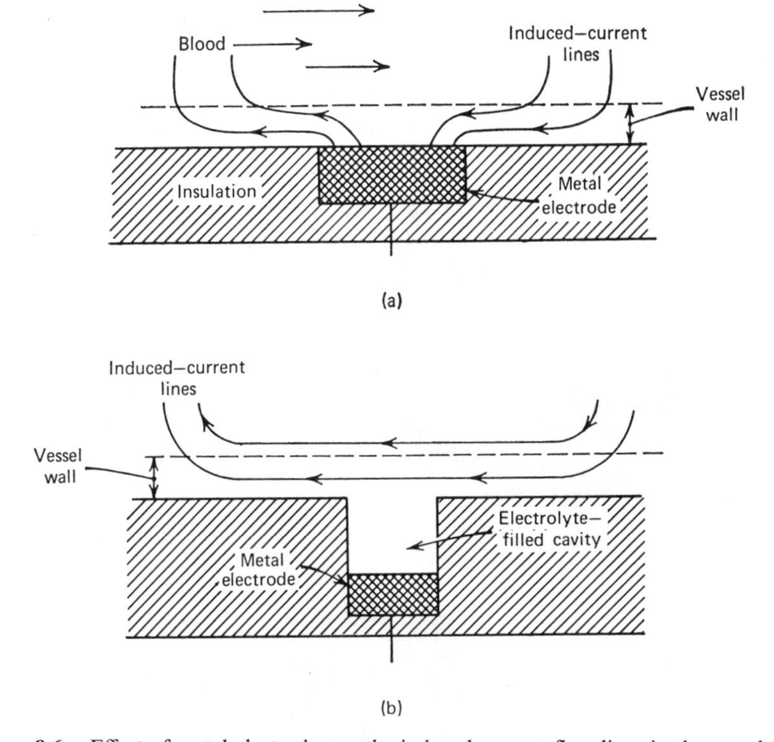

Figure 8.6. Effect of metal electrodes on the induced-current flow lines in the vessel wall and fluid: (a) metal electrode flush with the cuff; (b) recessed metal electrodes showing the greatly reduced induced current through the metal–electrolyte interface.

the true flow emf. Two solutions to this problem are possible. One is to use electrodes having a resistivity higher than, or similar to, the vessel wall [33] (e.g., a sintered metal oxide). The second, and more practical, solution is to recess [32] the metal electrodes so that they lie at the bottom of cylindrical, electrolyte-filled cavities. As shown in Figure 8.6(b), the potential gradient at the electrode surface and the magnitude of the induced current through the metal–electrolyte polarization layer will be greatly reduced.

8.1.4 Flow Probe Design and Application

The Electrodes. The electrode material, its surface finish, and its area are important factors to consider when a high sensitivity is demanded. To reduce both the noise generated by the electrode–electrolyte interface layer and the sensitivity of the flow emf loop to common mode pickup, it is important to use low-impedance electrodes. Wyatt [25, 32] has shown that platinized platinum electrodes have the lowest impedance and are the optimum choice when recessed in a cavity. However, when used in direct contact with the vessel wall, their low impedance is a disadvantage, since it causes an increased current flow from the wall into the electrode, resulting in a greater baseline error. Under such circumstances it would seem preferable to use bright platinum [32], but because of its higher impedance, the transducer has a larger noise and is more susceptible to common mode pickup.

Perivascular Flow Probes. A wide variety of blood flow transducer probes suitable for application to vessels as large as 3 cm down to vessels as small as 1 mm in diameter [34] have been described in the literature [35, 36]. Cuff-type probes, such as those illustrated in Figure 8.7(a), are most

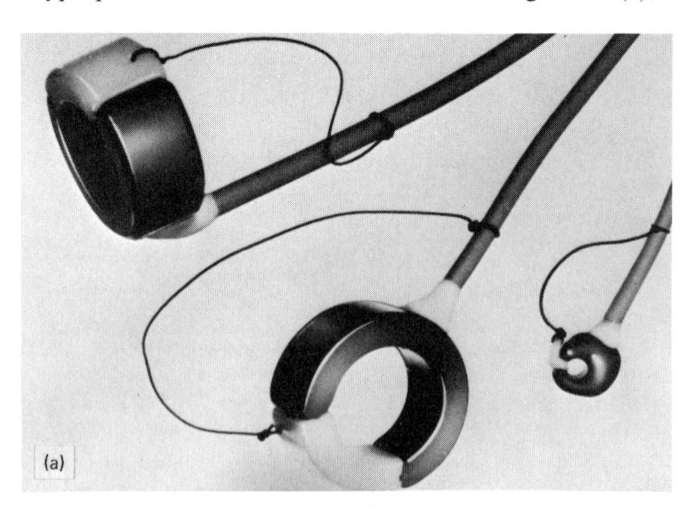

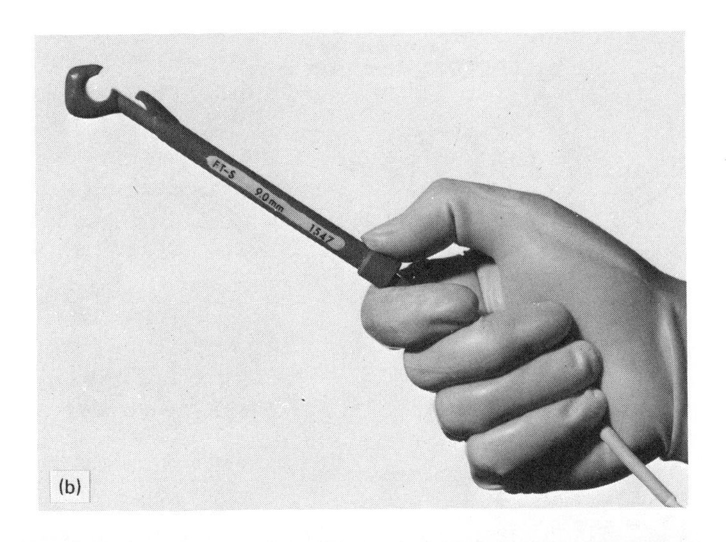

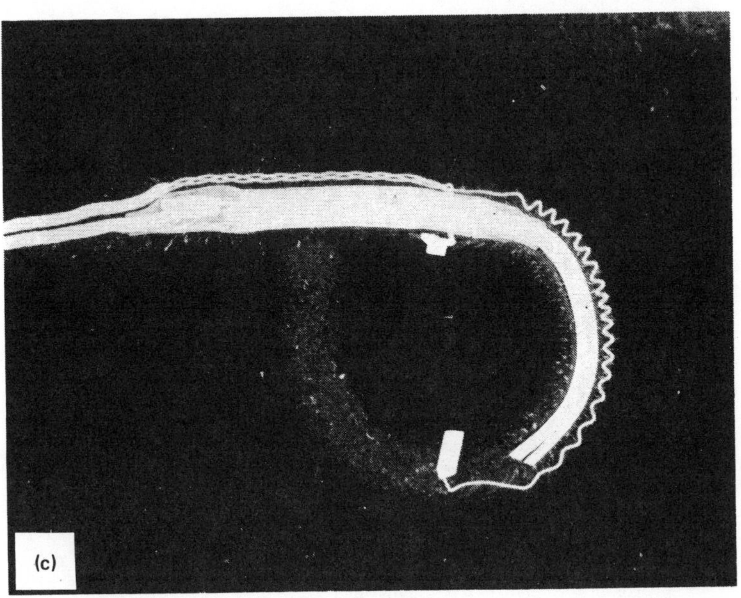

Figure 8.7. Examples of flow probes: (a) cuff-type perivascular probes; (b) clip-on type probe; (c) radiograph of the Williams–Barefoot probe showing the electrical components and shape of the magnetic field [(a) and (b), courtesy of In Vivo Metric Systems Inc., Redwood Valley, California; (c) reproduced, with permission, from Williams et al., Ch. 22 in *Blood Flow Measurement*, C. Roberts (ed.), Sector Publishing, London, 1972].

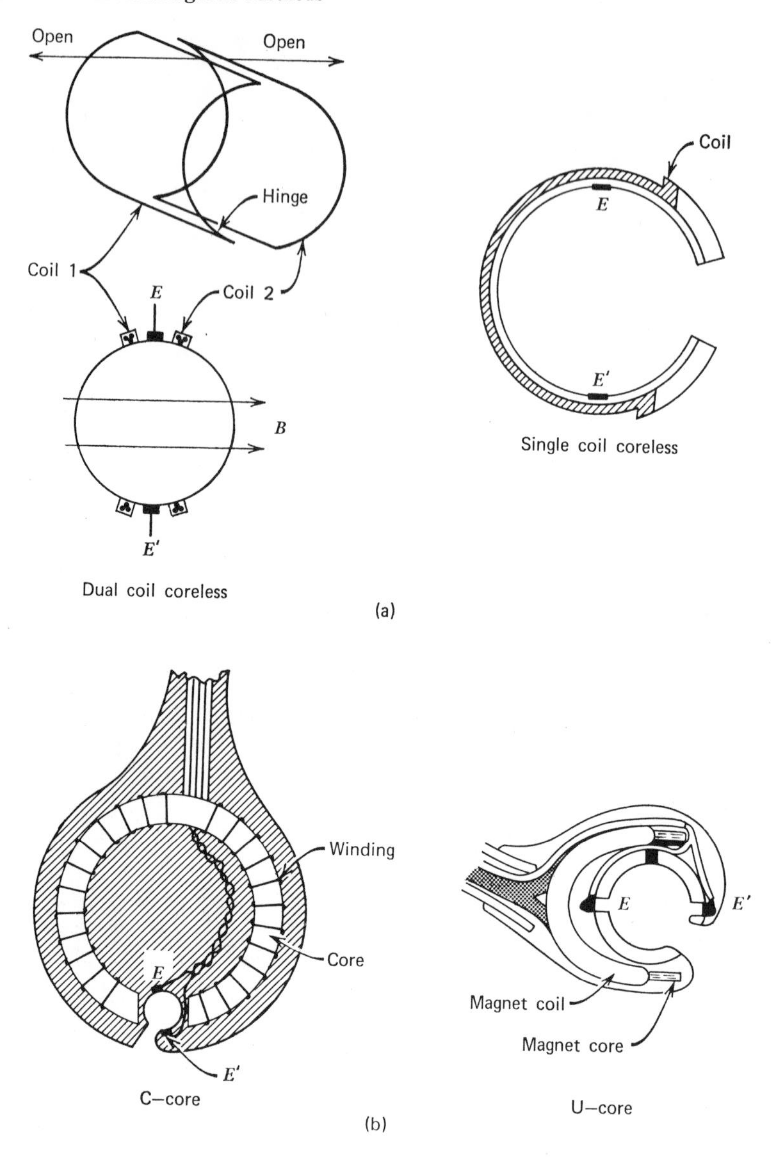

commonly used in research applications. The vessel is slipped through a small slot and is held in place by inserting the small shutter. To achieve proper contact between the electrodes and the vessel wall, it is necessary that the fit by a snug one, with preferably no more than a 10% diameter reduction [37]. As demonstrated by several researchers [38, 39], a 10% reduction can significantly affect the pressures in the vicinity of the cuff, even though the

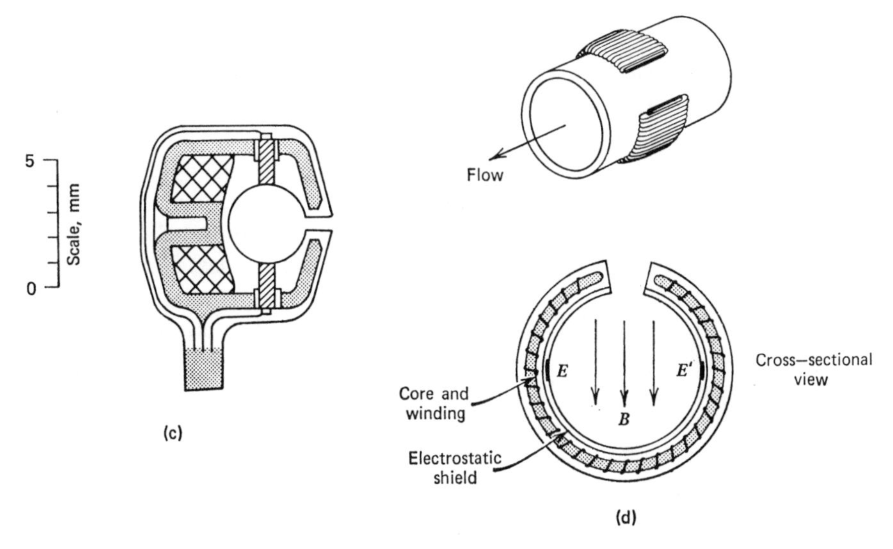

Figure 8.8. Examples of flow probe design: (a) coreless types; (b) the C-core and U-core types (adapted from Goodman [12]); (c) a 3-mm-i.d. split-field probe (adapted from Kolin and Vanyo [35]); and (d) toroidal core probe (adapted from Clark and Wyatt [46]).

flow waveform may not be too significantly altered. The difficulty with specifying a maximum reduction of only 10% is that a wide range of probe sizes are required, making the probe cost factor an important consideration.

For application during surgery on the human, the probes considered above are often somewhat inconvenient to handle and apply. Cannon [40] has detailed the requirements to be met in such circumstances and has developed the clip-on probe illustrated in Figure 8.7(b). The advantage of this probe is that it can be easily handled and its application does not require that the vessel be compressed.

For postoperative monitoring of cardiac output, it is desirable to use a flow probe that can be attached around the aorta during the operation and be readily extracted at a later time with a minimum of risk and discomfort to the patient. A probe designed to meet these requirements has been described by Williams et al. [41, 42] and is illustrated in Figure 8.7(c). It consists of an electrode–magnetic-field assembly contained within a flexible rubber tube that surrounds the vessel. A simple nylon snare attaches the end of the tube to the adjacent part and insures proper electrical contact of the electrodes with the vessel. To remove the probe, the nylon snare is released by pulling on the external thread: gentle traction is then applied to the tube, enabling it to uncoil from the vessel and be removed through the incision (second or third intercostal space) from the patient. Using such a probe, Williams et al. report that the cardiac output and pulsatile aortic waveform was continuously monitored for up to eight days postoperatively in 28 patients that had undergone open-heart surgery.

A variety of cuff transducer designs are illustrated in Figure 8.8. Shown in (a) are two coreless probes of the type developed by Kolin [43, 44]. The dual-coil variety, which uses two nearly rectangular coils shaped around a cylinder, is hinged to allow insertion of the vessel. The other version uses a single coil with a slot for insertion. The primary advantage of the coreless construction is that the coils conform to the vessel shape, thereby making them both compact and light. But, because of the smaller flux density that can be achieved for a given temperature rise [36], they do have a smaller sensitivity than their cored counterpart. Wyatt [36] has given a detailed comparison of the cored and coreless types and has concluded that the coreless probes are most appropriate when the flow rate is reasonably large (e.g., for vessels 7 mm in diameter and greater).

The C-core and U-core probes shown in Figure 8.8(b) offer a high sensitivity and are most frequently used for the smaller-diameter vessels. Details of their construction have, for example, been described in detail by Cox et al. [34], Khouri and Gregg [45], and Goodman [12].

To achieve a good baseline stability and freedom from baseline errors, many authors have stressed the importance of achieving a very large insulation resistance between the magnet coils and the electrodes. Since the voltage across the coils may be 10^6 times larger than the flow emf's, it is essential that the leakage resistance be greater than $10^{10}\ \Omega$. This means using a "potting" material with a very high resistivity and impermeability to salt water. By providing an electrostatic shield between the magnet coils and electrodes, the effect of the dc leakage can be reduced and capacitive feedthrough can be nearly eliminated. To avoid the undesirable effects arising from eddy currents induced in the shield, Clark and Wyatt [46] advocate the use of a thin, high-resistivity, copper–nickel (48 $\mu\Omega$-cm) foil.

A split-pole magnet design, of the type described by Kolin and Vanyo is illustrated in Figure 8.8(c). It uses a single thickness of sheet iron as the core, bent into a somewhat distorted E-shape. The *three* poles of the magnet core serve to provide a magnetic flux that, although reasonably constant along the flow axis and the axis joining the two electrodes, has a large variation in the remaining direction. As a result, Clark and Wyatt [46] have criticized the design and have pointed out that the 10-mm version exhibits an 8% reduction in sensitivity when the flow changes from laminar to turbulent.

The design, fabrication, and performance of the flow probe illustrated in Figure 8.8(d) has been presented by Clark and Wyatt [46]. It uses a toroidal form, having a laminated permalloy C-core that is excited by two oppositely wound windings on each half of the core. A 0.0004-in. copper–nickel foil serves as an electrostatic shield. The 10-mm cuff-type probe shown in Figure 8.9 has a sensitivity of 0.35 $\mu V/cm^3$-sec. Probes of this type are compact, have a small mass, and a good sensitivity. Furthermore, it is claimed that because of their low leakage flux, mutual interaction problems between adjacent excited probes is greatly reduced.

Figure 8.9. Toroidal-type cuff probe of 10-mm-i.d. (reproduced, with permission, from D. M. Clark and D. G. Wyatt, *Med. Biolog. Eng.*, **7**, 185–190, 1969).

Intravascular Velometer Probes. The ability to measure phasic flow in some of the major vessels during routine cardiac catheterization is of self-evident diagnostic importance. But the difficulties of devising a suitable transducer probe are considerable, in part because of the problem of mounting a device on the tip of a cardiac catheter and in part because of the problem of making the device independent of the velocity profile. All the electromagnetic catheter-tip probes described in the literature essentially measure a flow velocity over a limited cross section of the vessel in which they are inserted. By making a suitable guess as to the velocity profile and by measuring the vessel cross-sectional area by X-ray examination, the phasic volumetric flow rate can be calculated.

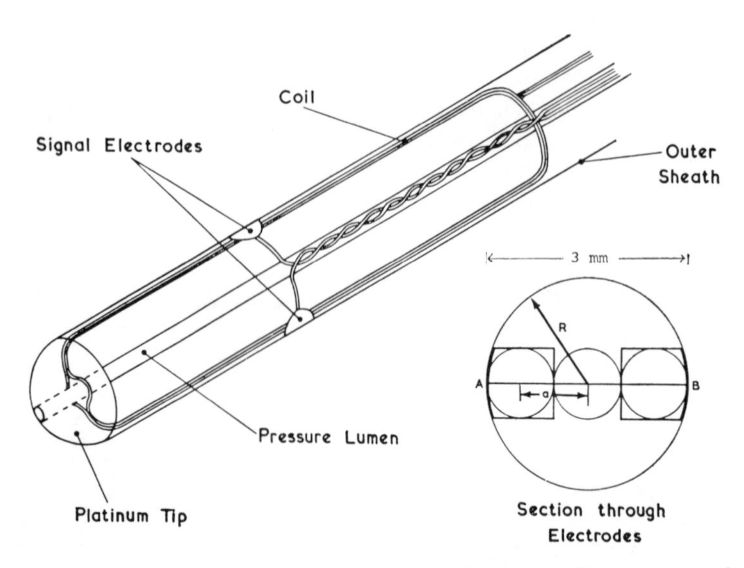

Figure 8.10. Catheter-tip electromagnetic flow velocity probe with a pressure lumen. The platinum tip is used as an earth connection (reproduced, with permission, from C. J. Mills and J. P. Shillingford, *Cardiovasc. Res.*, **1**, 263–273, 1967).

The first, and probably the most successful, electromagnetic catheter-tip velometer was described by Mills [47, 48] in 1966. As illustrated in Figure 8.10, it consists of a rectangular coil and a pair of electrodes placed on opposite sides of the catheter surface, where the radial component of the magnetic field is zero. The electrodes sense a flow emf generated by blood flowing around the probe contained within the vessel. The complete probe has an outside diameter corresponding to a F9 catheter* (3-mm o.d.) and contains a central pressure lumen enabling simultaneous measurements to be made of both the flow velocity and the pressure. It is found that when a sinusoidal excitation of 975 Hz is used, the frequency response is essentially flat to 35 Hz and the probe sensitivity is approximately 13 μV/(100 cm/sec). In vitro tests on the probe show that it is somewhat sensitive to the velocity profile: a 13% increase in the sensitivity was found to occur when the velocity profile changed from flat to laminar. Bevir's [49] finding that a probe of this type has a weighting function [see Eq. (4)] proportional to $1/r^4$, suggests that a considerable change in sensitivity should occur with angulation. However, this appears not to be the case. Mills and Shillingford report [48] that at an angle of 30° the sensitivity decreased by less than 3%, and at an angle of 60°, by less than 11%.

* Subsequent improvements have reduced this to F8 (2.5-mm o.d.).

The presence of the probe in a vessel increases the flow velocity: this can be allowed for in calculating the volumetric flow rate by simply subtracting the probe cross-sectional area from that of the vessel. Mills and Shillingford point out that for laminar flow the presence of the probe in the center of the vessel has a flattening effect on the velocity profile. Their tests indicate that the probe measures the average velocity in the annular region extending out to one probe radius from the probe surface.

The Mills probe has been used, without major difficulties, to measure the phasic flow in some major vessels of man during routine right-heart catheterization [48, 50–53]. Simultaneous records of the phasic flow and pressure were obtained. The fact that the probe can be autoclaved is an added convenience in its clinical application.

Several other catheter-tip electromagnetic velocity probes have also been described in the literature. For example, the probe developed by Spencer and Barefoot [54, 55], shown in Figure 8.11(a), uses a U-shaped core and is commercially available in catheter sizes ranging from F7 to F10 (the F8 and

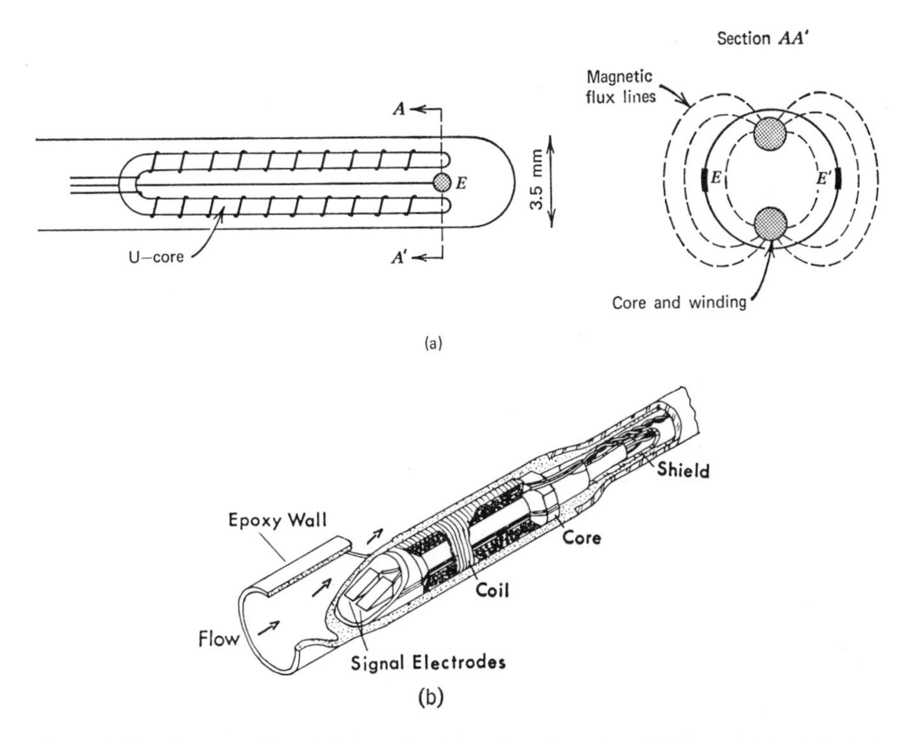

Figure 8.11. Some additional forms of catheter-tip velometers: (a) U-core type (adapted from Spencer and Barefoot [54]); (b) flow-through type (reproduced, with permission, from P. D. Stein and W. H. Schuette, *J. Appl. Physiol.*, **26**, 851–856, 1969).

F9 sizes contain a pressure port).* Although Spencer and Barefoot report the performance to be minimally satisfactory, a more recent report by Warbasse et al. [56] using the probe on experimental animals suggests that accurate results can be obtained. Some doubts concerning the safety of this probe have been expressed by Jones and Wyatt [57], who suggest that the surface temperature may rise to unsafe levels, thereby making it unsuitable for human investigations. A more recent paper by Buchanan and Shabetai [58] has discussed this aspect in more detail and has shown that Jones and Wyatt's conclusion was based on erroneous data and that both the Mills and Spencer-Barefoot probes are thermally safe, except possibly under prolonged operation under zero flow conditions.

Flow-through probes designed for intravascular use have been reported by Stein and Schuette [59] and Kolin et al. [60]. The Stein–Schuette probe, illustrated in Figure 8.11(b), is somewhat large in diameter and has the added disadvantage of a protrusion that makes its application in man rather hazardous. A similar disadvantage is inherent in the ingenious radial magnetic field sensor disclosed by Kolin [61].

More recently, Kolin [62] has described a method for intravascular flow measurement based on the use of an ac magnetic field placed external to the subject. The flow probe consists of a fine tubular structure with two electrodes located as shown in Figure 8.12. When inserted into a vessel, the two electrodes make contact with diametrically opposite inner regions of the vessel wall by virtue of the bend. Since the probe is flexible, it can be inserted through a small-diameter rigid tube into the vessel, where it will conform to to vessel shape.

The coaxial lead arrangement insures that the transformer-emf artifact is small.† Rotation of the probe until the flow signal is a maximum insures that the plane of the two electrodes is perpendicular to the field. An X-ray picture of the probe enables the vessel diameter to be determined, so that the flow emf can be related to the volumetric flow rate.

By eliminating the need for the field to be generated by the probe assembly, the scheme enables the flow probe to be made almost an order of magnitude smaller than was previously possible. Kolin describes a probe of 0.5-mm diameter but mentions that much smaller probes are technically feasible. Such a small diameter enables the probe to be introduced by the percutaneous technique of first inserting a fine hypodermic needle into the vessel via the skin and muscle and then feeding the probe through the hypodermic needle directly into the vessel.

* Carolina Medical Electronics, Inc., N.C.

† A three-electrode probe that essentially eliminates the transformer emf has been proposed and used by Gasking [63] and Biscar [64].

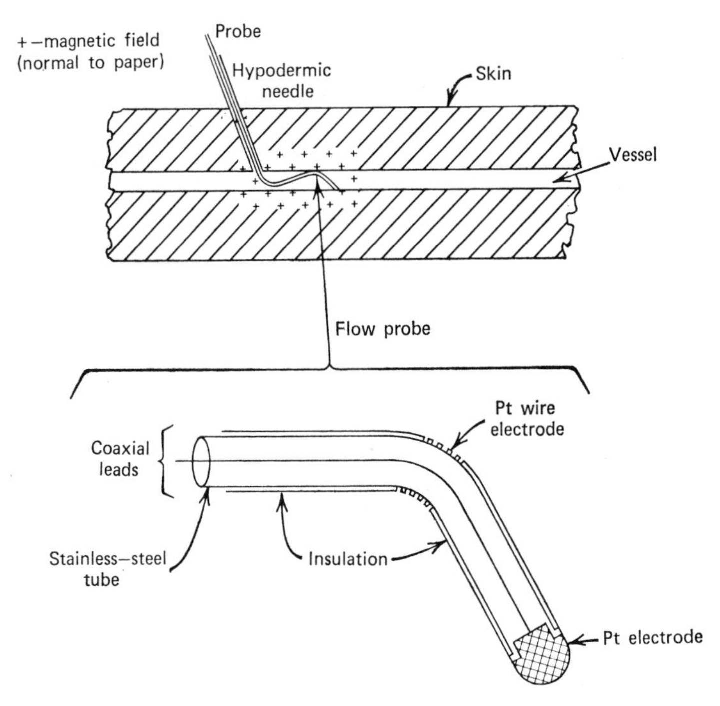

Figure 8.12. Intravascular flow-probe using an external magnetic field (adapted from Kolin [62]).

8.1.5 Electronic Systems

As discussed earlier, a variety of magnet-current excitation waveforms have been employed in an effort to improve the electromagnetic flowmeter performance. The sine wave and square wave can be considered the two basic waveforms around which most flowmeters have been designed; examples of their use will be given in the next two subsections.

Sine-Wave Systems. Ideally, for the sine-wave system, the transformer emf is in phase quadrature (90° out of phase) with the flow emf. As shown in Figure 8.13(a), the total instantaneous emf seen by the input amplifier is the sum of the two signals and can be written

$$V = V_f \sin \omega t + V_t(t),$$

where V_f is the peak amplitude of the flow emf and $V_t(t)$ is the instantaneous amplitude of the transformer emf. Now $V_t(t)$ is proportional to the rate of change of magnetic flux, but since the flux is proportional to sin ωt, we find by differentiation that $V_t(t) = K\omega \cos \omega t$. This enables the total emf to be written

$$V = V_f \sin \omega t + V_t \cos \omega t, \tag{5}$$

where $V_t = \omega K$ is the amplitude of the transformer emf and can have either a positive or negative sign, depending on the loop orientation with respect to

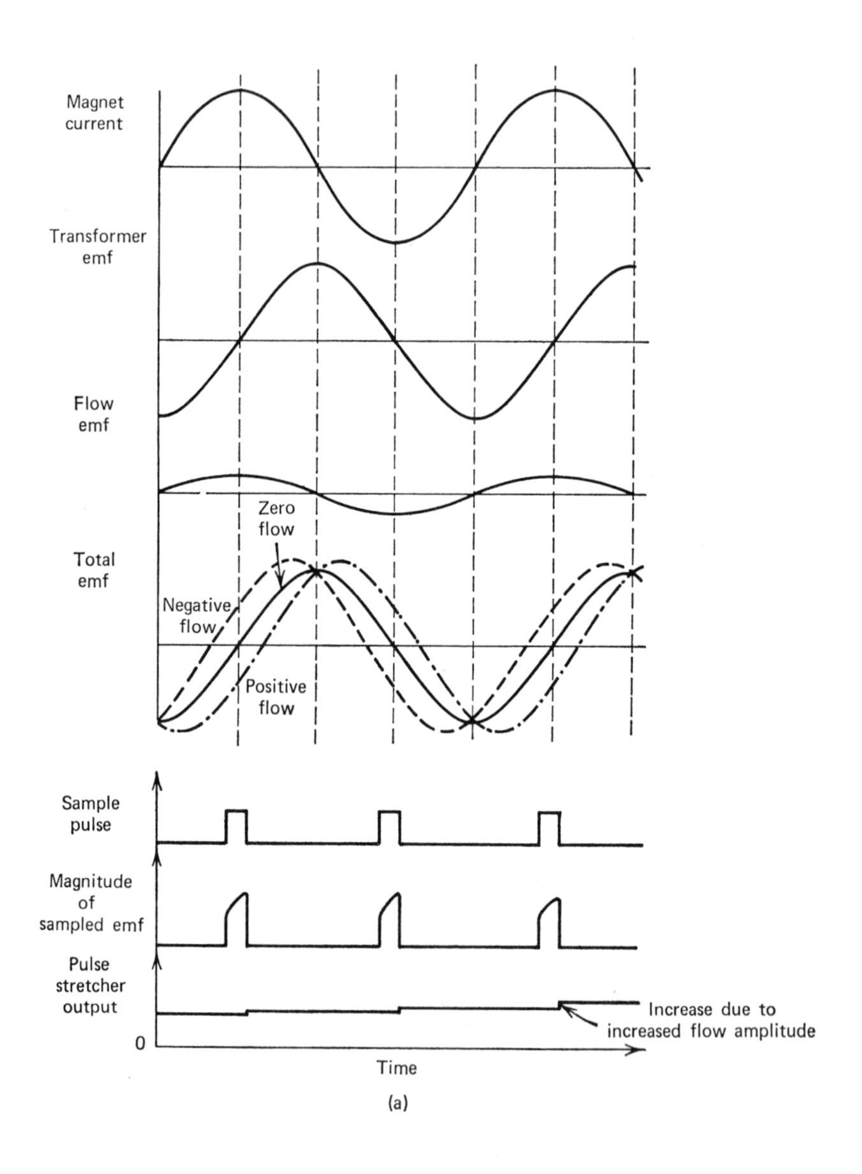

(a)

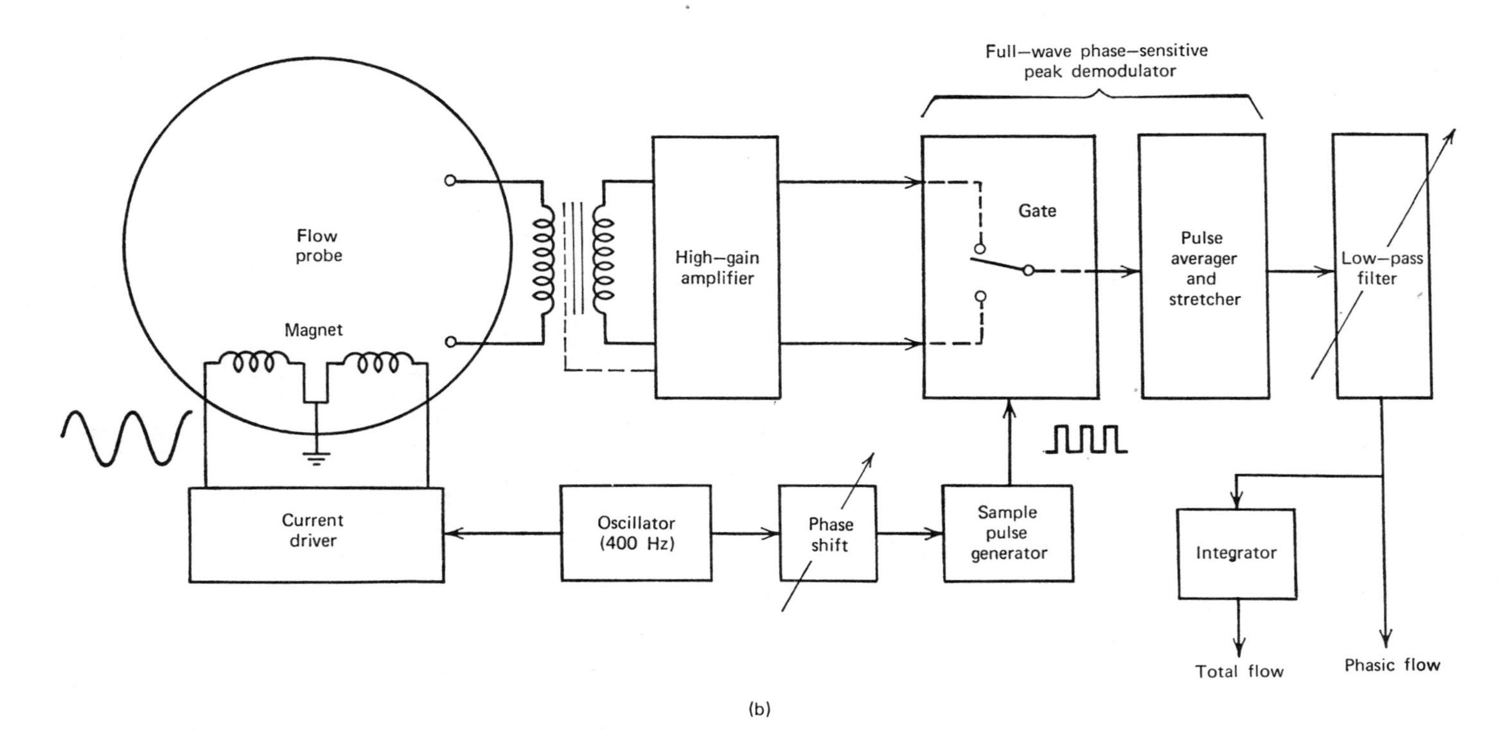

Figure 8.13. Gated sine-wave electromagnetic flowmeter system: (a) waveforms; (b) system block diagram.

the magnetic flux. Since the transformer emf increases with frequency, it is, as previously noted, important to use a low-excitation frequency.

Because the transformer emf is normally much greater than the flow signal, the change in the total signal waveform due to the flow emf will be small. To achieve good discrimination between the in-phase and quadrature signals, several approaches can be used. The two considered here are: full-wave peak detection and full-wave mean detection, of which the latter gives the best signal–noise ratio [65].

The full-wave peak detection scheme is based on the fact that the quadrature signal goes through zero as the flow emf passes through its maximum value. By using a narrow gate pulse to sample the total emf over the time interval indicated in Figure 8.13(a), a pulse signal can be derived whose mean pulse amplitude is independent of the quadrature amplitude but is proportional to the amplitude of the flow signal (the negative and positive areas of the quadrature signal cancel out in the averaging process). It will be evident that if the transformer emf is several orders of magnitude greater than the flow emf, the smallest error in the sample pulse timing will cause a significant baseline shift. Furthermore, any system imperfection that may cause part of the transformer emf to be converted to an in-phase signal will also result in a baseline shift. This means that great care must be taken in the electronic design to insure a sufficient degree of phase stability, so that baseline drift can be reduced to a minimum.

In the gated sine-wave system [27, 66, 67] shown in Figure 8.13(b), the probe signal is passed through a step-up transformer, the effect of which is to improve the signal–noise ratio and achieve a good common-mode signal rejection.

Overloading of the amplifier by the quadrature signal can be avoided either by insuring that the probe is properly balanced during construction or by providing a means for achieving some degree of quadrature suppression at the input transformer. The latter solution can be implemented through the use of an additional winding on the input transformer connected to a variable amplitude and phase voltage derived from the magnet-current source.

The full-wave phase-sensitive peak demodulator, which is activated by the gate pulses, samples the signal twice per cycle at times when the quadrature signal passes through zero. By averaging the sampled pulse over the sample interval and stretching its average value over the interval between samples, an output is derived that is proportional to the instantaneous flow but that still contains a small component of the sample pulse frequency. This can be eliminated by means of a low-pass filter.

A major problem with the gated sine-wave system is the difficulty in achieving adequate phase stability. Zero drift and an inability to make the mechanical zero (zero flow) equal to the electrical zero when the magnet

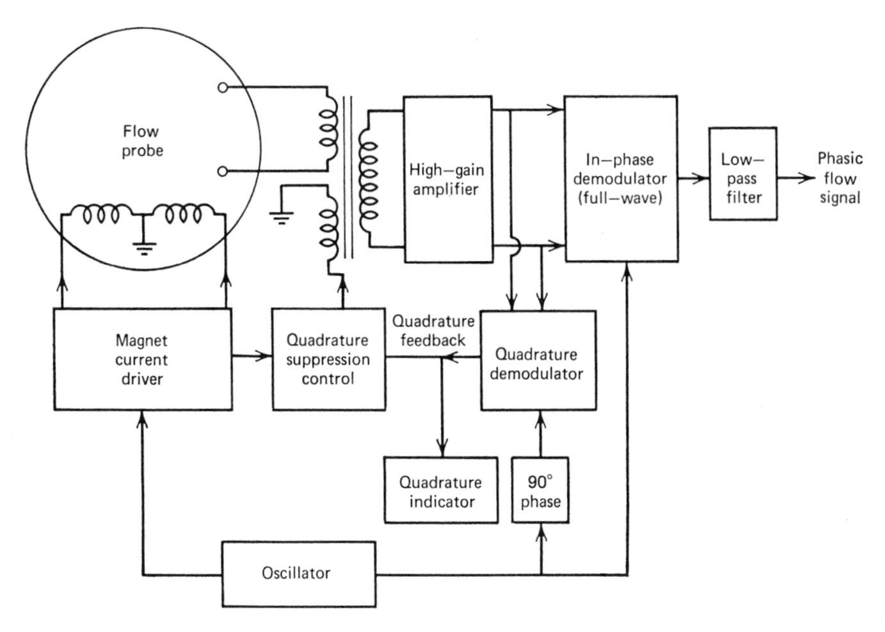

Figure 8.14. Sine-wave flowmeter system incorporating automatic quadrature suppression.

current is switched off makes the system difficult to use when the flow rates are small. These problems can be overcome by using the automatic quadrature-suppression scheme [6, 68] shown in Figure 8.14.

Reduction of the quadrature signal level at the amplifier input terminals is achieved through the use of a phase-sensitive detector that measures the quadrature signal and uses the resulting output to control a quadrature-suppression circuit [69]. An increase in the quadrature signal at the amplifier output terminals causes an increased quadrature-suppression signal to be applied via an extra winding on the input step-up transformer, thereby reducing the quadrature emf at the amplifier input terminals. The reduction of quadrature signal at the amplifier input is in fact equal to the gain of the quadrature feedback loop. Since this can be made fairly large, the phase stability required from the amplifier and in-phase demodulator can be greatly relaxed. Typically, an improvement by a factor of 50 can be achieved without causing instability. However, it should be noted that the quadrature suppression signal must still meet the original phase-stability requirements.

A useful feature of the system shown in Figure 8.14 is the quadrature-signal indicator, which serves as a guide to insure proper probe fit and electrical contact to the blood vessel. A further feature of the system is the use of a full-wave mean demodulator for the in-phase signal. The fact that the demodulator acts in a continuous rather than in a discrete mode enables a better signal–noise ratio to be achieved than is possible with the peak demodulator [65].

Square-Wave and Pulse Systems. The majority of commercially available electromagnetic flowmeters use either square-wave or pulse excitation. The main advantages to be gained with these waveforms over sinusoidal excitation are the relative ease with which the effects of the transformer emf can be circumvented, the less exacting phase-stability requirements for the amplifier and demodulator circuits, and the adaptability of the pulse-excitation system to achieve multiplexed operation for the simultaneous phasic flow measurement from several probes.

The transformer emf generated in pulse and square-wave systems is generally much greater than the quadrature amplitude arising from sinusoidal excitation. The difference of course arises from the different rates of change of the magnetic flux in the two systems. However, once the flux achieves a constant value, no further emf's are generated in the square-wave system until the next transition occurs, and ideally, one is simply left with the flow emf, which

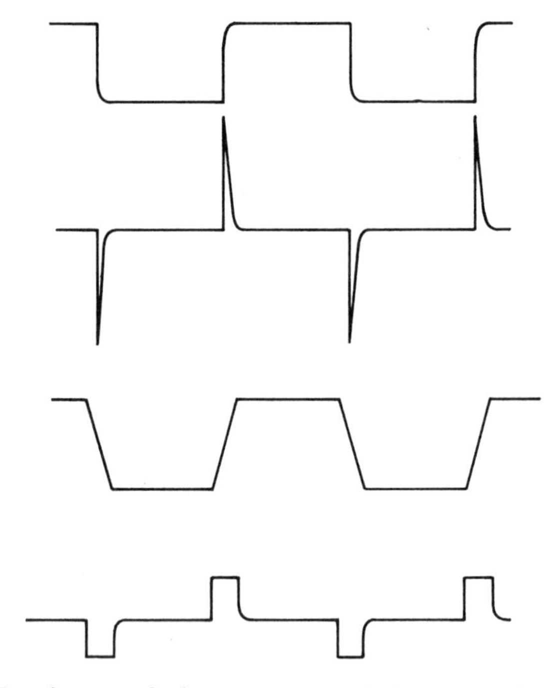

Figure 8.15. Transformer emf's for a square wave having exponential edges and for a trapezoidal wave.

can then be extracted in a relatively straightforward manner. A reduction in the amplitude of the transformer emf can be obtained by controlling the rate at which the magnet current is changed. As illustrated in Figure 8.15, the trapezoidal waveform results in a reduced transformer emf, but it also reduces the time interval over which the flow signal can be sampled.

A number of undesirable effects can result from the presence of a large transformer emf. One of these arises from the current flow that occurs around the electrode–electrolyte–amplifier circuit when the amplifier input impedance is too low. The effect of such a current is to cause a transient change in the polarization potential difference between the electrode and electrolyte [33]. Such a disturbance decays back to its equilibrium value rather slowly, causing a varying emf to be present during the flow-emf sampling interval. The simple answer to this problem is to design the preamplifier so that it has a high input impedance and either to insure that the capacitance of the shielded cables from the electrodes is sufficiently small or to use a "bootstrap" technique to reduce its effective value [70].

An additional problem caused by the large transformer emf results from overloading of the signal amplifier system. With ac coupled amplifiers, large overload signals can cause significant voltage changes to occur across the coupling and bias capacitors, resulting in a long time-constant recovery process that may distort the flow signal. The use of a simple dc coupled wide-band amplifier is precluded by the fact that there usually exists a fairly large ($\sim$0.1 V) and somewhat variable polarization potential difference between the two electrodes.

Hognestad [33, 71] has described a rather ingenious scheme to overcome this difficulty. As shown in the block diagram of Figure 8.16(a), the electrode signal passes into a low-gain dc coupled preamplifier and then into a higher-gain dc coupled amplifier that has a feedback circuit connected across it. When the switch S is closed, the two capacitors are connected to ground, making the feedback zero at the carrier frequency. For very low frequencies and dc, the feedback is effective and the net gain ends up close to unity. To avoid overloading problems associated with the use of capacitors, the switch S is opened during the transformer emf phase so that the amplifier gain is reduced to unity and no charging of the capacitors can occur. Thus, the arrangement can cope with the dc offset voltage appearing at the electrodes and avoids any amplifier saturation effects that might otherwise be caused by the transformer emf.

Switching of the feedback loop inevitably introduces some transients into the signal waveform. These can be eliminated by the gate, which is switched on for a somewhat shorter time interval than the flow signal is present for. An ac amplifier, demodulator, and a low-pass filter enable the flow signal to be extracted.

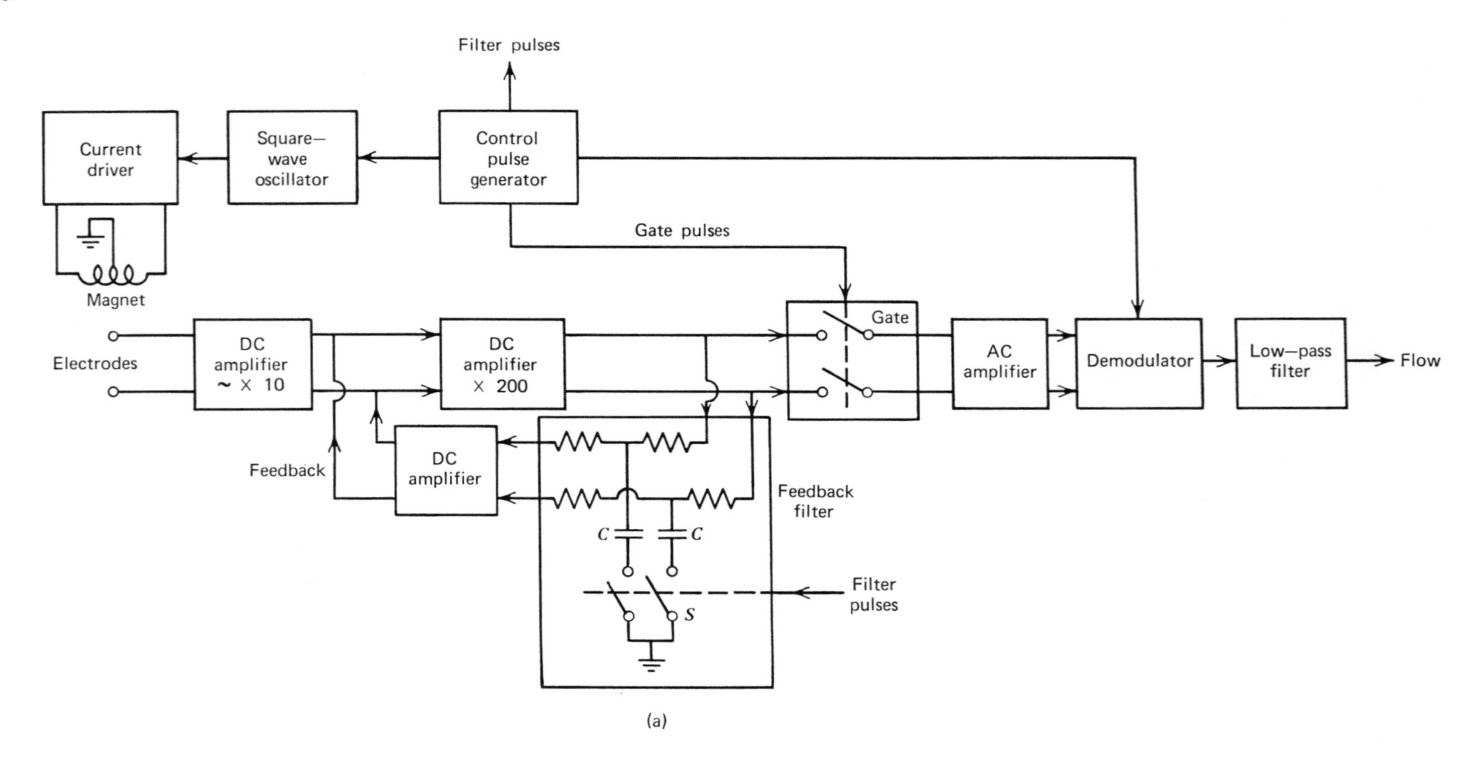
Filter pulses
Current driver
Square–wave oscillator
Control pulse generator
Gate pulses
Magnet
Electrodes
DC amplifier ~ × 10
DC amplifier × 200
Gate
AC amplifier
Demodulator
Low–pass filter
Flow
Feedback
DC amplifier
Feedback filter
C
C
Filter pulses
S

(a)

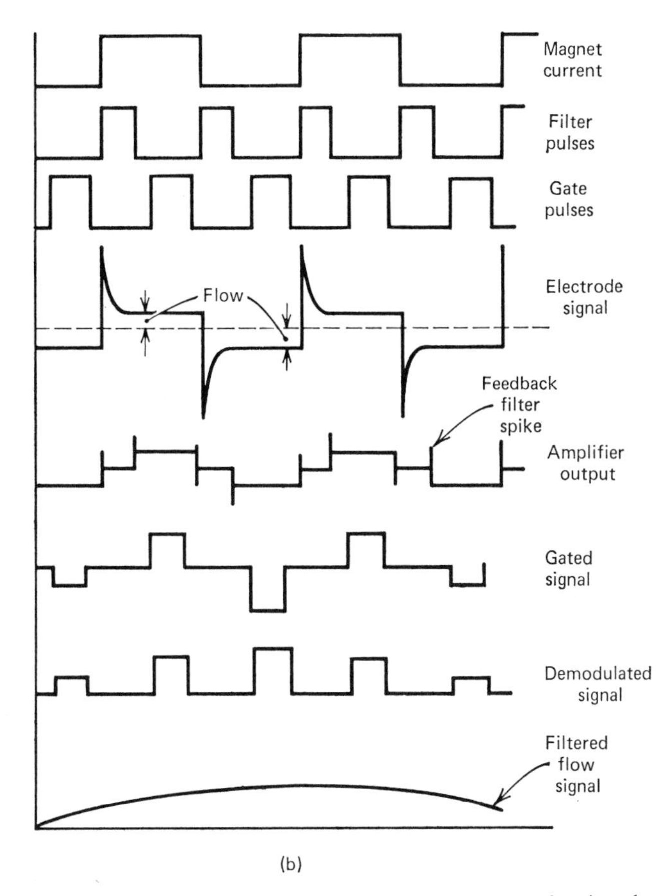

Figure 8.16. Square-wave flowmeter system: (a) block diagram showing the essence of the system; (b) important timing and signal waveforms (after Hognestad [71]).

An alternative way of avoiding the undesirable effects of the transformer emf and the polarization potential is to sample the amplifier output voltage when the magnetic field is zero and to use the resulting signal to correct the amplifier offset. A scheme of this form, first described by Moody [72], is illustrated in Figure 8.17 for a two-channel multiplexed flowmeter. The block diagram shows the signal processing for one of the flow probes: an identical arrangement, but with the pulse timing shown in the bottom half of (a), is used for the other probe.

The magnet current consists of positive and negative pulses separated by a time interval over which the magnetic field is zero. A feedback signal is

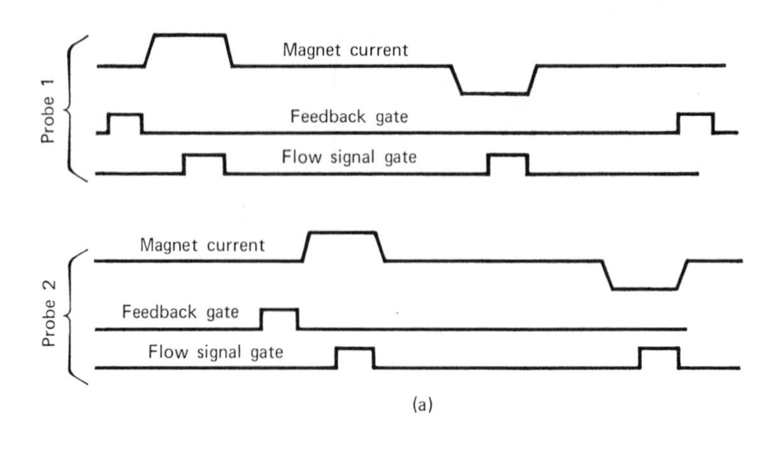

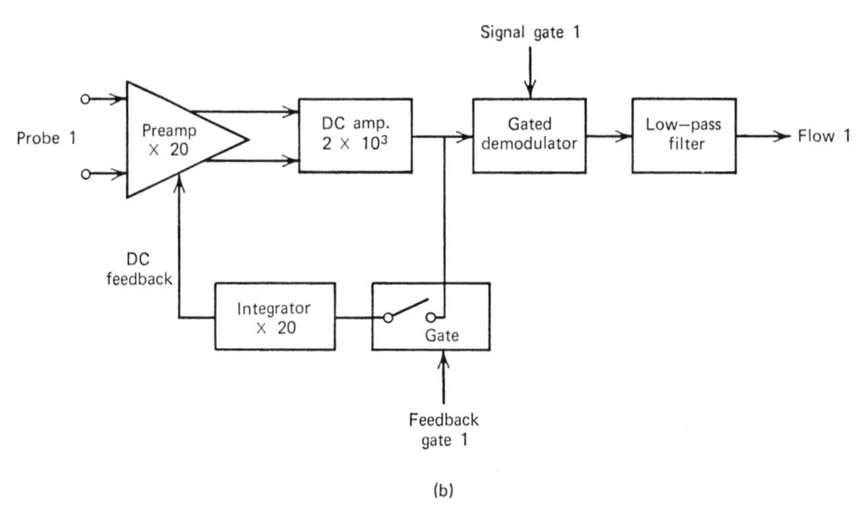

Figure 8.17. Two-channel pulsed flowmeter system: (a) timing pulses for the two channels; (b) block diagram of the signal processing portion of the flowmeter, (after Moody [72]).

derived once per cycle by sampling the amplifier output voltage during the zero field interval. The mean value of this sample is amplified, held constant over the remainder of the cycle, and applied as feedback to the preamplifier stage to correct for the dc offset error. The presence of gain in the feedback loop causes any input offset voltage to be attenuated by the time it reaches the output terminals.

During the transformer emf transient, the feedback gate is open, and even though the dc amplifier may saturate, no undesirable charge storage effects occur, enabling the amplifier system to recover very fast. The flow signal is extracted by a gated demodulator that operates over the time interval for which the magnetic field is constant.

8.2 ULTRASONIC FLOW TRANSDUCTION SYSTEMS

Ultrasonic flow measurement systems are based on either of two physical principles. The first is that the effective velocity of sound in a moving medium is equal to the velocity of sound relative to the medium plus the velocity of the medium. Thus, for example, a sound wave propagated upstream will have a smaller effective velocity than one propagated downstream. Since the difference in the two velocities is exactly twice the velocity of the fluid, a measurement of the difference enables the fluid velocity to be determined. The second principle is the change in frequency that occurs when an ultrasonic wave is scattered by a moving medium. It will be shown that the frequency shift (Doppler shift) of the scattered wave is directly proportional to the velocity.

8.2.1 Transit-Time and Phase-Shift Flowmeters

The average fluid velocity can be determined by measuring the difference in time that a pulse of ultrasound takes to travel upstream and downstream between two fixed points. For the purpose of analysis we consider the arrangement shown in Figure 8.18(a) in which two piezoelectric crystals A and B are placed at an angle Θ with respect to the flow axis and are separated by a distance D. The time taken for a pulse of ultrasound to travel between the two crystals can be found by noting that the component of fluid velocity along the line joining the two transducers is $v \cos \Theta$. If we assume the fluid flow velocity profile can be represented by an average velocity* $\hat{v}$, then the transit time is simply

$$T = \frac{D}{c \pm \hat{v} \cos \Theta}, \tag{6}$$

where c is the velocity of sound in the fluid and the plus and minus signs refer to the downstream and upstream transit times, respectively. By taking the difference of the upstream and downstream transit times, we find

$$\Delta T = \frac{2D\, \hat{v} \cos \Theta}{c^2 + \hat{v}^2 \cos^2 \Theta} \simeq \frac{2D\hat{v} \cos \Theta}{c^2} \tag{7}$$

* The velocity $\hat{v}$ is the flow velocity averaged along the path of the ultrasound. Gessner [73] has shown that for laminar flow $\hat{v} = 4\bar{v}/3$, and for turbulent flow, $\hat{v} = 1.07\bar{v}$, where $\bar{v}$ is the flow velocity averaged over the cross-sectional area.

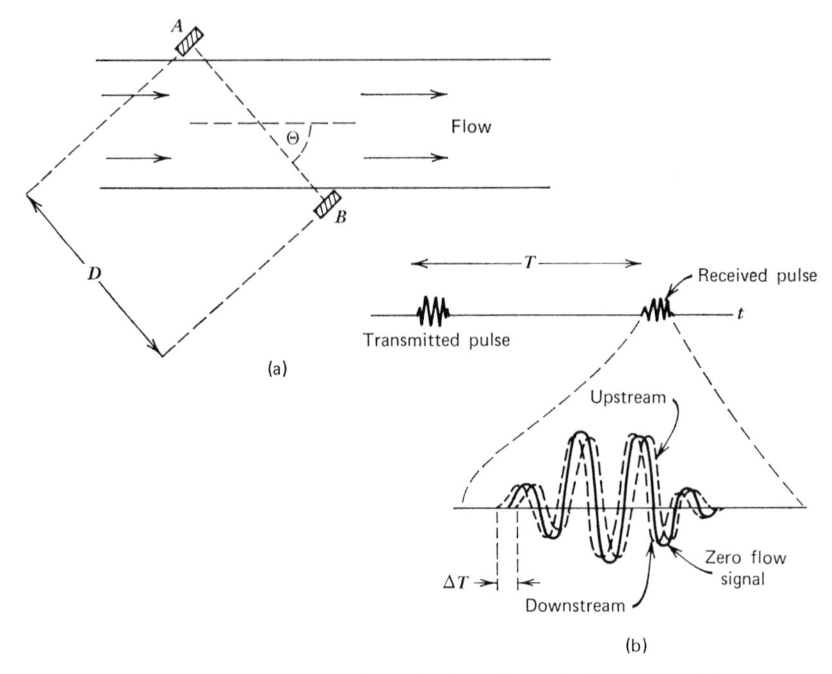

Figure 8.18. Principles of the pulsed transit-time ultrasonic flowmeter: (a) geometry of the transducers in relation to the tube or vessel; (b) transmitted and received pulse waveforms showing the transit time difference between the upstream and downstream transit times (after Franklin [87]).

if, as is the situation for physiological flow, $c \gg \hat{v} \cos \Theta$. As an example, we consider $D = 1.5$ cm, $\Theta = 30°$, $\hat{v} = 10$ cm/sec. Since the velocity of sound in blood is 1.5×10^5 cm/sec, we find from (7) that $\Delta T = 1.2 \times 10^{-9}$ sec. When the waveshape is a pulsed sinusoidal waveform, such as shown in Figure 8.18(b), this small time difference becomes difficult to measure with any reasonable degree of accuracy. Great care must be taken in the circuit design to insure that the effects of temperature on the zero drift are small. One way to circumvent this problem is to use the same pulse generator and receiver to measure both the upstream and downstream transit times [74, 75]. A system to achieve this is shown in Figure 8.19, where the switch S alternately connects the receiver and transmitter to the two transducers. Franklin et al. [74] have reported that the equivalent input zero drift of such a system can be less than 0.5 cm/sec over a 4-hour period. This quality of performance can only be achieved with a rather complex electronic system that must meet fairly stringent demands.

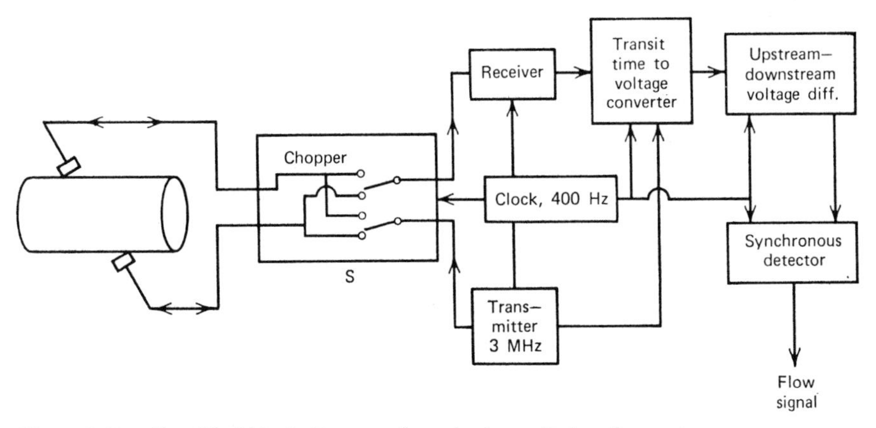

Figure 8.19. Simplified block diagram of a pulsed transit-time flowmeter.

An alternative method of measuring the upstream and downstream transit time difference is to measure the phase difference between a long pulse of ultrasound that is alternately propagated upstream and downstream. If the ultrasound is of frequency f, the phase difference $\Delta\phi$ can be expressed with the help of Eq. (7) as

$$\Delta\phi = \frac{4\pi f D\hat{v} \cos \Theta}{c^2}. \tag{8}$$

It can be seen from Eq. (8) that a larger phase difference can be obtained by using a higher excitation frequency. However, an upper limit is set by the rapidly increasing attenuation of ultrasound with increasing frequency.

Illustrated in Figure 8.20(a) is a phase-difference flow measuring system of the type described by Zamstorff et al. [76]. To facilitate the phase measurement, both the transmitted and received signals are mixed with a local oscillator to create two 10-kHz signals, which can be more readily compared to extract the phase angle. A serious difficulty with this system arises from the presence of multiple reflections in the blood vessel, which tend to create an error in the phase difference. More recently, Franklin et al. [77] have described an FM ultrasound source system which, it is claimed, overcomes this problem.

To avoid the noise and frequency limitation imposed by the electronic switches, Noble [78] has designed a two-frequency system that enables the upstream and downstream transit time difference to be found on a continuous basis.* As illustrated in Figure 8.20(b), two oscillators whose frequencies

* A similar system, based on Noble's work, has been described by Girard [79] and applied to the measurement of blood flow.

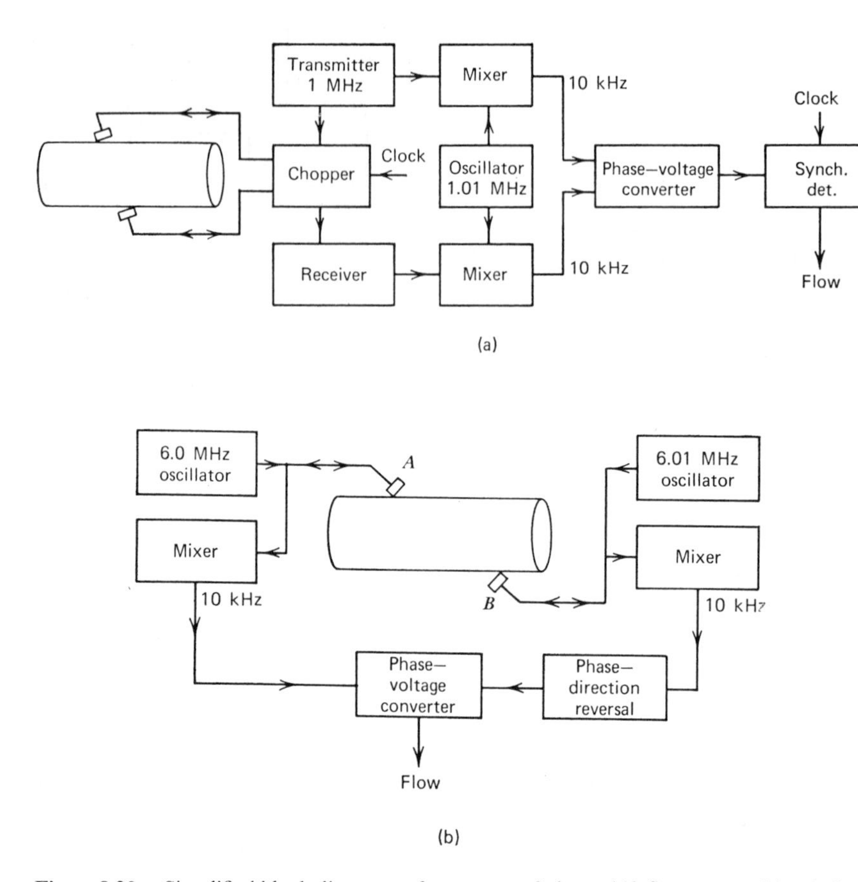

Figure 8.20. Simplified block diagrams of two types of phase-shift flowmeters: (a) switched system (after Zarnstorff et al. [76]); (b) dual-frequency continuous system (after Noble [78]).

differ by 10 kHz are used to excite the two crystals. Both crystals act simultaneously as transmitters and receivers. Thus, crystal A transmits 6.0 MHz and receives 6.01 MHz. The mixing of the two signals creates a 10-kHz-difference signal that contains the relevant phase information. By finding the phase difference between the two 10-kHz signals (one of which must have its phase direction reversed), an output is obtained that is linearly related to the flow velocity. Noble claims that this system has a sensitivity of approximately 1 cm/sec and frequency response of greater than 2 kHz.

A rather different method for ultrasonic flow-velocity measurements was used by Plass [80] for his intravascular probe. The system, as illustrated in Figure 8.21, makes use of a combination of phase and transit-time detection.

Two crystals are excited in antiphase with a pulse whose duration is less than the minimum transit time between crystals. The two received pulses occur at slightly different times and create at the two crystals emf's e_1 and e_2, which are summed in the gated amplifier. Ideally, the amplitudes of the two emf's will be equal so that the output voltage e can be written as

$$e = e_1 + e_2 = V \cos(\omega t + \phi) - V \cos(\omega t - \phi),$$

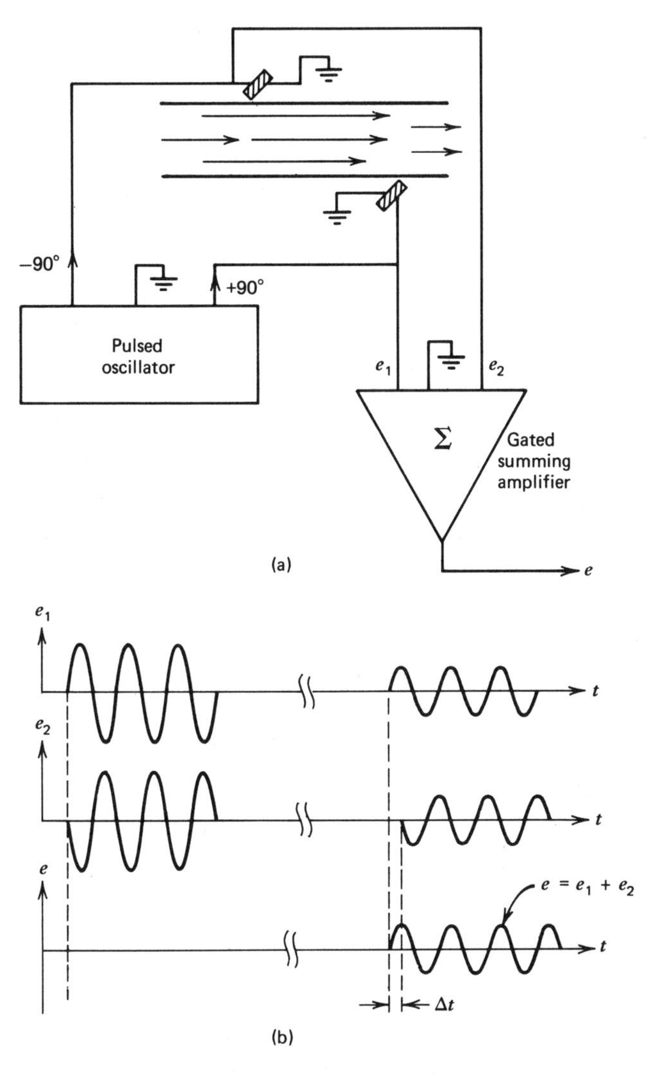

Figure 8.21. Principles of a pulsed phase-shift ultrasonic flow velocity system: (a) block diagram; (b) the effect of a flow velocity on the various waveforms.

where V is the received signal amplitude and 2ϕ is the total phase difference. The above equation can be expressed in the form

$$e = -2V \sin \phi \sin \omega t$$

$$= -\frac{2V\omega D\bar{v} \cos \Theta}{c^2} \sin \omega t$$

in which we have assumed that ϕ is small so that $\sin \phi \approx \phi$ and that 2ϕ is given by Eq. (8). Thus, it is seen that the output from the summing amplifier is proportional to the mean flow velocity. In practice, the two received signals will not have identical amplitudes; however, the amplitudes can effectively be made equal by passing e_1 and e_2 into two limiting amplifiers prior to the summation. This, in fact, was used in the system described by Plass.

The intravascular probe constructed by Plass used two crystals separated by a 2.7-cm path through which the blood could flow. Its outside diameter was 0.4 cm, and the crystals were excited at 5 MHz. Apart from its rather large diameter, the probe also suffered from having a large number of surfaces upon which blood could coagulate, thereby making it unsuitable for clinical application.

An intravascular flow probe based on the work of Plass has also been developed by Scheu et al. [81, 82]. Although the original version of this probe was somewhat bulky and lacked mechanical rigidity, more recent improvements [82–84] appear to have solved these problems. The probe, which is mounted on the end of a F7 catheter, has a 1.5-cm path length between the two crystals and an overall body length of 2.4 cm. In vitro tests [83] indicated that the sensitivity is somewhat dependent on hematocrit and temperature and is also significantly affected by angulation within the vessel. In vivo comparison of the flow velocity waveform with that simultaneously obtained from a perivascular electromagnetic flow transducer indicated good qualitative agreement.

A further development of Plass's work is the perivascular transducer reported by Rader et al. [85] as part of a totally implantable blood flow and pressure telemetry system. The two transducer crystals are mounted in a rigid cuff assembly designed to fit around the vessel. Few details are given of the performance of this particular system.

8.2.2 Doppler-Shift Flowmeters

Flow transduction, based on the frequency change that occurs when ultrasound is scattered by the particulate matter in a moving medium, has proved to be the simplest of the ultrasonic methods and one that can be readily used for long-term telemetry* of flow information from free-roaming animals [86, 87]. Perhaps the most serious drawback of the Doppler system (in its simplest form) is the inability to discriminate between positive and negative flow. It should also be emphasized that like all the ultrasonic methods, the Doppler system measures a flow velocity rather than the volumetric flow as is the case for the electromagnetic flowmeter.

Theory. A relation between the Doppler frequency change and the flow velocity can be obtained in the following manner. We assume, as illustrated in Figure 8.22, that the transmitting and receiving piezoelectric crystals are at angles of Θ and ϕ, respectively, in relation to the flow axis. The total

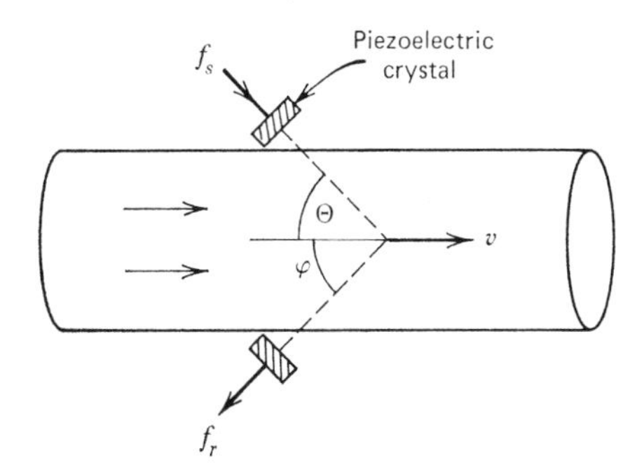

Figure 8.22. Doppler flow transducer, showing the angular relations between the flow velocity and the two piezoelectric crystals.

Doppler shift is the sum of two parts. The first can be found by noting that to an observer moving with the flow velocity v the transmitter crystal is moving away, and its frequency f_s appears as a frequency f_1 given by†

$$f_1 = \frac{f_s}{1 + \dfrac{v}{c} \cos \Theta}, \tag{9}$$

where c is the velocity of sound in the fluid. The second part can be found by observing that the scattering of ultrasound by the particulate matter in the fluid is equivalent to the transmission of a frequency f_1 from a virtual source moving with the fluid. Thus, to an observer fixed at the receiver crystal, the frequency f_1 will appear as a frequency f_r given by

$$f_r = f_1 \left(1 - \frac{v}{c} \cos \phi\right). \tag{10}$$

* Commercially available; e.g., Ward Associates, Huntingdon, Calif

† It appears that the derivations given by Wells [88] and Stegall et al. [89] are in error even though they arrive at the correct final approximate result.

From Eqs. (9) and (10), the Doppler frequency change can be written as

$$\Delta f = f_s - f_r = f_s - f_s\left(\frac{c - v\cos\phi}{c + v\cos\Theta}\right).$$

Assuming that $c \gg v$, this simplifies to

$$\Delta f \simeq \pm f_s(\cos\Theta + \cos\phi)\frac{v}{c}, \tag{11}$$

where the minus and plus signs have been introduced to account for flow toward and away from the crystal faces, respectively.

The most important feature of Eq. (11) is that Δf is directly proportional to the flow velocity, with a sign that indicates the direction. Furthermore, it should be noted that to obtain a large frequency change, it is desirable to have the crystals at a small angle. In practice this is limited by the increased difficulty of coupling the acoustic energy into the fluid and the increased attenuation arising from the greater path length. For $\Theta = \phi = 60°$, $v = 100$ cm/sec, and $f_s = 5$ MHz, and assuming $c = 1.5 \times 10^5$ cm/sec (the value for whole blood), we find that $\Delta f = 3.3$ kHz.

In deriving the equation for Δf, we considered scattering from a single region of fluid flow moving with a velocity v. In practice the situation is more complex, for there exists a distribution of velocities ranging from zero up to some maximum value. Furthermore, it should be noted that the radiation pattern of the two crystals results in radiation being transmitted and received over a range of angles. Both these factors cause the received wave to consist of a spectrum of frequencies [90–92] extending from f_s up to just beyond $f_s + \Delta f$, where Δf is the Doppler shift corresponding to the peak flow velocity.

System Design: Continuous Wave Systems. The simplest method for obtaining an output voltage proportional to the Doppler shift consists of mixing the transmitted and received signals to produce sum and difference frequencies. As illustrated in Figure 8.23, the difference frequency Δf can be converted into a proportional output voltage by using either a frequency discriminator or a zero crossing detector that yields an output voltage proportional to the number of zero crossings per unit time. Kato et al. [90] have shown that when the spectrum of frequencies generated by a laminar flow profile are accounted for, the output voltage for both forms of detection is exactly proportional to the mean flow velocity [93].

The simple system described above yields the same output voltage for flow velocities of the same magnitude but opposite directions. The inability to determine flow direction arises from the fact that the difference frequency Δf is present when either $f_r = f_s + \Delta f$, or when $f_r = f_s - \Delta f$ (i.e., corresponding to forward and reverse flow conditions). However, since the received

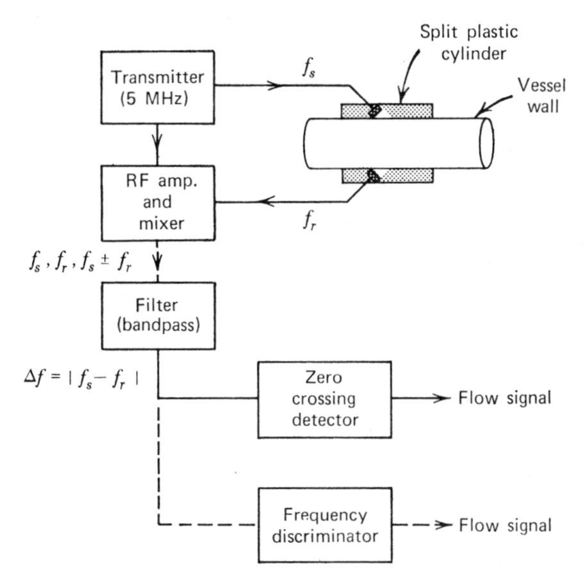

Figure 8.23. Block diagram of a nondirectional Doppler flow transduction system.

signal contains the flow direction information, it is possible, with some increase in the system complexity, to extract the sign of the difference frequency and thereby produce a directional Doppler system [94–98]. Details of some such systems will be described shortly.

A further aspect concerns the ability of the flowmeter to respond to flow variations. The system bandwidth is proportional to Δf, so that as Δf approaches zero for small flow velocities, the bandwidth also approaches zero. In practice this may not be too serious a problem: even for a flow velocity of around 1 cm/sec, the bandwidth will probably still be greater than 10 Hz. A somewhat more serious problem at low flow velocities arises from the decreased signal–noise ratio. Specifically, the pulsations of the vessel wall, as pointed out by Stegall et al. [89] and Flax et al. [99], give rise to low-frequency Doppler signals whose amplitudes are relatively large compared to those associated with the flow. For this reason it is desirable to insert a bandpass filter prior to the zero crossing detector to cut out the low-frequency components. This causes the output voltage to drop to zero when the flow velocity falls below that corresponding to the filter corner frequency. Typically this may be around 100 Hz corresponding to a 2 cm/sec flow velocity.

Several schemes have been proposed and used for extracting directional flow information from a continuous-wave Doppler system [98]. One method makes use of a local oscillator that differs in frequency from that of the transmitter by an amount that is greater than the maximum expected Doppler shift. If the transmitted frequency is f_s and that of the local oscillator is $f_s + \Delta f_m$, then a flow velocity corresponding to a Doppler shift of Δf will produce an output from the mixer containing the components $\Delta f_m \pm \Delta f$, depending on whether the flow is toward or away from the transmitter crystal. For zero flow velocity the output frequency will simply be Δf_m; for flow toward the crystal it will be $\Delta f_m + \Delta f$, and for flow away it will be $\Delta f_m - \Delta f$ (i.e., the output frequency displacement from Δf_m varies linearly with flow velocity). Such a scheme, as discussed on page 292, has been used by Light [96] for the transcutaneous monitoring of changes in human aortic flow.

One problem with the directional Doppler scheme described above arises from the stability of the local oscillator in relation to the transmitter oscillator. A small drift in either frequency causes an output flow to be erroneously registered. Mackay [98] has pointed out that this difficulty can be avoided by using a phase-lock loop to insure that the difference between the two frequencies always remains the same.

A second method for obtaining directional information from a Doppler system involves certain well-known single-sideband receiver techniques. Specifically, it uses a quadrature phase detector to separate the upper and lower Doppler sidebands. Such a scheme was first proposed and used by McLeod [94] and subsequently employed by Chiche et al. [97] for a catheter-tip velometer.

A block diagram of McLeod's system is shown in Figure 8.24(a). In this scheme the Doppler signal is added separately to two carrier frequency components that differ in phase by 90°. In point of fact, the RF signal will not consist solely of the Doppler signal: there will be a strong carrier frequency

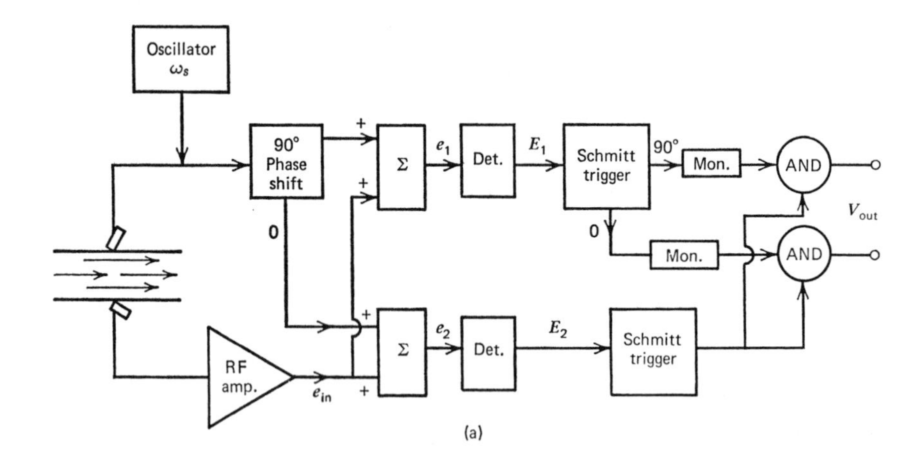

(a)

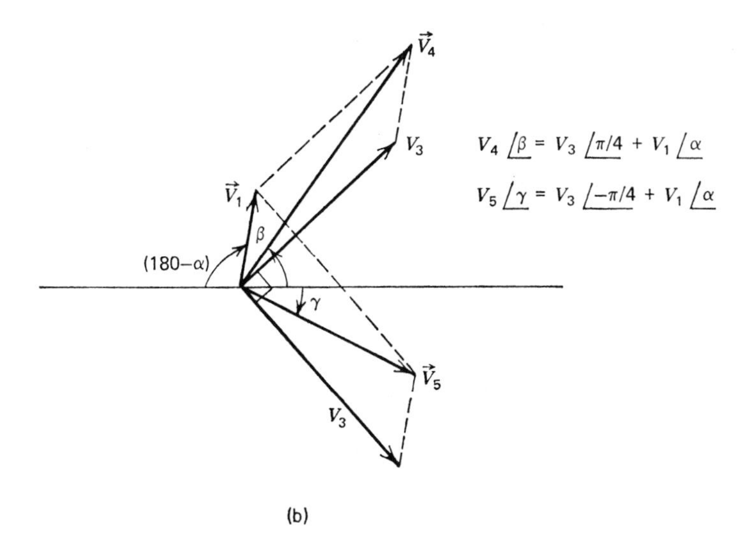

Figure 8.24. Directional CW Doppler flowmeter system: (a) block diagram; (b) phasor diagram (adapted from McLeod [94]).

component present caused partially by direct pickup of the transmitted signal. If the phase angle of this component is α, the total RF amplifier output can be written

$$e_{in} = V_1 \cos(\omega_s t + \alpha) + V_2 \cos[(\omega_s + \Delta\omega)t],$$

where the angular Doppler shift is denoted by $\Delta\omega$. If two carrier signals $V_3 \cos(\omega_s t - \pi/4)$ and $V_3 \cos(\omega_s + \pi/4)$ are added to e_{in} as shown in the block diagram, the summed signals will be given by

$$e_1 = V_4 \cos(\omega_s t + \beta) + V_2 \cos[(\omega_s + \Delta\omega)t]$$

$$e_2 = V_5 \cos(\omega_s t - \gamma) + V_2 \cos[(\omega_s + \Delta\omega)t],$$

where β and γ are the phase angles of the vectors $\vec{V}_4$ and $\vec{V}_5$ shown in Figure 8.24(b).

By squaring e_1 and e_2 and retaining only the low-frequency terms (corresponding to detection and low-pass filtering), we find that the following signals result:

$$\left.\begin{aligned} E_1 &= V_4 V_2 \cos(\Delta\omega t - \beta) \\ E_2 &= V_5 V_2 \cos(\Delta\omega t + \gamma) \end{aligned}\right\} \text{for } \Delta\omega > 0,$$

$$\left.\begin{aligned} E_1 &= V_4 V_2 \cos(\Delta\omega t + \beta) \\ E_2 &= V_5 V_2 \cos(\Delta\omega t - \gamma) \end{aligned}\right\} \text{for } \Delta\omega < 0.$$

Thus, the detection process results in two signals whose relative phase angles change from $(\beta + \gamma)$ to $-(\beta + \gamma)$ when the flow changes direction. To obtain an output voltage proportional to $\Delta\omega$ with a sign that reverses when $\Delta\omega$ changes sign, two zero-crossing detectors in the form of Schmitt triggers are employed. One of these Schmitt circuits produces both a normal and a complementary output, which are used to trigger two monostable circuits. The short pulses from these are AND-gated with the other Schmitt trigger output; as a result, only one pulse will emerge, depending on the sign of $\Delta\omega$. Thus, the average output voltage difference between the two terminals will be proportional to $\Delta\omega$ and will reverse sign when the flow reverses.

System Design: Pulse Wave Systems. Experimental information concerning spatial variation of the flow velocity in vessels is particularly valuable for fundamental hemodynamic research. Such information cannot be obtained from a continuous-wave Doppler system, which by its nature is incapable of distinguishing between echoes arising from different regions. On the other hand, by using a pulsed Doppler system, together with a range-gated detector, echoes arising from different positions can be discriminated and the velocity variation with distance can thereby be deduced. Systems of this type designed to determine the velocity profiles in blood vessels have been described by Baker [100] and Peronneau et al. [101, 102].

In the system described by Baker, a brief pulse of sinusoidal ultrasound is transmitted at a certain repetition frequency that is an exact submultiple of the oscillation frequency. This insures that all transmitted pulses have exactly the same shape. A phase detector is used to sample the phase shift of the returned echo with respect to a reference pulse. As pointed out by Baker, the amplitude of this phase difference varies in proportion to the Doppler frequency shift and therefore varies in proportion to the velocity of the region from which the echo originated. Unfortunately such a system lacks a means of determining the flow direction.

The rather more complex system described by Peronneau et al. [101b] overcomes this problem by using a single-sideband quadrature phase detector that separates out the upper and lower Doppler sidebands. As previously described, the phase relation of the two sidebands enables the flow velocity sign to be determined [94]. The oscillator frequency can be selected to be either 8 or 4 MHz, and the pulse has a repetition frequency of either 15.6 or 31.2 kHz, a pulse duration from 0.5 to 2 μS, and a range-gate delay of from 0 to 100 μS.

To obtain the velocity profile in a vessel for a given phase of the cardiac cycle, the ECG R-wave can be used as a synchronizing signal and the range-gate delay can be adjusted to cover the vessel diameter. By repeating the measurement for various delays from the R-wave, velocity profiles can be obtained showing the variation in velocity at a given point as a function of time. This technique assumes that the flow waveform is perfectly periodic, whereas in practice this is unlikely to be the case. To overcome this difficulty, Baker [100] and Peronneau et al. [102] have described multichannel systems that simultaneously measure the velocity at a number of fixed points across the vessel diameter, thereby enabling the velocity profile to be determined during a single cardiac cycle. Peronneau et al. report the development of an instrument that contains three identical 16-channel velocimeters to determine the three components of the velocity vector at 16 points across the vessel. By this means it should be possible to determine the instantaneous velocity vector and to compute the volume flow.

Intravascular Doppler Transducers. It appears that Stone et al. [103, 104] were the first to report the construction and use of a catheter-tip Doppler flow velocity transducer. As shown in Figure 8.25(a), an early model of the transducer consisted of two hemidisks of lead zirconate titanate separated by a thin mylar acoustical insulator. The hemidisks were resonant at 8 MHz, had a diameter of 1.5 mm, and were mounted at the tip of a 2.5-mm (F8) tube. One of the hemidisks acted as the transmitter, and the other as the receiver; they were connected to a simple nondirectional electronic system. From the

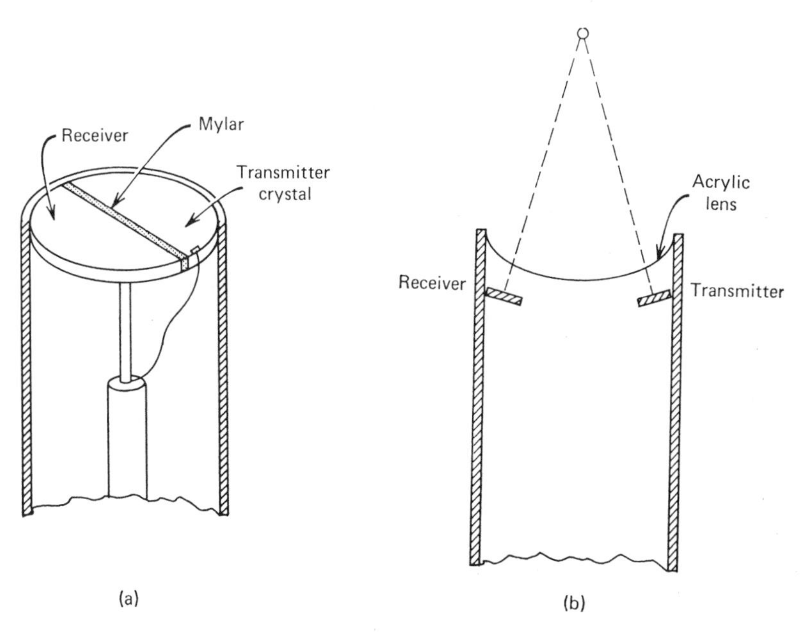

Figure 8.25. Examples of catheter-tip Doppler velometer transducers: (a) unfocused transducer (after Stone et al. [104]); (b) focused transducer (after Kalmanson et al. [106b]).

results of Schlieren measurements, Stone et al. report that the transducer measured flow velocity in a region from 0.5 to 4 cm beyond the tip. Using transducers of this type, Benchimol et al. [105] report flow velocity measurements in the superior vena cava, right atrium, and aorta in a large number of patients. Although the recordings are subject to some misinterpretation because of the absence of flow direction indication, the authors concluded that intravascular velometry using this technique was of clinical value.

Kalmanson et al. [106] have reported the development of several catheter-tip Doppler probes with the electronics necessary to make the output flow-direction-sensitive [97]. One such probe, illustrated in Figure 8.25(b), consists of two 8.4 MHz resonant crystals mounted at an angle to one another on an F9 catheter. An acrylic lens at the tip serves to focus the beam to a point approximately 0.5 cm ahead, thereby making it far more position-sensitive than the Stone probe discussed previously. Other probes described are one similar to that of Figure 8.25(b) but without the lens and a probe containing a single crystal (presumably with the metallization split on either side) with a diameter equivalent to an F7 catheter. Calibration tests on the latter show that it indicates the true velocity to within 6%, up to 100 cm/sec, but that it saturates at about 120 cm/sec. Furthermore, it is found that the electrical and hydrodynamic zeros coincide—a feature rarely true for electromagnetic probes. By mounting the probe on an F7-catheter controller, the tip could be aligned parallel to the blood flow to achieve optimal flow records, and moreover, the catheter could be readily manipulated through the aortic and mitral valves as well as into the pulmonary veins [106b]. In addition to extensive use of this probe on animals, certain human studies have also been undertaken [107].

Transcutaneous Flow Detection. The Doppler flowmeters described thus far have either relied on the placement of a transducer cuff around the vessel or have required the insertion of a probe into the vessel. On the other hand, the transcutaneous Doppler velometer illustrated in Figure 8.26 enables the flow in a superficial vessel to be assessed in a qualitative manner without surgical intervention. Originally described by Satomura and Kaneko [108], the transcutaneous method was later refined and applied to a wide range of problems by Rushmer and his co-workers [89, 109]. They showed that, in spite of its qualitative nature, it was capable of providing clinically useful information in such applications as the evaluation of arterial occlusive disease.

A clinical version of this instrument consists of a probe assembly whose tip contains the two angulated crystals.* Coupling of the ultrasonic energy between the crystals and the tissue is achieved with a suitable gel. Pulsatile

* Parks Electronics Laboratory, Beaverton, Oreg.

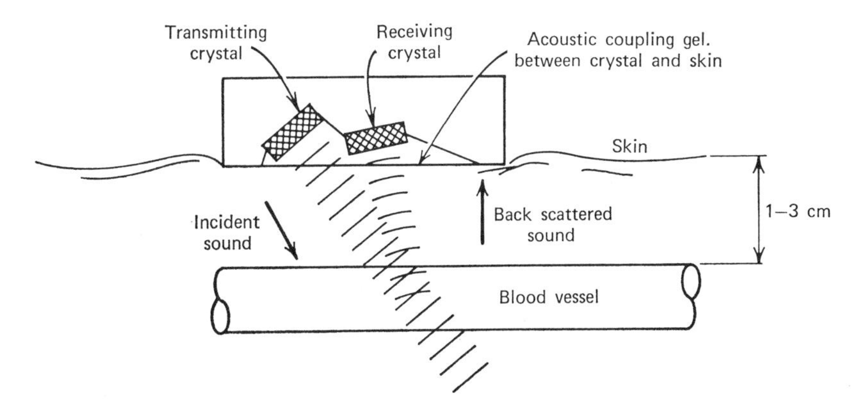

Figure 8.26. Illustrating the principles of operation of a transcutaneous Doppler flowmeter (reproduced, with permission from R. F. Rushmer, D. W. Baker, and H. F. Stegall, *J. Appl. Physiol.*, **21**, 554–566, March 1966).

flow in the vessel causes some movement of the vessel wall and surrounding tissue. This produces a Doppler frequency shift that will be superimposed on the shift arising from the blood velocity. Fortunately the Doppler shift from this cause is normally quite small, so that it can be removed from the flow signal by simply passing the detector signal through a high-pass filter. It is of course important that the corner frequency of such a filter be chosen rather carefully so that significant low-velocity flow signals should not be eliminated. Stegall et al. [89] suggest that a corner frequency of 200 Hz, corresponding to a flow velocity of around 6 cm/sec, adequately removes the effect of arterial wall motion when the carrier frequency is 5 MHz. Concerning the choice of excitation frequency, it is generally found that 5–10 MHz give the best results: the higher frequency gives better focusing and a shallower penetration depth [110], it also gives a larger frequency shift. Systems incorporating directional demodulation avoid possible misinterpretation arising from retrograde flow.

Although transcutaneous ultrasonic techniques would appear to yield information which relates to volume flow in only a qualitative manner, the possibility exists that quantitative information can be derived by using a pulse-wave Doppler system of the type previously described. Baker [100] has pointed out that by using such a system both the vessel diameter [111] and its angle with respect to the transducer can be determined (see Section 6.1.5 for a discussion of vessel diameter measurements). Knowing these quantities, it then becomes possible to compute the instantaneous volumetric flow.

Reagan et al. [112], using a CW directional Doppler instrument to determine the mean flow velocity and a pulsed echo instrument to find the vessel

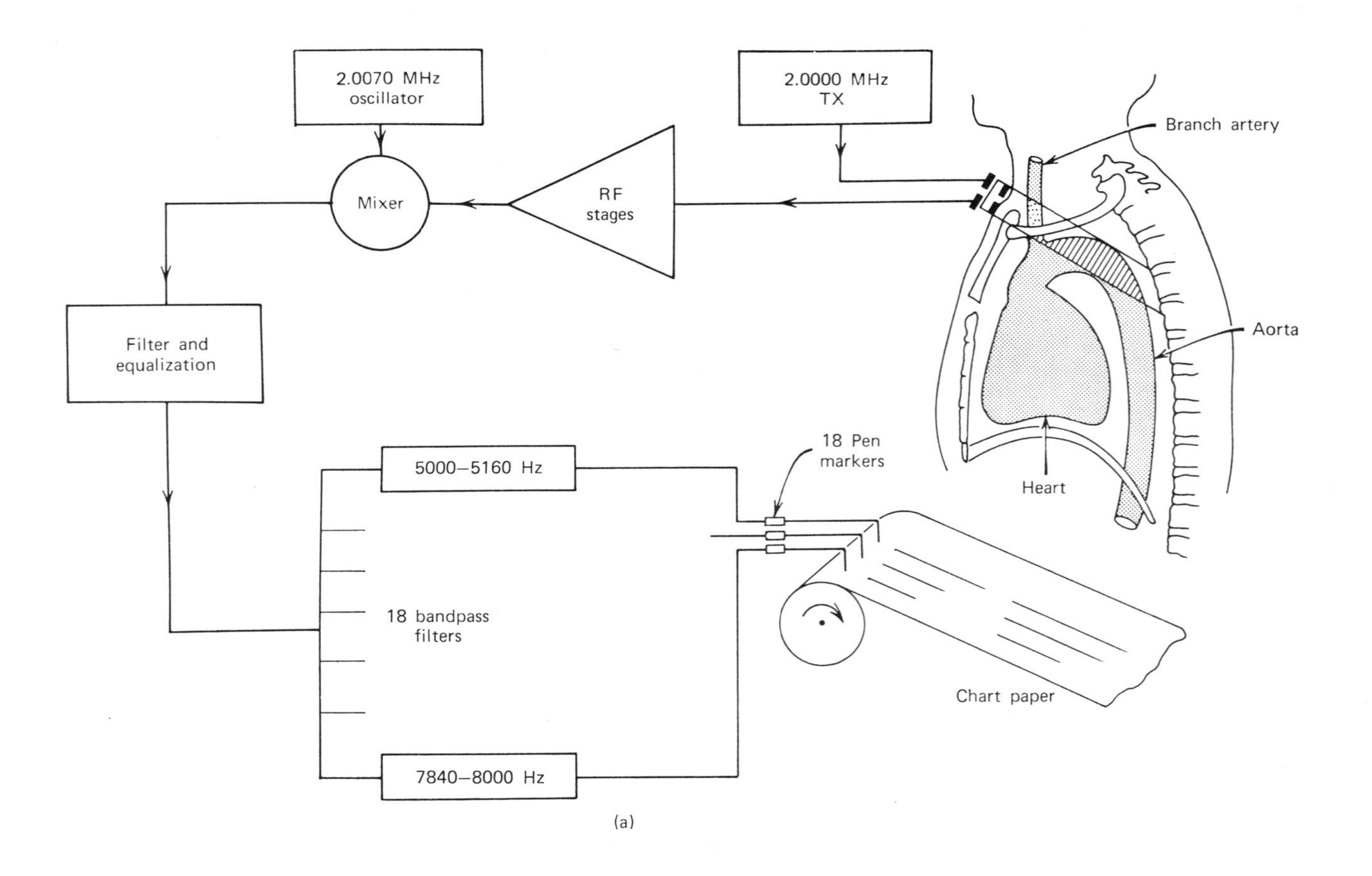
2.0070 MHz
oscillator
2.0000 MHz
TX
Branch artery
Mixer
RF
stages
Filter and
equalization
Aorta
18 Pen
markers
Heart
5000–5160 Hz
18 bandpass
filters
Chart paper
7840–8000 Hz

(a)

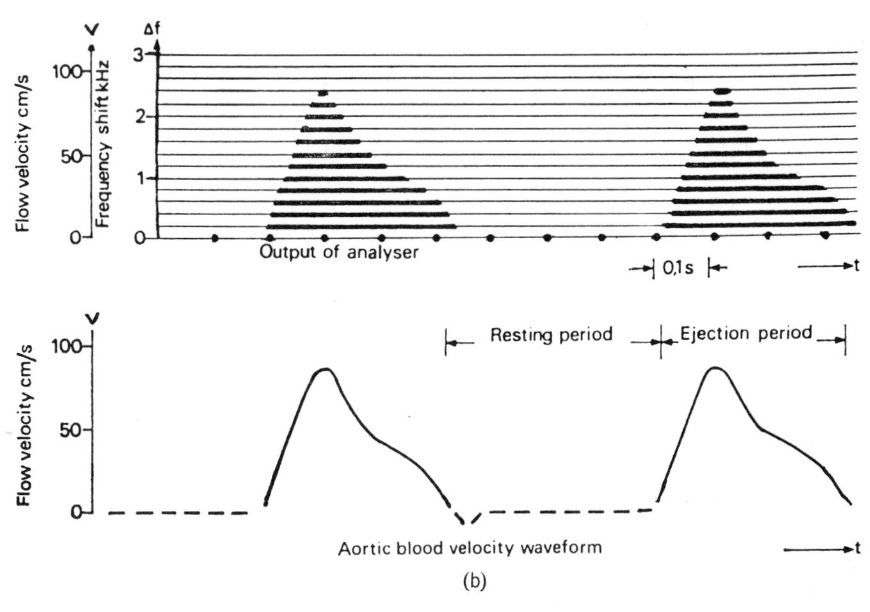

Figure 8.27. Directional Doppler ultrasound method for determining by transcutaneous means the aortic blood flow velocity: (a) block diagram of the system showing placement of the transducer on the suprasternal notch; (b) example of the chart recording, the envelope of which gives the time variation of the peak flow velocity (adapted from Light [114, 115]).

diameter, have measured the mean femoral artery flow in 18 patients. Although no accuracy check was made using an independent measurement method, it was noted that the mean flow rate for the 18 patients was in agreement with the values reported by other investigators using the indicator dilution technique.

More recently, a rather more complex system has been described by Miller and Histand [113] for measuring the instantaneous velocity profile and flow rate in the descending aorta. It employs an esophageal probe containing three pulsed Doppler transducers arranged at different angles to measure the instantaneous velocity vector at any given point across the vessel. A fourth crystal is used to measure the vessel diameter using the phase-lock technique described in Section 6.1.5. The complexity of the calculations and the fast rate at which information is produced required the use of a computer to assimilate and process the information, so that it could be presented in a digestible form. Undoubtedly, such a technique forms a powerful means for detailed hemodynamic studies.

In concluding this subsection on transcutaneous measurements, some mention should also be made of the work of Light [96, 114, 115] and Mackay [98] to obtain quantitative information on the blood flow and velocity in the aortic arch. By placing a 2-MHz direction resolving Doppler probe on the suprasternal notch and directing the beam toward the aortic arch, Light obtained the Doppler frequency spectrum associated with the blood flow in the aorta.

A block diagram of Light's system is shown in Figure 8.27(a). Since the local oscillator and the transmitter frequencies differ by 7.0 kHz, the output frequency in the absence of any flow will be 7.0 kHz. Hence, the presence of frequency components greater or less than 7.0 kHz will indicate the presence of velocity components away from or toward the transducer. A series of narrow-band filters select the various Doppler components and the presence or absence of a particular component is recorded on paper by means of a pen marker. Thus, the record, such as that shown in Figure 8.27(b), indicates the time over which a particular velocity is present or absent. The envelope of this series of lines gives the time variation of the peak flow velocity. If it can be assumed that the flow is turbulent and that in a portion of the aortic arch the flow is parallel to the ultrasound radiation, it follows that the integral of this envelope times the aortic cross-sectional area is equal to the aortic flow per cardiac cycle. The cardiac output will be greater than this because of coronary and branch artery flow. If an estimate of this branch flow can be made and the aortic diameter can be measured by radiological or ultrasound methods, it is possible to arrive at an approximate value of the cardiac output. Even if these additional quantities cannot be measured, it seems that the area under the envelope will be proportional to the cardiac output and therefore provides a useful means of monitoring changes in a given patient.

8.3 PRESSURE GRADIENT TECHNIQUE

The pressure gradient technique for measuring the instantaneous flow velocity is based on a mathematical relationship between the velocity and the pressure gradient along the vessel [116–118]. It can be shown that for a cylindrical rigid tube the instantaneous fluid velocity v averaged across the tube is related to the instantaneous pressure gradient along the tube by

$$\frac{-\Delta P}{\Delta x} = \frac{1.1\zeta}{g}\frac{dv}{dt} + \frac{12.8\mu v}{ga^2}, \qquad (12)$$

where $\Delta P/\Delta x$ is the pressure gradient (in cm H_2O/cm), ζ is fluid density (in gm/cm^3), g is 980 cm/sec^2, μ is viscosity in poise, a is inner diameter (in cm), and v is the average flow velocity (in cm/sec). The first term on the right is an inertial component whose value is usually large for strongly pulsatile flow but reduces to zero for steady flow conditions. The second term is a frictional component whose value is small compared to the inertial term under pulsatile conditions but entirely determines ΔP under steady-state conditions.

Thus, if a segment of an artery is cannulated and the static pressure is measured at two points separated by Δx, the average fluid velocity can be found by solving the differential equation given above. To find the instantaneous blood flow rate Q (in cm^3/sec), we write $Q = v\pi a^2$ and substitute into Eq. (12), yielding

$$\frac{-\Delta P}{\Delta x} = \frac{1.1\zeta}{\pi g a^2}\frac{dQ}{dt} + \frac{12.8\mu}{g\pi a^4}Q. \tag{13}$$

Since the second term contains the fourth power of the radius, it would appear that large errors will occur because of the difficulty in measuring a. Fortunately, as previously mentioned, the second term is small when the flow is dominated by the pulsatile component. However, it does determine the mean flow, and as a result, it is necessary either to measure the mean flow independently or to know the flow value at some instant of time (e.g., the flow is zero in the ascending aorta at the end of diastole).

The method can be applied in the larger vessels by using a special double lumen F6.5 catheter. It has been found that if the two lateral entrances to the lumens are spaced 4–6 cm apart, reasonable results can be achieved. Since the

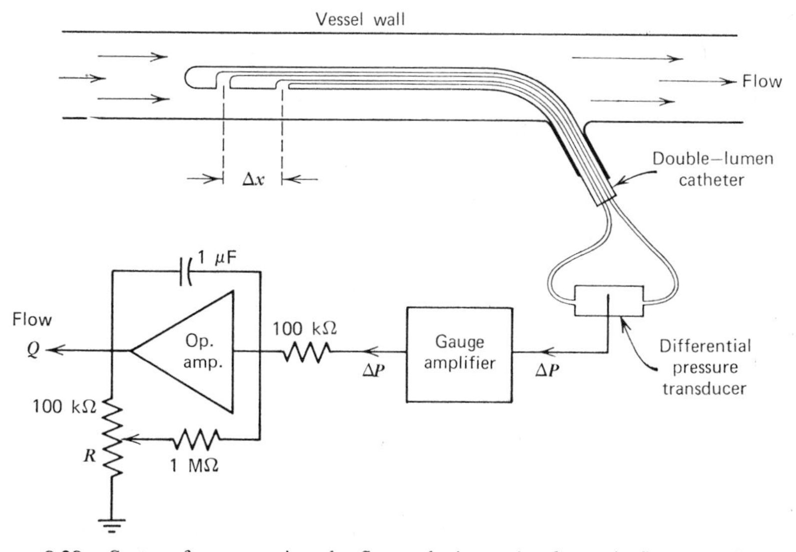

Figure 8.28. System for measuring the flow velocity and volumetric flow rate from the pressure gradient (adapted from Greenfield [116]).

accuracy depends on measuring the pressure difference, it is essential that the dynamic hydraulic properties of the two lumens be identical. To reduce the error in measuring ΔP, it is much better to use a differential transducer than to rely on taking the difference from two separate transducers. As shown in Figure 8.28, the ΔP signal is taken to an analog circuit to yield the time variation of Q directly [97]. The vessel radius, which can be determined from X-ray examination, enables the potentiometer R to be correctly set.

The chief virtue of this method is its *apparent* simplicity and the ease with which it can be used for clinical studies in patients undergoing cardiac catheterization. It was the first method to be applied clinically; however, it should be noted that great care must be taken to insure reasonably accurate results.

8.4 THERMAL TRANSPORT FLOW TRANSDUCERS

Two methods have been used for in vivo blood flow measurements based on the transport of heat [119]. In the first, heat is added at a constant rate and the difference between the upstream and downstream temperatures is measured. Since the transport of heat to the downstream temperature sensor depends on the flow rate, measurement of the temperature difference enables the flow to be determined. The second method relies on the change in heat transport from a heated element (e.g., a thermistor) with flow rate. Measurement of either the change in resistance of the element or the increased power necessary to maintain the temperature constant enables the flow velocity to be found.

8.4.1 The Thermostromuhr

Rein [120, 121] in 1929 was the first to make use of heat transport to a downstream sensor for physiologic flow studies. A version of Rein's *thermostromuhr* consists of a cuff assembly designed to fit around the vessel, with two thermocouples mounted at each end of a centrally located heating element. Although relatively simple to construct, the thermostromuhr suffered from a poorly defined thermal contact to the vessel and the surroundings and, partly as a result of this, exhibited large variations in sensitivity. Gregg et al. [122, 123], in a systematic study of the thermostromuhr's properties, pointed out many of the defects and, in addition, observed that both the upstream and downstream thermocouples indicated a temperature greater than the normal blood temperature. This suggested that heat conduction along the cuff or vessel wall and differential cooling caused by the blood flow were mainly responsible for the observed temperature difference. Partly as a result of these observations, the thermostromuhr fell into disrepute.

8.4.2 Intravascular Thermistor Probes

Methods based on the change in heat loss from a heated element have for many years formed an important means for studying the statics and dynamics of fluid and gas flow. For physiological flow measurements, thermocouples [124], thermistors [125–127] and, more recently, thin metal films [128–132] have been used as the sensing element. In essence, the system requires two temperature sensors: one to measure the temperature of the heat source and the other to measure the undisturbed blood temperature, thereby acting as a reference. The heat source (which can be one of the sensors) is usually maintained at no more than a few degrees above normal blood temperature in order to avoid blood damage and fibrin accumulation. Naturally, to achieve a reasonable frequency response, the mass of the heater and sensors must be small.

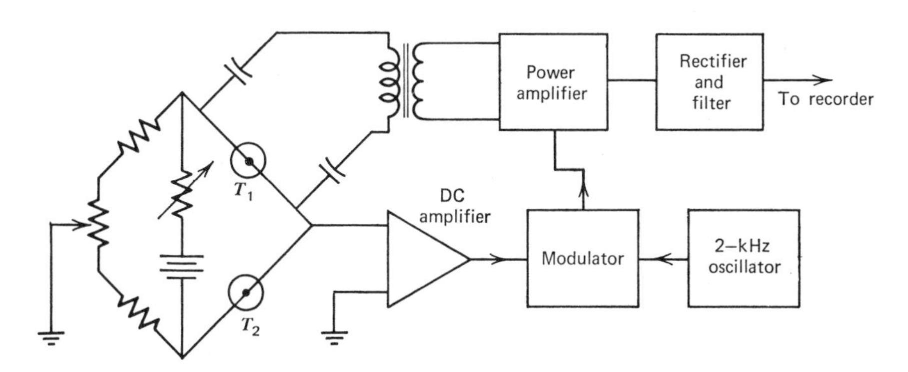

Figure 8.29. Block diagram of an isothermal thermistor flow probe according to the design of Katsura et al. [125].

Operation of the heater at a constant temperature, rather than allowing the heater temperature to vary as the flow changes, normally results in a greatly improved high-frequency response. In the isothermal catheter-tip probe described by Katsura et al. [125], two thermistors are mounted on opposite sides of the catheter: one acts as both a sensor and a heater, and the other acts as a temperature reference. As shown in Figure 8.29, thermistors T_1 and T_2 form part of a dc-excited bridge, with T_1 being maintained at a temperature a few degrees above ambient by 2-kHz power supplied from an amplifier. The bridge balance is sensed by dc amplifier whose output controls, by means of the modulator, the ac power to thermistor T_1. Thus, the feedback maintains a constant temperature difference between T_1 and T_2, and the power supplied to T_1 is a measure of the flow velocity. Katsura et al. report that the flow probe responded in 0.2 and 1.5 sec to step increases and decreases in the flow. The rather poor frequency response, the lack of directional indication, and the nonlinearity of the calibration above 15 cm/sec are evidently rather serious limitations of the design. An isothermal probe of a similar type, but using a fine heating coil surrounding T_1, was employed by Mellander and Rushmer [126] for venous flow measurements. The authors report that the frequency response was flat (5%) to 5 Hz and that the heater power varied almost linearly with flow velocity.

An interesting isothermal catheter probe having directional sensitivity and yielding an output proportional to the flow velocity has been developed by Grahn et al. [127]. Two thermistors are mounted on a specially designed tip plug in such a way that one is shielded from forward flow and the other from reverse flow. Each thermistor is maintained at a constant temperature with respect to a centrally located reference thermistor mounted right at the tip. It was experimentally observed in some earlier work by the authors that the power supplied to the thermistor was proportional to the logarithm of the flow velocity. This relationship was used in the system to obtain an output proportional to the velocity. The manner in which this was achieved consisted of measuring the power delivered to each thermistor, taking the logarithm, and using the difference from the two log converters as the output signal. By carefully matching the two velocity channels, the output was found to be equally sensitive in the forward and reverse directions, and in addition, it reversed sign with reversal of the flow direction. It was found that the frequency response was essentially flat to greater than 50 Hz, that the slow approach to zero flow when the flow was suddenly stopped (a common feature of many velocity probes) was eliminated, and that the calibration exhibited a smooth transition between forward and reverse flows about the zero.

8.4.3 Capillary Blood Flow Measurements

As shown by Hensel and co-workers [133–135], local capillary blood flow can be obtained from a measurement of the apparent thermal conductivity of the tissue.* A heat source in contact with tissue will lose heat by both conduction and blood flow transport. The latter is the cause of an apparent thermal conductivity change, whose magnitude has been found to be proportional to the capillary flow rate. Measurement of the apparent conductivity

* Measurment of the flow velocity in a single capillary can be made by using photometric methods to determine the transit time of a red blood cell along the vessel. Such methods have been recently reviewed by M. Intaglietta, *Microvasc. Res.*, **5**, 357–361 (1973).

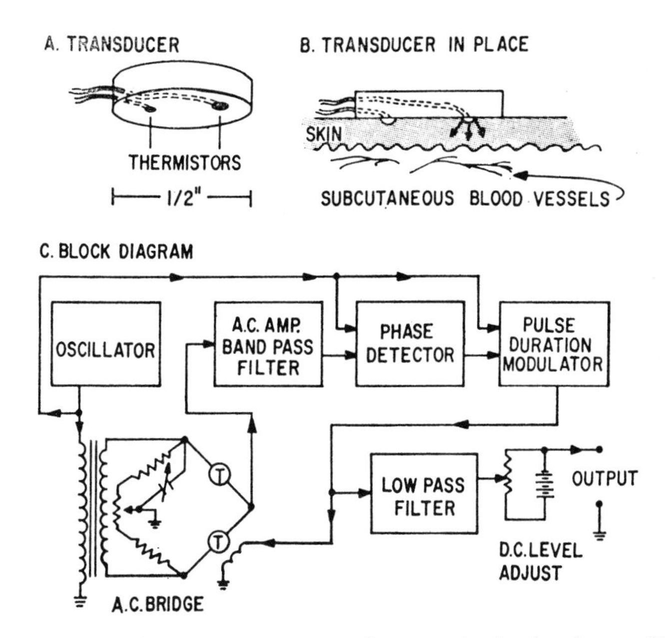

Figure 8.30. Isothermal transcutaneous system for measuring local surface capillary blood flow (reproduced, with permission, from D. C. Harding, R. F. Rushmer, and D. W. Baker, *Med. Biol. Eng.*, **5**, 623–626, Nov. 1967).

can be made using an isothermal heater and reference temperature sensor incorporated either in a needle probe for insertion within the tissue [133, 137] or within a disk for transcutaneous measurements [134–136].

The transcutaneous system described by Harding et al. [136] is illustrated in Figure 8.30. It consists of a half-inch-diameter disk containing two thermistors one of which is enclosed within a heating coil. The two thermistors are balanced in an ac bridge by using the imbalance signal to control the pulse width applied to the heater coil. As pointed out by the authors, calibration of the transducer in absolute terms is difficult; furthermore, placement of the disk is somewhat critical in that large errors may result when the disk is placed near a major vein or artery.

8.4.4 Thin-Film Velocity Probes

The application of heated thin metal films for intravascular flow velocity measurements was reported about the same time in 1968 by two independent groups [128–130]. Both groups developed flow probes less than 1 mm in diameter and successfully demonstrated the measurement of flow velocity profiles in experimental animals. The small probe size and the excellent frequency response when operated under isothermal conditions make the thin-film velometric method unique in its performance characteristics.

Two types of probe developed by Ling et al. [128] are illustrated in Figure 8.31 (a) and (b): one is designed to measure the flow velocity and the other to measure wall shear (i.e., the velocity gradient close to a vessel wall). Both

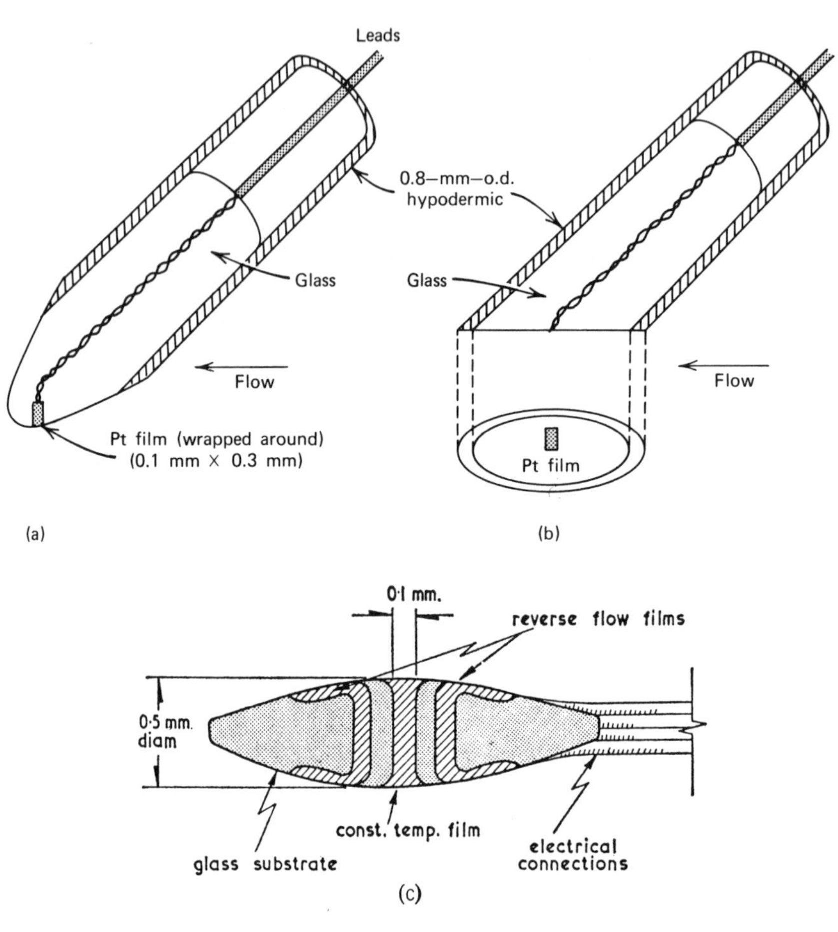

Figure 8.31. Thin-film flow velocity probes: (a) platinum velocity probe; (b) probe for measuring the velocity gradient; (c) directional flow probe [(a) and (b), adapted from Ling et al. [128]; (c), reproduced, with permission, from D. L. Schultz, D. S. Turnstall-Pedoe, G. de J. Lee, A. J. Gunning, and B. J. Belhouse, pp. 172–202 in *Circulatory and Respiratory Mass Transport*, G. E. W. Wolstenholme and J. Knight (eds.), Churchill, London 1969, courtesy of the Ciba Foundation, London].

probes contain a thin strip of platinum (0.1 mm × 0.3 mm) fused to a polished glass surface that forms a plug at the end of an 0.8-mm hypodermic needle. Accurate control of the needle tip is achieved by a micrometer attached to a plastic cuff that fits around the vessel; the depth of penetration through the vessel wall can be varied, thereby enabling the velocity profile to be measured. Measurements close to the vessel wall, where the velocity gradient is large, are best made using the shear probe, since in this region the gradient is fairly constant and the spatial resolution of the probe will be of less importance. A further point to note is that the asymmetrical position of the metal film results in different sensitivities for forward and reverse flows. Since the probe can be rotated to search for the maximum signal amplitude, this enables one to determine the flow direction at a given time in the cardiac cycle.

The dynamic response of the probe when operated under isothermal conditions is governed mainly by the heat capacity of the thin fluid boundary layer rather than by the film–substrate heat exchange. This is because the film temperature is controlled and forced to remain constant, whereas the boundary layer temperature can vary. Fortunately, the boundary layer is very thin, and as a result, the response for mean flow velocities of 100 cm/sec is flat from dc to around 10 kHz.*

Isothermal operation of the film at a temperature slightly above ambient fluid temperature can be achieved [138] using the circuit shown in Figure 8.32. To achieve a linear input–output relationship, Ling et al. [128] used an

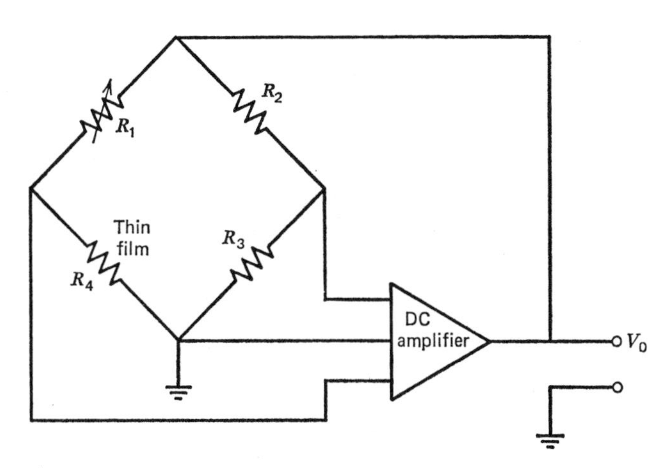

Figure 8.32. DC feedback bridge circuit for isothermal operation of a thin-film velocity sensor [138].

* The response is dependent on the flow velocity: it increases as the mean flow velocity increases, presumably because of the formation of a thinner boundary layer.

analog circuit to correct for the nonlinear velocity versus bridge output relation. Calibration was performed using an oscillating flow generator together with the results of well-established theory. Since the sensitivity is dependent on the fluid properties, calibration was carried out in blood under carefully controlled temperature conditions, the blood being taken from the animal being measured, so that hematocrit variations were eliminated.

Velocity profile measurements performed using blood flowing in a rigid

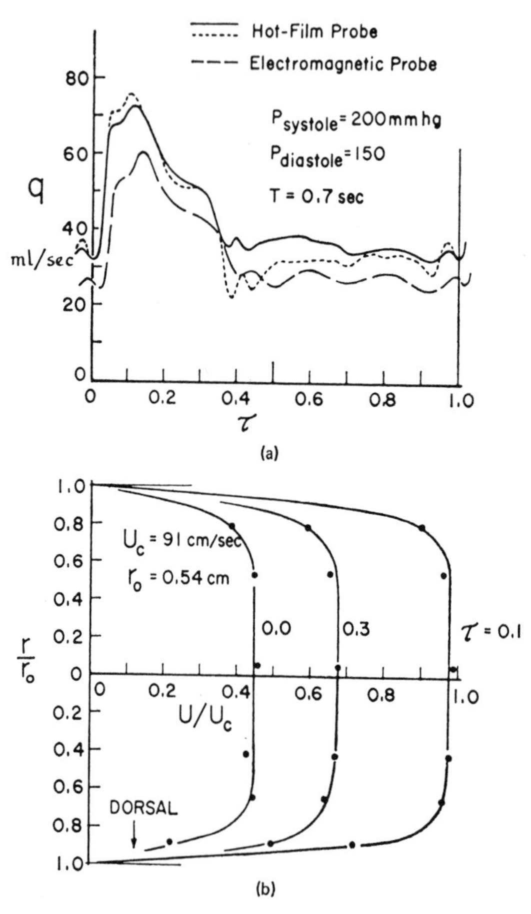

Figure 8.33. Measured total flow and velocity profiles in the thoracic aorta of a pig: (a) total flow; (b) normalized velocity profile, where U_c = central peak flow velocity, $\tau = t/T$, r_0 = inner radius (reproduced, by permission of the American Heart Association Inc., from S. C. Ling, H. B. Atabek, D. L. Fry, D. J. Patel, and J. S. Janicki: "Application of Heated-Film Velocity and Shear Probes to Hemodynamic Studies," *Circ. Res.*, **23**, 789–801, Dec. 1968).

circular conduit under steady conditions yielded the expected parabolic profile if the Reynolds number was less than 300; for larger numbers the profile tended to flatten. In vivo measurements on the thoracic aortic flow of pigs averaged over several hundred cardiac cycles exhibited the very pronounced flattening effect illustrated in Figure 8.33. Measurements on the shear wave at the wall showed that the peak shear stress was approximately one-third of the acute yield stress of endothelial cells.

Schultz et al. [129] used a somewhat different probe, consisting, as illustrated in Figure 8.31(c), of three thin films on a glass-bead substrate. The central film was maintained at a constant temperature using a dc feedback bridge (Figure 8.32); the two outer films were designed to detect flow reversal by measuring the change in heat transport from the central heated film. Measurements were conducted during routine cardiac catheterization to determine the velocity profiles in the aorta and pulmonary artery for patients suffering from mitral incompetence, pulmonary stenosis, aortic incompetence, and aortic stenosis.

A rather simpler, but directionally insensitive, probe using a single film element mounted at the tip of a double-lumen catheter (F7 or 8) has been described by Seed [131, 132]. It is reported that this catheter probe was used for routine measurements of the flow velocity and pressure in the aorta of patients undergoing cardiac catheterization.

8.5 VENOUS OCCLUSION PLETHYSMOGRAPHY

Measurement of the mean blood flow into an extremity or portion thereof is of importance for assessing the adequacy of peripheral flow, for diagnosing defects in the blood vessels and their control, and for assessing the results of vascular reconstructive surgery. Although there exist a number of methods for qualitatively determining the flow to a peripheral region [139–142], the only reliable method that is noninvasive and yet yields quantitative results is the venous occlusion plethysmographic (VOP) method [143, 144].

Basically the VOP technique consists of measuring the volume change in a limb segment when a proximally placed cuff is inflated to occlude just the venous return and a distally placed cuff is inflated to occlude both venous and arterial flow (a complete limb requires only the venous occlusion cuff). Since the venous and arterial flow *out* of the segment cease immediately after the two cuffs are inflated to their correct pressures, the initial rate at which the segment volume increases will be entirely the result of the arterial inflow. Hence, the slope of the volume-change curve (disregarding artifacts arising from the cuff inflation) will be equal to the arterial flow to the segment, and ideally, this should be equal to the preocclusion flow rate.

8.5.1 Water-Filled Plethysmographs

A commonly used method of determining the volume change consists of using a water-filled cuff that surrounds and is sealed to the segment being measured. As illustrated in Figure 8.34(a), a flexible rubber sleeve serves to contain the water between the cuff and a rigid outer container [145]. A transducer detects the volume of water displaced, and a record is produced that may be similar to that shown in Figure 8.34(b). From this record it will be noted that immediately following occlusion, the limb volume increases at a rate which initially remains fairly constant; thereafter, the inflow decreases and eventually a steady-state condition is reached [146]. This condition is determined by the increased venous pressure, which eventually reaches a high enough value to overcome the proximal venous cuff pressure, thereby enabling the inflow and outflow to the segment to equalize.

Since the fractional volume displacements are normally rather small (less than 1%), it is important to insure that the influence of temperature variations be reduced so that troublesome baseline drifts are avoided. Calibration of a water-filled plethysmograph can be achieved either by injecting a known volume of water into the plethysmograph or by injecting a known volume of air into the region above the water. Possible calibration errors arising from these techniques have been discussed by Dahn [145] and by Ardill et al. [147].

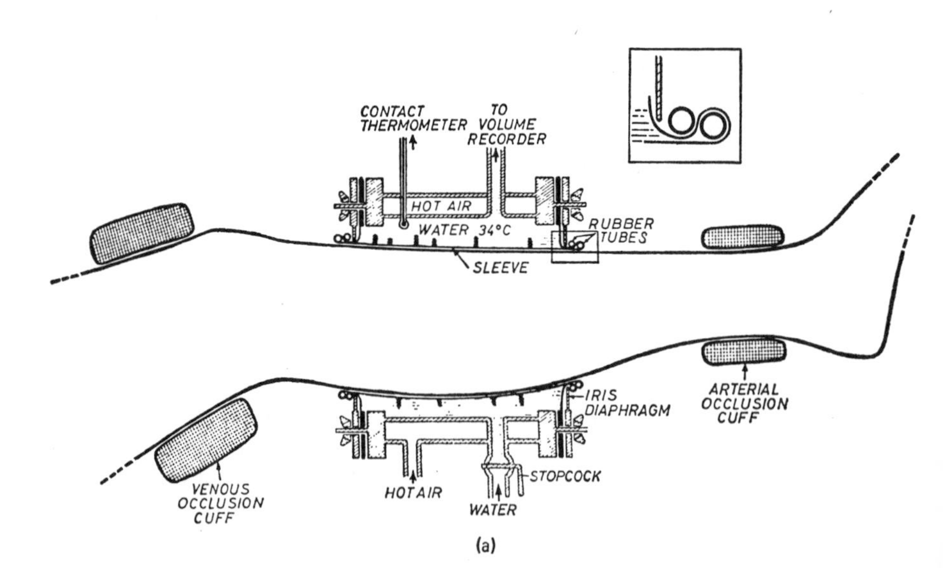

(a)

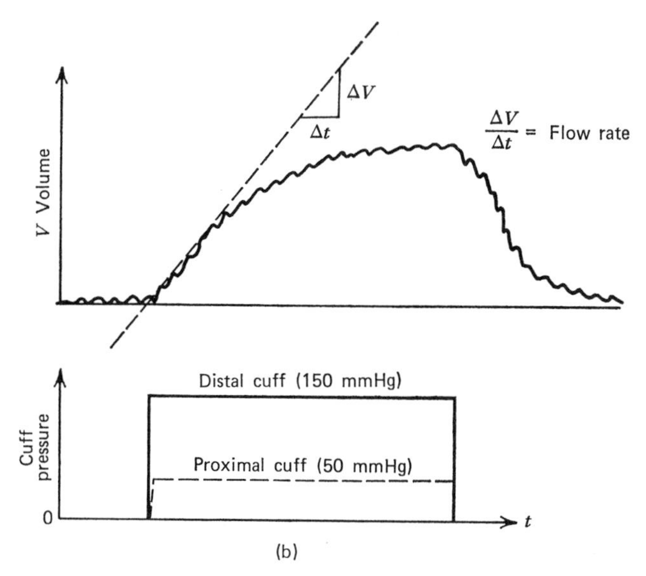

Figure 8.34. A sectional water-filled plethysmograph: (a) Details of construction; (b) sketch of typical record following proximal venous occlusion and distal arterial occlusion (reproduced, with permission, from I. Dahn, *Scand. J. Clin. Lab. Invest.*, **16**, 347–356, 1964).

8.5.2 Air-Filled Systems

Air rather than water can be used to transmit the limb volume changes to a suitable transducer. However, care must be taken to avoid leaks and special account must be taken of the higher thermal expansion coefficient. The use of air provides a much more normal environment for the limb, avoids possible errors arising from the hydrostatic pressure exerted by the water, results in a less cumbersome instrument, and responds much more rapidly, thereby enabling pulsatile volume changes to be more accurately recorded. To circumvent the problem of providing an airtight chamber, other techniques for determining the limb volume change can be employed.

One such method, first proposed by Figar [148, 149] in 1959, consists of measuring the change in electrical capacitance between the limb and a fixed outer electrode that surrounds it [150–153]. By using an additional outer (guard) electrode, surrounding the inner, "active" electrode, stray capacitance variations can be eliminated so that the measured capacitance is simply that of the active electrode to the limb. With careful design using polyurethane filter foam (97% air) to separate the limb surface from the active electrode, Wood and Hyman [150] achieved a linear capacitance versus fractional volume change relation. Although the sensitivity varied with arm diameter, the linear relation remained and the sensitivity could be found from the initial capacitance. By means of analog circuits, the progressive increase in capacitance following venous occlusion was differentiated and surveyed to determine the most consistent portion, and an output was displayed directly in terms of tissue perfusion (i.e., milliliters per 100 ml of tissue per minute).

A second method for determining limb volume changes using an air-filled enclosure is based on measuring the beat-to-beat air flow and integrating the result to obtain the total volume change following cuff inflation. This method proposed and developed by Jonson et al. [154, 155], makes use of a pneumotachograph (a flow impedance combined with a differential pressure transducer) to measure the instantaneous air flow and an integrator to derive the total volume change (Figure 8.35). In the absence of any cuff inflation, the average flow and volume change will be zero; when the proximal and distal cuffs are inflated to the correct pressures, the net area under the flow curve will be positive, and as a result, the volume displacement recording will rise in the pulsatile manner shown in Figure 8.35(b). Perfect sealing of the plethysmograph end walls to the limb is unnecessary if the impedance of any leak is large compared to the pneumotachograph impedance. In the design shown, a good seal is achieved through the use of a double-walled diaphragm whose inner region is connected to a vacuum pump.

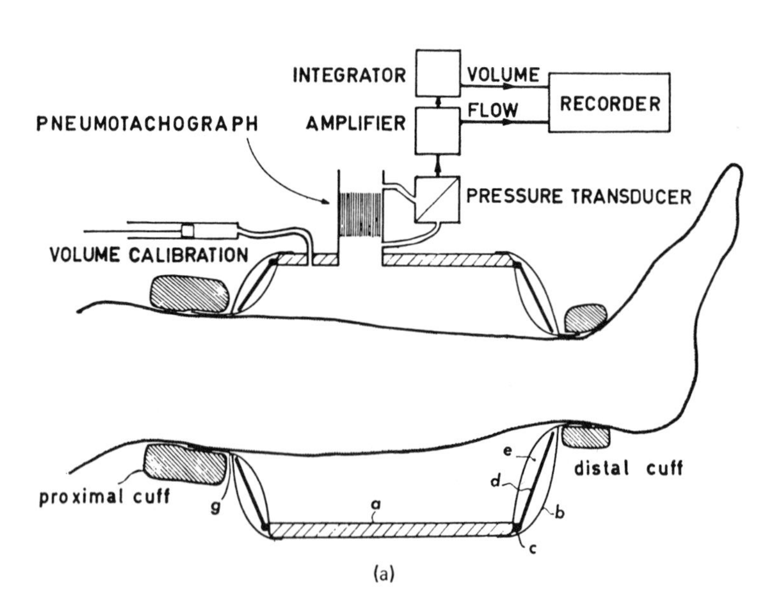

(a)

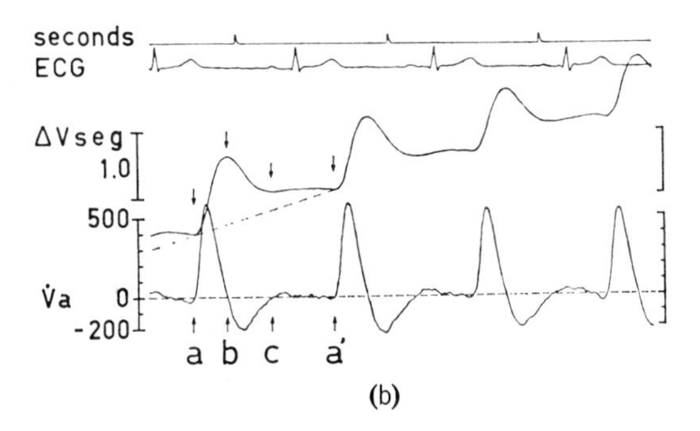

(b)

Figure 8.35. Sectional air-filled plethysmograph. (A), Details of construction: a, rigid acrylic cylinder; d, layered plastic overlapping plates, g, adhesive tape fastening extension of diaphragm to the limb; (B) flow (lower tracing) and volume record following cuff inflation (reproduced, with permission, from I. Dahn, B. Jonson, and R. Nilsen, *J. Appl. Physiol.*, **28**, 333–336, March 1970).

Using a piston pump to force air in and out of the plethysmograph, Dahn et al. [155] measured the system's frequency response. They found it to be essentially flat from dc to 25 Hz, which is quite sufficient to insure distortion-free measurements of the pulse pressure waveform. Nilsén [156] in a series of measurements on the calf of subjects with and without arterial occlusive disease has shown that the peak–peak flow and peak–peak volume pulsations provide a good means of discriminating different degrees of arterial disease. The use of this method, rather than a conventional water-filled plethysmograph, avoids having to produce hyperaemia* (which can be painful and perhaps risky) in order to measure the degree of arterial occlusion.

8.5.3 Strain-Gauge Plethysmography

The use of a mercury-in-rubber strain gauge (see Section 6.1.2) offers the possibility of a considerably more convenient method for deducing the volume change of a limb segment [142, 157–161]. Whitney [157] was the first to realize this and, using a specially designed gauge (the Whitney gauge), established that the results obtained correlated reasonably well with those obtained using a water-filled plethysmograph. Basically, the method consists of surrounding the limb segment with an elastic strain gauge and recording the fractional resistance change. Now, it was shown in Section 6.1.2 that for small extensions the fractional resistance change is related to the fractional

* Produced by a few minutes arterial occlusion in order to achieve a low transient vascular bed resistance.

length change by $\Delta R/R \simeq 2\Delta L/L$. If it is assumed that the fractional limb volume change is twice the fractional girth change (i.e., $\Delta V/V = 2\Delta L/L$), it follows that $\Delta V/V = \Delta R/R$. Thus, a measurement of the resistance change enables the volume change to be deduced [162].

Although there has been some controversy concerning the ability of the strain-gauge method to yield absolute results [141, 142, 162, 163], some further light on this matter has been shed through the work of Dahn and Hallbook [163]. These authors report the results of water plethysmographic and simultaneous elastic strain-gauge measurements on the calf. In their discussion of the results they state: "It would therefore appear justified to conclude that strain gauge plethysmography and water plethysmography are equally good methods for measuring arterial flow and venous emptying, but the values obtained with the two methods are not strictly comparable because the water pressure in the water plethysmograph tends to reduce the flow through the limb somewhat and to increase the rate of venous emptying." They also point out that placement of the strain gauge around the region of maximum girth is very important to insure good agreement with the water plethysmograph: displacement of the gauge a centimeter to either side can result in entirely different readings.

8.6 THE FICK AND RAPID-INJECTION INDICATOR DILUTION METHODS

The methods to be briefly described in this section are of considerable practical importance in that they allow the average flow through an organ to be determined without requiring major surgical intervention. Of the many variations of these methods that have been described in the literature, some are particularly suited to flow determinations of a particular organ or region, while others are of more general use. A proper review of the theory [164–169], sources of error, and a critical comparison of the various methods would require a great deal of space—far more than is available here. In view of this as well as the stated objective of this chapter to emphasize transduction techniques that yield pulsatile flow information, only a brief summary of the principles involved and some examples of their application will be presented.

8.6.1 Methods Based on the Fick Principle

In 1870 Fick stated a simple and self-evident principle that has provided the physiologist and clinician with one of the most reliable methods for measuring the average flow through organs. Quite simply, the Fick principle states that if the concentration of a certain indicator substance is known at the input and output sides of an organ and if the amount of this substance added to, or eliminated from, the organ per unit time is also known, then the volumetric flow rate can be found from

$$\text{Flow (l/min)} = \frac{\text{mg indicator removed or added/min}}{\text{Input–output concentration difference (mg/l)}},$$

or

$$Q = \frac{A}{c_i - c_0}.$$

This equation is valid if steady-state conditions are present at the time of measurement: it does not apply to the case discussed in Section 8.6.2, where a rapid injection of an indicator substance is made.

To illustrate the application of Fick's principle we shall consider the measurement of cardiac output using oxygen as the indicator substance. It is fairly self-evident that the amount of oxygen removed by the lungs per minute must be equal to the pulmonary flow times the venous–arterial oxygen-concentration difference. Now the amount of oxygen removed by the respiratory system can be determined by using, for example, a spirometer to measure the volume flow of respiratory gas and an analyzer to determine the inspired and expired oxygen difference. Samples of pulmonary artery blood and systemic arterial blood can be obtained by venous and arterial catheterization. An analysis of these samples enables c_i and c_0 to be found, thereby enabling the cardiac output to be calculated.

An alternative example of the application of Fick's principle in determining cardiac output is to inject an optical dye at a constant rate into the pulmonary artery and to measure its concentration photometrically in arterialized blood. The difficulty here is that recirculation causes the dye concentration to increase almost continuously, thereby tending to prevent the attainment of a steady-state condition. However, shortly following the start of the injection, before recirculation has had time to become effective, a steady-state plateau may be attained. If the concentration of dye in the arterial blood is measured during this time, the cardiac output can be successfully calculated.

One way around the recirculation problem is to use a substance that is eliminated somewhere in the circulatory path. Xenon, for example, is found to be released from blood as it passes through the lungs, and it returns only in small and predictable amounts back to the right side of the heart [170]. The measurement procedure consists of infusing ^{133}Xe at a constant rate into the inferior vena cava and sampling the blood in the pulmonary artery by means of a catheter. In addition, a femoral-artery blood sample is also taken to enable a small correction to be made for recirculation. Using standard liquid-scintillation counting techniques, the xenon concentration in the samples is determined, thereby enabling the pulmonary blood flow to be calculated.

8.6.2 Rapid-Injection Dilution Methods

Such methods involve the rapid injection of a bolus of a suitable indicator substance at the input side of an organ and the measurement of the time-varying indicator concentration at the output side. The concentration recording that results is called an *indicator dilution curve* (IDC).

Unlike methods that are based on Fick's principle, the rapid-injection method is a non-steady-state technique that relies on all the indicator added to the flow stream being transported to the output. If the indicator concentration at the output side is $c(t)$, then for a steady flow of Q (in l/min), the amount of indicator dI passing the output measuring point in a time interval dt at a time t is given by

$$dI = Qc(t)\,dt.$$

Integrating both sides from $t = 0$ to $t = \infty$ and noting that the total quantity of indicator in the bolus (I) is simply the integral of dI, we find that the flow is given by

$$Q = \frac{I}{\int_0^\infty c(t)\,dt}; \tag{14}$$

that is, the area under the IDC enables the flow to be found if the effects of recirculation can either be eliminated or ignored. A further point to note concerning the IDC is that the total volume of fluid contained between the injection and measurement sites is given by

$$V = Q \cdot t_m,$$

where

$$t_m = \frac{\int_0^\infty tc(t)\,dt}{\int_0^\infty c(t)\,dt} \tag{15}$$

is the mean transit time.

As shown in Figure 8.36, the shape of a typical IDC for cardiac output measurements consists of an initial delay followed by a "hill" with a down-slope shape that is close to an exponential decay but that is contaminated by the effects of recirculation. Diffusion of the indicator substance in the moving blood stream causes the IDC to be spread out, the amount of spreading being dependent on the mean transit time. Superimposed on the IDC may be small periodic fluctuations reflecting the pulsatile nature of the flow.

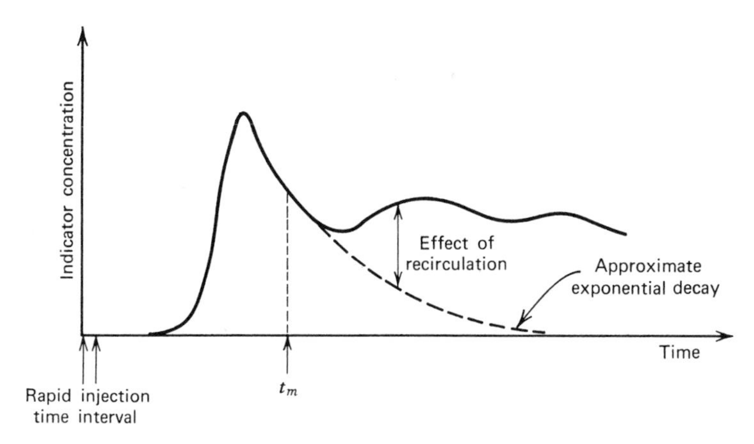

Figure 8.36. Indicator dilution curve resulting from the rapid injection of an indicator, showing the effects of recirculation.

To separate out the two components of the IDC so that the integral of $c(t)$ can be found without including the effects of recirculation, it is often assumed that the uncontaminated curve has an exponential downslope. By plotting the IDC in a log–linear manner, the exponential downslope is transformed into a straight line, which can then be extrapolated for large times, thereby enabling the required integral to be determined. The extrapolation and integration are often carried out with either a special purpose analog or digital computer, and the cardiac output is displayed or recorded immediately.

Many methods exist for implementing the rapid-injection technique. Dyes that alter the optical properties of blood are frequently used in clinical practice. One dye in particular—namely, indocyanine green—has the important property that its optical absorption peak occurs at 8050 Å, corresponding to the point in the spectrum (the isobestic wavelength) where the optical absorption coefficient of blood is essentially independent of the degree of oxygenation. This avoids the necessity of making any corrections for the degree of saturation of the sampled blood.

Measurement of the absorption coefficient can be made by continuously withdrawing blood from the sampling site through a catheter into a specially designed dichromatic densitometer [169]. Some corrections for the effects of catheter distortion on the IDC may have to be applied, depending on the physical arrangements. This last problem is avoided by using a fiber-optics catheter containing two separate fiber bundles, one to transmit light at two wavelengths from suitable sources and the other to transmit the light reflected by the blood at the catheter tip so that its intensity can be measured.

In this way an IDC can be recorded directly from the site at which the catheter tip is located [171, 172].

The use of a thermal indicator, in which temperature is the measured parameter, offers the important advantage that the effects of the indicator are eliminated in one pass around the circulatory system. As a result, repeated measurements can be made without encountering the problems associated with an accumulating background of indicator [173]. In its application for the measurement of cardiac output, the method normally consists of injecting a bolus of cold physiological saline into the right atrium. A thermistor probe located in the pulmonary artery can be used to record the resulting downstream temperature waveform.

To see how this waveform enables the flow to be determined, consider a volume V of injectate, of density ζ_I, specific heat χ_I at a temperature T_I, injected into the blood stream whose temperature is T_B. The amount of heat removed from the blood in warming the saline to a temperature T_B is therefore given by

$$I = V\zeta_I\chi_I(T_B - T_I).$$

Assuming that the injectate volume is small, the change in the amount of heat passing the sampling point is given approximately by

$$dI = Q\zeta_B\chi_B[T_B - T(t)]\,dt$$

where $T(t)$ is the temperature measured by the thermistor probe and Q is the flow rate. Integrating both sides of this equation from $t = 0$ to $t = \infty$, we find that the volume flow rate is given by

$$Q = \frac{V\zeta_I\chi_I(T_B - T_I)}{\zeta_B\chi_B\int_0^\infty [T_B - T(t)]\,dt}. \qquad (16)$$

One source of error with this method is the heat transfer to the bolus as it travels down the injection catheter. A way to correct this is to measure the temperature of the bolus as it emerges from the catheter and to integrate the resulting injectate temperature curve. This integral then enables the corrected form of Eq. (16) to be found.

It is of interest to note that the thermal method for measuring cardiac output can be made using a single venous puncture. Ganz et al. [174] have described a special double-catheter arrangement. The inner catheter with a thermistor probe at its tip can be advanced through the outer lumen so that the thermistor is located in the pulmonary artery. The outer catheter, which has a thermistor mounted at the side of its tip, is located in the right atrium and is used for the injection. Both the injectate and dilution curves can thereby be measured and the results integrated to yield the pulmonary artery flow.

REFERENCES

1. Fry, D. L. "General Considerations in Selecting A Flow Detection Technic," in R. F. Rushmer, Ed., *Methods in Medical Research*, Vol. XI. Year Book: Chicago, 1966, pp. 44–49.
2. Fry, D. L., and Ross, J. "Survey of Flow Detection Technics," in Ref. 1, pp. 50–69.
3. Roberts, C., Ed. *Blood Flow Measurement*. Williams and Wilkins: Baltimore, 1972.
4. Shercliff, J. A. *The Theory of Electromagnetic Flow Measurement*. Cambridge Univ. Press: Cambridge, 1962.
5. Kolin, A. "Electromagnetic Velometry. I. A Method For the Determination of Fluid Velocity Distribution in Space and Time." *J. Appl. Phys.*, **15**, 150–164 (February 1944).
6. Wyatt, D. G. "The Electromagnetic Blood Flowmeter." *J. Sci. Instrum.*, ser. 2, **1**, 1146–1152 (December 1968).
7. Ferguson, D. J., and Londahl, H. D. "Magnetic Meters: Effects of Electrical Resistance in Tissues on Flow Measurements and an Improved Calibration for Square-Wave Circuits." *Circ. Res.*, **14**, 917–929 (November 1966).
8. Gessner, U. "Effects on the Vessel Wall on Electromagnetic Flow Measurements." *Biophys. J.*, **1**, 627–637 (November 1961).
9. Edgerton, R. H. "The Effect of Arterial Wall Thickness and Conductivity on Electromagnetic Flowmeter Readings." *Med. Biol. Eng.*, **6**, 627–636 (November 1968).
10. Wyatt, D. G. "Dependence of Electromagnetic Flowmeter Sensitivity upon Encircled Media." *Phys. Med. Biol.*, **13**, 529–534 (October 1968).
11. Bevir, M. K. "The Effect of Conducting Pipe Connections and Surrounding Liquid on the Sensitivity of Electromagnetic Flowmeters." *J. Phys. D*, **5**, 717–729 (April 1972).
12. Goodman, A. H. "A Transistorized Squarewave Electromagnetic Flowmeter. II. The Flow Transducer." *Med. Biol. Eng.*, **7**, 133–141 (March 1969).
13. Dedichen, H., and Schenk, W. G. "Influence of Hematocrit Changes in Square-Wave Electromagnetic Flowmeter Calibration," in C. Cappelen, Ed., *New Findings in Blood Flowmetry*. Universitetsforlaget: Oslo, 1968, pp. 104–106.
14. Beck, R.; Morris, J. A.; and Assali, N. S. "Calibration Characteristics of the Pulsed-Field Electromagnetic Flowmeter." *Am. J. Med. Electron.*, **4**, 87–91 (April–June 1965).
15. Dennis, J., and Wyatt, D. G. "Effect of Hematocrit Value Upon Electromagnetic Flowmeter Sensitivity." *Circ. Res.*, **24**, 875–886 (June 1969).

16. Baker, R. C. "Solutions of the Electromagnetic Flowmeter Equation for Cylindrical Geometries." *Brit. J. Appl. Phys.* (*J. Phys. D*), **1**, 895–899 (July 1968).

17. Bevir, M. K. "The Predicted Effects of Red Blood Cells on Electromagnetic Flowmeter Sensitivity." *J. Phys. D*, **4**, 387–399 (March 1971).

18. Bevir, M. K. "The Theory of Induced Voltage Electromagnetic Flowmeters." *J. Fluid Mech.*, **43**, 577–590 (September 1970).

19. Shercliff, J. A. "The Effects of Nonuniform Magnetic Fields and Variations of Velocity Distribution in Electromagnetic Flowmeters," in Ref. 13, pp. 45–48.

20. Goldman, S. C.; Marple, N. B.; and Scolnick, W. L. "Effects of Flow Profile on Electromagnetic Flowmeter Accuracy." *J. Appl. Physiol.*, **18**, 652–657 (May 1963).

21. Bevir, M. K. "Long Induced Voltage Electromagnetic Flowmeters and the Effect of Velocity Profile." *Quart. J. Mech. Appl. Math.*, **24**, 347–372 (1971).

22. Wyatt, D. "Velocity Profile Effects in Electromagnetic Flowmeters," in Ref. 3, Chapter 15.

23. Rummel, T., and Ketelsen, B. "Inhomogenes Magnetfeld Ermöglicht Induktive Durchflubmessung bei Allen in der Praxis vorkommenden Stromungsprofilen." *Regelungstechnik*, **14**, 262–267 (1966).

24. Clark, D. M., and Wyatt, D. G. "The Effect of Magnetic Field Inhomogeneity on Flowmeter Sensitivity," in Ref. 13, pp. 49–54.

25. Wyatt, D. G. "Problems in the Measurement of Blood Flow by Magnetic Induction." *Phys. Med. Biol.*, **5**, 289–320 (January 1961); and **5**, 369–399 (April 1961).

26. Jochim, K. E. "The Development of the Electromagnetic Blood Flowmeter." *IRE Trans. Bio-Med. Electron.*, **BME-9**, 228–235 (October 1962).

27. Browning, C.; Pelling, D.; and Ledingham, J. M. "An Electromagnetic Flowmeter for Studying Changes of Cardiac Output in Unanesthetized Rats." *Med. Biol. Eng.*, **7**, 549–558 (September 1969).

28. Kolin, A. "Electromagnetic Rheometry and Its Application to Blood Flow Measurements." *Am. J. Physiol.*, **122**, 797–804 (June 1938).

29. Denison, A. B.; Spencer, M. P.; and Green, H. D. "A Square-Wave Electromagnetic Flowmeter for Application to Intact Blood Vessels." *Circ. Res.*, **3**, 39–46 (January 1955).

30. Denison, A. B., and Spencer, M. P. "Square-Wave Electromagnetic Flowmeter Design." *Rev. Sci. Instrum.*, **27**, 707–711 (September 1956).

31. Yanof, H. M.; Salz, P.; and Rosen, A. L. "Improvements in Trapezoidal-Wave Electromagnetic Flowmeter." *J. Appl. Physiol.*, **18**, 230–232 (January 1963).

32. Wyatt, D. G. "Baseline Errors in Cuff Electromagnetic Flowmeters." *Med. Biol. Eng.*, **4**, 17–45 (January 1966).

33. Hognestad, H. "Square-Wave Electromagnetic Flowmeter with Improved Baseline Stability"' *Med. Res. Eng.*, **5**, 28–33 (1966).

34. Cox, P.; Arora, H.; and Kolin, A. "Electromagnetic Determination of Carotid Blood Flow in the Anesthetized Rat." *IEEE Trans. Bio-Med. Electron.*, **BME-10**, 171–173 (October 1963).

35. Kolin, A., and Vanyo, J. "New Design of Miniature Electromagnetic Blood Flow Transducers Suitable for Semi-Automatic Production." *Cardiovasc. Res.*, **1**, 274–286 (July 1967).

36. Wyatt, D. G. "The Design of Electromagnetic Flowmeter Heads," in Ref. 13, pp. 69–74.

37. Bergel, D. H., and Gessner, U. "The Electromagnetic Flowmeter," in Ref. 1, pp. 70–82.

38. Greenfield, J. C.; Patel, D. J.; Mallos, A. J.; and Fry, D. L. "Evaluation of the Kolin Type Electromagnetic Flowmeter and the Pressure Gradient Technique." *J. Appl. Physiol.*, **17**, 372–374 (March 1962).

39. O'Rourke, M. F. "Impact Pressure, Lateral Pressure, and Impedance in the Proximal Aorta and Pulmonary Artery." *J. Appl. Physiol.*, **25**, 533–541 (November 1968).

40. Cannon, J. A. "The Requirements of the Clinician and Surgeon in the Design of Blood Flow Probes," in Ref. 13, pp. 88–90.

41. Williams, B. T.; Sancho-Fornos, S.; Clarke, D. B.; Abrams, L. D.; and Schenk, W. G. "Continuous, Long-Term Measurement of Cardiac Output After Open-Heart Surgery." *Ann. Surg.*, **174**, 357–363 (September 1971).

42. Williams, B.; Sancho-Fornos, S.; Clarke, D.; Abrams, L.; and Schenk, W. G. "Cardiac Output: Continuous Measurement After Open Heart Surgery," in Ref. 3, Chapter 22.

43. Kolin, A. "Electromagnetic Blood Flowmeters." *Science*, 23 October 1959, pp. 1088–1097.

44. Kolin, A., and Wisshaupt, R. "Single-Coil Electromagnetic Blood Flow Meters." *IEEE Trans. Bio-Med. Electron.*, **BME-10**, 60–67 (April 1963).

45. Khouri, E. M., and Gregg, D. E. "Miniature Electromagnetic Flowmeter Applicable to Coronary Arteries." *J. Appl. Physiol.*, **18**, 224–226 (January 1963).

46. Clark, D. M., and Wyatt, D. G. "An Improved Perivascular Electromagnetic Flowmeter." *Med. Biol. Eng.*, **7**, 185–190 (March 1969).

47. Mills, C. J. "A Catheter Tip Electromagnetic Velocity Probe." *Phys. Med. Biol.*, **11**, 323–324 (April 1966).

48. Mills, C. J., and Shillingford, J. P. "A Catheter Tip Electromagnetic Velocity Probe and its Evaluation." *Cardiovasc. Res.*, **1**, 263–273 (July 1967).

49. Bevir, M. K. "Sensitivity of Electromagnetic Velocity Probes." *Phys. Med. Biol.*, **16**, 229–232 (April 1971).

50. Wexler, L.; Bergel, D. H.; Gabe, I. T.; Makin, G. S.; and Mills, C. J. "Velocity of Blood Flow in Normal Human Venae Cavae." *Circ. Res.*, **23**, 349–359 (September 1968).

51. Gabe, I. T.; Gault, J. H.; Ross, J.; Mason, D. T.; Mills, C. J.; Shillingford, J. P.; and Braunwald, E. "Measurement of Instantaneous Blood Flow Velocity and Pressure in Conscious Man by a Catheter-Tip Velocity Probe." *Circulation*, **40**, 603–614 (November 1969).

52. Mason, D. T.; Gabe, I. T.; Mills, C. J.; Gault, J. H.; Ross, J.; Braunwald, E.; and Shillingford, J. P. "Applications of the Catheter-Tip Electromagnetic Velocity Probe in the Study of the Central Circulation in Man." *Am. J. Med.*, **49**, 465–471 (October 1970).

53. Mills, C. J.; Gabe, I. T.; Gault, J. H.; Mason, D. T.; Ross, J.; Braunwald, E.; and Shillingford, J. P. "Pressure-Flow Relationship and Vascular Impedance in Man." *Cardiovasc. Res.*, **4**, 405–417 (October 1970).

54. Spencer, M. P., and Barefoot, C. A. "Sensor Design for Electromagnetic Flowmeters," in Ref. 13, pp. 75–87.

55. Bond, R. F., and Barefoot, C. A. "Evaluation of an Electromagnetic Catheter Tip Velocity-Sensitive Blood Flow Probe." *J. Appl. Physiol.*, **23**, 403–409 (September 1967).

56. Warbassee, J. R.; Hellman, B. H.; Gillilan, R. E.; Hawley, R. R.; and Babitt, H. I. "Physiologic Evaluation of a New Catheter Tip Electromagnetic Velocity Probe. A New Instrument." *Am. J. Cardiol.* **23**, 424–433 (March 1969).

57. Jones, M. A. S., and Wyatt, D. G. "The Surface Temperature of Electromagnetic Velocity Probes." *Cardiovasc. Res.*, **4**, 388–397 (July 1970).

58. Buchanan, J. W., and Shabetai, R. "True Power Dissipation of Catheter Tip Velocity Probes." *Cardiovasc. Res.*, **6**, 211–213 (April 1972).

59. Stein, P. D., and Schuette, W. H. "New Catheter-Tip Flowmeter with Velocity Flow and Volume Flow Capabilities." *J. Appl. Physiol.*, **26**, 851–856 (June 1969).

60. Kolin, A.; Ross, G.; Grollman, J. H.; and Archer, J. "An Electromagnetic Catheter Flow Meter for Determination of Blood Flow in Major Arteries." *Proc. Nat. Acad. Sci.*, **59**, 808–815 (1968).

61. Kolin, A. "A Radial Field Electromagnetic Intravascular Flow Sensor." *IEEE Trans. Bio-Med. Eng.*, **BME-16**, 220–221 (July 1969).

62. Kolin, A. "An Electromagnetic Catheter Blood Flow Meter of Minimal Lateral Dimensions." *Proc. Nat. Acad. Sci.*, **66**, 53–56 (May 1970).

63. Gasking, J. "Measurement of Aortic Blood Flow Using an Extracorporial Magnetic Field," in Ref. 3, Chapter 17.

64. Biscar, J. P. "Three-Electrode Probe for Catheter-Type Blood Flowmeters," *IEEE Trans. Bio-med. Eng.*, **BME-20**, 62–63 (January 1973).

65. Wyatt, D. G. "Noise in Electromagnetic Flowmeters." *Med. Biol. Eng.*, **4**, 333–346 (July 1966).

66. Westersten, A.; Herrold, G.; Abbott, E.; and Assali, N. S. "Gated Sine-Wave Electromagnetic Flowmeter." *IRE Trans. Med. Electron.*, **ME-6**, 213–215 (December 1959).

67. Kolin, A. "Blood Flow Determination by Electromagnetic Method," in O. Glasser, Ed., *Medical Physics*, Vol. III. Year Book: Chicago, 1960, pp. 141–155.

68. Wyatt, D. G. "Electromagnetic Flowmeter for Use with Intact Vessels." *J. Physiol.*, **173**, 8P–9P (June 1964).

69. Hutcheon, I. C., and Harrison, D. N. "A Transistor Quadrature Suppressor for A.C. Servo Systems." *Proc. IEE*, B, **107**, 73–82 (January 1960).

70. Goodman, A. H. "A Transistorized Squarewave Electromagnetic Flowmeter. I. The Amplifier System." *Med. Biol. Eng.*, **7**, 115–132 (March 1969).

71. Hognestad, H. "Some Problems in Square-Wave Electromagnetic Flowmeter System Design," in Ref. 13, pp. 55–61.

72. Moody, N. F. "Square Wave Flowmeter." *Med. Res. Eng.*, **6**, 8 (1st quart., 1967).

73. Gessner, U. "The Performance of the Ultrasonic Flowmeter in Complex Velocity Profiles." *IEEE Trans. Bio-Med. Eng.*, **BME-16**, 139–142 (April 1969).

74. Franklin, D. L.; Baker, D. W.; and Rushmer, R. F. "Pulsed Ultrasonic Transit Time Flowmeter." *IRE Trans. Bio-Med. Electron.*, **BME-9**, 44–49 (January 1962).

75. Baker, D. W. "Pulsed Ultrasonic Flowmeter," in Ref. 1, pp. 107–117.

76. Zarnstorff, W. C.; Castillo, C. A.; and Crumpton, C. W. "A Phase-Shift Ultrasonic Flowmeter." *IRE Trans. Bio-Med. Electron.*, **BME-9**, 199–203 (July 1962).

77. Franklin, D. W.; Kemper, W. S.; and Pierson, E. E. "Frequency Modulated Ultrasound Transit Time Technique for Measurement of Fluid Velocity—Preliminary Report" (Paper 10-12). Proc. 8th Int. Conf. on Med. and Biol. Eng., Chicago, 1969.

78. Noble, F. W. "Dual Frequency Ultrasonic Fluid Flowmeter." *Rev. Sci. Instrum.*, **39**, 1327–1331 (September 1968).

79. Girard, J. P. "Debimetre Ultrasonore a Dephasage: Application au Debit Sanguin." *L'Onde Elect.*, **50**, 390–394 (May 1970).

80. Plass, K. G. "A New Ultrasonic Flowmeter for Intravascular Application." *IEEE Trans. Bio-Med. Eng.*, **BME-11**, 154-156 (October 1964).

81. Scheu, H.; Sager, O.; and Veragut, U. "Eine neue Methode zur Intravasalen Nessung von Stromungsgeschwindigkeiten: die Ultraschallsonde," *Klin. Wochenzeitschr.*, **43**, 608–611 (1965).

82. Scheu, H. D. *Pulsatile Flow Velocity of the Central Arterial Blood: Intravascular Measurement with the Ultrasound Probe. Bibl. Cardiol.*, No. 26. Karger: Basel, 1972, pp. 1–73.

83. Studer, U.; Fricke, G.; and Scheu, H. "Testing of an Improved Ultrasound Flowmeter: Technical Description and Results of Testing in Vitro." *Cardiovasc. Res.*, **4**, 380–387 (July 1970).

84. Fricke, G.; Studer, U.; Scheu, H. D. "Pulsatile Velocity of Blood in the Pulmonary Artery of Dogs: Measurement by an Ultrasound Gauge." *Cardiovasc. Res.*, **4**, 371–379 (July 1970).

85. Rader, R. D.; Meehan, J. P.; and Henriksen, J. K. C. "An Implantable Blood Pressure and Flow Transmitter." *IEEE Trans. Bio-Med. Eng.*, **BME-20**, 37–43 (January 1973).

86. Franklin, D. L.; Watson, N. W.; Pierson, K. E.; and Van Citters, R. L. "Technique for Radio Telemetry of Blood-Flow Velocity from Unrestrained Animals." *Am. J. Med. Electron.*, **5**, 24–28 (1966).

87. Franklin, D. L. "Techniques for Measurement of Blood Flow Through Intact Vessels." *Med. Electron. Biol. Eng.*, **3**, 27–37 (January 1965).

88. Wells, P. N. T. *Physical Principles of Ultrasonic Diagnosis.* Academic: London, 1969.

89. Stegall, H. F.; Rushmer, R. F.; and Baker, D. W. "A Transcutaneous Ultra-Sonic Blood-Velocity Meter." *J. Appl. Physiol.*, **21**, 707–711 (March 1966).

90. Kato, K.; Motomiya, M.; Izumi, T.; Kaneko, Z.; Shiraishi, J.; Omizo, H.; and Nakano, S. "Linearity of Readings on Ultrasonic Flow Meter." Digest, 6th Int. Conf. Med. Electron. and Biol. Eng., Tokyo, 1965, pp. 284–285.

91. Flax, S. W.; Webster, J. G.; and Updike, S. J., "Statistical Evaluation of the Doppler Ultrasonic Blood Flowmeter," in R. J. Gowan, C. E. Tucker, and J. K. Aikawa, Eds., *Biomedical Sciences Instrumentation*, Vol. VII. Instrument Society of America: Pittsburgh, 1970.

92. Arts, M. G. J., and Roevros, J. M. J. G. "On the Instantaneous Measurement of Blood Flow by Ultrasonic Means." *Med. Biol. Eng.*, **10**, 23–34 (January 1972).

93. Vatner, S. F.; Franklin, D.; and Van Citters, R. L. "Simultaneous Comparison and Calibration of the Doppler and Electromagnetic Flowmeters." *J. Appl. Physiol.*, **29**, 907–910 (December 1970).

94. McLeod, F. D. "A Directional Doppler Flowmeter." Digest, 7th Int. Conf. Med. Biol. Eng., Stockholm, 1967, p. 213.

95. Hirschberg, H. "Ultrasonic Techniques in Blood Flow Measurement," in Ref. 13, pp. 23–26.

96. Light, L. H. "Direction-Resolving Doppler System and Real-Time Analogue Spectral Recorder for Transcutaneous Aortovelography." Digest, 9th Int. Conf. Med. Biol. Eng., Melbourne, 1971, p. 228.

97. Chiche, P.; Kalmanson, D.; Veyrat, C.; and Toutain, G. "Enregistrement Transcutané du Flux Arteriel par Fluxmètre Directionnel à Effet Doppler. Description d'un Appareillage et Premiers Résultats." *Bull. Mém. Soc. Méd. Hôp. Paris* (*Ann. Med. Int.*), **119**, 87–95 (January 1968).

98. Mackay, R. S. "Non-invasive Cardiac Output Measurement." *Microvasc. Res.*, **4**, 438–452 (1972).

99. Flax, S. W.; Webster, J. G.; and Updike, S. J. "Pitfalls Using Doppler Ultrasound to Transduce Blood Flow." *IEEE Trans. Bio-med. Eng.*, **BME-20**, 306–309 (July 1973).

100. Baker, D. W. "Pulsed Ultrasonic Doppler Blood-Flow Sensing." *IEEE Trans. Sonics Ultrasonics*, **SU-17**, 170–185 (July 1970).

101a. Peronneau, P. A., and Leger, F. "Doppler Ultrasonic Pulsed Blood Flowmeter" (Paper 10-11). Proc. 8th Int. Conf. Med. Biol. Eng., Chicago, 1969.

101b. Peronneau, P.; Hinglais, J.; Pellet, M.; and Leger, F. "Velocimetre Sanguin par Effet Doppler a Emission Ultra-Sonore Pulsee." *L'Onde Elect.*, **50**, 369–384 (May 1970).

102. Peronneau, P.; Xhaard, M.; Nowicki, A.; Pellet, M.; Delouche, P.; and Hinglais, J. "Pulsed Ultrasonic Flowmeter and Flow Pattern Analysis," in Ref. 3, Chapter 2.

103. Stegall, H. F.; Stone, H. L.; and Bishop, V. S. "A Catheter-Tip Pressure and Velocity Sensor" (Paper 27.4). Proc. 20th Ann. Conf. Eng. Med. Biol., Boston, 1967.

104. Stone, H. L.; Stegall, H. F.; Bishop, V. S.; and Laenger, C. "Continuous Measurement of Blood Flow Velocity with an Intravascular Doppler Flowmeter." Digest of Tech. Papers, 7th Int. Conf. Med. Biol. Eng., Stockholm, 1967, p. 215.

105a. Benchimol, A.; Stegall, H. F.; Maroko, P. R.; Gartlan, J. L.; and Brener, L. "Aortic Flow Velocity in Man During Cardiac Arrhythmias Measured with the Doppler Catheter Flowmeter System." *Am. Heart J.*, **78**, 649–659 (November 1969).

105b. Benchimol, A.; Stegall, H. F.; Gartlan, J. L.; Barreto, E. C; Goldstein. M. R.; and Sandoval, J. "Right Atrium and Superior Vena Cava Flow Velocity in Man Measured with the Doppler-Catheter Flowmeter-Telemetry System." *Am. J. Med.*, **48**, 303–309 (March 1970).

106a. Kalmanson, D.; Toutain, G.; Novikoff, N.; Derai, C.; Chiche, P.; and Cabrol, C. "Le Cathétérisme Velocimetrique du Coeur et des Gros Vaisseaux par Sonde Ultrasonique Directionelle a Effet Doppler. Rapport Preliminaire." *Ann. Méd. Interne.*, **120**, 685–700 (November 1969).

106b. Kalmanson, D.; Toutain, G.; Novikoff, N.; and Derai, C. "Retrograde Catheterization of Left Heart Cavities in Dogs by Means of an Orientable Directional Doppler Catheter-Tip Flowmeter: A Preliminary Report." *Cardiovasc. Res.*, **6**, 309–318 (May 1972).

107. Kalmanson, D.; Derai, C.; and Novikoff, N. "Le Flux Tricuspidien Etudie Chez L'Animal et Chez L'Homme par Catheterisme Velocimetrique Directionnel: Aspect Normal Variations Physiologiques et Applications Diagnostiques." *Arch. Maladies Coeur Vaisseaux*, **64**, 854–873 (1971).

108. Satomura, S., and Kaneko, Z. "Ultrasonic Blood Rheograph." Proc. 3rd Int. Conf. on Med. Electron., London, 1960, pp. 254–258.

109. Rushmer, R. F.; Baker, D. W.; and Stegall, H. F. "Transcutaneous Doppler Flow Detection as a Nondestructive Technique." *J. Appl. Physiol.*, **21**, 554–566 (March 1966).

110. Yau, S. T., and Ashton, J. P. "Transcutaneous Measurement of Blood Flow by Ultrasound." *Bio-Med. Eng.*, **5**, 230–233 (May 1970).

111. McLeod, F. D. "The Pulsed Doppler Flow Probe as a Diameter Gage.' Digest, 9th Int. Conf. Med. Biol. Eng., Melbourne, 1971, p. 277.

112. Reagan, T. R.; Miller, C. W.; and Strandness, D. E. "Transcutaneous Measurement of Femoral Artery Flow." *J. Surg. Res.*, **11**, 477–482 (October 1971).

113. Miller, C. W., and Histand, M. B. "Nontraumatic Measurement of Blood Flow Velocity and Wall Motion in the Thoracic Aorta." Digest, 10th Int. Conf. Med. Biol. Eng., Dresden, 1973, p. 319.

114. Light, L. H. "Transcutaneous Observation of Blood Velocity in the Ascending Aorta in Man," in F. de Freitas, Ed., *Ballistocardiography and Cardiovascular Therapy. Bibl. Cardiol.*, No. 26. Karger: Basel, 1970.

115. Light, L. H., and Cross, G. "Cardiovascular Data by Transcutaneous Aortovelography," in Ref. 3, Chapter 11.

116. Greenfield, J. C. "Pressure Gradient Technique," in Ref. 1, pp. 83–93.

117. Fry, D. L. "The Measurement of Pulsatile Blood Flow by the Computed Pressure Gradient Technique." *IRE Trans. Med. Electron.*, **ME-6**, 259–264 (December 1959).

118. Gabe, I. T. "Determination of Arterial Blood Flow by the Pressure Gradient Technique," in Ref. 13, pp. 18–21.

119. Galle, K. R. "Thermal Flowmeters," in Ref. 1, pp. 94–106.

120. Rein, H. "Die Thermo-Stromuhr. Ein Verfahren zur fortlaufenden Messung der mittleren absoluten Durchflussmengen in uneroffneten Gefassen in Situ." *Z. Biol.*, **87**, 394–418 (June 1928).

121. Rein, H. "Die Thermo-Stromuhr. II Mitteilung. Arbeitsbedingungen und Arbeitsmöglichkeiten im Tierversuch," *Z. Biol.*, **89**, 195–201 (September 1929).

122. Gregg, D. E.; Pritchard, W. H.; Eckstein, R. W.; Shipley, R. E.; Rotta, A.; Dingle, J.; Steege, T. W.; and Wearn, J. T. "Observations on the Accuracy of the Thermostromuhr." *Am. J. Physiol.*, **136**, 250–262 (April 1942).

123. Shipley, R. E.; Gregg, D. E.; and Wearn, J. T. "Operative Mechanism of Some Errors in the Application of the Thermostromuhr Method to the Measurement of Blood Flow." *Am. J. Physiol.*, **136**, 263–274 (April 1942).

124. Bennett, H. S.; Sweet, W. H.; and Bassett, D. L. "Heated Thermocouple Flowmeter." *J. Clin. Invest.*, **23**, 200–208 (March 1944).

125. Katsura, S.; Weiss, R.; Baker, D.; and Rushmer, R. F. "Isothermal Blood Flow Velocity Probe." *IRE Trans. Med. Electron.*, **ME-6**, 283–285 (December 1959).

126. Mellander, S., and Rushmer, R. F. "Venous Blood Flow Recorded with an Isothermal Flowmeter." *Acta Physiol. Scand.*, **48**, 13–19 (1960).

127. Grahn, A. R.; Paul, M. H.; and Wessel, H. U. "A New Direction-Sensitive Probe for Catheter-Tip Thermal Velocity Measurements." *J. Appl. Physiol.*, **27**, 407–412 (September 1969).

128. Ling, S. C.; Atabek, H. B.; Fry, D. L.; Patel, D. J.; and Janicki, J. S. "Application of Heated-Film Velocity and Shear Probes to Hemodynamic Studies." *Circ. Res.*, **23**, 789–801 (December 1968).

129. Schultz, D. L.; Turnstall-Pedoe, D. S.; Lee, G. de J.; Gunning, A. J.; and Belhouse, B. J. "Velocity Distribution and Transition in the Arterial System," in G. E. W. Wolstenholme and J. Knight, Eds., *Circulatory and Respiratory Mass Transport*. Churchill: London, 1969, pp. 172–202.

130. Bellhouse, B., Clark, C., and Schultz, D. "Velocity Measurements with Thin Film Gauges," in Ref. 3, Chapter 26.

131. Seed, A. "Hot-Film Anemometry in the Human Aorta," in Ref. 3, Chapter 27.

132. Seed, W. A., and Wood, N. B. "Development and Evaluation of a Hot-Film Velocity Probe for Cardiovascular Studies." *Cardiovasc. Res.*, **4**, 253–263 (April 1970).

133. Hensel, H., and Ruef, J. "Fortlaufende Registrierung der Muskeldurchblutung am Menschen mit einer Calorimetersonde." *Pflüg. Arch.*, **259**, 267–280 (1954).

134. Hensel, H., and Bender, F. "Fortlaufende Bestimmung der Hautdurchblutung am Menschen mit einem electrischen Wärmeleitmesser." *Pflüg. Arch.*, **263**, 603–614 (1956).

135. Hensel, H. "Messkopf zur Durchblutungsregistrierung an Oberflächen," *Pflüg. Arch.*, **268**, 604–606 (1959).

136. Harding, D. C.; Rushmer, R. F.; and Baker, D. W. "Thermal Transcutaneous Flowmeter." *Med. Biol. Eng.*, **5**, 623–626 (November 1967).

137. Levy, L. L.; Stolwijk, J. A. J.; and Graichen, H. "Evaluation of Local Brain Blood Flow by Continuous Direct Measurement of Thermal Conductivity." Digest of the 7th Int. Conf. on Med. and Biol. Eng., Stockholm, 1967, p. 217.

138. Bellhouse, B. J., and Bellhouse, F. H. "Thin-Film Gauges for the Measurement of Velocity of Skin Friction in Air, Water, or Blood." *J. Sci. Instrum.*, **1**, 1211–1213 (December 1968).

139. Bruner, H. D., Ed. *Methods in Medical Research*, Vol. VIII. Year Book: Chicago, 1960, pp. 222–292.

140. Abramson, D. I. *Circulation in the Extremities*. Academic: New York, 1967.

141. Burger, H. C.; Horeman, H. W.; and Brakkee, A. J. M. "Comparison of Some Methods for Measuring Peripheral Blood Flow." *Phys. Med. Biol.*, **4**, 168–175 (October 1959).

142. Greenfield, A. D. M.; Whitney, R. J.; and Mowbray, J. F. "Methods for Investigating Peripheral Blood Flow." *Brit. Med. Bull.*, **19**, 101–109 (1963).

143. Greenfield, A. D. M. "Venous Occlusion Plethysmography," Ref. 139, pp. 293–301.

144. Siggaard-Anderson, J. "Venous Occlusion Plethysmography on the Calf: Evaluation of Diagnosis and Results in Vascular Surgery." *Danish Med. Bull.*, **17**, Suppl. (1970).

145. Dahn, I. "On the Calibration and Accuracy of Segmental Calf Plethysmography with a Description of a New Expansion Chamber and a New Sleeve." *Scand. J. Clin. Lab. Invest.*, **16**, 347–356 (1964).

146. Burton, A. C. *Physiology and Biophysics of the Circulation*, 2nd ed., Year Book: Chicago, 1972, Chapter 24.

147. Ardill, B. L.; Bhatnagar, V. M.; Fentem, P. H.; and Greenfield, A. D. M. "Clinical Use of Venous Occlusion Plethysmography." *Scand. J. Clin. Lab. Invest.*, **19**, Suppl. 99, 95–100 (1967).

148. Figar, S. "Electro-Capacitance Plethysmography." *Physiol. Bohemoslav.*, **8**, 275–280 (1959).

149. Figar, S. "A New Radio-Frequency Method for Measuring—for Medical Purpose—the Blood Supply in Various Parts of the Body." *Tech. Dig. (Prague)*, **1**, 489–493 (1959).

150. Hyman, C.; Burrap, D.; and Figar, S. "Bilateral Differences in Forearm Blood Flow as Measured with Capacitance Plethysmograph." *J. Appl. Physiol.*, **18**, 997–1002 (September 1963).

151. Willoughby, E. O. "A Constant Frequency, Differential Electronic Capacitance Plethysmograph." *Proc. Inst. Radio Electron. Eng. Australia*, **26**, 264–272 (August 1965).

152. Wood, J. R., and Hyman, C. "A Direct Reading Capacitance Plethysmograph." *Med. Biol. Eng.*, **8**, 59–70 (January 1970).

153. Sigdell, J. E. "A Theoretical Study of Capacitive Plethysmography." *Med. Biol. Eng.*, **9**, 447–457 (September 1971).

154. Jonson, B. "Pulse Plethysmography." *Scand. J. Clin. Lab. Invest.*, **19**, Suppl. 99, 106–107 (1967).

155. Dahn, I.; Jonson, B.; and Nilsén, R. "A Plethysmographic Method for Determination of Flow and Volume Pulsations in a Limb." *J. Appl. Physiol.*, **28**, 333–336 (March 1970).

156. Nilsén, R. "On the Clinical Use of Pulse Plethysmography of the Calf." *Scand. J. Clin. Lab. Invest.*, **25**, 391–412 (1970).

157. Whitney, R. J. "The Measurement of Volume Changes in Human." *J. Physiol.*, **121**, 1–27 (July 1953).

158. Brakkee, A. J. M., and Vendrik, A. J. H. "Strain-Gauge Plethysmography; Theoretical and Practical Notes on a New Design." *J. Appl. Physiol.*, **21**, 701–704 (March 1966).

159. Hallbrook, T.; Mansson, B.; and Nilsén, R. "A Strain Gauge Plethysmograph with Electrical Calibration." *Scand. J. Clin. Lab. Invest.*, **25**, 413–418 (1970).

160. Barendsen, G. J.; Venema, H.; and van den Berg, J. "Semicontinuous Blood Flow Measurement by Triggered Venous Occlusion Plethysmography." *J. Appl. Physiol.*, **31**, 288–291 (August 1971).

161. Needham, T. N. "The Measurement of Blood Flow: Strain Gauge Plethysmography." *Bio-Med. Eng.*, **7**, 266–269 (July 1972).

162. Sigdell, J. "A Critical Review of the Theory of the Mercury Strain-Gauge Plethysmograph." *Med. Biol. Eng.*, **7**, 365–371 (July 1969).

163. Dahn, I., and Hallbook, T. "Simultaneous Blood Flow Measurements by Water and Strain Gauge Plethysmography." *Scand. J. Clin. Lab. Invest.*, **25**, 419–428 (1970).

164. Bain, W. H., Ed. *Blood Flow Through Organs and Tissues.* Livingstone: Edinburgh, 1968.

165. Taylor, S. H. " Measurement of the Cardiac Output in Man." *Proc. Roy. Soc. Med.*, **59**, Suppl. 35–53 (1966).

166. Hamilton, W. F. " Measurement of the Cardiac Output," in W. F. Hamilton, Ed. *Handbook of Physiology: Circulation*, Sect. 2, Vol. I. Williams and Wilkins: Baltimore, 1962, Chapter 17.

167. Wood, E. H. "Symposium on Use of Indicator Dilution Technics in the Study of the Circulation." *Circ. Res.*, **10**, 378–581 (March 1962).

168. Carey, J. S., and Hughes, R. K. "Cardiac Output: Clinical Monitoring and Management." *Ann. Thor. Surg.*, **7**, 150–176 (February 1969).

169. Hill, D. W. *Electronic Techniques in Anaesthesia and Surgery*, 2nd ed., Butterworths: London, 1973, Chapter 8.

170. Ledingham, I. McA.; McGuinness, J. B.; Tindal, S. A. P.; Tilston, D.; and Gillespie, F. C. "Theoretical and Practical Considerations in the Measurement of Cardiac Output with Xenon^{133}," in Ref. 164, pp. 90–97.

171. Mook, G. A.; Osypka, P.; Sturm, R. E.; and Wood, E. H. "Fiberoptic Reflection Photometry on Blood." *Cardiovasc. Res.*, **2**, 199–209 (April 1968).

172. Hugenholtz, P. G.; Wagner, H. R.; Gamble, W. J.; and Polanyi, M. L. "Direct Read-Out of Cardiac Output by Means of the Fiberoptic Indicator Dilution Method." *Am. Heart. J.*, **77**, 178–186 (February 1969).

173. Hosie, K. F. "Thermal Dilution Technics." *Circ. Res.*, **10**, 491–504 (March 1962).

174. Ganz, W.; Donoso, R.; Marcus, H. S.; Forrester, J. S.; and Swan, H. J. C. "A New Technique for Measurement of Cardiac Output by Thermodilution in Man." *Am. J. Cardiol.*, **27**, 392–396 (April 1971).

CHAPTER NINE

Transducers for the Measurement of Ions and Dissolved Gases

In view of the vital role played by ions in the majority of biological processes, it is hardly suprising to find that a great deal of effort has been devoted to the development of transducers for measuring their concentration. Electrochemical transducers that are sensitive to ions of a specific type and that measure the "effective" ionic concentration are widely used for both clinical and research purposes. In particular, glass electrodes have for many years formed the standard method for measuring the hydrogen-ion concentration. More recently, glass electrodes that are specific to sodium and potassium ions and ion-exchange electrodes that are sensitive to a wide variety of anions and cations have been developed and used for clinical investigations. A most important aspect of these electrodes is their adaptability for in vivo measurements at the cellular level.

Along with the measurement of hydrogen-ion activity, the measurement of the partial pressures of oxygen and carbon dioxide in blood is an essential means for discovering the nature and origin of disturbances to a patient's acid–base equilibrium. Because of the clinical importance of blood-gas determination and because of the extensive use of oxygen electrodes in basic physiological research, this chapter also includes two sections on electrodes for partial pressure measurement.

To understand properly the principles of electrochemical transducers, it is necessary to be familiar with certain fundamental aspects of electrochemistry. A number of excellent books are available that cover this material at both the elementary [1, 2] and more advanced levels [3–6]. The brief review that follows is intended to give the reader a concise summary of those aspects of electrochemistry necessary for a proper understanding of the manner in which ion-sensitive electrodes operate.

9.1 FUNDAMENTAL ASPECTS OF ELECTROCHEMISTRY

9.1.1 Properties of Electrolytes

The transport of current through an electrolyte solution is governed by the density, type, charge, and mobility of the various ions present. Unlike metallic conductors, free electrons are not present in solution as independent entities; rather they move as integral parts of ions or molecules.

Pure water is a very poor conductor and ionizes according to

$$H_2O + H_2O \rightleftharpoons H_3^+O + OH^-,$$

where H_3^+O is a hydrated hydrogen ion (proton), commonly called a hydronium ion, and OH^- is a hydroxyl ion. The attachment of one or more water molecules to the proton to form H_3^+O [or possibly $H^+(H_2O)_4$] is an inherent property of the strongly polar water molecule. As shown in Figure 9.1(a), the water molecule consists of an oxygen atom bound to two hydrogen atoms through two O–H bonds at 104°. The attraction of electrons to the oxygen nucleus causes the electron cloud to be displaced toward the oxygen atom, resulting in a fairly large net dipole moment. The presence of a free ion in aqueous solution causes the surrounding water molecules to be orientated and attracted to the ion, as illustrated in Figure 9.1 (b) and (c). In fact, most ions in aqueous solution become hydrated to some degree and many of the properties of the ion are controlled by the degree of hydration rather than by the intrinsic ionic properties. One such property is the ionic mobility, which is greatly reduced by the viscous drag resulting from the hydration shell.

Weak electrolytes, such as acetic acid, exhibit a change in conductivity with dilution, which can be explained in terms of the variation in the degree of dissociation of the substance. For a binary electrolyte BA, dissociation occurs according to the equilibrium expressed by

$$BA \rightleftharpoons B^+ + A^-,$$

where the equilibrium is displaced to the right as the dilution increases, until, at infinite dilution, complete dissociation occurs.

For *strong electrolytes*, such as KCl, the degree of dissociation cannot entirely explain the observed conductivity change with dilution. To account for experimental measurements properly, it is necessary to consider the role of interionic interactive effects. In a KCl solution the K^+ and Cl^- ions will mutually interact through Coulombic forces. On an atomic scale the distribution of ions will not be completely random: the K^+ ions will attract a cloud of Cl^- ions so that on the average the K^+ ions are effectively surrounded by Cl^- ions. Similarly, the Cl^- ions will be surrounded by K^+ ions. The effect of this ionic distribution on the movement of ions under the influence of a field is to reduce the ion transport velocity. As the K^+ ion moves to the negative electrode, the surrounding Cl^- ion cloud moves in the opposite direction, thereby creating a local space-charge that tends to restore the ions

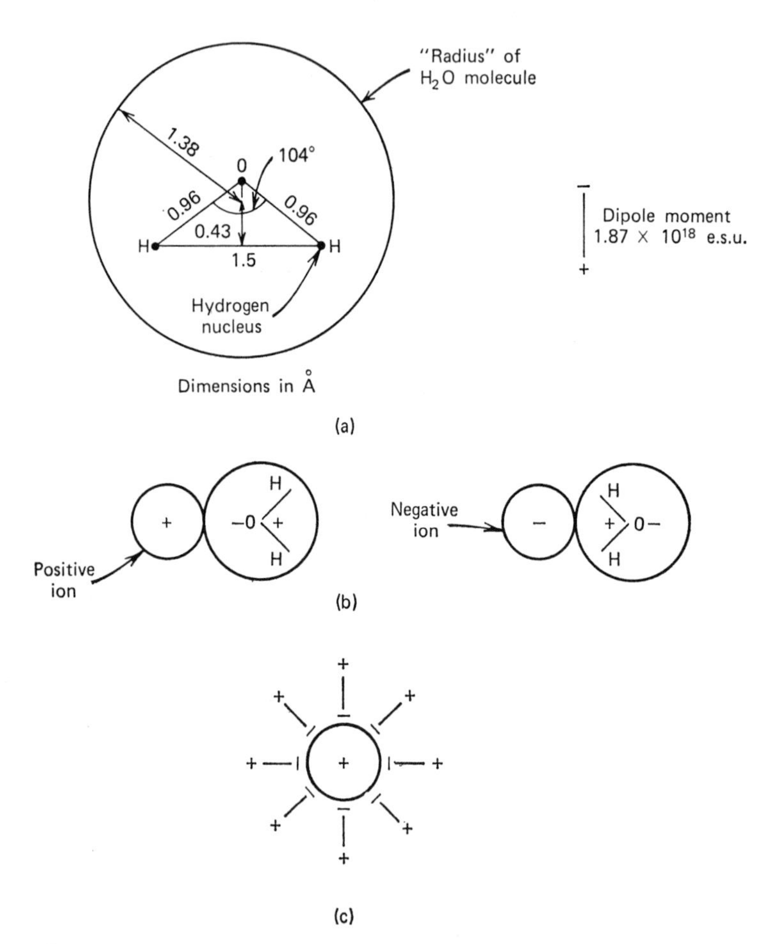

Figure 9.1. Structure of the water molecule: (a) dimensions according to the model of Bernal and Fowler (*J. Chem. Phys.*, **1**, 535 [1933]); (b) water molecule orientation when attached to positive and negative ions; and (c) schematic representation of the hydrolysis of a positive ion.

to their original positions. The net result is a reduction in the ion transport speed. Furthermore, the hydration of the Cl^- ions results in the K^+ ions being subject to an increased viscous drag. It follows therefore that interionic forces cause a decreased conductance: only for very large dilutions, when the interactions are negligible, will the conductance vary in a manner that can be predicted from the degree of dilution.

The same interionic effects are also of importance in determining the availibility of an ion to participate in a chemical reaction. Indeed, the ionic concentration is not necessarily a true reflection of the solution properties. Only at infinite dilution will the ionic concentration be a useful parameter in describing the properties.

A much more meaningful quantity is the ionic *activity*, which in essence expresses the availability of a given ion species to participate. Although a rigorous thermodynamic definition of the activity could be given, it is sufficient for our purposes to define the ion activity as the concentration of ions that, when interionic effects are absent, would produce the same effects as the real solution. Thus, the activity* a can be expressed as

$$a = \gamma C,$$

where C is the concentration and γ is the activity coefficient. When the solution is infinitely dilute, $\gamma = 1$ and the activity is equal to the concentration.

In a simple electrolyte solution with a single univalent anion and cation, the *mean ionic activity* ($a_\pm$) is related to the *mean ionic activity coefficient* ($\gamma_\pm$) by

$$a_\pm = \gamma_\pm C. \tag{1}$$

If the electrolyte anions and cations have activities of a_- and a_+ and activity coefficients of γ_- and γ_+, respectively, then

$$a_+ = \gamma_+ C$$

$$a_- = \gamma_- C.$$

Multiplying these two equations and taking the square root, we find

$$\sqrt{a_+ a_-} = \sqrt{\gamma_+ \gamma_-}\ C. \tag{2}$$

Comparison of Eqs. (1) and (2) shows that $a_\pm = \sqrt{a_+ a_-}$ and $\gamma_\pm = \sqrt{\gamma_+ \gamma_-}$. Thus, the mean activity of the ions can be expressed in terms of the individual ion activities.

* The activity is normally expressed in terms of the *molality* (i.e., moles per kilogram of solvent) rather than in terms of the *molarity* (moles per liter of solution). The two differ considerably when the concentration is large.

A great deal of theoretical and experimental work has gone into the development of expressions for the variation of the activity coefficient with ionic concentration. The most successful theory is that developed by Debye and Huckel, which has been extended by a number of workers to improve the accuracy at higher concentrations. The basic Debye–Huckel equation [5] at 25°C is

$$\log(\gamma_{\pm}) = \frac{-0.51\, z_+ z_- \sqrt{\mu}}{1 + 3.3 \times 10^7 a_i \sqrt{\mu}}, \tag{3}$$

where z_+ and z_- are the valences of the cation and anion, respectively; a_i is the effective diameter of the hydrated ion in solution; and μ is the *total ionic strength*. This last quantity is defined by the sum over all ions in the solution:

$$\mu = \tfrac{1}{2} \sum z_i C_i, \tag{4}$$

where C_i is the concentration of the ith ion of valence z_i. A most important aspect of this definition is that for dilute solutions the mean activity coefficient of a given electrolyte is approximately constant in all solutions having the same total ionic strength.

The Debye–Huckel equation is found to give excellent agreement with measured values if the solution is fairly dilute. More specifically, it gives results that are accurate to a few percent for uni-univalent electrolytes (e.g., NaCl) when the concentration is less than 0.1 normal. For electrolytes having higher valence the range of validity decreases.

9.1.2 Half-Cells and Their Potentials

When certain metal electrodes are immersed in a solution containing their ions, an equilibrium is quickly established whereby the rate at which metal atoms lose electrons and pass into solution is exactly balanced by the rate at which metal ions in solution deposit on the electrode as metal atoms. The equilibrium, for a metal of valence z can be expressed by

$$\mathrm{M} \rightleftharpoons \mathrm{M}^{+z} + ze^-.$$

During the process of establishing thermodynamic equilibrium, a charge redistribution occurs in the immediate vicinity of the metal–solution interface and establishes an equilibrium potential difference between the metal and electrolyte. For a potential to exist under equilibrium conditions, it is necessary that there be one or more regions where the net charge density is nonzero. Such a region, called the space-charge region, exists in the immediate vicinity of the metal–solution interface.

According to the theory proposed by Helmholtz, the space-charge region consists of two regions of opposite charge, one located at the metal surface and the other just within the solution. Stern* extended the concepts developed by Helmholtz and others and proposed that, within the electrolyte, the space-charge region consisted of a *compact* layer of charge formed by ions at the closest distance of approach to the interface and a more *diffuse* layer, which extended out much further from the interface. The compact layer is subject to much greater electrostatic forces and is more securely bound than the diffuse layer. As illustrated in Figure 9.2, the thickness of the compact layer is roughly the radius of a hydrated ion, while the diffuse layer, in a dilute solution, may be in the order of 50 Å. As the concentration increases, so the diffuse layer thickness decreases.

Not all metals reach an equilibrium state with water. Some, such as sodium, react with water until the electrode is fully consumed. Certain noble metals, such as platinum or gold, are examples of metals whose exchange reaction with water is normally dominated by impurities rather than by the intrinsic properties of the metal itself.

For those metals that reach a thermodynamic equilibrium state, the potential difference is a well-defined, although nonmeasurable, quantity. Any attempt to measure the potential requires a second metal electrode in the solution to complete the electrical circuit. This second electrode itself generates a metal–electrolyte potential, so that the net measured potential is the difference between the two electrode potentials.† Unsuccessful attempts have been made to express theoretically the potential of a single electrode in terms of quantities that can be measured. Evidently, success with this approach would enable the potential difference of all electrodes to be determined in an absolute manner.

Because of this difficulty, it is sensible from an operational viewpoint to define one electrode to have zero potential and to measure all other electrode potentials with respect to it. By international agreement, the hydrogen electrode when operating in a certain specified manner has been assigned a potential of exactly zero.

The *standard hydrogen electrode* system [13, 14] consists of a platinum electrode with an electrodeposit of platinum black, immersed in an acid. If the hydrogen ion activity of the acid is 1 mole/liter (pH = 0) and hydrogen gas is bubbled through the solution aroung the electrode so that its partial pressure (P_{H_2}) is 1 atm, the potential is defined to be zero at *all* temperatures. Ignoring the hydration of the hydrogen ion, the electrode reaction can be represented by

$$H_2 \text{ (aq. soln.)} \rightleftharpoons 2H \text{ (adsorbed on metal)} \rightleftharpoons 2H^+ \text{ (aq. soln.)} + 2e^-.$$

* See, for example, Section 40 in Ref. 3.

† This assumes that all other sources of potential change within the system can be neglected.

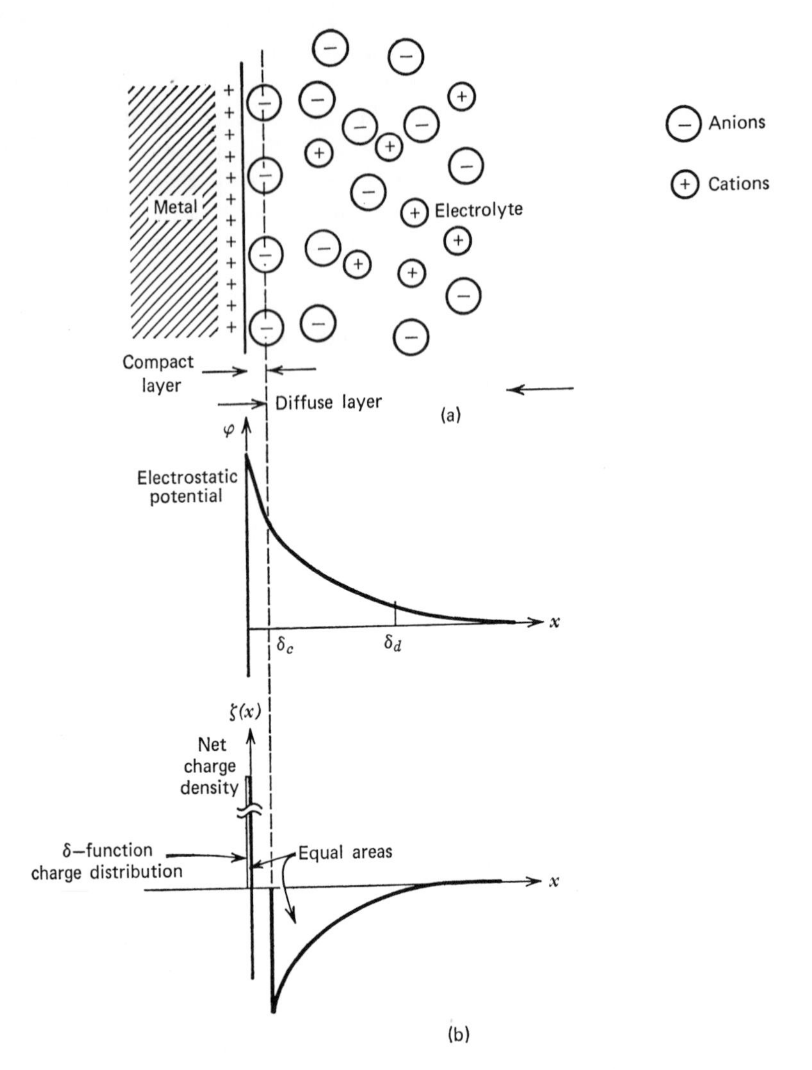

Figure 9.2. Structure of the double layer according to the model proposed by Stern (*Z. Elektrochem.*, **30**, 508 [1924]): (a) ion distribution near the interface; (b) charge density and electrostatic potential. If δ_c ($\sim$ 2Å) is the closest distance of approach of an ion to the surface, the net charge density for $0 < x < \delta_c$ will be zero. For $x > \delta_c$ the electrostatic potential decays exponentially with distance. The "characteristic" distance δ_d for a uni-univalent electrolyte $\simeq$ 10 Å for a 0.1M concentration and is $\simeq$ 1000 Å for a $10^{-5}M$ concentration.

In this process the hydrogen atoms adsorbed on the metal surface go into solution as hydrogen ions leaving behind a negative charge. Thus, the platinum electrode acts both as a catalyzer for the equilibrium and a means by which electrons can be supplied or delivered: it does not enter into the reaction in the manner of a metal–ion electrode.

The potential generated by the hydrogen electrode can be classified as a *redox* (oxidation-reduction) potential. Redox potentials can be defined [3] as those potentials resulting from reactions in which two phases exchange electrons and for which the electrode serves only as a means for this exchange. For example, if a platinum electrode is immersed in a solution containing ferrous and ferric ions, the exchange reaction

$$Fe^{3+} + e^- \rightleftharpoons Fe^{2+}$$

occurs, and platinum supplies or accepts electrons. An additional example of a redox electrode is a platinum electrode immersed in a solution containing chloride ions and chlorine gas bubbled around the electrode. The oxidation-reduction reaction can be represented by

$$2Cl^- \rightleftharpoons Cl_2 + 2e^-,$$

and again, electrons are supplied to or from the platinum.

If the activity of the ions in solution is unity, and, in the case of a gas, if the partial pressure is 1 atm, the equilibrium potentials, when measured at 25°C with respect to a standard hydrogen electrode, are called *standard potentials*. The standard potentials for some of the more important electrodes used in biological work and their reaction equations are listed in Table 9.1.

When the ion activity or partial pressure differs from the standard conditions, the half-cell potentials are no longer equal to the standard potentials. It can be shown [3] that if an electrode involves a reaction of the form

$$\alpha A + \beta B \rightleftharpoons \gamma C + \delta D + ze^-, \tag{5}$$

so that z electrons are transferred, the equilibrium potential is given by the *Nernst equation* expressed in the following form:

$$E = E^0 + \frac{RT}{zF} \ln \left(\frac{a_C{}^{\gamma} a_D{}^{\delta}}{a_A{}^{\alpha} a_B{}^{\beta}} \right) \tag{6}$$

where R is the gas constant, F is Faraday's constant, T is the absolute temperature, E^0 is the standard electrode potential, and a is the activity. The factor RT/F is equal to 0.0256 V at 25°C.

As an example, consider the reaction of a copper electrode immersed in a solution of its ions:

$$Cu \rightleftharpoons Cu^{2+} + 2e^-.$$

Table 9.1 Standard Potentials of Half-Cells at 25°C

Cell	Electrode reaction	Potential, V
Metal–ion potentials:		
Al^{3+}/Al	$Al \rightleftharpoons Al^{3+} + 3e^-$	−1.66
Zn^{2+}/Zn	$Zn \rightleftharpoons Zn^{2+} + 2e^-$	−0.763
Fe^{2+}/Fe	$Fe \rightleftharpoons Fe^{2+} + 2e^-$	−0.440
Ni^{2+}/Ni	$Ni \rightleftharpoons Ni^{2+} + 2e^-$	−0.250
Pb^{2+}/Pb	$Pb \rightleftharpoons Pb^{2+} + 2e^-$	−0.126
$Ag/AgCl$	$Ag + Cl^- \rightleftharpoons AgCl + e^-$	+0.2224
Hg/Hg_2Cl_2	$2Hg + 2Cl^- \rightleftharpoons Hg_2C_2l + 2e^-$	+0. 2681
Cu^{2+}/Cu	$Cu \rightleftharpoons Cu^{2+} + 2e^-$	+0.337
Cu^{+}/Cu	$Cu \rightleftharpoons Cu^{+} + e^-$	+0.521
Hg_2^{2+}/Hg	$2Hg \rightleftharpoons Hg_2^{2+} + 2e^-$	+0.797
Ag^{+}/Ag	$Ag \rightleftharpoons Ag^{+} + e^-$	+0.7991
Au^{3+}/Au	$Au \rightleftharpoons Au^{3+} + 3e^-$	+1.50
Au^{+}/Au	$Au \rightleftharpoons Au + e^-$	+1.68
Redox potentials:		
Cr^{3+}/Cr	$Cr^{2+} \rightleftharpoons Cr^{3+} + e^-$	−0.40
H^{+}/H_2	$H_2 \rightleftharpoons 2H^{+} + 2e^-$	0.0000 (std.)
Cu^{2+}/Cu	$Cu^{+} \rightleftharpoons Cu^{2+} + e^-$	+0.153
Fe^{3+}/Fe^{2+}	$Fe^{3+} \rightleftharpoons Fe^{2+} + e^-$	+0.7701
Cl^{-}/Cl_2	$2Cl^{-} \rightleftharpoons Cl_2 + 2e^-$	+1.3583

By comparing this reaction with Eq. (5), we find that $\alpha = 1$, $\beta = 0$, $\gamma = 1$, $\delta = 0$, and $z = 2$. Further, since the activity of a pure solid is normally assumed to be unity, Eq. (6) yields

$$E = E^0 + \frac{RT}{2F} \ln (a)$$

where a is the activity of the Cu^{2+} ions and E^0, from Table 9.1, is equal to 0.377 V. Thus, if a is greater than unity, E is greater than E^0, and if less than unity, it is less than E^0.

As a second example, consider the redox electrode reaction

$$2Cl^- \rightleftharpoons Cl_2 + 2e^-.$$

Again applying Eq. (6) and interpreting the activity of Cl_2 to be the partial pressure (P_{Cl_2}), we find

$$E = E^0 + \frac{RT}{F} \ln \left(\frac{\sqrt{P_{Cl_2}}}{a_{Cl^-}} \right).$$

If the partial pressure is 1 atm and E^0 is obtained from Table 9.1, then

$$E = 1.3583 - \frac{RT}{F} \ln (a_{\text{Cl}^+}).$$

As a final example, we consider the hydrogen electrode whose reaction was considered earlier. Applying Eq. (6) and noting that E^0 is assigned the value of zero, the electrode potential is given by

$$E = \frac{RT}{F} \ln \left(\frac{a_{\text{H}^+}}{\sqrt{P_{\text{H}_2}}} \right). \tag{7}$$

9.1.3 Electrochemical Cells Under Equilibrium Conditions

An electrochemical cell consists of two half-cells whose electrolytes are in electrical contact. The cell emf depends not only on the difference in the two half-cell potentials but also on any liquid junction potentials that may be present.

For the Daniel cell shown in Figure 9.3(a), if the two solutions have metal–ion activities of unity, the cell can be represented by

$$\text{Zn}/\text{Zn}^{2+}(a = 1) \,\vdots\, \text{Cu}^{2+}(a = 1)/\text{Cu},$$

where a phase boundary is represented by a single oblique line and the broken line represents a membrane permeable to all ions. The purpose of the membrane is to prevent free mixing of the two solutions but to allow ions to flow

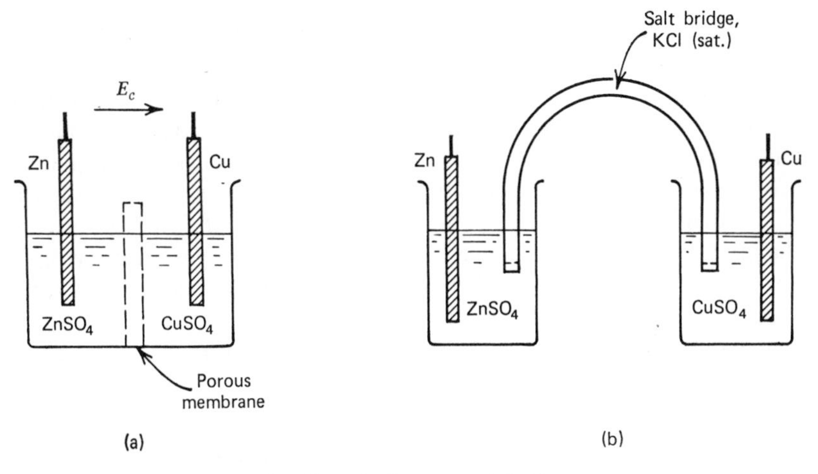

Figure 9.3. The Daniel cell with and without a salt bridge.

from one solution to the other. In the absence of any current (equilibrium condition), the cell emf at 25°C is given by*

$$E_c = E^0_{Cu^{2+}/Cu} - E^0_{Zn^{2+}/Zn}$$

if the liquid junction potential is neglected. From Table 9.1 we find that

$$E_c = +1.100 \text{ V}.$$

More generally, if the activities of the two solutions differ from unity the cell potential is given by

$$E_c = 1.100 + \frac{RT}{2F} \ln \left(\frac{a_{Cu^{2+}}}{a_{Zn^{2+}}} \right).$$

It is important to note that the above expression assumes that the potential between the two solutions is negligibly small. In point of fact, this may not be the case: potentials of several tens of millivolts can occur. To eliminate such potentials, a *salt bridge* can be used as illustrated in Figure 9.3(b). A salt bridge normally consists of a tube filled with a saturated or highly concentrated solution of KCl.† The two ends of the bridge solution are in electrical communication with the two solutions to be joined but are plugged sufficiently so as to prevent excessive mixing. As will be shown, the most important feature of such a bridge is that the two liquid/liquid junctions generate only a very small emf (a few millivolts), often negligibly small in comparison to the cell emf. When a salt bridge is used in the Daniel cell and the liquid/liquid junction potentials are neglected the cell is represented by

$$Zn/Zn^{2+}//Cu^{2+}/Cu$$

where the double slash represents the elimination of the liquid junction potential.

In general, liquid/liquid junctions consisting either of two different electrolytes or of two different concentrations of the same electrolyte produce a potential difference. The reason for this can be seen by considering a junction consisting of two different concentrations of a simple electrolyte such as NaCl. The diffusion coefficient of Na^+ ions is less than the Cl^- ions, so that in the junction region the negative ions move more readily toward the region of lower concentration leaving behind the slower positive ions. As a result, an electric field is produced in the junction region that, in the absence of any net current flow, constrains the positive and negative ions to move at the same

* The international sign convention is followed, whereby the cell emf is expressed as the potential of the right-hand solution with respect to the left-hand solution.

† Other solutions such as KNO_3, NH_4NO_3, and RbCl are also suitable.

rate. It can be shown that a potential difference given by [3]

$$E_j = \frac{\mu_+ - \mu_-}{\mu_+ + \mu_-} \frac{RT}{zF} \ln\left(\frac{a_2}{a_1}\right) \tag{8}$$

occurs across the junction. In this expression, μ_+ and μ_- are the mobilities of the positive and negative ions, z is the valence, and a_2 and a_1 are the ionic activities. Since μ and the diffusion coefficient are proportional, Eq. (8) can be expressed in terms of the diffusion coefficients by simply replacing the mobility by the corresponding diffusion coefficient.

Alternatively, Eq. (8) can be simplified by defining the *transport number* of an ion i by

$$t_i = \frac{\mu_i}{\sum \mu},$$

where the sum is over all ion types in the solution. For the case in hand,

$$t_+ = \frac{\mu_+}{\mu_+ + \mu_-}, \qquad t_- = \frac{\mu_-}{\mu_+ + \mu_-},$$

which, when substituted into Eq. (8), yields

$$\begin{aligned} E_j &= (t_+ - t_-) \frac{RT}{zF} \ln\left(\frac{a_2}{a_1}\right) \\ &= (2t_+ - 1) \frac{RT}{zF} \ln\left(\frac{a_2}{a_1}\right). \end{aligned} \tag{9}$$

As an example, consider the junction

$$\text{NaCl } (0.01M)//\text{NaCl } (0.001M).$$

Since $t_+ = 0.392$ at 25°C, Eq. (9) becomes

$$\begin{aligned} E_j &= (2 \times 0.392 - 1) \times 0.026 \ln (10) \\ &= -12.96 \text{ mV}, \end{aligned}$$

where, in accordance with the international convention, the potential is that of the right-hand solution with respect to the left-hand solution. It will be observed from Eq. (8) that when the two ionic mobilities are the same, the potential becomes zero.

If a cell has two identical electrodes but the solution concentrations in which each electrode is immersed differ, an emf will be produced that may in part be caused by the difference in the half-cell potentials and in part by the liquid junction potential. Since the emf of such a cell arises from differences in ionic concentration, it is called a *concentration cell.*

In the case of two dissimilar electrolyte types, the liquid junction potential generally depends on the detailed nature of the junction transition region. However, if the junction is of the continuous mixture type, the equation for the potential is that derived by Henderson [3], namely,

$$E_j = \frac{\sum \mu_j (C_j'' - C_j')/z_j}{\sum \mu_j (C_j'' - C_j')} \frac{RT}{F} \ln \left(\frac{\sum \mu_j C_j''}{\sum \mu_j C_j'} \right) \tag{10}$$

where the prime and double prime refer to solutions 1 and 2, respectively; subscript j is the jth ion type; z_j is the ion charge expressed in units of the electronic charge magnitude; and the sums are over all ion types.

Consider, for example the junction

$$\text{HCl } (0.1M)//\text{KCl } (4.16M)$$

Then, from Eq. (10),

$$E_j = \frac{4.16(\mu_{K^+} - \mu_{Cl^-}) - 0.1(\mu_{H^+} - \mu_{Cl^-})}{4.16(\mu_{K^+} + \mu_{Cl^-}) - 0.1(\mu_{H^+} + \mu_{Cl^-})} \frac{RT}{F} \ln \left(\frac{4.16(\mu_{K^+} + \mu_{Cl^-})}{0.1(\mu_{H^+} + \mu_{Cl^-})} \right).$$

Assuming the same mobility values as for an infinite dilution (i.e., $\mu_{K^+}/\mu_{Cl^-} = 0.963$, $\mu_{H^+}/\mu_{Cl^-} = 4.60$) and that $T = 298°K$, we find $E_j = 4.6$ mV.

It is evident from the above example that since $\mu_{K^+} \approx \mu_{Cl^-}$, the more concentrated the KCl is relative to the HCl solution, the smaller will be the liquid junction potential. This is illustrated in Table 9.2 for two different KCl and HCl concentrations.

Table 9.2 Some Liquid/Liquid Junction Potentials[a] at 25°C

Potentials, mV	KCl 4.2M	KCl 0.1M
HCl, 0.1M	+4.6	+26.9
HCl, 0.01M	+3.0	+9.1
NaOH, 0.1M	−0.4	−19.2
NaOH, 0.01M	+2.3	−4.5

[a] Potentials are that of the KCl solution with respect to the other electrolyte expressed in mV (values taken from Bates [13]).

Salt bridges are very frequently used in electrochemical measurements on biological fluids and normally involve two liquid junction potentials. For the system

solution X/salt bridge/solution Y

the two junction potentials should exactly cancel if the solutions X and Y are identical. For different solutions the two potentials will normally be unequal;

however, if the salt bridge solution is very concentrated compared to X and Y, the two liquid junction potentials will be small, thus yielding a small system potential.

The liquid junction potential for the system solution X/solution Y can be very much greater than the total potential generated when the two solutions are joined by a salt bridge. To illustrate this point, consider the junction

$$\text{HCl}\ (0.1M)/\text{KCl}\ (0.1M).$$

From Table 9.2, the potential is 26.9 mV. On the other hand, for the system

$$\text{HCl}\ (0.1M)/\text{KCl (sat.)}/\text{KCl}\ (0.1M),$$

Table 9.2 and Eq. (8) yield $E_j = 4.6 - 1.8 = 2.8$ mV. Thus, the salt bridge nearly eliminates the potential generated by the direct junction. In doing so, it also reduces the variation in potential arising from changes in the ion activity. A further possible advantage of the salt bridge is to eliminate the direct junction of two solutions that react chemically with one another.

9.1.4 Electrochemical Cells Under Nonequilibrium Conditions

The passage of a current through an electrode disturbs the equilibrium potential $E(0)$ resulting in a new potential $E(i)$, which depends on the current density. The change in potential is called the *overvoltage* or *overpotential*, η. Thus,

$$\eta = E(i) - E(0),$$

and depending on the direction of the current, η can be either positive or negative. From a practical standpoint, a knowledge of the variation of η with current is of great importance. In all measurements involving electrochemical cells, a current, even though it be very small, passes through the cell during the process of measurement. It is evidently of significance to know how much current can be passed without appreciably affecting the equilibrium cell emf.

When η is nonzero, the electrode is said to be *polarized* and the cell to be operating *irreversibly*. If the current is sufficiently small so that the equilibrium electrode reaction rates are not appreciably disturbed, the electrode potential will be close to the equilibrium value and the electrode is said to be operating *reversibly*.

Vetter [3] identifies four independent physical mechanisms that can give rise to an overvoltage:

1. The charge transfer process through the electrode double layer
2. The diffusion of reactants toward, and away from, an electrode
3. The chemical reaction at the electrode
4. The process of inclusion or release of metal atoms into or from the metal crystal lattice.

If the mechanisms are assumed to be independent of one another, the total overvoltage can be written as the sum

$$\eta = \eta_t + \eta_d + \eta_r + \eta_c, \tag{11}$$

where

η_t = charge-transfer overvoltage
η_d = diffusion overvoltage
η_r = reaction overvoltage
η_c = crystallization overvoltage.

In what follows, a brief account will be given of each physical mechanism and the way in which it affects the total overvoltage.

Charge-Transfer Overvoltage. At a metal–ion electrode under equilibrium conditions, the transfer of ions from the metal into solution is exactly balanced by the deposition of ions on the metal surface, where they recombine with the metal lattice. This charge exchange occurs across the compact double layer in the manner illustrated in Figure 9.4. For metal ions to pass into solution, an energy barrier must be overcome whose "height" represents the energy required for dissolution. For ions to be deposited, a smaller energy barrier must be surmounted, representing the energy required for deposition of a metal ion on the metal surface.

The dissolution current density J_+, which is equal to J_- under equilibrium conditions, is called the *exchange current density* J_0. Since the ratio of the cell current to the exchange current represents the deviation of the cell from equilibrium conditions, it is evident that the larger J_0, the smaller will be the charge transfer overvoltage for a given total cell current.

If current is supplied or extracted from an electrode, the net flow of ions across the double layer must change. This is achieved through a change in the activation energies brought about through a change in the electrostatic potential in the compact double layer. If, as shown in Figure 9.4(b), the direction of the current is such as to demand an increased ionic dissolution rate, the activation energy for dissolution will decrease and that for deposition will increase. The increase and decrease are exactly sufficient to enable the ionic flow rate to satisfy the demands of the cell current. Furthermore, the change in electrostatic potential across the compact double layer is equal to the charge-transfer overvoltage.

It can be shown from a first-order analysis based on the above physical model that the overvoltage component η_t is related to the current density J by

$$\frac{J}{J_0} = \exp\left(\frac{\alpha z \eta_t F}{RT}\right) - \exp\left(\frac{-(1-\alpha) z \eta_t F}{RT}\right), \tag{12}$$

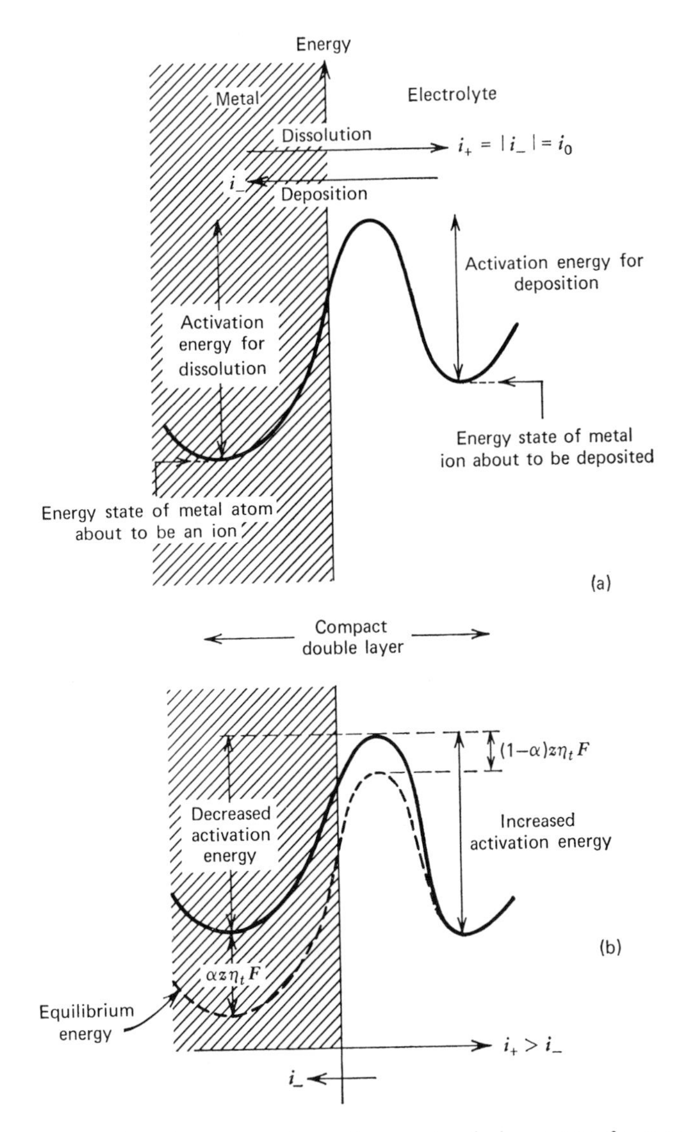

Figure 9.4. Illustrating the energy of reacting species during a transfer reaction at a metal–ion electrode: (a) equilibrium energy; (b) nonequilibrium energy of reacting species at a metal anode, showing how the charge-transfer overvoltage η_t causes a change in the activation energies.

where α is the *transfer coefficient* $(0 \leqslant \alpha \leqslant 1)$ representing the fraction of η_t that decreases the dissolution activation energy. For large currents Eq. (12) reduces to

$$\frac{J}{J_0} = \exp\left(\frac{\alpha z \eta_t F}{RT}\right)$$

or

$$\eta_t = \frac{RT}{\alpha z F} \ln \frac{J}{J_0} = -\frac{RT}{\alpha z F} \ln J_0 + \frac{RT}{\alpha z F} \ln J. \tag{13}$$

Hence, a graph of η_t versus $\ln J$ should yield a straight line whose intercept and slope enable αz and J_0 to be determined. Such a plot is called a Tafel plot. Both the low- and high-current regions are encompassed in the normalized graph of current density versus overvoltage shown in Figure 9.5.

From a practical point of view it is found that with electrodes whose exchange current density is fairly small, the charge-transfer mechanism is the rate-determining process for small electrode current densities—that is, η_t is the major contribution to the total overvoltage η. For hydrogen electrodes using platinum, $J_0 = 4$ μA/cm^2, and for gold, $J_0 = 0.9$ μA/cm^2. Assuming

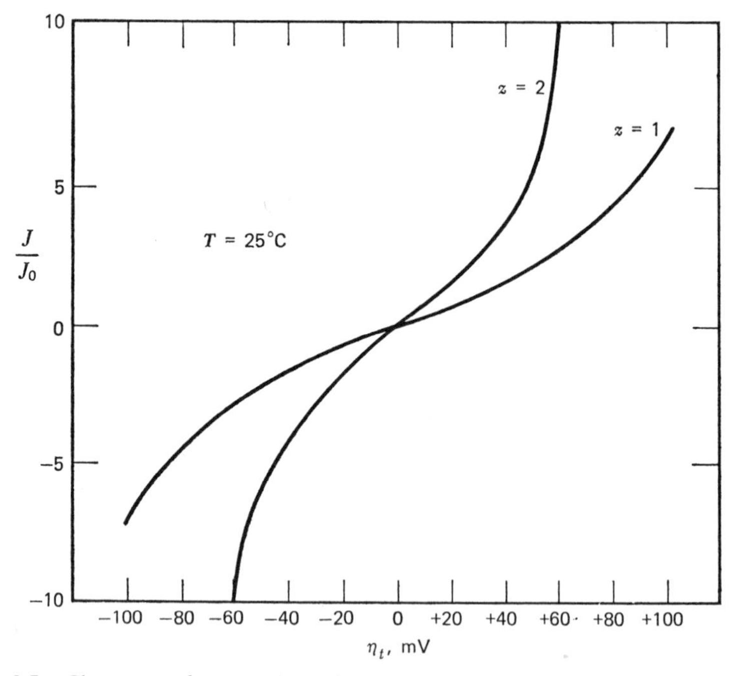

Figure 9.5. Charge-transfer overvoltage characteristics for a metal–ion electrode, according to Eq. (12), for $\alpha = 0.5$. The curve for $z = 1$ is also the charge-transfer overvoltage characteristic for a redox electrode.

that $\alpha = 0.5$, it can be seen that a Pt electrode having an effective surface area of 1 cm^2 and passing a current of 4 μA will have an overvoltage of around 25 mV. On the other hand, for a Ag/Ag^+ electrode in a 0.1M solution $J_0 = 4.5$ A/cm^2, making η_t a negligibly small part of the total overvoltage.

Diffusion Overvoltage. Ionic transport in an electrolyte can occur either through the process of diffusion brought about by the existence of a concentration gradient or throguh the process of drift under the influence of an electric field. If, as shown in Figure 9.6, current is passed through a Ag/

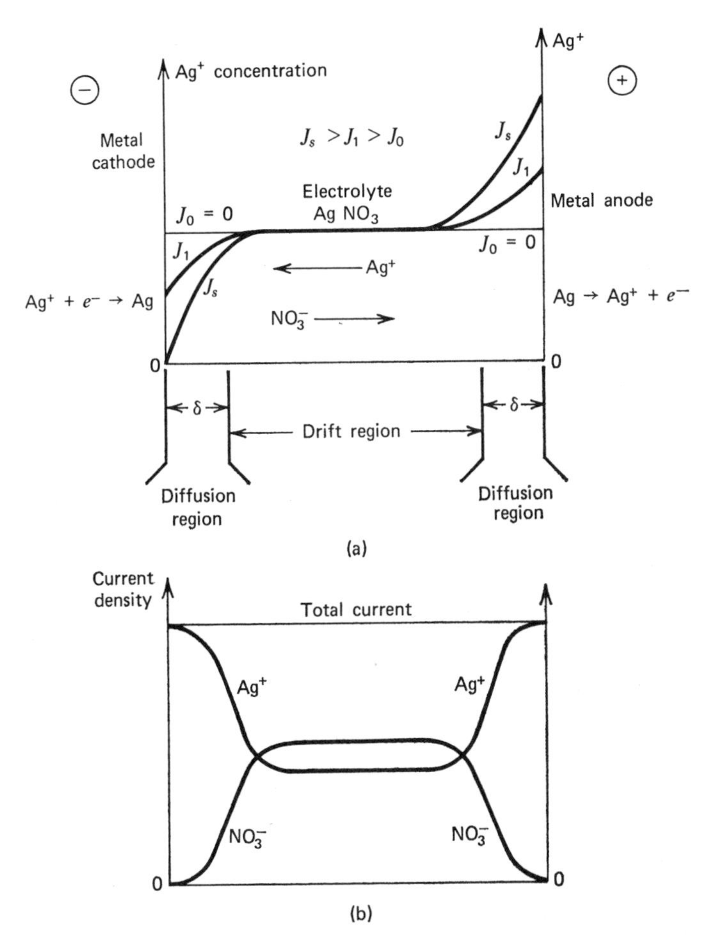

Figure 9.6. Diffusion effects in a $Ag/AgNO_3/Ag$ concentration cell: (a) variation of silver-ion concentration across the cell for three different cell current densities; (b) showing the variation of the current density components across the cell. The Ag^+ transport number is slightly less than that for NO_3^-, so that a somewhat greater proportion of the current is carried by the NO_3^- ions in the "drift" region.

$AgNO_3/Ag$ concentration cell, Ag^+ ions will be deposited at the negative electrode and released from the positive electrode. The release of ions at the anode causes the concentration of silver ions to be greater immediately adjacent to the anode than in the bulk. Evidently the larger the current density, the larger will be the concentration increase and diffusion current density. Similarly, at the cathode the silver-ion density is depleted, resulting in a diffusion current density directed toward the cathode.

It will be recalled that the potential generated by a metal–ion electrode depends not only on the type of electrode but also on the ionic activity immediately adjacent to the metal electrode. Hence, a local concentration change resulting from the depletion or accumulation of ions at an electrode gives rise to a net change in the cell potential. For the cell illustrated, the total potential change arises from the sum of the magnitudes of the decrease at one electrode and the increase at the other electrode. If diffusion is the only rate-determining process, the total overvoltage of an electrode will be equal to the diffusion overvoltage η_d.

As illustrated in Figure 9.6, the concentration of silver ions adjacent to the cathode varies from the equilibrium value at zero current to a value that is essentially zero when the current density reaches a certain limiting value, J_s. The *limiting current density* corresponds to the maximum rate at which ions can be supplied to the electrode from the bulk of the solution.

An equation for the diffusion overvoltage for the Ag/Ag^+ electrode can be found by first applying the Nernst equation to the expression for the diffusion overvoltage, namely, $\eta_d = E(i) - E(0)$. This yields

$$\eta_d = \frac{RT}{F} \ln a_0 - \frac{RT}{F} \ln a_b = \frac{RT}{F} \ln \frac{a_o}{a_b}, \tag{14}$$

where a_0 and a_b are the metal-ion activities at the electrode surface and in the bulk of the solution, respectively. Now the diffusion current density is proportional to the gradient of the ion activity. Assuming that the gradient at the electrode surface is proportional to $(a_0 - a_b)$, it follows that the electrode current density is given by

$$J \propto (a_0 - a_b)$$

or

$$J = k(a_0 - a_b).$$

But $J = J_s$ when $a_0 = 0$; hence,

$$\frac{J}{J_s} = 1 - \frac{a_0}{a_b},$$

which, when substituted into Eq. (14), enables the magnitude of the diffusion overvoltage to be written as

$$|\eta_d| = \frac{-RT}{F} \ln\left(1 - \frac{J}{J_s}\right). \tag{15}$$

From the graph of Eq. (15) presented in Figure 9.7, it will be noted that the overvoltage tends to infinity as J approaches J_s. The reason for this behavior arises from the approach of the activity to zero at the electrode surface; this, from the Nernst equation, causes the potential to approach infinity. However, in practice, before this occurs, other electrode processes become important and cause the current to increase again.

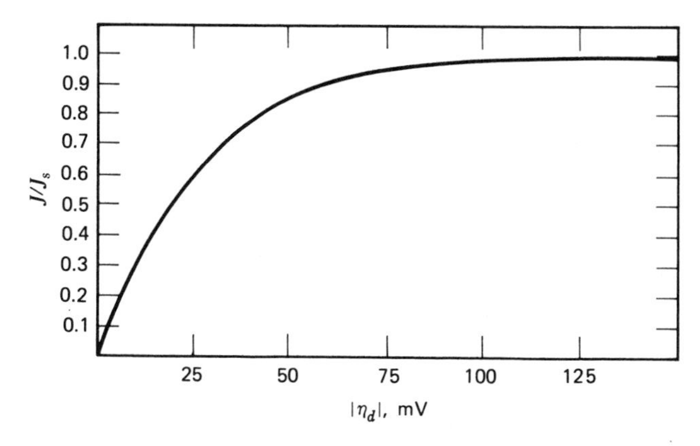

Figure 9.7. Diffusion overvoltage characteristic as given by Eq. (15), at 25°C.

The distance from the electrode surface over which the diffusion current is important relative to the drift current is typically around 0.05 cm for metal–ion electrodes in a stationary electrolyte. When the solution is stirred fairly rapidly, this reduces to approximately 0.001 cm. The effect of stirring enables ions to be supplied at a greater rate to the electrode, thereby increasing the limiting current or, when the electrode current is maintained constant, decreasing the diffusion overvoltage.

From a practical viewpoint it is important to note that the effects of diffusion often govern the overvoltage characteristics of a cell at higher electrode current densities but may be dominated by the charge-transfer effects as equilibrium conditions are approached.

Reaction Overvoltage. A reaction overvoltage arises when a slow chemical process (a partial reaction) becomes a rate-determining factor in the total electrode reaction. Suppose, for example, that the deposition of a metal ion involves a prior partial reaction to make the ion available and that this process is rate-limiting. If the concentration of reactants is constant, then the concentration of the products of this partial reaction will depend on the cell current density. The higher the current density, the smaller will be the concentration of metal ions adjacent to the electrode surface and, consequently, the larger will be the overvoltage. The reaction overvoltage, like the diffusion overvoltage, arises from a concentration change at the electrode surface. It is because of this that both effects are often treated under the more general heading of *concentration overvoltage*, whose value is equal to the sum of the diffusion and reaction overvoltages.

The rate at which a reaction proceeds in the presence of a constant concentration of reactants sets an upper limit to the current density. If reaction processes are rate-limiting, then the electrode overvoltage versus current characteristics can be expected to exhibit a saturation phenomenon similar to that shown in Figure 9.7.

Crystallization Overvoltage. The process by which metal ions deposited on a metal electrode surface are incorporated into the crystal lattice is potentially a rate-limiting mechanism for the overall electrode reaction. Since the process involves an activation energy, it is reasonable to expect that an increase in the crystallization rate would involve a change in potential across the metal–solution interface. This potential change can be identified as the crystallization overvoltage. In practice it is normally very small and difficult to measure.

Resistance Polarization. The sources of overpotential described so far are not the only reasons why the potential of an electrolytic cell varies with current. Potential changes arising from the ohmic resistance of the electrolyte, from the concentration gradient in the diffusion layer, and from the effects of surface films on the electrode surface can be important from a practical point of view. For convenience, these additional potential changes are called *resistance polarization.*

Polarization arising from the conductivity of the electrolyte can be expected to obey Ohm's law. It can be decreased if a supporting electrolyte (one that does not participate in the electrode reactions) is added in. The diffusion layer described above is also a cause of resistance polarization for two reasons. First, the current flowing through the layer produces an ohmic potential difference between the two boundaries of the layer. Since the conductivity of the layer is nonuniform and varies with current, the potential difference will not obey a simple linear law. Second, the variation of concentration with distance in the diffusion layer produces a liquid/liquid junction potential (diffusion potential) in the manner described in Section 9.1.3. It can be shown that the result of these two effects for a simple univalent electrolyte produces a total resistance polarization exactly equal to the diffusion overpotential as given by Eq. (15). Finally, resistance polarization may be caused by the formation of a thin semiconducting film on the surface of the metal electrode. Both diffusion potentials and ohmic potentials can arise from such a film.

9.2 PROPERTIES OF REFERENCE ELECTRODES

The electrochemical measurement of ion activity basically involves two electrodes: an *indicator electrode* and a *reference electrode*. As its name implies, the indicator electrode is designed to sense the quantity being measured and therefore should respond in a well-defined and reproducible manner to variations in ion activity. The reference electrode is required to provide electrical continuity to the test solution in such a manner that its potential is essentially independent of any changes in the test solution. Since all electrodes are temperature-dependent, it is desirable that the indicator and reference electrodes be designed so that their temperature coefficients cancel one another.

When the indicator electrode is an ion-responsive glass (see Section 9.4), two reference electrodes are normally used. An inner reference electrode immersed in a suitable standard electrolyte provides electrical contact to the inner surface of the glass electrode. The solution under test, which is in contact with the outer glass surface, is joined to an outer reference electrode by a suitable salt bridge. Any potential changes between the two electrodes reflects changes in the glass electrode potential, which can then be related to alterations in ion activity within the test solution.

As stated by Janz and Ives [15] and discussed by Covington [16], satisfactory performance of reference electrodes requires that they possess the following qualities: reversibility, reproducibility, and stability.

The degree of reversibility required is usually fairly easy to achieve, since with modern potential measuring instruments, the current drawn can be very small. However, if the electrode is designed for cellular application, the small surface area can result in high current densities even though the current flowing may be in the 10^{-10} A range. In such circumstances it is necessary to insure that the electrode employed has a sufficiently high exchange current density for the overvoltage to be neglected. Reproducibility refers not only to the ability to fabricate electrodes having essentially the same electrochemical properties but also to the ability of the electrodes to respond to temperature and concentration changes without significant hysteresis. The final quality, stability, refers to the electrode properties remaining unchanged over a long-term experiment. Unfortunately, most electrodes suffer from long-term degradation, generally because of the action of electrode "poisons." A simple way around this problem is to couple the electrode to the test solution via a salt bridge.

9.2.1 The Hydrogen Electrode

In Section 9.1.2 it was pointed out that the potential of the standard hydrogen electrode [13, 14] is defined to be zero for all temperatures. An important reason for the choice and acceptance of this electrode as the zero reference is its reproducibility. In this regard it is unmatched by any other type of electrode: pairs of carefully prepared hydrogen electrodes immersed in the same acid should exhibit bias potentials of less than 10 μV.

As previously discussed, the hydrogen electrode consists of a platinized platinum electrode immersed in an acid solution with hydrogen gas bubbled through it. The platinization greatly increases the effective surface area (perhaps by 2000 times), thereby reducing the overvoltage; it also acts as a catalyzer for the electron exchange process.

Unfortunately the electrode is rather susceptible to a variety of poisons. Poisons in the form of oxidizing agents are reduced at the electrode surface causing the molecular hydrogen in solution adjacent to the electrode to be reduced in concentration, thereby changing the electrode potential. Other forms of poisons may be reduced and deposit themselves on the metal surface or may be preferentially adsorbed on the surface, thereby reducing the surface area available for catalysis and reducing the working life of the electrode. As a result of these problems and the need for a supply of pure hydrogen gas, the hydrogen electrode is rarely used for routine measurements. Rather, it is used as a standard against which other electrodes can be periodically checked and as a means for periodically checking the pH of standard reference solutions (see Section 9.3.2).

9.2.2 Silver–Silver Chloride Electrodes [15, 17]

Electrodes consisting of a metal in an electrolyte containing its ions are generally called *electrodes of the first kind.* Both the silver–silver chloride and mercury–mercurous chloride electrodes are examples of electrodes of the second kind. This class of electrode consists of a metal immersed in an electrolyte that forms a compound on the metal surface consisting of the metal ions and the electrolyte anions.

The silver–silver chloride electrode consists of either pure silver or platinum with a deposit of silver and a porous layer of silver chloride on the surface. The electrode is reversible to chlorine ions. When immersed in a solution containing ions and when acting as an anode, chlorine ions combine with silver to form AgCl; when acting as a cathode, chlorine ions pass into solution from the AgCl layer, thereby depleting it.

The presence of the sparingly soluble AgCl layer is essential for the proper electrode functioning. As will be shown, it maintains the silver-ion activity in the electrolyte at the electrode surface inversely proportional to the chlorine-ion activity.

The presence of solid AgCl in water insures that the solution close to the AgCl is saturated with Ag^+ and Cl^- ions and an equilibrium exists, which can be expressed by

$$\text{AgCl (solid)} \rightleftharpoons Ag^+ + Cl^-. \qquad (16)$$

For this case the concentrations of the two ions will be equal. Now the rate at which dissolution occurs is a constant, and since equilibrium exists, it must be exactly balanced by the rate of association of Ag^+ and Cl^- ions. It is reasonable to expect that the rate of association will be proportional to the activities of the two ion types—that is,

$$(a_{Ag^+}) \cdot (a_{Cl^-}) = \text{constant}.$$

The presence of solid AgCl in a solution that already contains Cl^- ion through the dissociation of another substance does not change the dissociation rate of AgCl. Hence, it follows that the Ag^+ activity must be reduced in order to maintain the same association rate. Thus, the *solubility product* given by

$$K_s = (a_{Ag^+}) \cdot (a_{Cl^-}) \qquad (17)$$

is, for a given temperature, independent of the Cl^- and Ag^+ activities, and is equal to 1.78×10^{-10} at 25°C. For pure water we find that $a_{Ag^+} = a_{Cl^-} = 1.33 \times 10^{-5}$ moles/liter, while in a solution for which $a_{Cl^-} = 1.0$, we find $a_{Ag^+} = 1.78 \times 10^{-10}$ moles/liter.

The electron exchange process at the silver surface occurs through

$$\text{Ag} \rightleftharpoons Ag^+ + e^-;$$

that is, the potential of the Ag–AgCl electrode is that of a Ag–Ag^+ electrode in which the Ag^+ activity is determined by the process in Eq. (16). It follows from the Nernst equation that

$$E = E^0_{Ag/Ag^+} + \frac{RT}{F} \ln (a_{Ag^+}),$$

which can be expressed in terms of the Cl^- activity by using Eq. (17):

$$E = E^0_{Ag/Ag^+} + \frac{RT}{F} \cdot \ln (1.78 \times 10^{-10}) - \frac{RT}{F} \cdot \ln (a_{Cl^-}).$$

Making use of the standard electrode potential value given in Table 9.1, the Ag–AgCl potential at 25°C is given by

$$E = 0.2224 - 0.0256 \ln (a_{Cl^-}).$$

Experimentally it is found that the Ag–AgCl electrode closely follows the Nernst equation for a wide range of Cl^- activities. In very concentrated solutions of KCl, the *solubility* of AgCl increases by several orders of magnitude above that for a dilute solution due to complex anion formation, but this does not alter the value of K_s given above. However, care must be taken to insure that the chloride layer is not dissolved away: presaturating the KCl solution with AgCl prevents this from occurring.

In practice, $0.1M$ HCl, $0.1M$, $1.0M$, or saturated KCl is used to form a reference Ag–AgCl electrode. The advantage of the more concentrated KCl solutions arises from the small liquid-junction potential so that a salt bridge is not required.

Potentials of the AgCl–Ag electrode for various KCl molarities are shown in Table 9.3. Also shown is the isothermal temperature coefficient of the cell

$$\mathrm{Pt/H_2/HCl}\ (a = 1)//\text{solution } X/\mathrm{AgCl/Ag}.$$

The isothermal temperature coefficient gives the change in the total cell emf when the cell as a whole is raised by ΔT. The other temperature coefficient, $(dE/dT)_{th}$, gives the change in cell emf when the hydrogen electrode is kept at 25°C and the rest of the cell is raised by ΔT. The two temperature coefficients are related by the temperature coefficient for the standard hydrogen electrode

$$\left(\frac{dE}{dT}\right)_{iso} = \left(\frac{dE}{dT}\right)_{th} - 0.87 \qquad \text{(in mV/°C)}.$$

Silver–silver chloride electrodes can be prepared in the form of foil or wire using either pure silver or silver deposited on platinum. The silver on platinum electrodes are generally found to be superior in terms of stability and reproducibility. They can be prepared by (1) electrodepositing Ag on Pt and then by using the electrode as an anode in either HCl or KCl solution to electroform an AgCl layer on the surface; (2) by the thermal decomposition of a silver oxide paste on Pt to form pure silver and then by electrolytically converting part of the silver to silver chloride; or (3) by the thermal decomposition of a paste consisting of silver oxide and silver chlorate [15, 17].

As stated by Covington [16], next to the hydrogen electrode the Ag–AgCl electrode is probably the most reproducible and certainly the most reliable and convenient reference electrode. Pairs of carefully prepared electrodes, after an initial aging period, often have bias potentials (potential difference between two electrodes in the same solution) of less than 50 μV and are stable to less than 10 μV for long periods of time. They can be fabricated in

Table 9.3 Electrode Potentials and Temperature Coefficients of Some Electrodes of the Second Kind[a]

Cell	Solution X, $M = \text{mole/l}$	Electrode potential, V	$\left(\frac{dE}{dT}\right)_{th}$,[b] mV/°C	$\left(\frac{dE}{dT}\right)_{iso}$,[c] mV/°C
$X/AgCl/Ag$	$0.01M$ KCl	+0.343	+0.617	−0.25
	$0.1M$ KCl	+0.288	+0.431	−0.44
	$1.0M$ KCl	+0.235	+0.250	−0.62
	$3.5M$ KCl	+0.205	+0.14	−0.73
	Sat. KCl	+0.199	−0.14	−1.01
$X/Hg_2Cl_2/$ Hg	$0.01M$ KCl	+0.388	+0.94	+0.07
	$0.1M$ KCl	+0.333	+0.79	−0.08
	$1.0M$ KCl	+0.280	+0.59	−0.28
	$3.5M$ KCl	+0.247	+0.47	−0.40
	Sat. KCl	+0.241	+0.22	−0.65

[a] From A. J. de Bethuene, in C. A. Hampel, Ed., *Encyclopedia of Electrochemistry*, Reinhold: New York, 1964, p. 433.
[b] $(dE/dT)_{th}$ is the temperature coefficient when the hydrogen reference electrode remains at 25°C and the other electrode temperature is varied.
[c] $(dE/dT)_{iso}$ is the temperature coefficient when the complete cell is varied in temperature.

the form of a microprobe suitable for intracellular measurement of chloride ion activity [18], as well as for potential measurements at the cellular level.

Certain poisons affect the stability and useful life of Ag–AgCl electrodes. For example, it has been found that 0.064 mole % of KBr changes the electrode potential by approximately 1 mV: the presence of oxygen in acid solution also affects the potential. In biological tissue certain reactions can cause the chloride layer to become depleted to such an extent that the electrode becomes essentially useless.

9.2.3. Mercury–Mercurous Chloride (Calomel) Electrodes [13, 19]

The calomel electrode consists of a mercurous chloride (Hg_2Cl_2) layer, perhaps 0.5 cm thick, on the surface of pure mercury, electrical contact to the mercury being made by a platinum wire. When used as a reference electrode, either saturated, $1N$ or $0.1N$ KCl solutions are used. The saturated solution is often preferred because of its small junction potential with other less concentrated solutions.

Like AgCl, mercurous chloride is only weakly soluble in water. The equilibrium can be expressed by

$$Hg_2Cl_2 \rightleftharpoons Hg_2^{2+} + 2Cl^-,$$

with a solubility product given by

$$K_s = (a_{Cl^-})^2 \cdot (a_{Hg_2^{2+}})$$
$$\simeq 1 \times 10^{-18} \qquad \text{at } 25°C.$$

The presence of chlorine ions in the solution causes the Hg_2^{2+}-ion activity to decrease to a value inversely proportional to the square of the Cl^- activity. Since the electrode potential is also determined by the equilibrium

$$2Hg \rightleftharpoons Hg_2^{2+} + 2e^-,$$

it follows that

$$E = E^0_{Hg/Hg_2^{2+}} + \frac{RT}{F} \ln (a_{Hg_2^{2+}})$$

$$= E^0_{Hg/Hg_2^{2+}} + \frac{RT}{F} \ln (1 \times 10^{-18}) - \frac{2RT}{F} \ln (a_{Cl^-}).$$

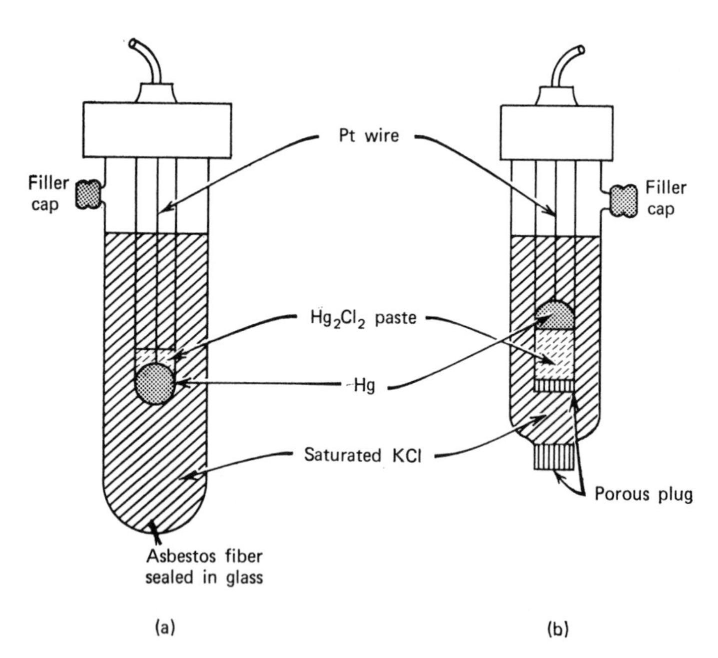

Figure 9.8. Some examples of calomel "dip-type" electrodes: (a) using an asbestos "plug" sealed in the glass container; (b) using porous plugs.

From Table 9.1, $E^0_{Hg/Hg_2^{2+}} = 0.797$ V, enabling the calomel electrode potential to be written

$$E = 0.268 - \frac{2RT}{F} \ln (a_{Cl^-}),$$

experimental values for which are given in Table 9.3.

Some examples of calomel reference electrodes designed to be dipped into the test solution are shown in Figure 9.8: in (a) the saturated KCl and the test solution are joined by the fluid flow that occurs along the asbestos fiber, while in (b) the liquid junction occurs at the porous plug. Even though the calomel electrode is inferior in many respects to the Ag–AgCl electrode, it is still the preferred electrode of many investigators when miniaturization is not important.

9.3 MEASUREMENT OF pH

9.3.1 Meaning and Definition of pH

The measurement of the degree of acidity or alkalinity of a solution is of fundamental importance in analytical chemistry as well as in clinical biochemistry. A solution is acid when the hydronium-ion activity is greater than the hydroxyl-ion activity and is alkaline when the reverse is true.

For ultrapure water the H_3^+O and OH^- activities are equal and the equilibrium can be expressed by

$$2H_2O \rightleftharpoons H_3^+O + OH^-.$$

The equilibrium constant is given by

$$K = \frac{(a_{H^+}) \cdot (a_{OH^-})}{(a_{H_2O})^2}.$$

Since water is only weakly dissociated, the denominator can be regarded as constant and incorporated into K to yield the ion activity product:

$$K_W = (a_{H^+}) \cdot (a_{OH^-}).$$

If an acid is added to the water, the hydrogen acitvity increases and the hydroxyl activity decreases by an amount equal to that required to maintain the activity product constant. Since the activities may vary by many orders of magnitude, it is convenient to compress the scale by using as a measure of the acidity the base-10 logarithm of the hydrogen-ion activity. The pH is defined by [13]

$$\text{pH} = -\log (a_{H^+}). \tag{18}$$

For pure water at 25°C, $K_W = 1.008 \times 10^{-14}$ or $\sqrt{K_W} \simeq 1 \times 10^{-7}$, and since the two activities are equal, $(a_{H^+}) = 1 \times 10^{-7}$, or pH = 7.0. It follows that for an acid, pH < 7.0 and for an alkaline solution, pH > 7.0

The measurement of pH is most conveniently carried out by means of a suitable electrochemical cell, preferably one that responds linearly to pH changes and that is insensitive to ions other than hydrogen. Unfortunately, the basic problem concerned with such a measurement is that it is not possible to design an electrochemical cell to measure only the hydrogen-ion activity: all measurements involve two or more ion activities. Further, since presently known thermodynamic methods do not permit an exact calculation of an individual ion activity, it follows that a determination of pH according to the definition given by Eq. (18) requires certain theoretical assumptions. As a result the accuracy of pH measurement in terms of Eq. (18) is limited to ±0.01 pH units [20].

Because of this difficulty, it has been found convenient to use an operational pH definition based on standard buffer solutions [13, 20]. In the U.S. scale the buffer solutions have a pH value based on a value of the chloride-ion activity calculated from the Debye–Huckel theory. In the British system 0.05M potassium hydrogen phthalate is *defined* to have a pH of exactly 4.0 at 15°C. This definition corresponds to the true value given by Eq. (18) to within ±0.01 pH units. By defining a solution to have a certain pH value, the pH of other buffer solutions can be determined. Through the use of these standard buffers, a pH-measuring instrument can be calibrated and the pH of an unknown solution determined. With a cell of the form

indicator electrode/solution X//reference electrode,

in which the liquid junction potentials are small, if the cell emf's for two standard buffers, 1 and 2, are E_1 and E_2, then the cell emf for the test solution is related to the unknown pH by

$$\frac{\mathrm{pH}_x - \mathrm{pH}_1}{\mathrm{pH}_2 - \mathrm{pH}_1} = \frac{E_x - E_1}{E_2 - E_1}.$$

This equation assumes a linear relation between the pH and the cell emf. Evidently the closer the pH of the buffer solutions are to the unknown pH, the better will be the accuracy and the smaller will be the error from any nonlinearity.

9.3.2 The Hydrogen pH Electrode

The hydrogen pH electrode [13, 14] is primarily used for checking the response of glass electrodes and for measuring the pH of standard buffer solutions. Because of its susceptibility to poisons, the hydrogen electrode cannot be used with many solutions; furthermore, the added inconvenience of requiring a source of pure hydrogen gas makes its use rather rare.

An equation for the potential of a hydrogen electrode was derived earlier in this chapter: it is

$$E = \frac{RT}{F} \ln \left(\frac{a_{H^+}}{\sqrt{P_{H_2}}} \right)$$

which can be rewritten in terms of the pH by making use of Eq. (18):

$$E = \frac{-2.303RT}{F} \left(\text{pH} - \frac{1}{2} \log \frac{760}{P_{H_2}} \right),$$

where the partial pressure of hydrogen is expressed in millimeters of mercury. Thus, the potential is linearly related to the pH and the slope of the line is $-2.303RT/F$.

The two examples of hydrogen-ion electrodes shown in Figure 9.9 both incorporate twin platinum electrodes for checking electrode deterioration. The salt bridge in (a) can be eliminated by using an Ag–AgCl electrode dipping into the solution being tested. According to Mattock [21], both electrodes shown in Figure 9.9 give stable and reproducible emf's to within ± 0.1 mV in a matter of minutes.

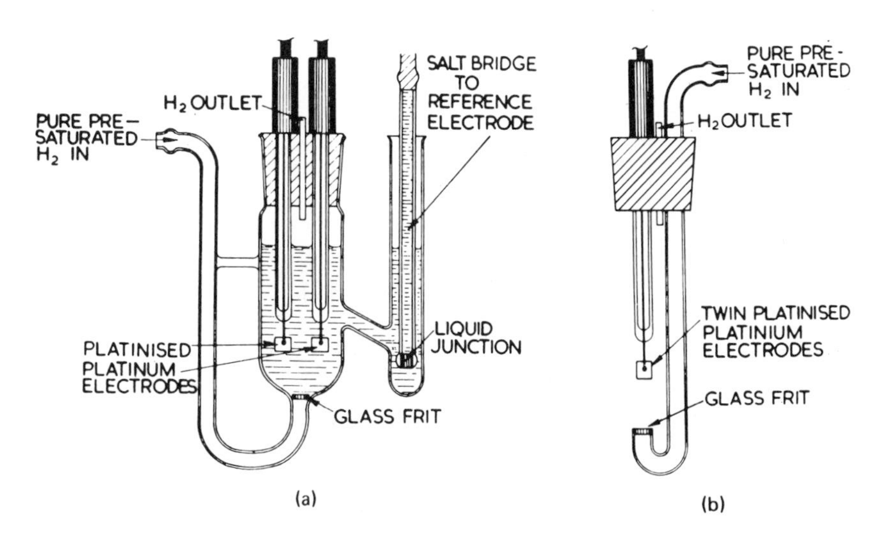

Figure 9.9. Examples of hydrogen pH electrodes: (a) container type; (b) immersion-type (reproduced, with permission, from G. Mattock, "Laboratory pH Measurements" in *Advances in Analytical Chemistry and Instrumentation*, Vol. 2, C. N. Reilley, (ed.), Wiley, New York, 1963).

9.3.3 Antimony pH Electrodes [13, 22, 23]

A thin layer of antimonous oxide (Sb_2O_3) is normally present on the surface of antinomy. When immersed in an electrolyte containing hydrogen ions, the oxidation-reduction reaction

$$Sb_2O_3 + 6H^+ + 6e^- \rightleftharpoons 2Sb + 3H_2O$$

occurs. The electrode potential can be found by applying the Nernst equation as given by Eq. (6), to the above equilibrium, yielding

$$E = E^0 + \frac{RT}{F} \ln (a_{H^+})$$

$$= E^0 - \frac{2.303RT}{F} \cdot \text{pH},$$

where E^0 is the standard potential of the Sb–Sb_2O_3 electrode and it has been assumed that the activities of antimony, antimonous oxide, and water are all unity. In practice, it is found that E^0 is a somewhat variable quantity (approximately 0.25 V); however, the slope of the pH characteristic is close to the ideal value of 59 mV per pH unit at 25°C.

The presence of oxidizing and reducing agents significantly disturbs the potential of antimony electrodes. When used in living tissue, the presence

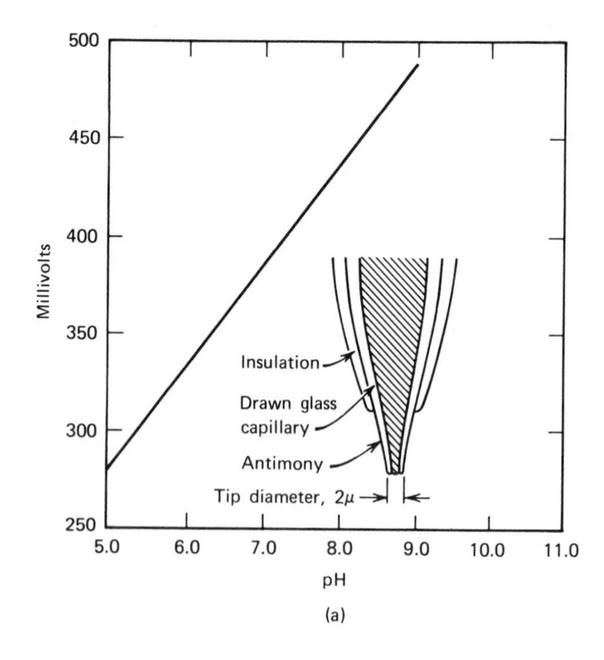

(a)

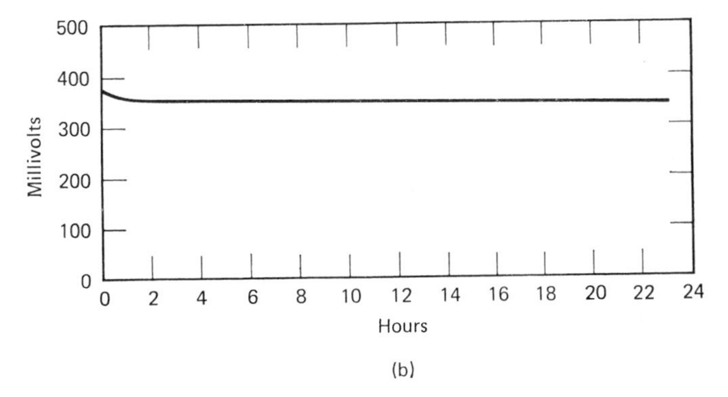

Figure 9.10. Characteristics of a thin-film antimony pH microelectrode. (a) pH calibration with an AgCl–KCl (sat) reference electrode, at 27°C; (b) drift characteristic in physiological saline (from Transidyne Electrophysiology Catalog, 1971; reproduced with permission of Transidyne Corp., Mich.).

of a variable oxygen tension can be expected to introduce a considerable uncertainty in the pH reading. In spite of these problems, antimony electrodes have found useful application for measurements at the cellular level. Although earlier electrodes used solid antimony, some of the more recent versions use sputtered antimony on glass. The purity of the sputtering process might be expected to yield electrodes of good reproducibility and better stability than the solid electrodes. Microelectrodes using sputtered Sb films on glass have proved useful for recording the approximate pH and its variations within cells. An example is shown in Figure 9.10 (inset), together with the calibration curve and drift characteristic in physiological saline.

9.4 GLASS ELECTRODES

When a thin glass membrane separates two electrolytes, a potential difference is observed across the glass. It is found that this *glass-electrode potential* varies in a reproducible and well-defined manner with the activities of hydrogen and other ions in the electrolytes [8, 11, 13]. Further, it is found that by a proper choice of the glass composition, the potential often varies as the log of the activity of a specific ion and may be essentially independent of the other ion activities.

In order to understand the origin of the potential, its variation with ion activity and the dependence on the glass composition, it is necessary to consider briefly the structure of glass [24].

Glasses, like liquids, have no long-range order and, on a macroscopic scale, can be regarded as randomly organized structures. However, on the microscopic scale it is found that a sufficient degree of order exists to enable a meaningful description to be given of the probable arrangement of the atoms with respect to one another. According to the model proposed by Zachariasen [25], which is illustrated in Figure 9.11, the silicate glasses consist of a network composed of silicon atoms lying at the center of a tetrahedron formed by four oxygen atoms. The arrangement is such that no long-range structural order results.

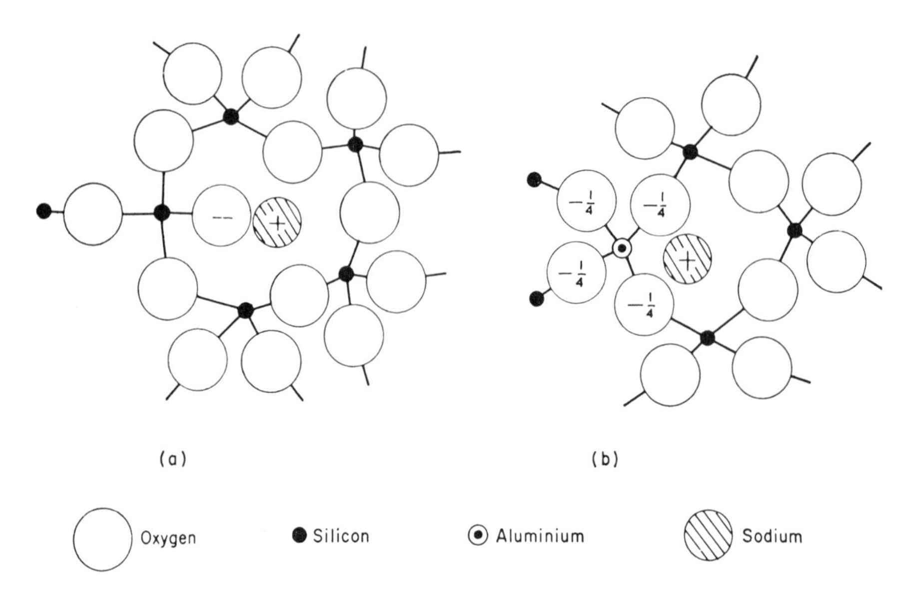

Figure 9.11. A two-dimensional representation of the structure of glass: (a) sodium silicate glass; (b) sodium alumina silicate glass; (reproduced, with permission, from J. O. Isard, Ch. 3 in *Glass Electrodes for Hydrogen and Other Cations*, G. Eisenman (ed.), Dekker, New York, 1967).

The presence of an alkali metal oxide in the glass causes some of the oxygen–silicon bonds to be broken. Each metal cation is bonded to a negatively charged oxygen ion that is bonded to only one silicon atom. The fairly weak metal bond coupled with the existence of suitable interstitial sites endows the metal ion with a reasonable degree of mobility. It is found that for sodium silicate glasses, the electrical conduction arises from sodium ions moving from one interstitial position to another. Since conduction is by an activated process, it is reasonable to expect that the resistivity will vary with temperature as $\exp(-E_a/kT)$, where E_a is the activation energy. This is usually found to be the case for most ion-selective glasses.

A further feature of the alkali-metal ion-bonding is the relative ease with which the metal ion can be exchanged for a H^+ ion. It is through the process of ion exchange that the glass electrode is endowed with its ability to respond to H^+ and other ions. By modifying the glass lattice by incorporating various elements into the silica glass, it is possible to synthesize a glass so that it acts as a cation exchanger sensitive to an ion of a particular type.

As an example we consider a glass consisting of 11 mole % Na_2O, 18 mole % Al_2O_3, and 71 mole % SiO_2 (NAS 11–18). The aluminum atoms are incorporated into the random silica network as shown in Figure 9.11(b), with the Na^+ ions bonded in an interstitial position to the negatively charged oxygen ions. The bonding is such as to make the glass a particularly efficient cation exchanger for Ag^+ ions.

9.4.1 Origin and Theory of the Glass Electrode Potential

The potential developed across a glass membrane separating two electrolytes arises from the cation exchange process at the two interfaces and the diffusion of ions within the glass. Thus, the total electrode potential can be written

$E = E_{b1}$	$+E_{b2}$	$+E_d$.
Phase-boundary potential soln. 1	Phase-boundary potential soln. 2	Diffusion potential

Since we are primarily interested in the change in electrode potential that occurs when one of the solutions is changed and the other remains constant, E_{b2} can be regarded as constant, so that

$$E = E_x + E_{b1} + E_d. \tag{19}$$

Now suppose that ions I are exchanged for ions J in the glass and that an equilibrium exists of the form

$$I^+(\text{glass}) + J^+(\text{soln.}) \rightleftharpoons I^+(\text{soln.}) + J^+(\text{glass}).$$

It can be shown [24, 26] that the boundary potential arising from this cation exchange process is given by

$$E_{b1} = \text{constant} + \frac{RT}{F} \ln (a_i + Ka_j), \tag{20}$$

where a_i and a_j are the cation activities in solution 1,

$$K = \left(\frac{a_i}{a_j}\right) \cdot \left(\frac{a_j^*}{a_i^*}\right),$$

is an ion-exchange constant, and a^* is the ion activity just inside the glass.

The presence of an intruding cation in the glass with a mobility greater than the ion it replaced results in a greater diffusion flux for this ion. Since the higher mobility cation tends to diffuse faster, a net charge imbalance will occur within the glass. The electric field that results causes the high-mobility ion to be restrained to a greater degree than the low-mobility ion and thereby insures that the net flux due to each cation type are identical. Thus, the diffusion potential arises from the equilibrium requirement that there be no change in the charge distribution within the glass.

It can be shown that the diffusion potential can be expressed as [26]

$$E_d = \text{constant} + \frac{RT}{F} \ln \left(\frac{a_i + K(\mu_j^*/\mu_i^*)a_j}{a_i + Ka_j} \right) \tag{21}$$

where μ^* is the ion mobility in the glass. Substituting Eqs. (20) and (21) into Eq. (19) and incorporating the various constants into a single term E^0, we find

$$E = E^0 + \frac{RT}{F} \ln \left[a_i + K \left(\frac{\mu_j^*}{\mu_i^*} \right) a_j \right]$$

or

$$E = E^0 + \frac{RT}{F} \ln (a_i + K_{ij} a_j), \tag{22}$$

where the constant K_{ij} expressing the relative sensitivity of the electrode potential to the two ion types is equal to $K(\mu_j^*/\mu_i^*)$. In the absence of any general multi-ion theory, it is tempting to generalize Eq. (22) to the form

$$E = E^0 + \frac{RT}{F} \ln \left(a_i + \sum_{j=1}^{N} K_{ij} a_j \right). \tag{23}$$

It has been found that although Eq. (23) describes the behavior of certain multi-ion mixtures, it is not generally applicable.

If ion I is H^+ and ion J is Na^+, then Eq. (22) can be written

$$E = E^0 + \frac{RT}{F} \ln (a_{H^+} + K_{H^+/Na^+} \cdot a_{Na^+}). \tag{24}$$

Evidently the smaller the value of $(K_{H/Na}\, a_{Na})$, the closer the characteristics of the electrode will be to the ideal linear E-versus-pH relationship. The graph of Eq. (22) shown in Figure 9.12 illustrates how the range of linear operation depends on the value of $(K_{H/Na}\, a_{Na})$. It will be observed that the *selectivity constant* K_{ij} and the activity a_j determine the range of linearity. If the pH response is to be linear in the highly alkaline range, it is necessary that the selectivity constant be small; otherwise, small concentrations of sodium will cause significant errors.

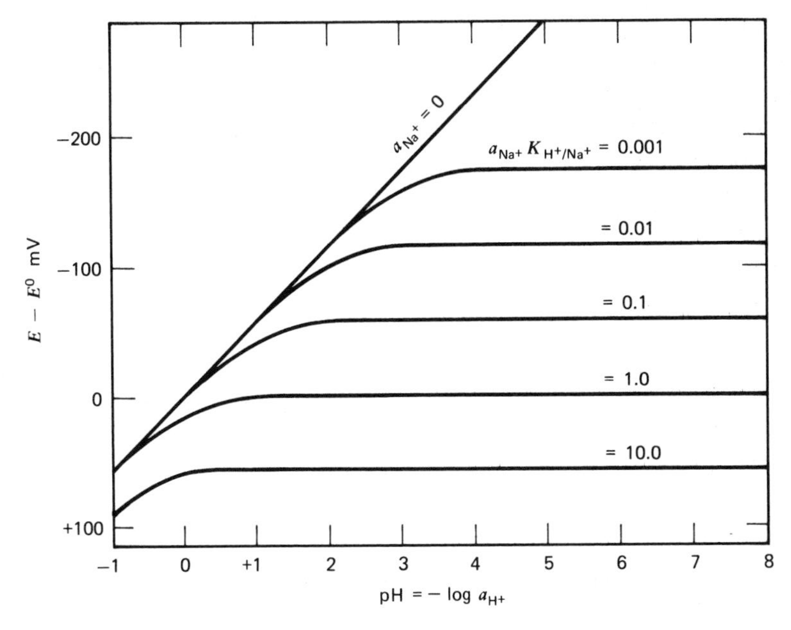

Figure 9.12. Graphical presentation of Eq. (24) showing the effect of selectivity and sodium activity on the pH response linearity of a glass electrode.

9.4.2 Practical Aspects of Glass pH Electrodes [8, 10]

One of the first glasses to be used commercially for pH measurement consisted of 22 mole % Na_2O, 6 mole % CaO and 72 mole % SiO_2 (NCaS 22–6) corresponding to Corning Glass code number 0150. In 1*N* NaOH the sodium error becomes significant at pH = 9. With the more recent lithium oxide glasses such as LAS 14–4, the range is increased to pH = 13 in the presence of 1*N* NaOH, as illustrated in Figure 9.13. It should be noted that an error occurs not only in strongly alkaline solutions but also in concentrated acid solutions. The *alkaline error* in the presence of sodium can be satisfactorily accounted for in terms of Eq. (24) when the two terms in parenthesis are dissimilar; however, a modified theory is required to account for the error when the two terms are nearly the same. The origin of the *acid error* has been disputed for a number of years; the reader is referred to Bates [13, pp. 319–322] for a discussion of the various theories proposed.

The penetration of water into silica glasses to form a *hydrated silica layer* is particularly evident with the pH-sensitive glasses. There appears to be an intimate connection between the hydroscopicity and pH function, which

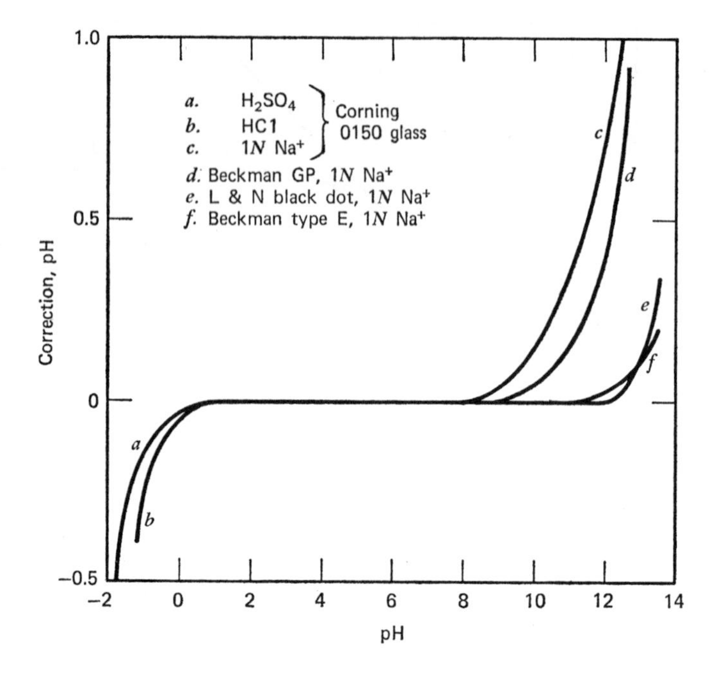

Figure 9.13. Alkaline and acid error for a number of commercial glass pH electrodes (reproduced, with permission, from R. M. Bates, *Determination of pH: Theory and Practice*, Wiley, New York, 1964).

probably arises from the greatly enhanced diffusion constant of cations in hydrated layers of glass compared to nonhydrated glass. The thickness of the hydrated layer has been found to vary from a few monolayers (~10 Å) to ~10 μm depending on the composition [27].

Ideally, if the test solution is identical to the reference solution the potential difference across the glass should be zero. In practice, this in not normally found to be the case and an *asymmetry potential* occurs whose value depends on the pH, prior history of the electrode, and temperature. It seems likely that differences in the degree of hydration or dehydration of the two surfaces has an important influence on this small, but sometimes significant, offset potential.

The high resistivity of glass, and consequently the high resistance between the two glass surfaces of a glass electrode, causes certain problems in measuring the potential. It was previously pointed out that since conduction through the glass is by a cation activation process, the resistance is a sensitive function of temperature. To avoid measurement error arising from the high source resistance and also to avoid error from significant disturbance to the electrode equilibrium condition, it is essential that the potential-recording device have a high internal resistance compared with the highest resistance expected from the electrode. Glass pH electrodes having a glass thickness of about 100 μm typically have resistances in the range 10^7–10^{10} Ω, although even higher resistances may be encountered in glass microelectrodes.

With modern solid-state electrometers an input resistance of $>10^{13}$ Ω and an input leakage current of $<10^{-13}$ A is readily achieved. This is sufficient for most pH electrodes. Higher input resistances, to meet the demands of certain glass microelectrodes, can be achieved either through the use of a guarded gate MOS transistor input stage or by using a vibrating-reed capacitor chopper.

A further aspect concerned with the potential measurement is the problem of electrostatic interference to which all high-impedance measurements are very susceptible. Single or double electrostatic shields are often an integral part of a glass electrode design and, when used in conjunction with a carefully shielded experimental arrangement, usually enable this source of interference to be eliminated.

An important aspect of glass electrode design concerns the choice of a suitable *inner* reference electrode [28, 29]. Generally, either the calomel or Ag–AgCl electrode is used immersed in either dilute HCl (often 0.1*N*) or a buffered chloride solution. However, it should be noted that dry connections to the glass membrane, using, for example, a silver deposit or silver paint [30], have met with a reasonable degree of success.

The properties that an inner solution should possess have been described by Dole [29]: it should have a buffer capacity sufficient to cope with any alkali ions leached out of the glass, should not attack the glass, and should have a concentration such as to insure long-term stability of the reference electrode. With regard to this last point it should be noted that in contrast to the external reference electrode, for which it is desired to eliminate any liquid junction potentials by using a concentrated salt-bridge solution, no such requirement exists for the inner electrode. By using a more dilute solution (e.g., 0.1*N* HCl), the problem of the high solubility of AgCl in concentrated chloride solutions (see p. 346) is avoided.

The choice of a suitable inner and outer reference electrode combination is governed by the desire to achieve a small isothermal temperature coefficient for the system and to have a cell emf of zero at some fixed pH value. These requirements will be examined by considering the effects of temperature on the various components of the total cell emf.

9.4.3 Effects of Temperature

If the pH-sensitive glass is regarded as an ideal hydrogen electrode, the cell emf can be written [28]

$$E_c = \frac{2.3kT}{F}\,\text{pH} + E_O - E_I, \tag{26}$$

where E_O is the "standard" potential of the outer reference electrode system

std. H_2 electrode/soln. X/ref. soln. B/ outer ref. electrode

and $-E_I$ is the potential of the inner reference system

inner ref. electrode/ref. soln. A/std. H_2 electrode.

If it is assumed that $(E_O - E_I)$ varies linearly with temperature, that is,

$$E_O - E_I = E_a + bT, \tag{27}$$

then from Eq. (26), dE_c/dT will be zero when

$$\frac{dE_O}{dT} - \frac{dE_I}{dT} = \frac{-2.3k}{F}\,\text{pH}_{\text{iso}}. \tag{28}$$

Thus, the temperature coefficient can only be zero at a specific pH value, pH_{iso}, called the *isopotential pH*. For example, if we choose $\text{pH}_{\text{iso}} = 7.0$, then at 25°C, Eq. (28) can be written as

$$\frac{dE_O}{dT} - \frac{dE_I}{dT} = -1.4\ \text{mV/°C}. \tag{29}$$

If, in addition, it is required that $E_c = 0$ at pH $= 7.0$, then from Eq. (26),

$$E_O - E_I = -1.4 \times 10^{-3}T. \tag{30}$$

Using either a saturated calomel or saturated Ag–AgCl outer electrode and an inner Ag–AgCl electrode, it is possible to find an inner filling solution that simultaneously satisfies both Eqs. (29) and (30) as well as meeting the other requirements previously described [28, 31a].

Figure 9.14 illustrates the effects of temperature on the pH characteristics for a cell with $E_c = 0$ at pH $= \text{pH}_{\text{iso}} = 7.0$. It should be noted that, based on the assumption that $E_I - E_O$ varies linearly with temperature, there is no zero shift and the slope varies linearly with the absolute temperature. In practice it is found that arising from a quadratic temperature term, there is a small zero-dependence, which usually amounts to no more than a few tenths of a millivolt per degree centigrade. The slight zero shift and the slope-dependence can be corrected for in a practical pH meter through the use of a resistance temperature sensor immersed in the test solution.

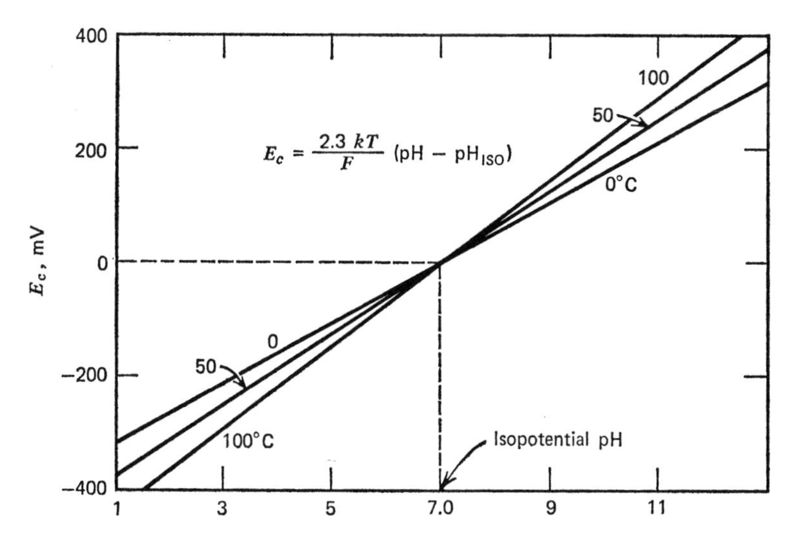

Figure 9.14. Effect of temperature on a glass pH electrode system having a cell emf of zero at the isoelectric pH value of 7.0.

9.4.4 Glass pH Macroelectrodes

In Figures 9.15 and 9.16 some example of glass electrodes designed for measuring the pH of solutions are shown.* The electrode system illustrated in Figure 9.15 uses an inner Ag–AgCl electrode immersed in a suitable buffered chloride solution, in combination with a calomel external reference electrode. By incorporating the external electrode into an outer glass sleeve, as shown in Figure 9.16(c), a combination unit results that is capable of measuring the pH of smaller sample volumes. In this particular example, the fiber liquid junction is coaxial to the pH sensitive glass.

In order to measure smaller sample volumes or to measure the pH of a flowing system, the capillary-type system illustrated in Figure 9.17 is often used. It consists of a fine capillary of pH-sensitive glass surrounded by a sealed reference electrode. The sample to be measured is drawn into the capillary by suction and the open end is immersed in salt-bridge solution containing the other reference electrode. An important advantage of this

* A totally different type of glass (SiO_2) electrode for measuring Na^+, K^+ and H^+ ion activities, has been described by Bergveld [31b]. It consists of a SiO_2–Si insulated-gate field-effect transistor structure in which the gate consists of the test solution A change in the ion activities at the solution–SiO_2 interface produces a change in the induced channel charge and hence changes the drain current.

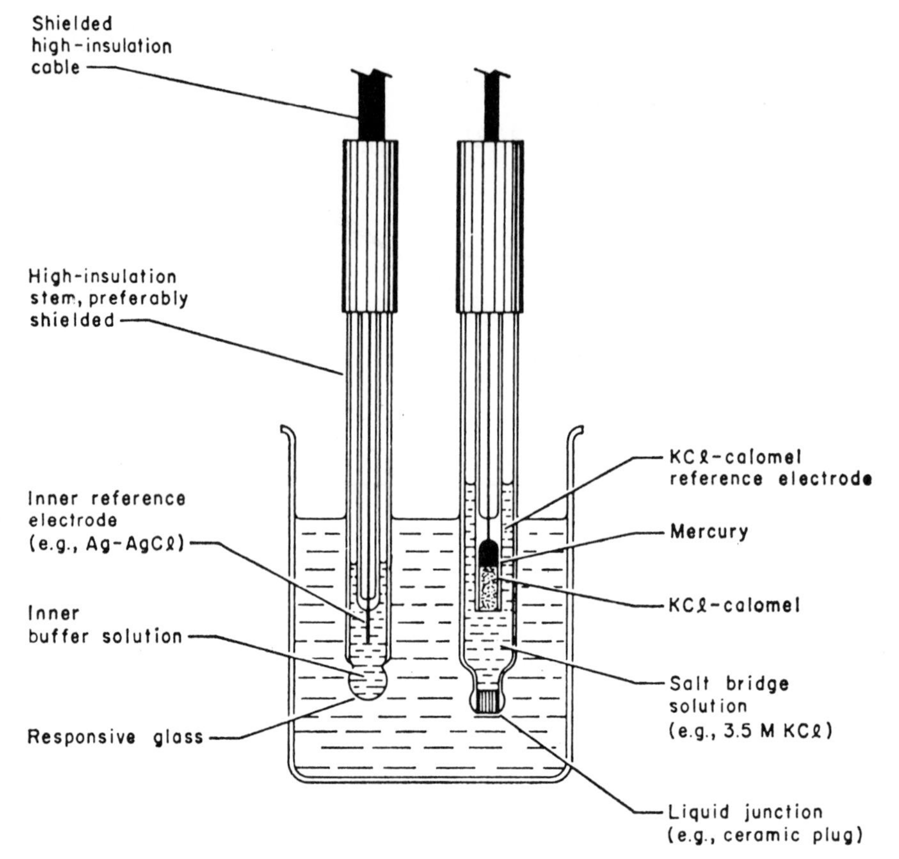

Figure 9.15. Typical pH measurement system using a glass electrode and an external calomel reference electrode (reproduced, with permission, from G. Mattock and D. M. Band, Ch. 2 in *Glass Electrodes for Hydrogen and Other Cations*, G. Eisenman (ed.), Dekker, New York, 1967).

system is that it enables measurements to be made on very small samples of biological fluids under anaerobic conditions.

The capillary-type electrode forms the basis of most in vitro systems for measuring the pH of blood. Whole blood is a highly buffered suspension whose pH lies in the range 7.35–7.45 for the normal adult. To determine the acid–base status [32] by equilibriating the blood with known concentrations of CO_2 and also to detect significant changes from the norm, an accuracy of ± 0.01 pH units is required, relative to a standard buffer solution. To achieve this, special precautions are required to insure that coagulation does not occur,

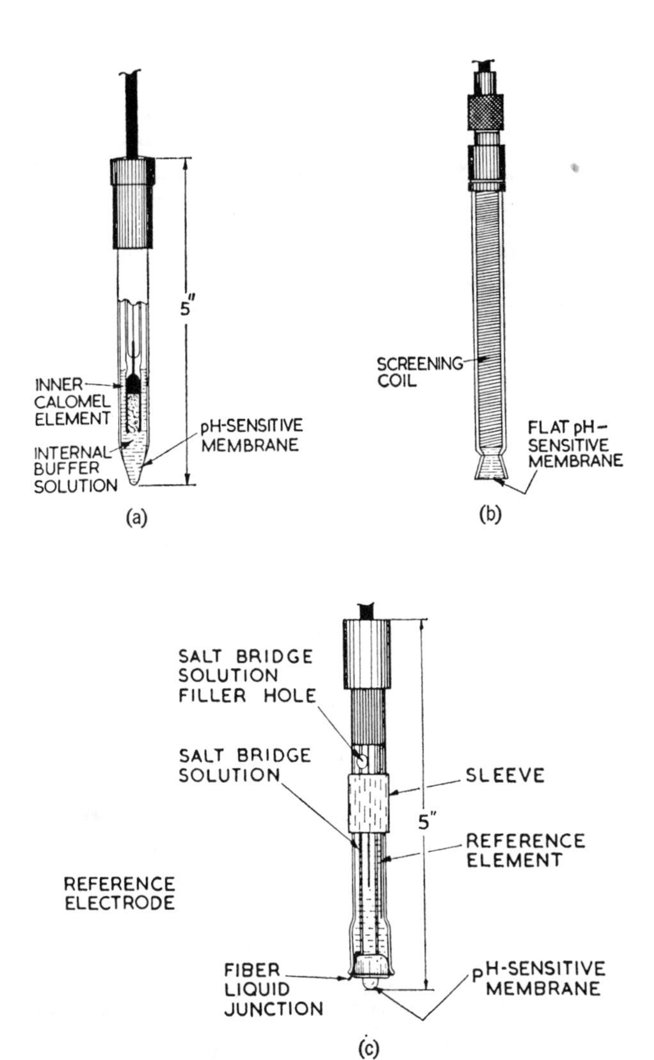

Figure 9.16. Examples of glass pH electrodes: (a) bulb-type with calomel inner electrode; (b) electrostatically shielded flat-membrane type; and (c) combination unit with inner and outer Ag–AgCl electrodes (reproduced, with permission, from G. Mattock, pp. 35–121, in *Advances in Analytical Chemistry and Instrumentation*, Vol. 2, C. N. Reilley (ed.), Wiley, New York, 1963).

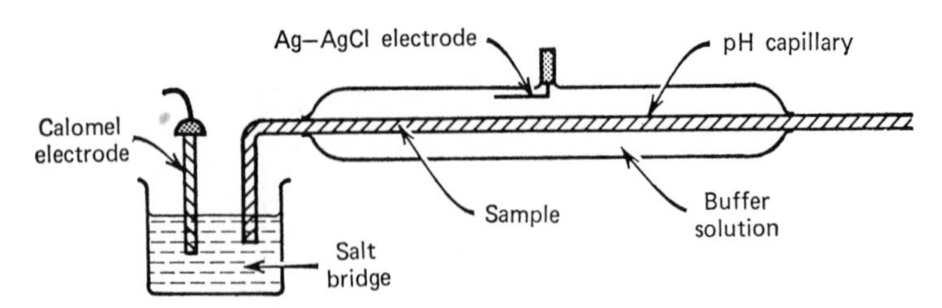

Figure 9.17. Illustrating the principle components of a glass capillary system for measuring the pH of small volumes under anaerobic conditions.

to prevent loss of CO_2, and to insure that the sample is measured under accurately controlled temperature conditions.

Figure 9.18 illustrates the basis of the blood pH-measuring system developed by Astrup and Schroeder [33] and refined by Siggaard-Anderson [32]. Thermostatically controlled 1% NaCl insures that both the reference electrode assembly and the capillary assembly are to within 0.1°C of the required temperature (normally either 37° or 38°C). The use of a conducting fluid rather than pure water enables a sufficient degree of electrostatic shielding to be achieved so that additional shielding is not necessary. A blood sample, whose volume should be about 20 μl, is drawn into the pH-sensitive glass capillary by suction via a polyethylene tube. The end of this tube is then

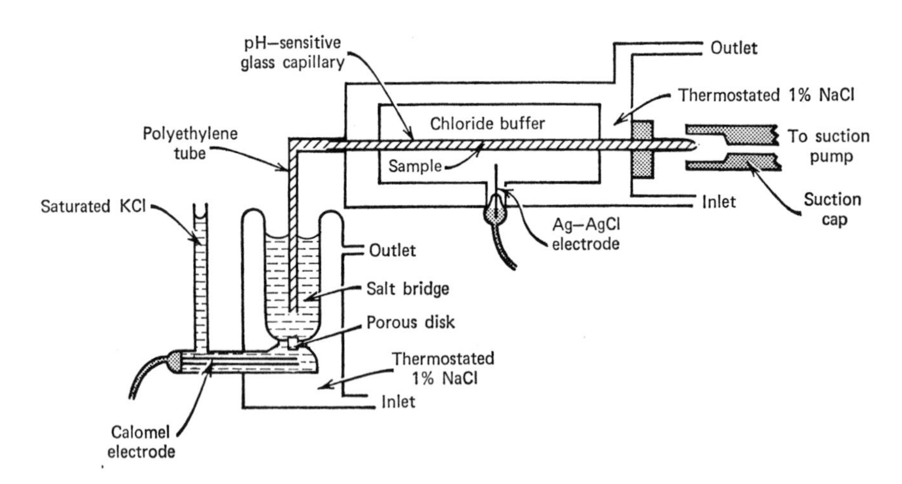

Figure 9.18. Principles of an in vitro glass capillary system designed for measuring the pH of whole blood at 38°C (after Siggaard-Andersen [32]).

transferred into a bridge solution, which forms a liquid junction with a saturated KCl–calomel electrode.*

Calibration of the system is normally carried out with the help of two buffer standards whose pH at 38°C are 6.840 and 7.384. One standard serves to set the "zero," and the other, to set the "slope" (normally the slope is somewhat less than the theoretical value of 60.7 mV/pH at 38°C).

In attempting to achieve the desired accuracy problems may be encountered from the blood–KCl (saturated) open-capillary liquid junction. Saturated KCl causes the red cells to become crenated and the proteins to coagulate, thereby introducing considerable uncertainty in the value of the liquid junction potential. Maas [35] noted that the liquid junction potential between blood and normal saline (0.160*M*) is very small. In addition he noted that by using standard buffers modified through the addition of NaCl, the blood/buffer-liquid junction potential can also be small. Thus, by using normal saline as the bridge solution and employing the modified buffers for calibration, he was able to avoid the problems arising from the use of concentrated KCl. Comparison of the results obtained with the normal saline bridge to those obtained with saturated KCl showed a standard deviation of 0.002 pH units. Generally, with careful calibration and proper attention to the various precautions, a standard deviation of 0.006 pH units with respect to a standard buffer can be achieved. However, as pointed out by Mattock and Band [20], the accuracy in terms of hydrogen-ion activity is probably no better than ± 0.02 pH units.

Most in vivo pH measurements on the human have either been directed to the determination of blood pH or to the determination of pH within the gastrointestinal tract. Two examples of in vivo blood pH measurement will be considered.

An indwelling catheter with a pH-sensitive glass tip [Figure 9.19(a)] has been reported by Staehelin et al [36] to provide a useful and effective means of monitoring acid–base changes in patients undergoing major surgery, in a state of shock, or under intensive-care treatment. A calomel or silver chloride electrode held in contact with the skin establishes the reference half-cell. Proper electrical contact is achieved by using an electrolyte paste or jelly and a specially designed rubber·cuff to hold the electrode in place. The authors report that with care, stable arterial and venous pH-monitoring can be carried out for periods of many hours.

An alternative approach to in vivo blood pH-monitoring has been reported by Band and Semple [37] using the miniature combination electrode assembly illustrated in Figure 9.19(b). The small diameter (0.5–0.8 mm) pH-sensitive

* Although shown separately in Figure 9.18, the calomel electrode can be incorporated into a single unit with the capillary [34].

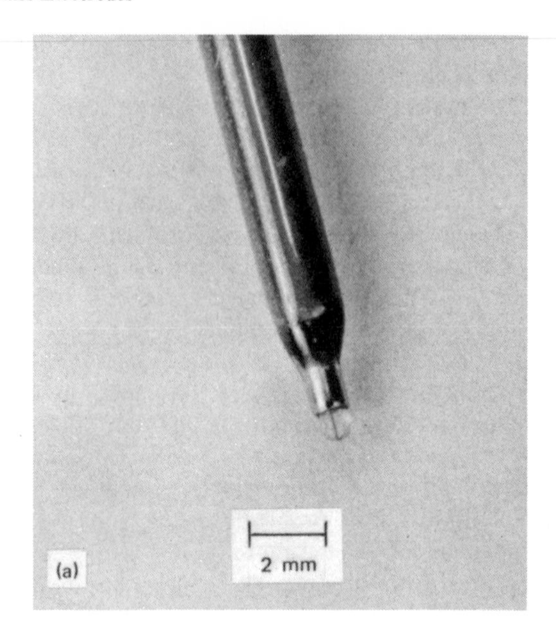

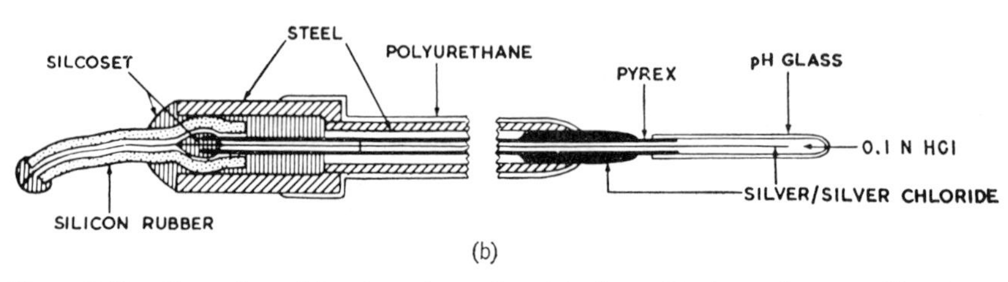

(b)

Figure 9.19. Examples of in vitro electrodes: (a) glass pH electrode on a 6F catheter (courtesy, Beckman Instruments, California); (b) needle electrode for insertion into a modified Cournand intra-arterial needle (reproduced, with permission, from D. M. Band and S. J. G. Semple, *J. Appl. Physiol.*, **22**, 854–857, 1967).

sealed glass tube and coaxial Ag–AgCl external reference electrode fits inside the lumen of a modified Cournand intra-arterial needle. When the needle is inserted into an artery, blood flows up the lumen and passes through the annular space between the electrode and inner wall of the needle. Blood is allowed to escape from the needle at a defined rate—perhaps 2 ml/min—so that the electrode responds rapidly (<0.5 sec) to any arterial pH changes.

The second important in vivo application of pH electrodes is for studying the pH properties of the gastrointestinal (GI) tract [38–40]. Either glass or antimony electrodes (see Section 9.3.3) are incorporated in a small "pill" package that also includes a reference electrode, power source, amplifier, and transmitter circuits [41, 42]. The self-contained pH-sensitive pill is sufficiently small for it to pass freely down the GI tract when swallowed by the subject. As it does so, it transmits to a nearby receiver the pH level, enabling a continuous record of pH level as a function of position in the GI tract to be obtained [43]. With the aid of such a system it has been possible to study gastric secretion [44], the effects of various foodstuffs, environmental conditions, and psychological state on the pH response [39]. Further, in certain special cases, the system has enabled useful diagnostic information to be obtained on subjects suffering from various GI disorders.

9.4.5 Glass pH Microelectrodes

The successful development of glass microelectrodes [8, 11, 45] with tip diameters of less than 1 μm have enabled in vivo measurements of intracellular pH [46] to be performed on cells with diameters of less than 10 μm. The wide variety of special pH-sensitive glass microelectrodes that have been designed and employed for such work can generally be classified into either of the two categories: sealed electrodes and unsealed (capillary) electrodes.

Two examples of sealed electrodes are shown in Figure 9.20. The electrode

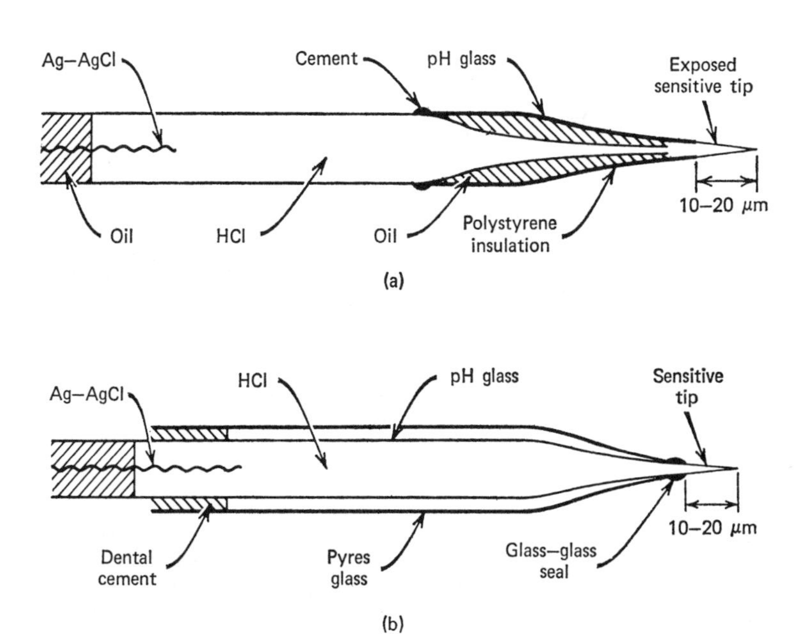

Figure 9.20. Examples of closed-tip pH microelectrodes: (a) polystyrene-insulated electrode [47]; (b) glass-insulated electrode.

of Figure 9.20(a) uses a pH-sensitive glass (NCaS 22–6) capillary pulled to a fine point and insulated with polystyrene to within approximately 20 μm of the tip [45, 47–49]. A non-pH-responsive glass micropipette containing a suitable electrolyte and an Ag–AgCl electrode is cemented to the pH glass and the space between the two is filled with an insulating oil. Khuri [47] reports that this type of electrode can be made with tip diameters of about 1 μm and a corresponding internal resistance of about 10^8 Ω. Selected electrodes whose

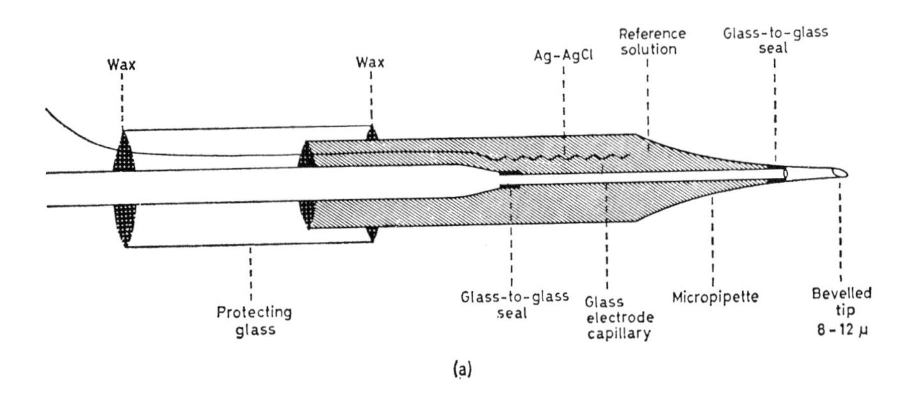

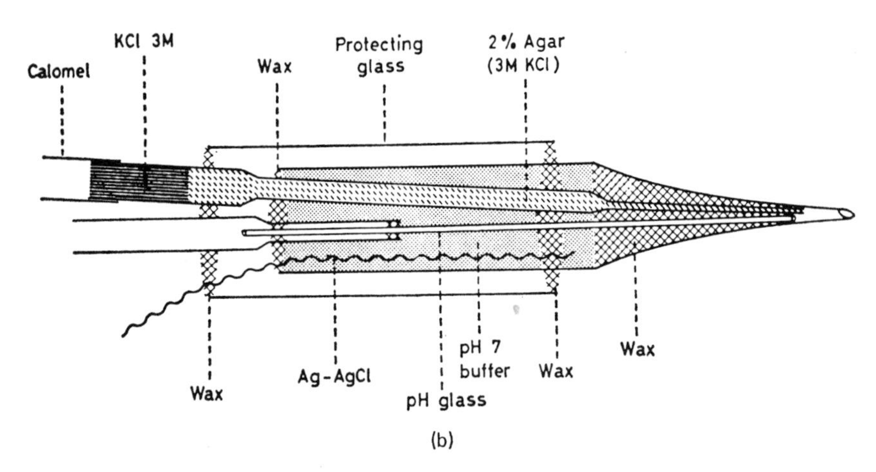

Figure 9.21. Capillary-type glass pH microelectrodes: (a) Glass–glass sealed electrode; (b) combination electrode incorporating the "external" reference electrode (reproduced with permission of Springer-Verlag, Berlin-Heidelberg-New York, from R. N. Khuri, S. K. Agulian, H. Oelert, and R. I. Harik: "A Single Unit pH Glass Ultramicro Electrode," *Pflügers Arch. ges. Physiol.*, **294**, 291–294, 1967, and from R. N. Khuri, S. K. Agulian, and R. I. Harik: "Internal Capillary Glass Microelectrodes with a Glass Seal for pH, Sodium and Potassium," *Pflügers Arch. ges. Physiol.*, **301**, 182–186, 1968).

pH slopes were greater than 50 mV/pH unit were found to have a linear potential response over the range 2–12 pH units at 25°C. Deterioration of the insulating layer or holes caused by imperfect insulation coverage can cause the electrode shank to become pH responsive thereby resulting in an erroneous reading when the tip and the shank are in differing solutions.

The electrode shown in Figure 9.20(b) avoids this problem by using an outer non-pH-responsive glass. The two glasses are sealed close to the tip by means of a microforge, forming a glass–glass seal. Details of the fabrication of this type of electrode have been described by Hinke [18, 50], who also reports that electrode resistance values are in the range 10^9–10^{12} Ω. Hinke points out that an electrometer with an input resistance approximately 10^{15} Ω and a stability of 100 μV/h is desirable if satisfactory results are to be obtained with the highest-resistance electrodes. Kostyuk et al. [51] have also described this type of electrode and report that tip diameters of less than 0.5 μm can be readily achieved.

Two examples of the internal capillary type of pH electrode are shown in Figure 9.21, both of which are the work of Khuri and his colleagues [49, 52, 53]. The simpler version shown in (a) operates by sucking the solution under test into the fine, pH-sensitive glass capillary and measuring the potential developed between the outer Ag–AgCl electrode and an external reference microelectrode. The electrode response time is approximately 40 sec, and a sample volume of approximately 0.01 μl is required.

The combination electrode [45, 53] incorporating the external calomel electrode within the same structure has the great advantage of only requiring a single micropuncture of the cell in order to obtain a reading. This is somewhat offset by the larger tip diameter ($\sim$5 μm) and considerably more complex construction. Khuri et al. [53] report that under in vitro conditions volumes less than 0.05 μl can be measured with a standard error of $\pm$0.02 pH units.

Some mention should also be made of the open-tip pH-sensitive glass microelectrodes developed by Lavallée [54]. Electrolyte-filled glass microelectrodes having tip diameters of less than 1 μm are found to indicate potentials that differ substantially from those measured with larger diameter electrodes. If, as illustrated in Figure 9.22, the small-diameter microelectrode is part of a symmetrical electrolyte system, a nonzero potential is observed. By breaking the tip so as to increase the diameter, the excess potential (*tip potential*) disappears.

Lavallée and Szabo [55, 56] suggest that the tip potential probably arises from a "double layer" charge on the inside glass wall, which, because of the asymmetry, results in a potential along the length of the microelectrode. For a pH-sensitive glass electrode, Lavallée proposed that the charge distribution (and therefore the potential) is affected by the pH of the electrolyte

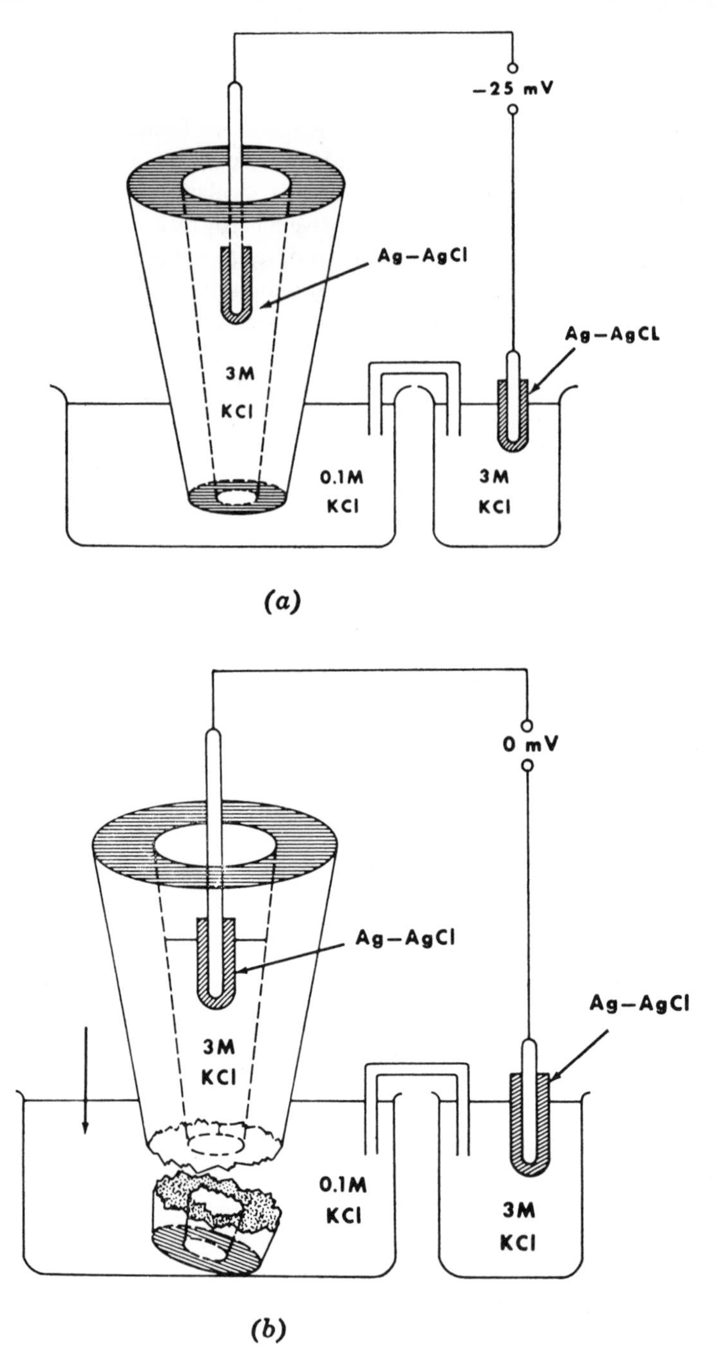

Figure 9.22. Effect of tip potential: (a) small-diameter glass microelectrode, exhibiting a tip potential of 25 mV; (b) elimination of tip potential by breaking the tip (reproduced, with permission, from M. Lavallée and G. Szabo, Ch. 6 in *Glass Microelectrodes*, M. Lavallée et al. (eds.), Wiley: New York, 1969).

within and outside the glass wall. It was observed that the sensitivity of NCaS 22–6 glass electrodes, filled with $0.5M$ KCl of pH 7, to changes in in the pH of the test solution was typically 30 mV/pH and that the electrodes exhibited a linear potential characteristic over the range 2–9. The low internal resistance of these electrodes ($\sim 10^8\ \Omega$), compared to the sealed electrodes, and a fast response time (~ 2 sec) are obvious advantages.

9.5 ELECTRODES FOR ANION AND CATION MEASUREMENTS

9.5.1 Glass Electrodes [8, 11]

In the previous section it was pointed out that through a proper selection of the glass composition it is possible to change the relative sensitivity of the electrode to various cation types. With the exception of the H^+ ion, it is unfortunately not possible at the present time to achieve a composition that is sensitive to just one cation type and is insensitive to all others. As a measure of the sensitivity of a glass, we reconsider Eq. (22), which expresses the glass potential for an ideal two-ion electrolyte:

$$E = E^0 + \frac{RT}{F} \ln (a_i + K_{ij} a_j),$$

where K_{ij} is the *selectivity*, expressing the relative sensitivity of the electrode to ion j as compared to ion i on a mole-for-mole basis. Thus, if $K_{ij} = 0.1$, ion j will be only one-tenth as effective as ion i in changing the electrode potential.

The relative values of K_{ij} for differing ion types can be experimentally determined and expressed in terms of the relative sensitivities of the electrode to certain ions. For example, the sodium glass NAS 11–18 has a selectivity order given by [57]

$$Ag^+ > H^+ > Na^+ \gg K^+, Li^+$$

and an electrode potential of

$$E = E^0 + \frac{RT}{F} \ln (a_{Na^+} + 10a_{H^+} + 0.005a_{K^+}) \tag{31}$$

when only the cations Na^+, H^+, and K^+ are present. Equation (31) shows that this electrode is 200 times more sensitive to sodium than to potassium. Hence, when measuring mammalian extracellular fluid for which the K^+ concentration is $5 \times 10^{-3}M$, the Na^+ concentration is $153 \times 10^{-3}M$ and the pH is close to 7, the influence of the H^+ and K^+ cations on the electrode potential can be entirely neglected.

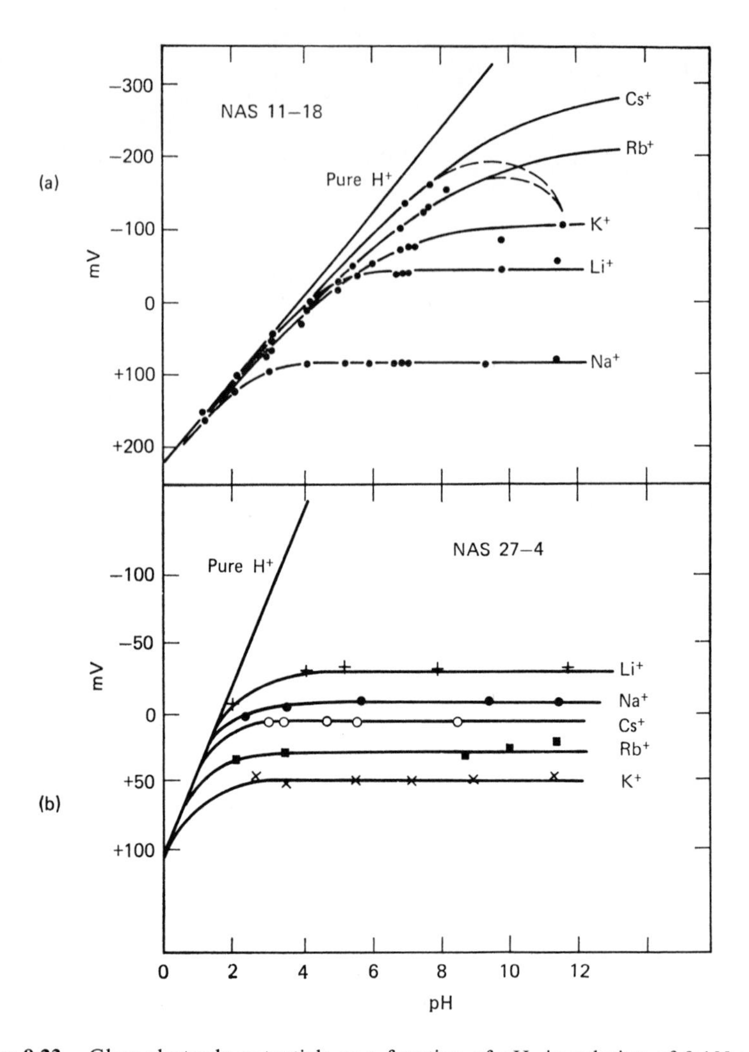

Figure 9.23. Glass electrode potentials as a function of pH, in solution of 0.1N cation concentration: (a) sodium selective glass; (b) potassium selective glass (reproduced, with permission, from G. Eisenman, pp. 213–369, in *Advances in Analytical Chemistry and Instrumentation*, Vol. 4, C. N. Reilley (ed.), Wiley: New York, 1965).

The response of an NAS 11–18 electrode to equal molar strengths of different cations of varying pH is illustrated in Figure 9.23(a). The graph shows that for low pH values, the potential is strongly influenced by the pH, reflecting the influence of the middle term in Eq. (31). However, for higher pH values, the potential is independent of pH and is found to vary linearly with the pNa^+ $[= -\log(a_{Na^+})]$ value having a slope that is nearly equal to the Nernst value of $2.3RT/F$.

Although Na^+ can be measured sucessfully in most biological fluids without interference, this is not often the case for K^+-selective glass electrodes. The higher concentration of Na^+ in extracellular fluids and the poor relative selectivity make it necessary to correct for the Na^+ activity by an independent measurement. For the potassium selective glass NAS 27–4 the selectivity order is (Figure 9.23(b))

$$H^+ > K^+ > Rb^+ > Cs^+ > Na^+ > Li^+.$$

If the H^+-ion activity is small, the glass electrode potential for the two cations K^+ and Na^+ can be expressed as

$$E = E^0 + \frac{RT}{F} \ln (a_{K^+} + 10a_{Na^+}).$$

Thus, in extracellular fluid the potential is strongly influenced by changes in Na^+ activity. This difficulty has been overcome by several investigators by an additional measurement of Na^+ using a sodium-selective glass [45, 58]. For most intracellular measurements, since the K^+ concentration is more than 10 times greater than the Na^+ concentration, the interference can be neglected.

Sodium- and potassium-selective glass microelectrodes [49–52] are similar to the pH electrodes shown in Figures 9.20 and 9.21 but use the appropriate cation selective glass. The inner reference solution for K^+ determination is typically $0.1M$ KCl and for Na^+ determination is $0.1M$ NaCl.

As an additional example we consider the glass capillary-type microelectrode described by von Stackelberg [59], which enables either pH or pNa to be determined with sample volumes as small as 10^{-4} μl. As illustrated in Figure 9.24(a), the electrode uses a fine glass capillary that is 5–10 mm in length and 5–10 μm in diameter and that is sealed to a glass shaft. Surrounding the capillary is an outer glass tube of 1 mm diameter containing a reference solution that consists of either $0.1N$ NaCl (for the Na electrode) or $0.1N$ HCl (for the pH electrode). It was reported that the slope of the characteristic for both electrode types was within a few millivolts of the Nernst value. Furthermore, as is evident from Fig 9.24(b), the soldum electrode has a highly linear characteristic over the range of physiological interest.

9.5.2 Liquid and Solid-State Ion-Exchange Membrane Electrodes

Glass is not the only electrode material capable of a selective Nernst response to ions of a given type. For many years it has been realized that certain solid-state and liquid substances exhibit a selective permeability to ions of a particular type and show a Nernst response to the ion activity [60–62]. More recently, through the discovery of new materials that exhibit improved selectivity [63] and also through an improved understanding of the mechanism of ion transport [64], a wide range of ion-selective electrodes have become commercially available. Table 9.4, which is extracted from the commercial literature, illustrates this range and summarizes the more important electrode properties.

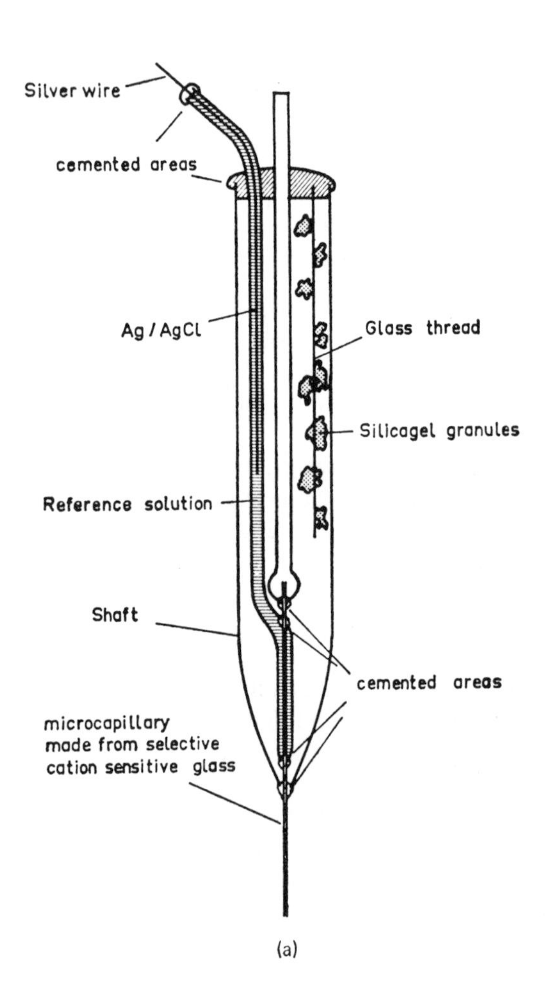

(a)

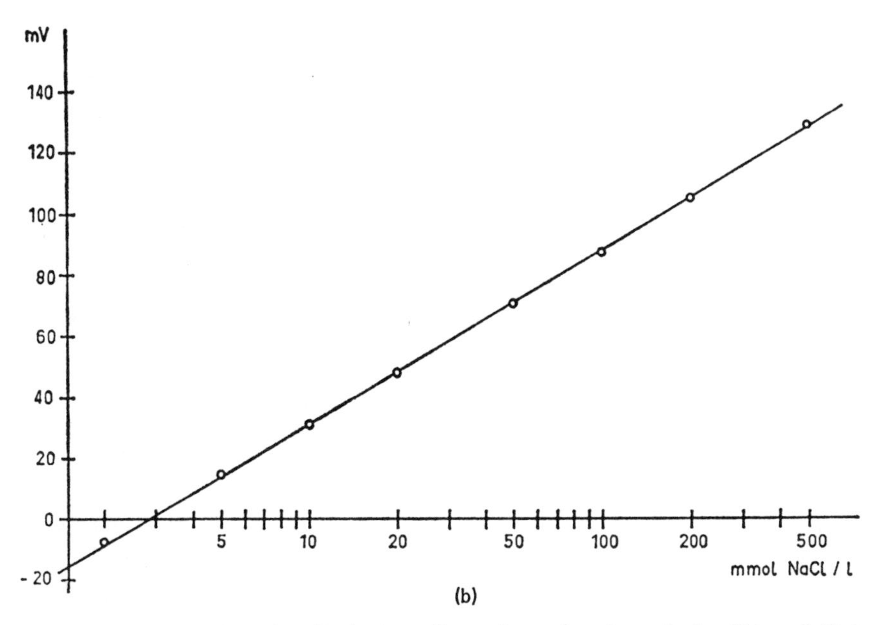

Figure 9.24. Properties of a 10^{-4}-μl capillary glass microelectrode for H^+ and Na^+ measurement. (a) constructional details; (b) sodium response (reproduced with permission of Springer-Verlag, Berlin-Heidelberg-New York, from W. F. von Stackelberg: "A 0.1 Nanoliter Glass Capillary Electrode," *Pflügers Arch.*, **321**, 274–282, 1970).

The manner in which an ion-selective membrane generates a potential difference can best be understood by considering an ion-selective membrane separating two electrolytes containing the ion in differing concentrations. Under equilibrium conditions the potential difference across the membrane is such as to balance exactly the flux of ions moving across the membrane by diffusion from the solution of higher concentration to that of lower concentration. The membrane potential can be written as

$$E = \frac{RT}{zF} \ln \left(\frac{a_1}{a_2} \right)$$

where the activity of the two electrolytes is denoted by a and z is the ion valence. Since one of the electrolytes acts as a reference, the total cell emf can be expressed in terms of the ion activity in the test solution:

$$E = E^0 + \frac{RT}{zF} \ln (a_t)$$

$$= E^0 - \frac{2.3RT}{zF} \, \text{p(test)},$$

Table 9.4 Some Solid-State and Liquid Membrane Electrodes[a]

Ion	Ion-exchange medium	Operating range[b] (moles/liter)	pH range	Electrode resistance $M\Omega$	Interferences: Selectivity constants
Br^-	Silver Bromide (crystal)	1 to 5 $\times 10^{-6}$	0 to 14	<10	$Cl^- = 2.5 \times 10^{-3}$, $I^- = 5 \times 10^3$, $CN^- = 1.2 \times 10^4$, $OH^- = 3 \times 10^{-5}$ $NH_3 = 0.5$
Ca^{++}	Liquid organic	1 to 10^{-5}	pCa $< pH < 10$	<500	$Ba^{++} = Sr^{++} = Ni^{++} = Mg^{++} = 10^{-2}$, $Na^+ = K^+ = 10^{-3}$
Cl^-	Silver chloride (polycrystalline)	1 to 5 $\times 10^{-5}$	$0 < pH < 13 - pCl$	<10	$Br^- = 300$, $I^- = 2 \times 10^6$, $CN^- = 5 \times 10^6$, $OH^- = 0.012$, $NH_3 = 8$: S^{--} must be absent
Cu^{++}	CuS–Ag_2S mixture	1 to 10^{-5}	0 to 14	<1	Ag and Hg are poisons and must be absent: high levels of Cl^- and Br^- will complex Cu^{++} solns.: $Fe^{3+} = 10$.
F^-	LaF_3 single crystal	1 to 10^{-6}	$0 < pH < 12 - pF$	<5	$Br^- = Cl^- = I^- = NO_3^- = HCO_3^- = 10^{-3}$, $OH^- = 0.1$
I^-	Silver iodide (crystal)	1 to 5 $\times 10^{-8}$	0 to 14	<10	$Cl^- = 10^{-6}$, $Br^- = 2 \times 10^{-4}$, $CN^- = 0.4$, $S_2O_3^{--} = 10^{-5}$; S^{--} and strong reducing agents must be absent
K^+	Solid organic	1 to 10^{-7}	0 to 14	<500	$Cs^+ = 0.5$, $Rb^+ = 2$, $NH_4^+ = 0.01$, $Ag^+ = 0.002$, $Na^+ = 2 \times 10^{-4}$.
K^+	Liquid organic	1 to 10^{-5}	2 to 11	<100	$Cs^+ = 20$, $Rb^+ = 10$, $NH_4^+ = 0.02$, $Na^+ = 0.012$
Ag^+ or S^{--}	Silver sulfide (crystalline)	1 to 10^{-7}	0 to 14	<10	No significant interferences.

[a] Data extracted from Corning Ion Selective Electrode Catalog, 1972, and Beckman Select-Ion Electrode Catalog, 1972.

[b] The range of *linear* operation may be less than the range given.

where E^0 incorportates the half-cell electrode potentials and the activity potential of the reference solution.

A liquid ion exchanger consists of a solution of a certain high-molecular-weight substance in a water insoluble organic solvent. The solute molecule bears a charge opposite to that of the ion to be transported and acts as a site for its transportation through the liquid-membrane phase. Through the appropriate choice of a transport-site molecule the membrane can be made selectively permeable to either anions or cations of a certain type.

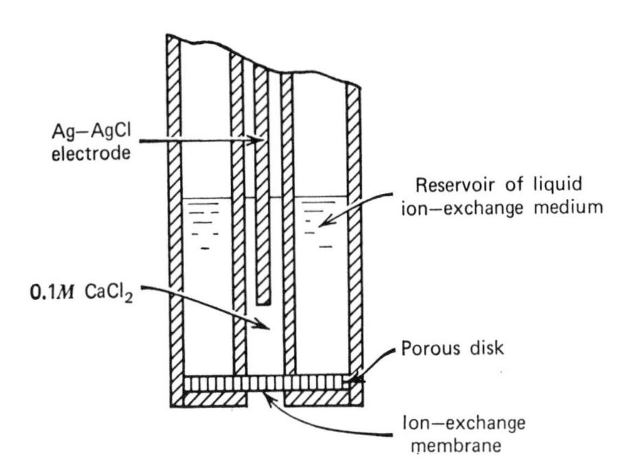

Figure 9.25. Liquid ion-exchange electrode for Ca^{++} activity measurements. The exchange media may, for example, consist of a 0.1M calcium salt of didecyl phosphoric acid in dioctylphenylphosphonate [62].

An example of a liquid membrane electrode permeable to Ca^{++} ions is illustrated in Figure 9.25. A reservoir of the organic exchange medium is used to insure saturation of the porous filter. In essence, the filter acts as a structural support or container for the liquid-membrane medium. By using an internal reference solution of calcium chloride with an Ag–AgCl electrode, stable half-cell potentials are established between the metal and the electrolyte as well as between the electrolyte and the liquid-membrane phase. As noted in Table 9.4, this electrode has a sensitivity to Ca^{++} that is 1000 times greater than that for sodium or potassium. However, considerable interference arises from the hydrogen ion, making the electrode subject to appreciable error when the test solution pH is much below 6.

As illustrated in Figure 9.26, the sodium error is only appreciable at low

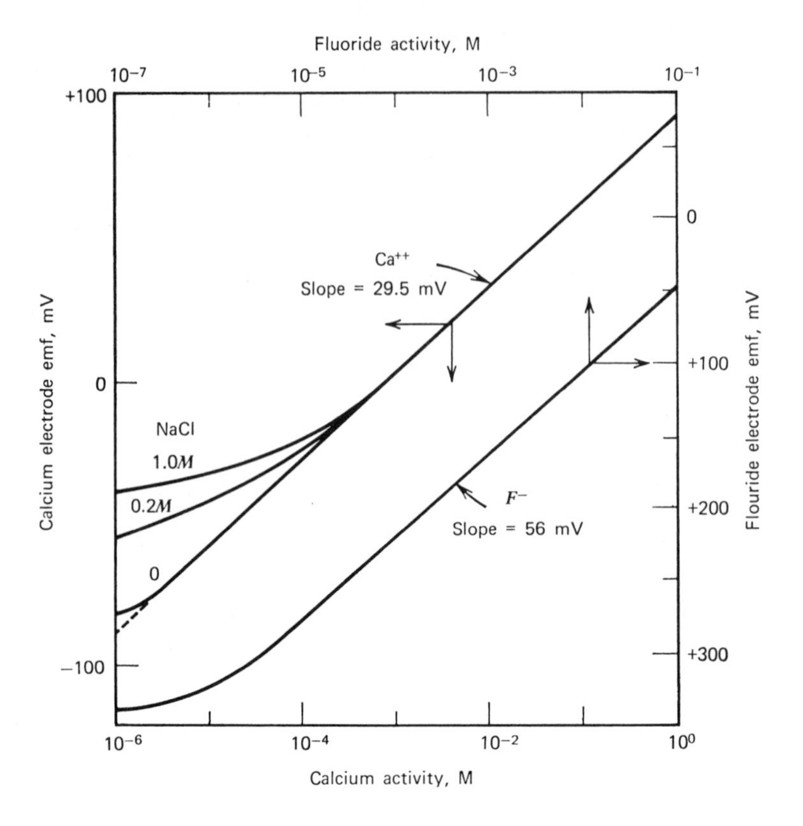

Figure 9.26. Calibration curves for a calcium liquid membrane electrode and a fluoride crystal membrane electrode (adapted from J. W. Ross, Ch. 2, in *Ion Selective Electrodes*, R. A. Durst (ed.), National Bureau of Standards, Pub. 314, Washington, D. C., Nov. 1969).

calcium activities and for high sodium concentrations. It should also be noted from this graph that the response is very close to the ideal except for very low activities where the solubility of the liquid membrane medium in the test solution sets the limit of sensitivity.

Solid-state membranes based on single crystals of rare-earth fluorides, polycrystalline silver sulfide, fused mixtures of silver sulfide and silver chloride or bromide, metal sulfides in a matrix of silver sulfide, and a variety of solid organic materials have been found to exhibit selective electrode properties [62, 65, 66].

The fluoride-ion electrode based on a thin single crystal of lanthanum fluoride (LaF_3) is of particular industrial importance [67]. Transport of the fluoride ion through such a crystal occurs through a lattice-defect vacancy movement process. Essentially the LaF_3-crystal membrane prevents all ions except those with the same ionic charge and radius as the fluoride ion from moving through the crystal. The permeability to F^- ions results in a Nernstian response over a wide range of activity.

As described by Frant and Ross [67] the fluoride electrode uses a disk-shaped crystal of LaF_3, from 1 to 2 mm thick, with a mixed inner reference solution of 0.1M NaF and 0.1M KCl, and an Ag–AgCl electrode. As shown in Figure 9.26, the response is essentially Nernstian with a lower limit of $10^{-6}M$ set by the solid solubility of the LaF_3 crystal in the test solution. The principal source of interference is the OH^- ion, which has an ionic radius similar to that of the F^- ion. To avoid significant error from this source, the test solution pH should be less than 13 minus the pF.

One interesting application of the lanthanum fluoride electrode concerns its use for monitoring the fluoride-ion activity in the mouth. Graf and Muhlemann [69a] and later Clark and Dowdell [69b] have described a miniaturized form of electrode for the radiotelemetric study of fluoride-ion activity in dental plaque and saliva. A partial denture, incorporating the electrode and a transponder, enables the activity to be monitored under in vivo conditions.

9.5.3 Liquid Ion-Exchange Microelectrodes

The construction and application of liquid ion-exchange microelectrodes for the intracellular measurement of Ca^{++}, Mg^{++}, Cl^-, and K^+ have been reported by Orme [68] and Khuri er al. [70]. Some examples are shown in Figure 9.27.

In all four electrodes the liquid organic ion-exchange medium is trapped at the tip of the Pyrex glass micropipette. The inner reference solution for type (a) is contained within an inner glass micropipette. Orme [56] states that with this type of arrangement, the electrode resistance can be considerably reduced. In electrode (b) direct contact is made to the exchange medium with the Ag–AgCl electrode. Even though the electrode is nonreversible the very small current densities result in a stable half-cell potential for the chloride liquid ion-exchanger medium.

For the small diameter microelectrodes ($\sim 1\ \mu m$) the electrode resistance can be very large (10^9–$10^{12}\ \Omega$) necessitating special care in the fabrication to avoid ohmic leakage paths. Furthermore, special precautions are required to avoid errors arising from the electrometer input characteristics as well as from external sources of interference.

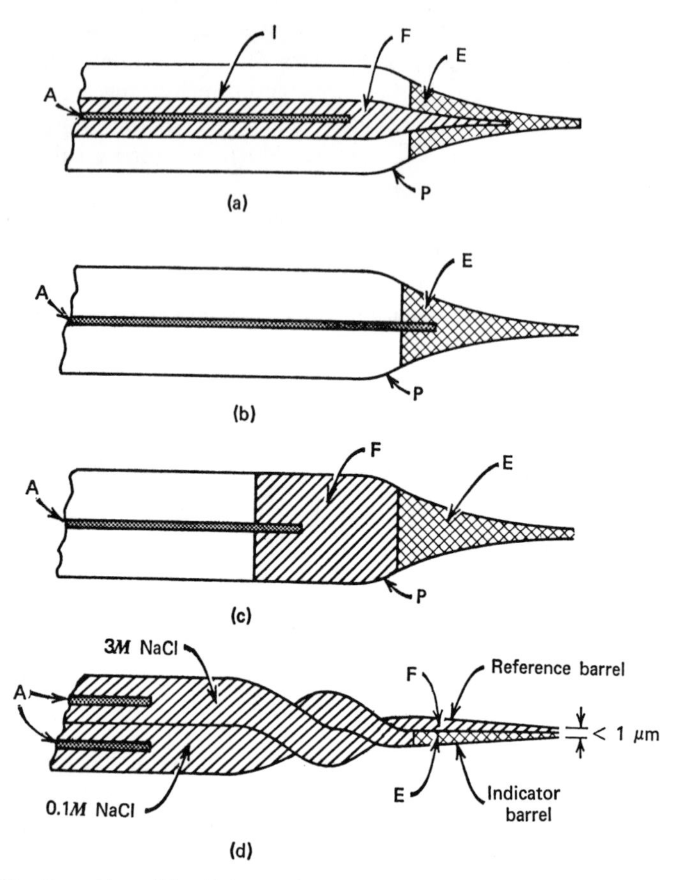

Figure 9.27. Examples of liquid ion exchanger microelectrodes: (a) with an inner microelectrode reference electrode; (b) with direct contact to the ion-exchange medium by the Ag–AgCl electrode; (c) with a liquid junction to the exchange medium; and (d) combination electrode system A, Ag–Cl electrode; E, liquid ion-exchange medium; F, reference solution; I, Pyrex inner micropipette; P, Pryex outer micropipette (after F. W. Orme, Ch. 17 in *Ion Selective Electrodes*, R. A. Durst (ed.), National Bureau of Standards, Special Pub. 314, Nov. 1969, and R. N. Khuri et al., *J. Appl. Physiol*, **32**, 419–422, 1972).

9.6 THE OXYGEN ELECTRODE

In the higher animals, oxygen plays an essential role in maintaining cellular viability. As a result, a great deal of effort has been devoted to developing simple and effective means for measuring the oxygen content in both fluids and tissue. In tissue, for example, the manner in which the local oxygen concentration varies in relation to the distance of the tissue from the capillaries reflects the local consumption, the availability, and transport to the tissue of oxygen. A measurement of the local oxygen content can be made if the transducer is sufficiently small for its presence not to disturb the local conditions. Further, it is necessary that the amount of oxygen consumed by the transducer be sufficiently small for depletion of the oxygen concentration not to be significant except in the immediate vicinity of the electrode. Transducers to meet these requirements will be discussed later in this section.

9.6.1 Oxygen Content and Oxygen Saturation

In discussing the problems of oxygen transducer design it is important to be clear on the meaning of various terms that quantitate the amount of oxygen present. The oxygen *content* or *concentration* in solution may be expressed either by the volume of oxygen (at 0°C and 760 mmHg) present, or by the number of oxygen equivalents present in a given volume of solution. The units normally employed are milliliters per 100 ml; milliliters per liter: or milliequivalents per liter.

If a solution is in equilibrium with a gas mixture containing oxygen, the oxygen content of the solution will, in general, depend on the oxygen partial pressure. Since the equilibrium partial pressure is usually simpler to measure than the oxygen content, the amount of oxygen present is often specified in terms of the oxygen partial pressure (P_{O_2}) and expressed in millimeters of mercury. The term *oxygen tension* is identical to *oxygen partial pressure* and is often preferred when discussing the amount of oxygen in biological media.

If the oxygen is in simple solution rather than in reversible chemical combination with one of the constituents of the solution, the oxygen tension is directly proportional to the oxygen content (Henry's law). In the case of blood, the oxygen is primarily in reversible chemical combination with hemoglobin, and as a result, the content is nonlinearly related to the partial pressure. At higher partial pressures the oxygen-carrying capacity of the hemoglobin molecules is fully used, causing the oxygen content to saturate. A convenient measure of the blood oxygen content is the *oxygen saturation** defined by:

$$\text{Oxygen saturation} = \frac{\text{Blood oxygen content}}{\text{Blood oxygen capacity}} \times 100.$$

Direct measurement of the oxygen saturation can be made on whole blood by the methods of transmission and reflection oximetry [71, Chapter 12; 72].

* Strictly speaking the oxygen saturation is defined in relation to the content of the hemoglobin; however, since the oxygen content in simple dissolved form is normally negligibly small compared to the hemoglobin content, the definition given yields the same result.

Since this section is concerned with one particular method of measuring oxygen tension—namely, the oxygen electrode—it should be pointed out that a number of other methods exist that may be more appropriate or more accurate under certain circumstances. The oxygen content can be measured by releasing the dissolved and bound oxygen and then measuring the amount released either manometrically (e.g., the Van Slyke method) or by gas chromatography [71–74]. Direct measurement of blood oxygen saturation can be performed on either whole or hemolized blood by spectrophotometric transmission or reflection techniques [71, 75]. The reflection oximeter using fiber optics [76], the transmission (ear) oximeter [71, 77], and oximeters using a combination of both transmission and reflection [78] enable oxygen saturation measurements to be made under in vivo conditions. More recently, in vivo determinations of P_{O_2} and P_{CO_2} in both blood and tissue have been made using a mass spectrometer to analyze the gases diffusing through a membrane-covered catheter tip [79–81].

9.6.2 Principles of the Oxygen Electrode

In its simplest form, the oxygen electrode consists of a noble metal (usually platinum) immersed in the medium to be measured and biased negatively with respect to a suitable reference electrode. By means of the system shown in Figure 9.28(a) the current–voltage characteristics of the electrode can be obtained for solutions containing various concentrations of dissolved oxygen. The characteristics illustrated in Figure 9.28(b) exhibit an initial current increase followed by a region where the current becomes essentially independent of the voltage. It is in this saturation region that the current is found to be proportional to the oxygen content.

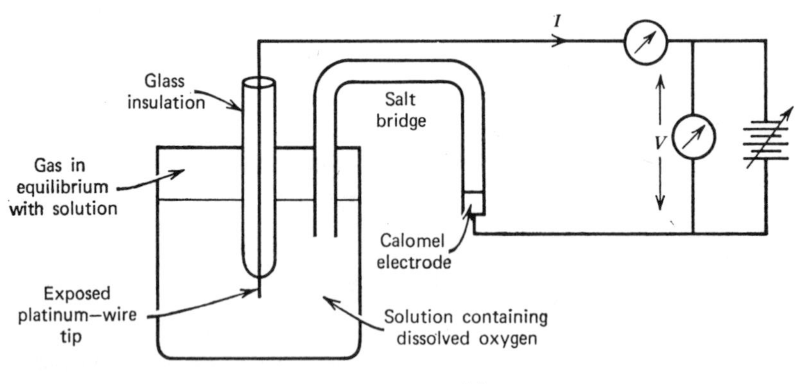

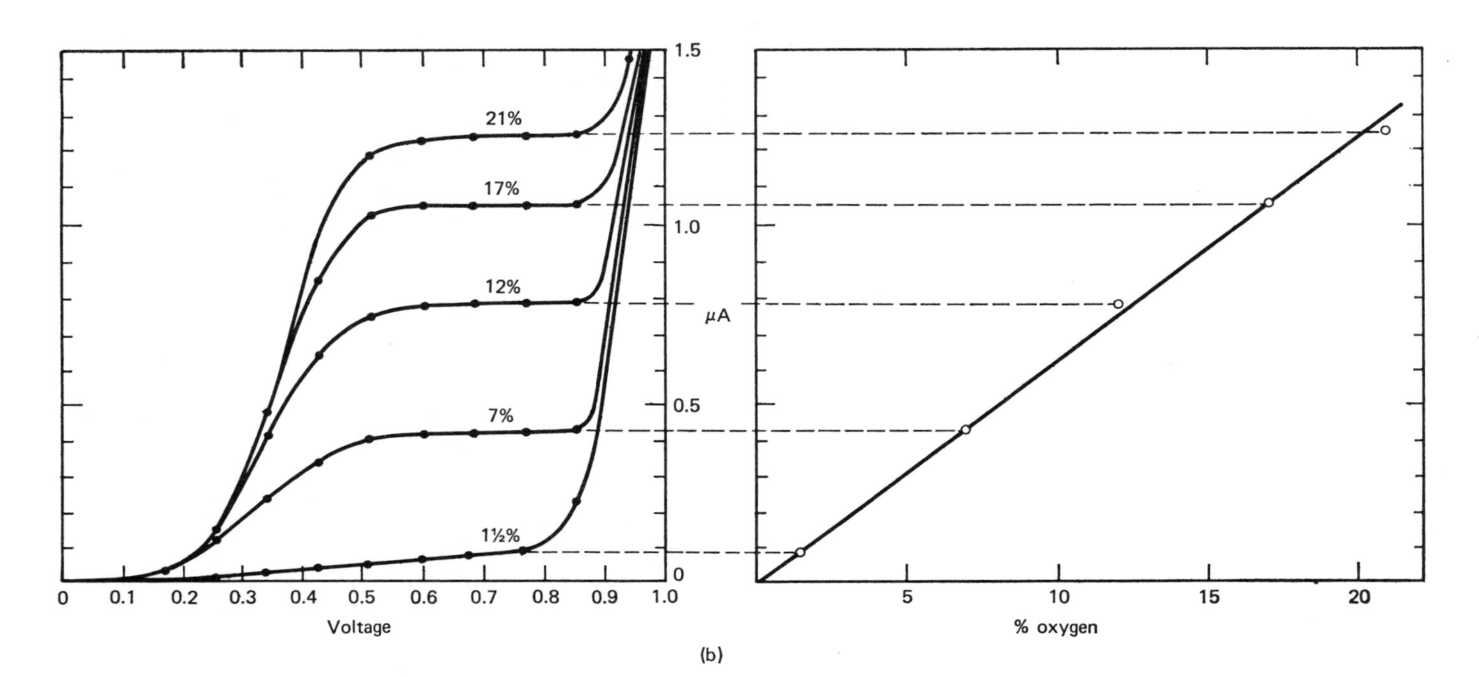

Figure 9.28. The oxygen electrode: (a) measurement system; (b) polarogram taken with the system shown in (a) together with the calibration graph, for 0.1M KCl solution equilibrated with various oxygen partial pressures (adapted, with permission, from R. A. Olson et al., *J. Gen. Physiol.*, **32**, 681–702, 1949).

The cathode current arises from a two-step oxygen-reduction process that is believed to be of the form [82]

$$O_2 + 2H_2O + 2e^- \longrightarrow H_2O_2 + 2OH^-$$

$$H_2O_2 + 2e^- \longrightarrow 2OH^-.$$

Although the details of each step are the subject of some dispute, it appears certain that all the hydrogen peroxide is fully reduced under normal circumstances. Thus, four electrons are supplied for every molecule of oxygen reduced.

In order to understand the origin of the electrode characteristics, it is necessary to refer to the discussion of the charge transfer and diffusion overvoltages contained in Section 9.1.4. For small applied emf's, the cathode current is determined primarily by the exchange current density and the change in activation energies brought about by the applied emf. For larger emf's the diffusion mechanism dominates, and as a result, any increase in emf causes the oxygen activity at the electrode surface to decrease, which causes the current to increase. When the applied emf is sufficient to reduce the oxygen activity at the interface close to zero, the current saturates and becomes essentially independent of the emf. As will be shown, the saturation current depends on the electrode surface area, the undisturbed oxygen tension, and the diffusion constant and solubility of oxygen in the medium. Physically, the saturation current condition corresponds to the maximum rate at which oxygen can diffuse to the cathode when the cathode is acting as a perfect oxygen sink.

9.6.3 Theoretical Aspects [83–86]

Some insight into the properties of practical bare metal electrodes can be gained by examining the properties of an ideal spherical electrode immersed in an infinite medium whose undisturbed oxygen tension is p_O. If the medium is consuming no oxygen, the oxygen tension p is governed by the diffusion equation:

$$\frac{\partial p}{\partial t} = D_O \nabla^2 p, \tag{32}$$

where D_O is the diffusion constant for oxygen in the medium [82a].

In order to determine the oxygen tension at any distance r from the center of the spherical electrode of radius a, it is necessary to solve Eq. (32) subject to the appropriate boundary conditions. If the emf is applied to the electrode at time $t = 0$ and if the emf is sufficient to make the oxygen tension at the electrode surface zero—that is, $p(a, t) = 0$—then the oxygen tension can be shown to be given by

$$p(r, t) = p_O\left[\left(1 - \frac{a}{r}\right) + \frac{a}{r}\,\text{erf}\left(\frac{r - a}{2\sqrt{D_O t}}\right)\right], \tag{33}$$

where the tabulated function erf (y) is defined by

$$\text{erf}\,(y) = \frac{2}{\sqrt{\pi}}\int_0^y e^{-u}\,du. \tag{34}$$

It will be noted from Eq. (33) that the oxygen tension reaches a final steady-state value given by the first term:

$$p(r, \infty) = p_O\left(1 - \frac{a}{r}\right).$$

Since this function varies rather gradually with r, the steady-state diffusion field extends quite a long way out from the electrode surface.

In the graph of Eq. (33) shown in Figure 9.29, the normalized oxygen tension is plotted against the normalized radius for various times following the application of the emf to the electrode [86]. It will be observed that for

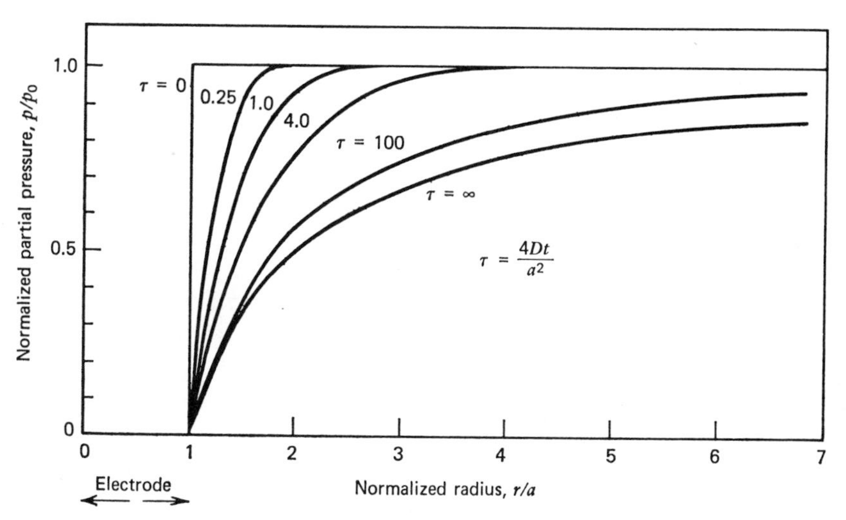

Figure 9.29. Oxygen tension distribution resulting from the transient application of an emf to an ideal spherical electrode embedded in an infinite medium (reproduced, with permission of Springer-Verlag, Berlin-Heidelberg-New York, from W. Grunewald, "Einstellzeit der Pt-Elektrode bei Messungen nicht stationarer O_2-Partialdrucke," *Pflügers Arch.*, **322**, 109–130, 1971).

small times, the oxygen demanded by the electrode can be supplied from quite a small volume of the medium; however, for longer times, the oxygen close to the electrode becomes depleted and the diffusion field becomes much more extensive.

An expression for the electrode current can be found from the oxygen tension gradient at the electrode. Thus, by differentiating Eq. (33), putting $r = a$, and noting that four electrons are required for each molecule of oxygen consumed, it can be readily shown that the current is given by [83, 86]

$$I(t) = 16\pi F\alpha_O D_O a\left(1 + \frac{a}{\sqrt{\pi D_O t}}\right) p_O, \tag{35}$$

where α_O is the solubility of oxygen in the medium and F is Faraday's constant. The steady-state current is given by

$$I_f = 16\pi F\alpha_O D_O a p_O, \tag{36}$$

which is used as a normalizing factor in Figure 9.30. Most important, it will be noted that the current is directly proportional to the undisturbed oxygen tension. However, it also is proportional to the solubility and diffusion constant, the values for which may not be known with any accuracy.

The graph of Figure 9.30 shows that initially the current drops quickly toward the final value but that the last 20% of the tail is very slow. It can be

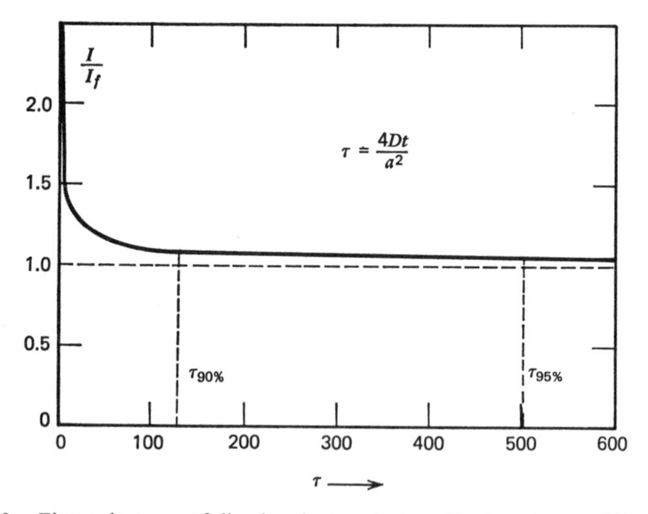

Figure 9.30. Electrode current following the transient application of an emf for a spherical electrode in an infinite medium (reproduced, with permission of Springer-Verlag, Berlin-Heidelberg-New York, from W. Grunewald: "Einstellzeit der Pt-Elektrode bei Messungen nicht stationarer O_2-Partialdrucke," *Pflügers Arch.*, **322**, 109–130, 1971).

shown from Eq. (35) that the time taken to reach 95% of the final value is given by

$$t_{95\%} = 120 \frac{a^2}{D_O}.$$

For example, if $a = 10$ μm and the oxygenated medium is water at 37°C ($D_O \simeq 3.2 \times 10^{-5}$ cm^2/sec), we find that $t_{95\%} = 4$ sec. But if $a = 100$ μm the time increases to 400 sec. In practice, much shorter response times can be expected because of movement of the fluid from convection currents and local sources of oxygen (e.g., capillaries close to the electrode).

For large-area electrodes movement of the fluid around the electrode has a major effect on the current. The fresh supply of oxygen brought in by the moving fluid compensates for the oxygen reduced by the electrode, thereby increasing the diffusion gradient and electrode current. For small electrodes (~1 μm), the effect of flow is found to be much smaller and may be negligible. The reason for this appears to be the formation of a hydrodynamic boundary layer of essentially stationary fluid that remains attached to the electrode surface. If the boundary layer thickness is much greater than the electrode radius, most of the diffusion field will lie within this layer, and as a result, the electrode current should be flow-independent. For example, Cater [87] reports that bare 1-μm electrodes are insensitive to stirring.

In tissue, the presence of a network of capillaries carrying oxygenated blood can be expected to have a major influence on the response-time and spatial resolution of a bare metal electrode. In the ideal physical model assumed for the mathematical derivation outlined above, sources of oxygen within the diffusion field were ignored. In practice, an appreciable number of capillaries can be expected to intersect or lie close to the sensitive surface of a large-diameter electrode. These capillaries act as limited oxygen sources, thereby increasing the "average" oxygen-tension reading and reducing the response time to transient changes in oxygen tension. Even an approximate mathematical treatment of this problem is very difficult. The model assumed by Hudson [84], in which the capillaries are represented by a spherical surface at a constant oxygen tension, is undoubtedly more realistic than the one assumed above.

A significant practical problem associated with the use of bare metal electrodes, especially when immersed in a medium containing proteins, is electrode "poisoning." It appears that the long-term drift reported by many investigators is at least partially caused by protein deposition on the cathode, whose effective area is thereby decreased, causing the current to fall.

Additional problems associated with the bare metal electrode are: the relatively large diffusion field, resulting in a poor spatial resolution; the sensitivity of all but the smallest electrodes to fluid flow; and the difficulty of calibration when the oxygen-diffusion properties of the medium are unknown. All these deficiencies can be avoided through the use of an appropriate oxygen-permeable membrane covering the electrode.

If the thickness of the membrane is sufficient to entirely confine the diffusion field within the membrane, the electrode will respond only to the oxygen tension at the membrane surface. This condition also insures that the electrode will be insensitive to flow. Furthermore, since the diffusion properties of the membrane remain constant, the calibration should be independent of the medium into which the electrode is inserted.

The conditions necessary to insure that the diffusion field is confined within the membrane have been examined by Hudson [84], Grunewald [85] and others, based on a simple spherical-electrode geometry. For a spherical electrode of radius a covered by a membrane of outer radius b and thickness $(b - a)$, the oxygen tension in an infinite medium is given by

$$p(r) = p_O\left\{1 - \frac{b/r}{[1 + (\alpha_O D_O/\alpha_m D_m)(b/a - 1)]}\right\} \tag{37a}$$

for $r \geqslant b$, and

$$p(r) = p_O\left\{1 - \frac{[1 + (\alpha_O D_O/\alpha_m D_m)(b/r - 1)]}{[1 + (\alpha_O D_O/\alpha_m D_m)(b/a - 1)]}\right\} \tag{37b}$$

for $b \geqslant r \geqslant a$, where α_m and D_m are the solubility and diffusion constants for oxygen in the membrane and p_O is the undisturbed oxygen tension in the medium.

The normalized graph of Eq. (37) shown in Figure 9.31 illustrates the effect of the ratio $\alpha_O D_O/\alpha_m D_m$ on the diffusion field for a membrane thickness equal to twice the metal electrode radius. As this ratio increases, so the diffusion field is increasingly confined to the membrane. The condition for confinement can be found from Eq. (37) by noting that the oxygen tension at the membrane surface should approach p_O. Substituting $p \to p_O$ and $r = b$ into Eq. (37) yields

$$\left(\frac{b - a}{a}\right)\frac{\alpha_O D_O}{\alpha_m D_m} \gg 1, \tag{38}$$

which can be satisfied if the membrane is thick compared to the metal-sphere radius. Since the electrode response time is proportional to the thickness squared, a limit is imposed by the transient response requirement. It can be shown that if Eq. (38) is satisfied, the 0%-to-95% response time is given by [86]

$$t_{95\%} \approx \frac{(b - a)^2}{2D_m}. \tag{39}$$

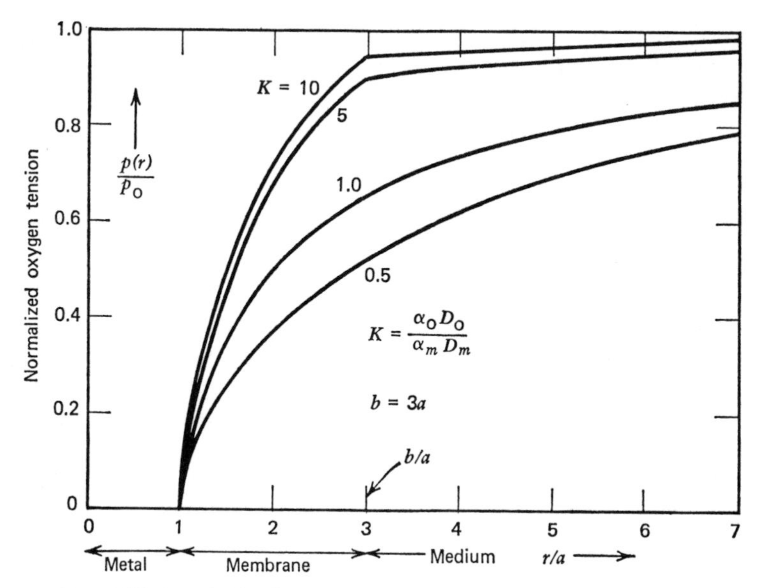

Figure 9.31. Diffusion field of a membrane-covered electrode. The membrane outer surface radius is three times the metal electrode radius.

For example, with a Teflon ($D_m = 3.4 \times 10^{-7}$ cm^2/sec) membrane 5 μm thick, the 95% response time is 0.25 sec; this increases to 25 sec when the thickness is 50 μm. Thus, if a short response time is required, a membrane material with a high diffusion constant and a low solubility coefficient should be chosen.

Teflon is reported by Berkenbosch [88a] to have an oxygen solubility coefficient of $\alpha_m = 0.19$ cm^3 O_2/cm$^3 \cdot 760$ mmHg and a diffusion coefficient of $D_m = 3.4 \times 10^{-7}$ cm^2/sec at 37°C. The corresponding figures for blood plasma are $\alpha_O = 0.023$ and $D_O = 1.7 \times 10^{-5}$. Hence, for an electrode of 2.5-μm radius covered by a 5-μm layer of Teflon,

$$\left(\frac{b-a}{a}\right)\frac{\alpha_O D_O}{\alpha_m D_m} = 11.9,$$

which is sufficiently greater than 1 to insure that the diffusion field lies within the membrane. The steady-state current sensitivity (amps per millimeter of mercury of O_2) can be computed from the expression given by Grunewald [85] for the current:

$$I_f = 16\pi F \cdot \frac{b\alpha_O D_O p_O}{\left[1 + \frac{\alpha_O D_O}{\alpha_m D_m}\left(\frac{b}{a} - 1\right)\right]}, \tag{40}$$

yielding, $S = I_f/p_O = 5.7 \times 10^{-12}$ A/mmHg.* In the absence of the membrane the sensitivity can be calculated from Eq. (36) as $S = 2.5 \times 10^{-11}$ A/mmHg. Hence, an 80% reduction in sensitivity is one of the penalties incurred in obtaining greatly improved spatial resolution and flow-independence. At 50 mmHg O_2 pressure the teflon covered electrode consumes 3×10^{-13} cm^3 of O_2 per second. This corresponds to the amount of oxygen consumed per second by a 3.5-μm-radius spherical volume in the cerebral cortex of a dog.

9.6.4 Open and Recessed Electrodes

Shown in Figure 9.32 are some examples of open and recessed electrodes of the type sometimes used for both tissue and fluid oxygen-tension measurements. The open-ended electrodes of the general forms shown in (a) and (b) have been reported by many invesitgators; sometimes a thin oxygen-permeable coating is used to prevent or retard electrode poisoning [82, 87].

The recessed electrode shown in Figure 9.32(c) was first described by Davies [82] and Brink in 1943. It contains a cylindrical recessed region filled with agar, saline, collodion, or some other medium through which the

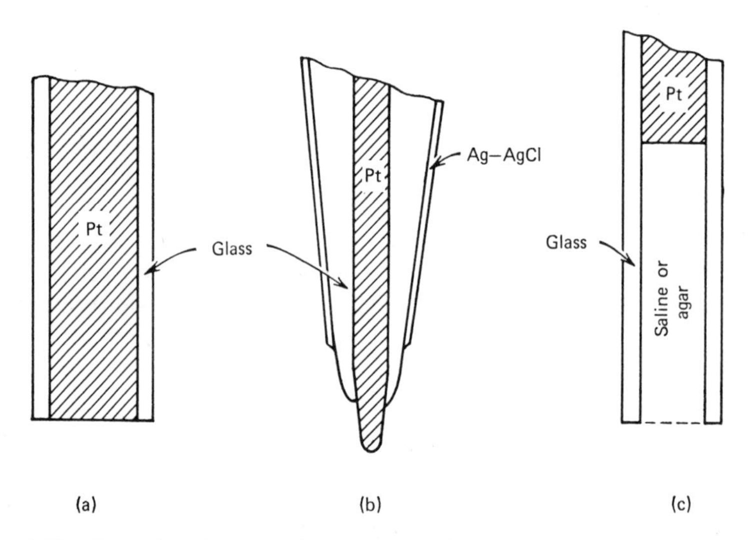

Figure 9.32. Examples of open and recessed P_{O_2} electrodes: (a) Flush-ended electrode; (b) micropipette type with a surface Ag–AgCl reference electrode; (c) recessed electrode filled with either saline or agar.

* If α is expressed in cm^3 $O_2/cm^3 \cdot 760$ mmHg, the expression must be divided by $(760 \cdot 22.4 \times 10^3 \cdot T/273)$, where T is the absolute temperature.

oxygen from the test solution can diffuse to the cathode. If the diffusion field is confined to the recess, the current will depend on the known properties of the recess medium rather than on the oxygen-diffusion properties of the medium being measured. Thus, it has the important advantage of enabling absolute P_{O_2} measurements to be made in a medium whose diffusion properties are unknown.

To insure that the diffusion field does not extend beyond the end of the recess, measurement of the electrode current must be made prior to the attainment of steady-state conditions. From a one-dimensional model of diffusion in the recess, it can be shown [83] that the electrode current at a time t following the application of an emf is given by

$$I(t) = 4FA\alpha_r p_O \sqrt{\frac{D_r}{\pi t}}, \tag{41}$$

where A is the electrode area, p_O is the undisturbed oxygen tension, and α_r and D_r are the solubility and diffusion constant for oxygen in the recess medium. Equation (41) is valid if the diffusion field is confined to the recess and that equilibrium is attained prior to the application of the emf. Thus, the current at any fixed time t after applying the emf, is proportional to the oxygen tension.

If the diffusion field extends beyond the recess, Eq. (41) no longer applies. Typically, for a recess 1 mm long, t must be less than 20 sec. In addition, long time intervals are required between successive measurements in order to allow equilibrium to be restored. By making the cathode area very small, the diffusion field can be confined essentially to the recess and the steady-state current will be proportional to the oxygen tension. A glass-insulated microelectrode of this type having a recessed gold cathode and a diameter of 1 μm has been described by Whalen et al. [88b]. The authors report that the electrode has a response time to full equilibrium of 25 msec and that it performs satisfactorily for intracellular P_{O_2} measurements under in vivo conditions.

9.6.5 The Clark-Type Electrode

A major step in the development of oxygen electrodes having a sufficient degree of long-term stability and convenience for clinical measurements was proposed by Clark [89]. Basically, the idea presented and exploited by Clark was to use an electrolyte solution contained *within* the electrode assembly to transport oxygen from an oxygen-permeable membrane to the metal cathode. As illustrated in Figure 9.33(a), a thin oxygen-permeable film is stretched across the electrode tip, allowing oxygen to diffuse through a thin electrolyte layer to the cathode. No electrical contact is made to the medium

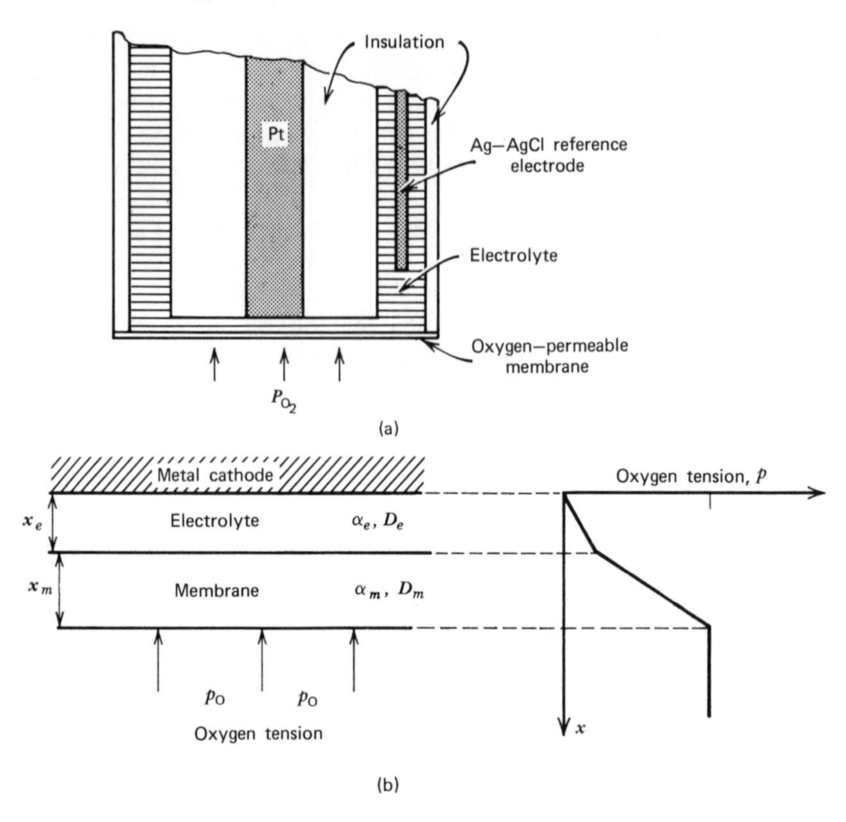

Figure 9.33. The Clark electrode: (a) simplified illustration of the construction; (b) first-order one-dimensional model also showing the oxygen tension distribution throughout the system.

being measured; instead, the reference electrode is incorporated *within* the electrode assembly. This most important feature of the electrode enables oxygen tension to be measured in nonconducting media (i.e., gaseous mixtures).

A first-order diffusion model of the Clarke electrode is illustrated in Figure 9.33(b). The membrane–electrolyte–electrode system is considered to act as a one-dimensional diffusion system with the partial pressure at the membrane surface equal to the equilibrium partial pressure p_O and that at the cathode equal to zero. It can be shown that [90] the steady-state electrode current is given by

$$I = \frac{4FA\alpha_m D_m p_O}{x_m}\left[1 - \frac{1}{1 + (x_m D_e \alpha_e / x_e D_m \alpha_m)}\right]. \tag{42}$$

where A is the electrode area and the diffusion and solubility constants of the membrane and electrolyte are denoted with the subscripts m and e, respectively.

From Eq. (42) is will be noted that if

$$x_m D_e \alpha_e \gg x_e D_m \alpha_m, \tag{43}$$

then

$$I \simeq \frac{4FA\alpha_m D_m p_O}{x_m},$$

which is independent of the electrolyte-layer thickness and diffusion properties. Condition (43) is satisfied fairly readily, since $\alpha_e D_e$ is normally quite a bit larger than $\alpha_m D_m$. For example, if a Teflon membrane of thickness (x_m) 25 μm and a cathode area of 2×10^{-6} cm^2 ($\sim$8-μm radius) are used, we find that the electrode sensitivity is given by

$$S = \frac{I}{p_O} \simeq 1 \times 10^{-12} \text{A/mmHg}.$$

In practice, since the cathode radius is comparable to the membrane thickness, considerable lateral diffusion will occur, resulting, perhaps, in an order of magnitude increase in sensitivity from that given above [91].

The response of Clark-type electrodes to transient changes in oxygen tension have been theoretically and experimentally examined by Berkenbosch [88]. He finds that if the membrane rather than the electrolyte layer controls the diffusion, so that condition (43) is satisfied, the 95% response time is given by

$$t_{95\%} \simeq \frac{0.37 x_m^{\,2}}{D_m}.$$

For the 25-μm Teflon membrane previously considered, $t_{95\%} = 6.9$ sec at 37°C, which is in good agreement with the experimental results reported by Severinghaus [91]. By using a thinner membrane, the response time can be reduced. However, the electrolyte-layer thickness must also be reduced so that the electrode current remains insensitive to changes in electrolyte thickness brought about, for example, by changes in hydrostatic pressure.

Temperature changes significantly affect the electrode sensitivity. Berkenbosch [88, 90] points out that both the oxygen solubility and diffusion constant of the membrane are exponentially dependent on the temperature. Thus, the sensitivity varies as

$$S \propto e^{-E_A/RT},$$

where E_A is the activation energy of the product $\alpha_m D_m$.

Heitman et al. [92] report that the values of E_A for Teflon and polypropylene are 4.35 and 5.6 kcal/mole, respectively. Thus, for a Teflon membrane, it can be readily shown that on decreasing the temperature from 38°C to 28°C, the sensitivity reduces by 20%. Such a large change requires either accurate temperature control or a compensation system such as the one described by Berkenbosch and Riedstra [90].

Some mention should also be made of the properties desired for the reference electrolyte. Severinghaus [91] points out that at low pH the electrode current becomes pH-dependent, probably because of a change in the oxygen-reduction reaction. Since a reduction in pH can occur from CO_2, which readily diffuses through the membrane to form carbonic acid, it is important that oxygen electrodes for blood and tissue measurements be properly stabilized. A strong phosphate buffer solution of pH 7, with 0.1M KCl and a chloride reversible electrode are sometimes used.

In order to illustrate the design and application of Clark-type electrodes, examples of in vitro and in vivo electrodes for blood P_{O_2} measurements and microelectrodes for tissue measurements will be presented.

9.6.6 Some Examples of Clark-Type Electrodes

Clark electrodes of the type shown in Figure 9.34 are widely used for clinical P_{O_2} determinations of blood [92] and other biological fluids. The design illustrated [93] contains a 25-μm-diameter platinum wire sealed in glass with the tip exposed by polishing the end. A polypropylene membrane 25 μm thick traps a thin layer of electrolyte between it and the glass–platinum tip. Severinghaus suggests that polypropylene is superior to both Teflon and polyethylene for whole blood measurements [91]. The design illustrated is reported [93] to have the following characteristics at 37°C: (1) a 99% response in 25 sec, (2) a 1% linearity from 0 to 100% oxygen saturation, (3) an electrode current with no oxygen corresponding to 0.5% of O_2, (4) a temperature coefficient of 3%/°C, (5) a sensitivity of about 2×10^{-11} A/mmHg O_2, (6) a drift of less than 1% between calibration and measurement, and (7) no detectable effect from carbon dioxide.

Severinghaus [91] also discusses the effect of fluid flow on the electrode current and points out that for a stationary fluid, diffusion gradients eventually occur in the fluid, causing the reading to decrease. Other reasons for a decreased P_{O_2} reading in whole blood are also discussed.

Of considerable importance in achieving accurate results is good temperature regulation. Nonsaturated whole blood has a 7%/°C P_{O_2} temperature coefficient, which, when added to the 3%/°C for the electrode, results in an overall coefficient of 10%/°C. Regulation to ±0.1°C is therefore required in order to achieve a ±1% accuracy.

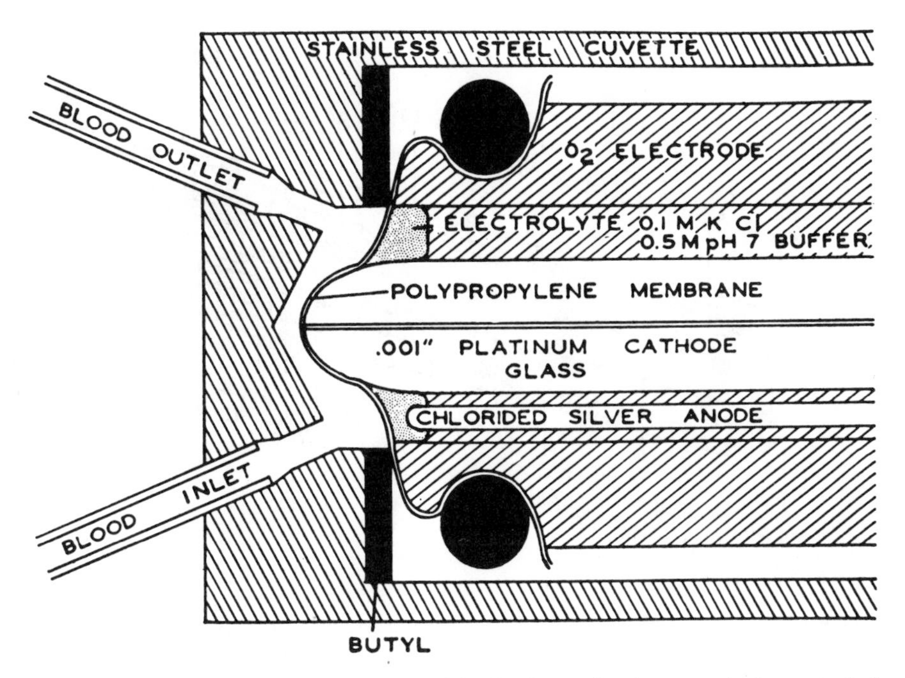

Figure 9.34. Clark type electrode mounted in the form of a thermostatically controlled cuvette, designed for measuring the oxygen tension of whole blood (reproduced, with permission, from J. W. Severinghaus, pp. 1475–1487 in section 3, Vol. 2, *Handbook of Physiology*, American Physiological Society, Bethesda, Maryland, 1965).

A number of needle and catheter-tip Clark electrodes have been described that are suitable for in vivo clinical use [94–96]. The design of Kimmich and Kreuzer [95], which is similar to their respiratory gas electrode [97], is illustrated in Figure 9.35. It uses a ring-shaped cathode formed by platinum foil wrapped around a cylinder of PVC or glass and covered by an outer cylinder. By using a ring rather than a solid circular electrode, a larger surface area can be obtained without causing the diffusion field to spread out significantly into the fluid and thereby cause the electrode to be flow-sensitive. With a Teflon membrane 6 μm thick, the electrode sensitivity is about 0.9×10^{-9} A/mmHg O_2. This is approximately equivalent to the sensitivity of a solid circular cathode electrode 100 μm in diameter, with the same membrane thickness.

Experimental measurements in blood at 37°C showed that with a 6-μm membrane the signal varied by only 6% when the flow velocity was changed from about 0 to 100 cm/sec. This is the same flow-dependence as would be

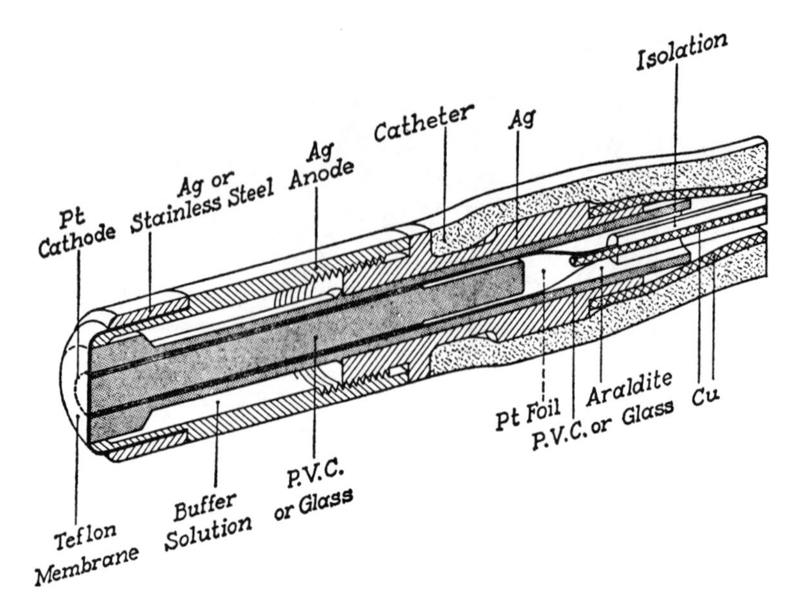

Figure 9.35. Example of a catheter-tip oxygen sensor designed for in vivo arterial measurements. The external diameter is 2 mm (reproduced with permission of S. Karger, Basel-New York, from H. P. Kimmich and F. Kreuzer, "Catheter PO_2 Electrode with Low Flow Dependency and Fast Response," *Progr. Resp. Res.*, **3**, 100–110, 1969).

observed with a 7-μm-diameter circular electrode. In gas the electrode had a 95% response time of 0.3 sec, with essentially no flow-dependence. In blood the response time was 0.4 sec at high flow velocities, but it increased to 1.0 sec at 10 cm/sec.

Measurements on a dog with the electrode positioned in the aortic arch demonstrated that the respiratory P_{O_2} fluctuations could be readily followed; shorter-term fluctuations with heart beat were also observed [98].

Many of the microelectrodes designed for measuring and studying oxygen diffusion surrounding capillaries use either a bare metal cathode or a membrane covered Pt or Au cathode with an external reference electrode [87, 99, 100]. Microelectrodes of the Clark type incorporating a reference electrode within the structure are of course more complex to fabricate, but they do enable the absolute P_{O_2} to be determined in a very localized manner. Such electrodes were first described by Silver [101] and later by Bicher and Knisely [103], who used a somewhat more reproducible method of fabrication.

Silver's electrode, illustrated in Figure 9.36, consists of a Pt wire 10–25 μm in diameter that has been electropolished to reduce its tip diameter to around

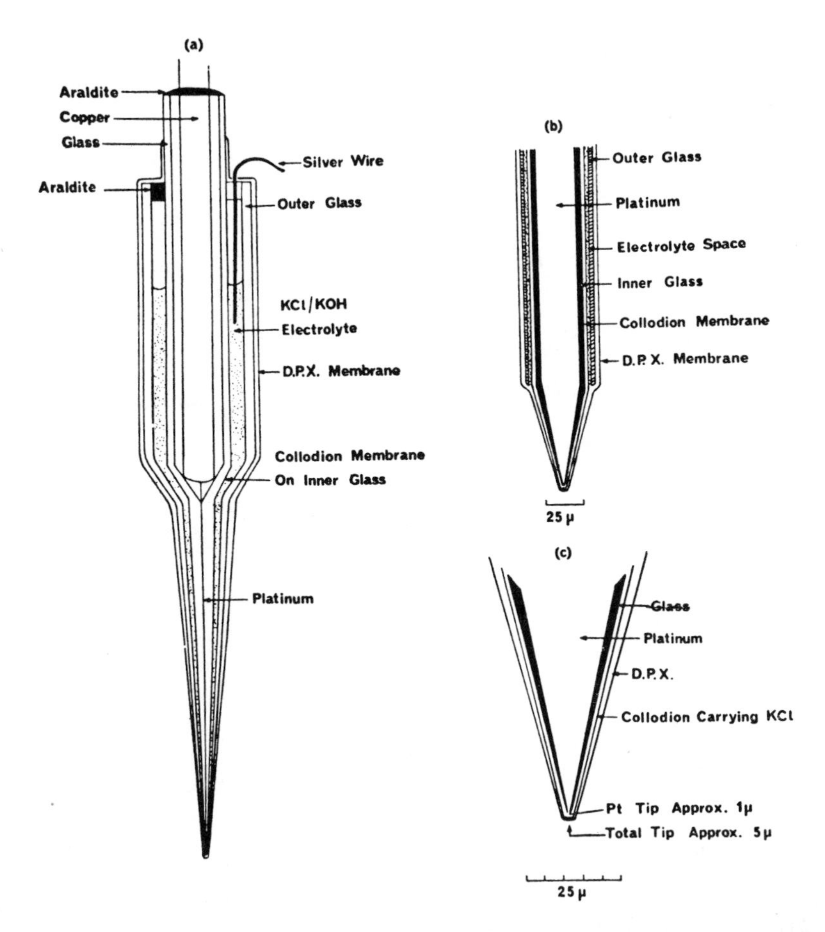

Figure 9.36. Details of the construction of a Clark-type microelectrode: (a) complete assembly; (b) details of the thin end; and (c) details of the tip showing the outer DPX layer and a collodion-carrying KCl layer covering the exposed Pt tip (reproduced, with permission, from I. A. Silver, *Med. Electron. Biolog. Eng.*, **3**, 377–387, 1965).

1 μm. The glass-insulated platinum wire is covered with a thin layer of collodion by dipping. After hardening, the electrode is dipped into an electrolyte solution so that the collodion becomes conducting and thereby provides an electrical pathway from the platinum tip to the electrolyte reservoir containing a silver electrode. An oxygen permeable membrane is formed by a thin layer of the hystological mounting resin DPX. Electrodes constructed in this manner were reported to have a 97% response time of approximately 0.5 sec, a

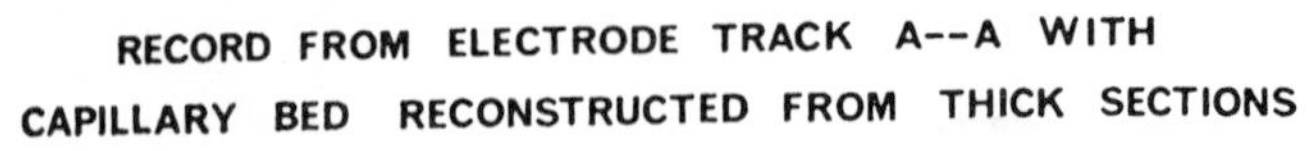

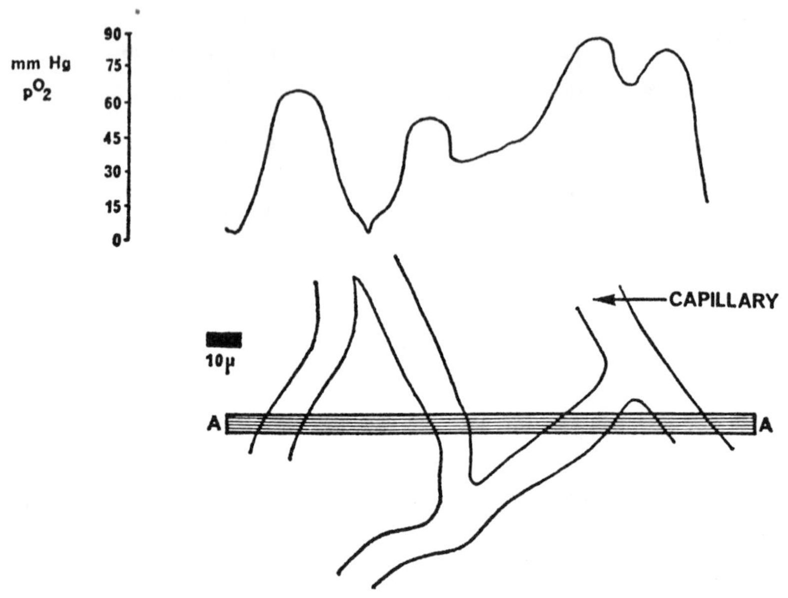

Figure 9.37. Variation of P_{O_2} in the cerebral cortex. The path taken by the electrode tip in relation to the cortical capillaries is shown below. The capillaries were not penetrated by the electrode (reproduced, with permission, from I. A. Silver, *Med. Electron. Biolog. Eng.*, **3**, 377–387, 1965).

sensitivity of 5×10^{-12} A/mmHg O_2, a tip diameter of less than 5 μm, and a spatial resolution of around 4 μm for the smallest electrodes.

Figure 9.37 shows a P_{O_2} recording obtained by Silver [101] with this electrode as the tip is advanced through the cerebral cortex of a rabbit. From a knowledge of the tip position in relation to the capillary structure, the oxygen diffusion field between capillaries can be mapped [100, 102].

9.7 CARBON DIOXIDE ELECTRODES

In conjunction with P_{O_2} and pH measurements on whole blood, the measurement of P_{CO_2} forms an essential ingredient for quantitatively assessing the extent of any disturbance to a patient's acid–base balance [106]. Furthermore, it should be noted that P_{CO_2} measurements by themselves can have an important clinical significance. For example, one of the most sensitive signs of impending ventilatory failure is an increased arterial P_{CO_2}.

There are three techniques of importance for the determination of blood P_{CO_2}: (1) the whole blood CO_2 content–pH method, (2) the Astrup tonometer technique, and (3) the CO_2 electrode method [32]. A careful comparison of these three methods with regard to error has been reported by Bartschi et al. [107]. They conclude that the CO_2 electrode yielded the most satisfactory results in terms of scatter and directional error. Further, in terms of convenience and measurement time, the P_{CO_2} electrode is vastly superior.

The CO_2 electrode was first described by Stowe et al. [108] in 1957 and was significantly improved through the work of Severinghaus and Bradley [109]. The basic principle of the electrode is to allow the unknown CO_2 source to equilibrate with an aqueous solution and to measure some property of this solution that is changed by this process. Since CO_2 reacts with water to form carbonic acid, an obvious property to measure is the pH. In fact, as will be shown, the pH varies as the logarithm of P_{CO_2}.

A cuvette-type electrode system [93] designed for whole blood P_{CO_2} determinations is illustrated in Figure 9.38. A thin Teflon membrane, through which CO_2 can readily diffuse, enables the blood CO_2 to equilibrate with the sodium bicarbonate–KCl solution trapped within the nylon stocking. The change in pH is measured by means of a glass electrode that consists of a pH-sensitive glass membrane and inner and outer reference electrodes. It will be shown that the presence of sodium bicarbonate almost doubles the electrode sensitivity. The addition of KCl enables the external calomel electrode to operate in a reversible manner, thereby stabilizing the electrode potential.

When an aqueous solution is equilibrated with CO_2, carbonic acid (H_2CO_3) results. The concentration of H_2CO_3 is proportional to the CO_2 tension:

$$H_2CO_3 = \alpha P_{CO_2}, \tag{44}$$

where α is the solubility of CO_2 in water. Now carbonic acid dissociates according to

$$H_2CO_3 \rightleftharpoons H^+ + HCO_3^- \tag{45}$$

and

$$HCO_3^- \rightleftharpoons H^+ + CO_3^{--},$$

where the second dissociation is very weak and will be ignored in the analysis. In the concentrations normally used, the sodium bicarbonate can be assumed fully dissociated:

$$NaHCO_3 \longrightarrow Na^+ + HCO_3^-.$$

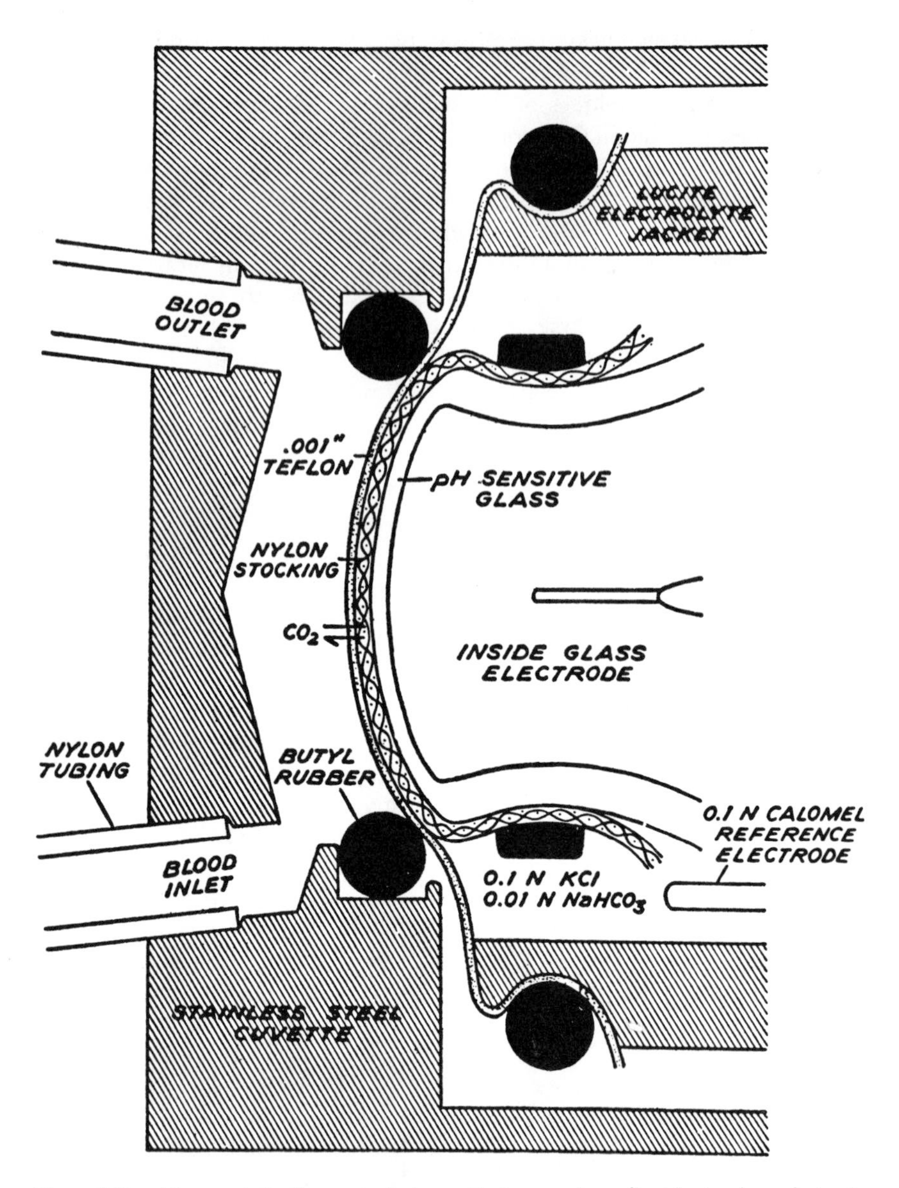

Figure 9.38. Thermostatically controlled cuvette-type carbon dioxide tension electrode (reproduced, with permission, from J. W. Severinghaus, Ch. 61, pp. 1475–1487 in Section 2, Vol. 2, *Handbook of Physiology*, American Physiological Society, Bethesda, Maryland, 1965).

Under these circumstances, it can be shown from the dissociation equations for water and carbonic acid together with the charge neutrality equation that the hydrogen-ion activity is related to the P_{CO_2} by

$$\alpha P_{CO_2} = \frac{(a_{H^+})^2 + (a_{H^+})(a_{Na^+}) - K_w}{K_1}, \tag{46}$$

where K_w is the ionic activity product for water and K_1 is the first dissociation constant for H_2CO_3.

For pure water $a_{Na^+} = 0$, and since K_w is very small compared to the other term, Eq. (46) recudes to

$$\text{pH} = -\tfrac{1}{2} \log (K_1 \alpha P_{CO_2}). \tag{47}$$

If sodium bicarbonate is present in solution with a concentration of 0.001—0.01 M, then $a_{Na^+} \gg a_{H^+}$, and if K_w is ignored, Eq. (46) reduces to

$$\begin{aligned} \text{pH} &= -\log \frac{K_1 \alpha P_{CO_2}}{a_{Na^+}} \\ &= -\log P_{CO_2} - \log \left(\frac{\alpha K_1}{a_{Na^+}} \right). \end{aligned} \tag{48}$$

From Eqs. (47) and (48) is will be noted that the sensitivity of the electrode ($S = d\,\text{pH}/d \log P_{CO_2}$) is doubled through the addition of sodium bicarbonate. It will also be noted that the pH varies linearly with log P_{CO_2}, so that a 10-fold increase in P_{CO_2} decreases the pH by only 1.0 pH unit.

It is found that the electrode response time is a complex function of many variables and in addition also depends on the magnitude and direction of the step change in CO_2. Severinghaus [91] has examined the variation with membrane type (Silastic, polyethylene, rubber, Teflon), membrane thickness (6–50 μm), and bicarbonate ion concentration. He finds that the response time decreases, as expected, with membrane thickness but that very long response times occur for small (<10 mmHg) P_{CO_2} values. Severinghaus found that Teflon and Silastic membranes give the best performance: Teflon gives good accuracy and long-term stability; Silastic, because of its higher CO_2 permeability, gives a better response time.

The response time increases with both increasing $NaHCO_3$ concentration and electrolyte-layer thickness. It is suggested that at low P_{CO_2} values where the response time may be in the range of minutes, it is better to use $NaHCO_3$ concentrations of 0.001 M or less. However, this does result in some sacrifice in electrode sensitivity and stability.

A number of blood gas analysis systems are commercially available that incorporate pH, P_{O_2} and P_{CO_2} electrodes as an integrated temperature-controlled unit.* One such system uses a Silastic membrane CO_2 electrode that, it is claimed, has a 98% response time of 45 sec, a ±1% error limit, and a range of 10–260 mmHg CO_2 in 0.1 mmHg steps.† The 200-μl blood sample is analyzed for all three variables in less than 90 sec. Furthermore, by means of an internal computation system, it automatically computes the total CO_2 content, the plasma bicarbonate concentration $[HCO_3^+]$ and, following the insertion of the externally measured hemoglobin content, the base excess or deficit. Calibration of the system is carried out semiautomatically by means of two cylinders of analyzed gas: one to set the zero and the other to set the slope.

Although the above discussion has been restricted in application to blood P_{CO_2} measurements, it should also be noted that considerable importance is attached to CO_2-tension measurements in tissue and other biological fluids. Hertz and Siesjo [110] have developed a CO_2 electrode, similar to the Stowe electrode but of reduced dimensions and improved response time. The electrode diameter of 1 cm is still far too large for meaningful tissue measurements; however, it has been found useful for measuring the CO_2 tension on surfaces [111].

An important development in achieving a miniaturized CO_2 sensor has been the work reported by Niedrach [112] on the fabrication and testing of a sensor mounted at the tip of a plastic tube approximately 1.5 mm in diameter. The sensor, which is of the Severinghaus type, is small enough to be inserted via a suitable cannula into a blood vessel. Ulmer et al. [113] have used a production version of this sensor to measure the arterial P_{CO_2} for the purpose of automatically controlling the ventilation of patients in a respiratory care unit. They report that the electrode has a 90% response time of roughly 45 sec, which, although rather long, is adequate for this particular application. A further point to be noted concerns the susceptibility of the sensor to calibration changes when the electrode membrane is disturbed. In view of this, perhaps a more satisfactory (although expensive) sensor for tissue CO_2 measurements is the mass spectrometer attached to a catheter with a CO_2-permeable membrane on the tip [79–81]. It was in this manner that Brantigan et al. [81] studied dynamic changes in CO_2 and O_2 tensions within the myocardium.

* Blood pH, P_{CO_2}, P_{O_2} System, Radiometer Corp., Copenhagen; Digital Blood Gas Analyzer, Instrumentation Lab. Inc., Lexington, Mass.

† Model 165 pH/Blood Gas System, Corning Scientific Instruments, Medfield, Mass.

9.8 ENZYME ELECTRODES

A class of electrodes based on an electrochemical process combined with an immobilized enzyme provides an important means of measuring the concentration of certain biochemical substances. Updike and Hicks [114] first described such a scheme for measuring glucose concentration; subsequently, Guilbault and Montalvo [115, 116] discussed a method for measuring urea concentrations [117].

In the method of Updike and Hicks, the enzyme, glucose oxidase, is immobilized in a layer of acrylamide gel 25–50 μm thick and held in contact with the plastic membrane of a Clark-type oxygen electrode, as illustrated in Figure 9.39(a). If the electrode surface is in contact with a solution containing glucose and oxygen, diffusion of both the glucose and the oxygen into the enzyme gel layer occurs. The diffusion of oxygen through the plastic membrane of the oxygen electrode is reduced in the presence of glucose owing to some of the oxygen being used in the following enzyme-catalyzed reaction:

$$\text{Glucose} + O_2 \xrightleftharpoons{\text{Glucose oxidase}} \text{Gluconic acid} + H_2O_2 .$$

Thus, the presence of glucose causes hydrogen peroxide to be formed and the oxygen consumed in the process causes the oxygen flux reaching the electrode to be reduced, thereby decreasing its current.

If the oxygen concentration in the solution is great enough for it not to cause any rate limitation and if the glucose concentration is not too large, it is found that the glucose concentration and the decrease in measured oxygen tension are linearly related. The response time depends on the thickness of the plastic and gel membranes. For 98% response, Updike and Hicks found the time interval to be in the range from 30 sec to 3 min.

With the single electrode, the electrode current responds not only to the glucose concentration but also depends on the oxygen tension of the test solution. To avoid this difficulty Updike and Hicks used the dual-cathode arrangement of Figure 9.39(b), in which the enzyme gel of one of the cathodes is made inactive by heating so that it responds only to oxygen. By taking the difference between the two cathode currents, an output signal is obtained that is proportional to the glucose concentration and that is essentially independent of the oxygen tension.

Guilbalt [116] has described an alternative enzyme electrode for glucose determination in which the glucose oxidase is in direct contact with a platinum cathode poised at a potential sufficient to cause the hydrogen peroxide to be

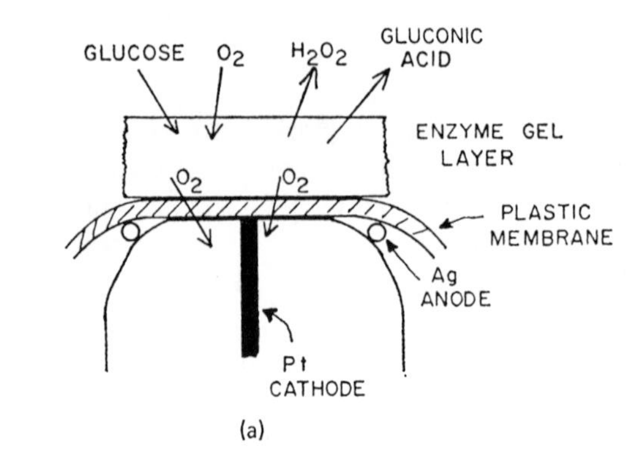

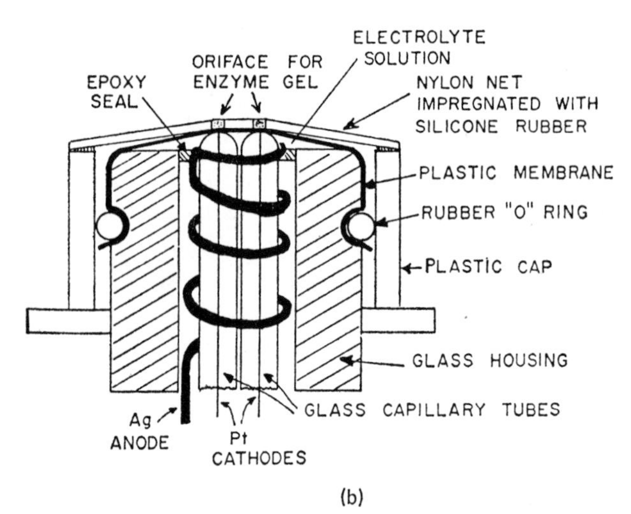

Figure 9.39. Enzyme electrode for glucose concentration measurements: (a) principles; (b) dual-cathode electrode (reproduced, with permission, from S. J. Updike and G. P. Hicks, *Nature*, **214**, 986–988, June 3rd 1967).

electro-oxidized.* Either the rate of change of electrode current or the total steady-state current produced can be used as a measure of the glucose concentration.

In the urea-specific enzyme electrode described by Guilbault and Montalvo [115, 116], the enzyme, urease, was immobilized in polyacrylic gel. The urease

* Chang et al. [118] have described a glucose sensor based on a specially designed fuel cell operating in a glucose-diffusion-controlled mode.

catalyzes the hydrolysis of urea according to

$$\text{Urea} \xrightleftharpoons{\text{Urease}} NH_4^+ + HCO_3^-.$$

Thus, by detecting the concentration of ammonium with an electrochemical sensor, the concentration of urea can be deduced. To use the electrode for the assay of urea in blood, it was necessary to used a multielectrode system to avoid the interference errors arising from the Na^+, K^+, and NH_4^+ ions normally present in blood.

REFERENCES

1. Lyons, F. H. *Introduction to Electrochemistry.* Heath: Boston, 1967.
2. Denaro, A. R. *Elementary Electrochemistry.* Butterworths: London, 1965.
3. Vetter, K. J. *Electrochemical Kinetics, Theoretical and Experimental Aspects.* Academic: New York, 1967.
4. Harned, H. S., and Owen, B. B. *The Physical Chemistry of Electrolytic Solutions*, 3rd ed., Reinhold: New York, 1958.
5. Kortum, G. *Treatise on Electrochemistry*, 2nd ed., Elsevier: Amsterdam, 1965.
6. Eyring, H., Ed. *Physical Chemistry: An Advanced Treatise*, Vol. XI, *Electrochemistry.* Academic: New York, 1970.
7. Ives, D. J. G., and Janz, G. J., Eds. *Reference Electrodes; Theory and Practice.* Academic: New York, 1961.
8. Eisenman, G., Ed. *Glass Electrodes for Hydrogen and Other Cations.* Dekker: New York, 1967.
9. Durst, R. A., Ed. *Ion Selective Electrodes.* Special Pub. No. 314, National Bureau of Standards: Washington, D.C., 1969.
10. Eisenman, G.; Mattock, G.; Bates, R.; and Freedman, S. M. *The Glass Electrode.* Wiley: New York, 1966.
11. Lavallée, M.; Shanne, O. F.; and Hébert, N. C., Eds. *Glass Microelectrodes.* Wiley: New York, 1969.
12. Feder, W., Ed. "Bioelectrodes." *Ann. N.Y. Acad. Sci.*, **148**, Art. 1, 1–287 (1968).
13. Bates, R. G. *Determination of pH: Theory and Practice.* Wiley: New York, 1964.
14. Hills, G. J., and Ives, D. J. G. "The Hydrogen Electrode," in Ref. 7, Chapter 2.
15. Janz, G. J., and Ives, D. J. G. "Silver Silver Chloride Electrodes," in Ref. 12, pp. 210–221.
16. Covington, A. K. "Reference Electrodes," in Ref. 9, pp. 107–142.

17. Janz, G. J. "Silver-Silver Halide Electrodes," in Ref. 7, Chapter 4.

18. Hinke, J. A. M. "Glass Microelectrodes in the Study of Binding and Compartmentalization of Intracellular Ions," in Ref. 11, Chapter 16.

19. Hills, G. J., and Ives, D. J. G. "The Calomel Electrode and Other Mercury-Mercurous Salt Electrodes," in Ref. 7, Chapter 3.

20. Mattock, G., and Band, D. M. "Interpretation of pH and Cation Measurements," in Ref. 8, Chapter 2.

21. Mattock, G. "Laboratory pH Measurements," in *Advances in Analytical Chemistry and Instrumentation*, Vol. II. Wiley: New York, 1963, pp. 35–121.

22. Ives, D. J. G. "Oxide, Oxygen and Sulfide Electrodes," in Ref. 7, Chapter 7.

23. Bates, R. G., and Covington, A. K. "Behaviour of the Glass Electrode and Other pH Responsive Electrodes in Biological Media," in Ref. 12, p. 70.

24. Isard, J. O. "The Dependence of Glass-Electrode Properties on Composition," in Ref. 8, Chapter 3.

25. Zachariasen, W. H. "The Atomic Arrangement in Glass." *J. Am. Chem. Soc.* **54**, 3841-3851 (October 1932).

26. Doremus, R. H. "Diffusion Potentials in Glass," in Ref. 8, Chapter 4.

27. Eisenman, G. "The Ion-Exchange Characteristics of the Hydrated Surface of Na^+ Selective Glass Electrodes," in Ref. 11, Chapter 3.

28. Bates, R. G. "Inner Reference Electrodes and Their Characteristics," in Ref. 11, Chapter 1.

29. Doyle, M. *The Glass-Electrode.* Wiley: New York, 1941.

30. Portnoy, H. D. "The Construction of Glass Electrodes," in Ref. 8, Chapter 8.

31a. Wegman, D., and Simon, W. "Glaseleklroden-Messkette mit isothermen Schnittpunkt bei pH = 7.0 zur pH—Messung unter extremen Bedingungen." *Helv. Chim. Acta*, **47**, 1181–1187 (1964).

31b. Bergveld, P. "Development, Operation, and Application of the Ion-Sensitive Field-Effect Transistor as a Tool for Electrophysiology." *IEEE Trans. Biomed. Eng.*, **BME-19**, 342–351 (September 1972).

32. Siggaard-Andersen, O. *The Acid-Base Status of the Blood*, 3rd ed., Williams and Wilkins: Baltimore, 1956.

33. Astrup, P., and Schrøder, S. "Apparatus for Anaerobic Determination of the pH of Blood at 38°C." *Scand. J. Clin. Lab. Invest.*, **8**, 30–32 (1956).

34. Severinghaus, J. W. "Design of Capillary pH Electrode Incorporating an Open Liquid Junction and Reference Electrode in a Single Unit." *Scand. J. Clin. Lab. Invest.*, **17**, 614–616 (1965).

35. Maas, A. H. J. "pH Determination in Body Fluids Using a Cell with an Isotonic Sodium Chloride Bridge." *J. Appl. Physiol.*, **30**, 248–250 (February 1971).

36. Staehelin, H. B.; Carlson, E. N.; Hinshaw, D. B.; and Smith, L. L. "Continuous Blood pH Monitoring using an Indwelling Catheter." *Am. J. Surg.*, **116**, 280–285 (August 1968).

37. Band, D. M., and Semple, S. J. G. "Continuous Measurement of Blood pH with an Indwelling Arterial Glass Electrode." *J. Appl. Physiol.*, **22**, 854–857 (1967).

38. Kunz, H. J.; Norby, T. E.; and Rogers, C. H. "A pH Measuring Radio Capsule for the Alimentary Canal." *Am. J. Dig. Dis.*, **16** (NS), 739–743 (August 1971).

39. Demling, L.; Classen, M.; and Thebis, J. "Telemetry of Gastric H-ion Concentration with the Glass Electrode," in L. Demling and K. Bachmann, Eds., *Biotelemetrie*. Thieme: Stuttgart, 1970, pp. 265–275.

40. Yarbrough, D. R.; McAlhany, J. C.; Cooper, N.; and Weidner, M. G. "Evaluation of the Heidelberg pH Capsule." *Am. J. Surg.*, **117**, 185–192 (February 1969).

41. Mackay, R. S. *Biomedical Telemetry: Sensing and Transmitting Biological Information for Animals and Man.*, 2nd ed., Wiley: New York, 1970.

42. Jacobson, B. "Endoradiosonde Techniques—A Survey." *Med. Electron. Biol. Eng.* **1**, 165–180 (1963).

43. Kitagawa, K.; Nishigon, T.; Murato, N.; Nishimoto, K.; and Ikegami, I. "A New Radio Capsule with Micro Glass Electrode for the Telemetry of the Gastrointestinal pH and Its Clinical Use." Digest, 6th Int. Conf. on Med. Electron. and Biol. Eng. Tokyo, 1965, pp. 216–217.

44. Starney, L. S.; Hamilton, T.; Sircus, W.; and Smith, A. N. "Evaluation of the pH-Sensitive Telemetering Capsule in the Estimation of Gastric Secretory Capacity." *Am. J. Dig. Dis.*, **11** (NS), 753–760 (1966).

45. Khuri, R. N. "Ion-Selective Electrodes in Biomedical Research," in Ref. 9, Chapter 8.

46a. Waddell, W. J., and Bates, R. G. "Intracellular pH." *Physiol. Rev.*, **49**, 285–329 (April 1969).

46b. Paillard, M. "Direct Intracellular pH Measurement in Rat and Crab Muscle." *J. Physiol.*, **223**, 297–319 (June 1972).

47. Khuri, R. N. "pH Glass Microelectrode for *in vivo* Applications." *Rev. Sci. Instrum.*, **39**, 730–732 (May 1968).

48. Khuri, R. N. "Glass Microelectrodes and their Uses in Biological Systems," in Ref. 8, Chapter 18.

49. Khuri, R. N. "Cation and Hydrogen Microelectrodes in Single Nephrons," in Ref. 11, Chapter 13.

50. Hinke, J. A. M. "Cation-Selective Microelectrodes for Intracellular Use," in Ref. 8, Chapter 17.

51. Kostyak, P. G.; Sorokina, Z. A.; and Kholodova, Yu. D. "Measurement of Activity of Hydrogen, Potassium and Sodium Ions in Striated Muscle Fibers and Nerve Cells," in Ref. 11, Chapter 15.

52. Khuri, R. N.; Agulian, S. K.; and Harik, R. I. "Internal Capillary Glass Microelectrodes with a Glass Seal for pH, Sodium and Potassium." *Pflüg. Arch.*, **301**, 182–186 (1968).

53. Khuri, R. N.; Agulian, S. K.; Oelert, H.; and Harik, R. I. "A Single Unit pH Glass Ultramicro Electrode." *Pflüg. Arch.*, **294**, 291–294 (1967).

54. Lavallée, M. "Intracellular pH of Rat Atrial Muscle Fibers Measured by Glass Micropipette Electrodes." *Circ. Res.*, **15**, 185–193 (1964).

55. Lavallée, M., and Szabo, G. "Cation Sensitive Glass Micro-electrodes for Intracellular Measurements." Digest, 6th Int. Conf. on Med. Electron. and Biol. Eng. Tokyo, 1965, pp. 568–569.

56. Lavalleé, M., and Szabo, G. "The Effect of Glass Surface Conductivity Phenomena on the Tip Potential of Micropipette Electrodes," in Ref. 11, Chapter 6.

57. Eisenman, G. "The Electrochemistry of Cation-Sensitive Glass Electrodes," in C. N. Reilley, Ed., *Advances in Analytical Chemistry and Instrumentation*, Vol. IV. Wiley: New York, 1965, pp. 213–369.

58. Freedman, S. M. "H^+ and Cation Analysis of Biological Fluids in the Intact Animal," in Ref. 8, Chapter 16.

59. von Stackelberg, W. F. "A 0.1-Nanoliter Glass Capillary Electrode." *Pflüg. Arch.*, **321**, 274–282 (1970).

60. Sollner, K. "Membrane Electrodes," in Ref. 12, pp. 154–179.

61. Pungor, E., and Toth, K. "Ion-Selective Membrane Electrodes." *Analyst*, **95**, 625–648 (July 1970).

62. Ross, J. W. "Solid-State and Liquid Membrane Ion Selective Electrodes," in Ref. 9, Chapter 2.

63. Rechnitz, G. A. "New Directions for Ion-Selective Electrodes." *Analytical Chemistry*, **41**, 109A–113A (1969).

64. Eisenman, G. "Theory of Membrane Electrode Potentials: An Examination of the Parameters Determining the Selectivity of Solid and Liquid Ion Exchanges and of Neutral Ion-Sequestering Molecules," in Ref. 9, Chapter 1.

65. Covington, A. K. "Heterogeneous Membrane Electrodes" in Ref. 9, Chapter 2.

66. Durst, R. A. "Analytical Techniques and Applications of Ion-Selective Electrodes," in Ref. 9, Chapter 11.

67. Frant, M. S., and Ross, J. W. "Electrode for Sensing Fluoride-Ion Activity in Solution." *Science*, **154**, 1553–1554 (December 1966).

68. Orme, F. W. "Liquid Ion Exchanger Microelectrodes," in Ref. 10, Chapter 17.

69a. Graf, H., and Muhlemann, H. R. "Oral Telemetry of Fluoride Ion Activity." *Arch. Oral. Biol.*, **14**, 259–263 (March 1969).

69b. Clark, N. G., and Dowdell, L. R. "A Radiotelemetric Method for the Study of pH and Fluoride-Ion Concentration in Dental Plaque and Saliva." *Med. Biol. Eng.*, **11**, 159–163 (March 1973).

70a. Khuri, R. N.; Agulian, S. K.; and Wise, W. M. "Potassium in the Rat Kidney Proximal Tubules in Situ: Determination by K^+-Selective Liquid Ion-Exchange Microelectrodes." *Pflüg. Arch.*, **322**, 39–46 (1971).

70b. Khuri, R. N.; Hajjar, J. J.; and Agulian, S. K. "Measurement of Intracellular Potassium with Liquid Ion-Exchange Microelectrodes." *J. Appl. Physiol.*, **32**, 419–422 (March 1972).

71. Hill, D. W. *Electronic Techniques in Anaesthesia and Surgery*, 2nd ed. Butterworths: London, 1973.

72. Nilsson, N. J. "Oximetry." *Physiol. Rev.*, **40**, 1–26 (January 1960).

73. Lukas, D. S., and Ayres, S. M. "Determination of Blood Oxygen Content by Gas Chromatography." *J. Appl. Physiol.*, **16**, 371–374 (1961).

74. Hill, D. W. "Methods of Measuring Oxygen Content of Blood," in J. P. Payne and D. W. Hill, Eds., *Oxygen Measurements in Blood and Tissues*. Churchill: London, 1966.

75. Zijlstra, W. G., and Mook, G. A. *Medical Reflection Photometry*. Van Gorcum: Assen, Netherlands, 1962.

76. Mook, G. A.; Osypka, P.; Sturm, R. E.; and Wood, E. H. "Fibre Optic Reflection Photometry on Blood." *Cardiovasc. Res.*, **2**, 199–209 (1968).

77. Paul, W., and Woolf, C. R. "A Ear Oximeter Using D.C. Operational Amplifiers." *Can. J. Physiol. Pharmacol.*, **45**, 1001–1009 (November 1967).

78. Janssen, F. J. "The Principle Design and Features of a New Hb-Oximeter." *Med. Biol. Eng*, **10**, 9–22 (January 1972).

79. Brantigan, J. W.; Gott, V. L.; Vestal, M. L.; Fergusson, G. J.; and Johnston, W. H. "A Nonthrombogenic Diffusion Membrane for Continuous in vivo Measurement of Blood Gases by Mass Spectrometry." *J. Appl. Physiol.*, **28**, 375–377 (March 1970).

80. Gardner, T. J.; Brantigan, J. W.; Perna, A. M.; Bender, H. W.; Brawley, R. K.; and Gott, V. L. "Intramyocardial Gas Tensions in the Human Heart During Coronary Artery-Saphenous Vein Bypass." *J. Thoracic Cardiovasc. Surg.*, **62**, 844–850 (December 1971).

81. Brantigan, J. W.; Gott, V. L.; and Martz, M. N. "A Teflon Membrane for Measurement of Blood and Intramyocardial Gas Tensions by Mass Spectroscopy." *J. Appl. Physiol.*, **32**, 276–282 (February 1972).

82. Davies, P. W. "The Oxygen Cathode," in W. L. Nastuk, Ed., *Physical Techniques in Biological Research*, Vol. IV. Academic: New York, 1962, Chapter 3.

82a. Hoare, J. P. *The Electrochemistry of Oxygen*. Wiley: New York, 1968.

83. Kolthoff, I. M., and Lingane, J. J. *Polarography*, Vol. I, 2nd ed. Interscience: New York, 1952, Chapter 2.

84. Hudson, J. A. "Measurement of Oxygen Tension by the Oxygen Cathode." *Med. Biol. Eng.* **5**, 207–223 (May 1967).

85. Grunewald, W. "Diffusion Error and O_2 Consumption of the Pt Electrode during PO_2 Measurements in the Steady State." *Pflüg. Arch.*, **320**, 24–44 (1970).

86. Grunewald, W. "Response Time of the Pt Electrode with Measurements of Non-stationary Oxygen Partial Pressures." *Pflüg. Arch.*, **322**, 109–130 (1971).

87. Cater, D. B. "The Measurement of PO_2 in Tissues," in F. Dickens and E. Neil, Eds. *Oxygen in the Animal Organism.* IUB Symposium Series, Vol. 31. Pergamon: Oxford, 1964.

88a. Berkenbosch, A. "Time Course of Response of the Membrane-Covered Oxygen Electrode." *Acta Physiol. Pharmacol. Neerl.*, **14**, 300–316 (1967).

88b. Whalen, W. J.; Nair, P.; and Ganfield, R. A. "Measurements of Oxygen Tension in Tissues with a Micro Oxygen Electrode." *Microvasc. Res.*, **5**, 254–262 (May 1973).

89. Clark, L. C. "Monitor and Control of Blood and Tissue Oxygen Tension.' *Trans. Am. Soc. Artif. Internal Organs*, **2**, 41–46 (1956).

90. Berkenbosch, A., and Riedstra, J. W. "Temperature Effects in Amperometric Oxygen Determinations with the Clark Electrode." *Acta Physiol. Pharmacol. Neerl.*, **12**, 144–156 (1963).

91. Severinghaus, J. W. "Measurement of Blood Gases: PO_2 and PCO_2," in Ref. 12, pp. 115–132.

92. Heitmann, H.; Buckles, R. G.; and Laver, M. B. "Blood PO_2 Measurements: Performance of Microelectrodes." *Resp. Physiol.*, **3**, 380–395 (1967).

93. Severinghaus, J. W. "Blood Gas Concentrations," in W. O. Renn and H. Rahn, Eds. *Handbook of Physiology*, Sect. 3, Vol. II. American Physiological Society: Washington, D.C., 1965, Chapter 61.

94. Charlton, G.; Read, D.; and Read, J. "Continuous Intrarterial PO_2 in Normal Man using a Flexible Microelectrode." *J. Appl. Physiol.*, **18**, 1247–1251 (1963).

95. Kimmich, H. P., and Kreuzer, F. "Catheter PO_2 Electrode with Low Flow Dependency and Fast Response," in F. Kreuzer, Ed., *Progress in Respiration Research*, Vol. III. Karger: Basel, 1969, pp. 100–110.

96. Lubbers, D. W. et al. "Principle of Construction and Application of Various Platinum Electrodes," in Ref. 95, pp. 136–146.

97. Kolmer, H. H., and Kreuzer, F. "Continuous Polarographic Recording of Oxygen Pressure in Respiratory Air." *Resp. Physiol.*, **4**, 109–117 (1968).

98. Purves, M. J. "Information of Physiological Value Derived From Continuous Measurement of Oxygen Tension of Blood in Vivo," in Ref. 95, pp. 79–88.

99. Whalen, W. J.; Riley, J.; and Nair, P. "A Microelectrode for Measuring Intracellular PO_2." *J. Appl. Physiol.*, **23**, 798–801 (May 1967).

100. Lubbers, D. W. "The Meaning of the Tissue Oxygen Distribution Curve and its Measurement by Means of Pt-Electrodes," in Ref. 95, pp. 112–123.

101. Silver, I. A. "Some Observations on the Cerebral Cortex with an Ultramicro, Membrane-Covered Oxygen Electrode." *Med. Biol. Eng.* **3**, 377–387 (October 1965).

102. Silver, I. A. "The Measurement of Oxygen Tension in Tissues," in Ref. 74, pp. 135–153.

103. Bicher, H. I., and Knisely, M. H. "Brain Tissue Reoxygenation Time, Demonstrated with a New Ultramicro Oxygen Electrode." *J. Appl. Physiol.*, **28**, 387–390 (March 1970).

104. Updike, G. P., and Hicks, S. P. "The Enzyme Electrode." *Nature*, 3 June 1967, pp. 986–988.

105. Christian, G. D. "Electrochemical Methods for Analysis of Enzyme Systems," in S. N. Levine, Ed., *Advances in Biomedical Engineering and Medical Physics*, Vol. IV. Wiley: New York, 1971, pp. 95–161.

106. Filley, G. F. *Acid-Base and Blood Gas Regulation.* Lea and Febiger: Philadelphia, 1971.

107. Barschi, F.; Haab, P.; and Held, D. R. "Reliability of Blood PCO_2 Measurements by the CO_2-Electrode, The Whole-Blood C_{CO_2}/pH Method and the Astrup Method." *Resp. Physiol.*, **10**, 121–131 (1970).

108. Stow, R. W.; Baer, R. F.; and Randall, B. F. "Rapid Measurement of the Tension of Carbon Dioxide in Blood, *Arch. Phys. Med.* **38**, 646–650 (1957).

109. Severinghaus, J. W., and Bradley, A. F. "Electrodes for Blood PO_2 and PCO_2 Determination." *J. Appl. Physiol.*, **13**, 515–520 (1958).

110. Hertz, C. H., and Siesjo, B. "A Rapid and Sensitive Electrode for Continuous Measurement of PCO_2 in Liquids and Tissue." *Acta Physiol. Scand.*, **47**, 515–520 (1958).

111. Ingvar, D. H.; Siesjo, B.; and Hertz, C. H. "Measurement of Tissue PCO_2 in the Brain." *Experientia*, **15**, 306 (1959).

112. Niedrach, L. W. *Electrochemical Sensors for Continuous Monitoring of Blood Gases and pH.* Report No. 73CRD194, General Electric Co., Schenectady, N.Y., June 1973.

113. Ulmer, H. V.; Erdman, W.; and Schulz, V. "A New Method for Continuous Bloodgas Controlled Ventilation by Arterial PCO_2 Catheter-Electrodes." Vol. I, Digest, 10th Int. Conf. Med. Biol. Eng., Dresden, 1973, p. 145.

114. Updike, S. J., and Hicks, G. P. "The Enzyme Electrode." *Nature*, 3 June 1967, pp. 986–988.

115. Guilbault, G. G., and Montavo, J. G. "Urea-Specific Enzyme Electrode." *J. Am. Chem. Soc.*, **91**, 2164–2165 (1969).

116. Guilbault, G. G. "Enzyme Electrodes for Biomedical Analysis," Vol. II, Digest, 10th Conf. Med. Biol. Eng., Dresden, 1973, p. 54.

117. Christian, G. D. "Electrochemical Methods for Analysis of Enzyme Systems," in Ref. 105, pp. 95–161.

118. Chang, K. W.; Aisenberg, S.; Soeldner, J. S.; and Hiebert, J. M. "Basic Principle and Performance of a Viable Glucose Sensor Suitable for Implantation." Vol. II, Digest, 10th Int. Conf. Med. Biol. Eng., Dresden, 1973, p. 56.

CHAPTER TEN

Electrodes for the Measurement of Bioelectric Potentials

A pair of electrodes, normally consisting of two metal–electrolyte half-cells, is required for measuring the potential difference between two points in a biological system. Each electrode forms an interface between a system in which conduction occurs through ion movement and a system involving electronic-type conduction. The change from ionic to electronic conduction that occurs at the electrode–electrolyte interface can be regarded as a process of energy conversion, and as a result, the biopotential electrode can be considered to act as a transducer.

At first sight it may seem that the properties, design, and application of potential sensing electrodes is a straightforward topic that hardly merits a complete chapter let alone a complete book [1]. But on closer examination it is found that even the simplest of electrodes has a complex behavior.* It can introduce noise, result in a poor common-mode rejection, result in frequency distortion, and introduce nonlinearities. Furthermore, for some applications, the physical constraints imposed by the nature of the measurement (e.g., intracellular potential measurements) requires careful attention to the design in order to insure that the electrical and mechanical distortions are sufficiently small to be neglected.

The first part of this chapter is devoted to an examination of electrode behavior in terms of the physical mechanisms occurring at the metal–electrolyte interface. Circuit models are introduced, based on the theoretical characteristics, to represent the small-signal behavior. Unfortunately, these models

* See [2] for a good elementary summary of electrode properties and applications.

involve circuit elements whose values are frequency-dependent and thereby detract from their usefulness for nonsinusoidal waveforms. However, some approximate circuit models are also presented that enable rough calculations to be made when transient or complex periodic waveforms are present.

In the latter part of this chapter the problems of electrode design are considered for the measurement of surface potentials such as ECG and EEG and for the measurement of potentials at the cellular level.

10.1 ELECTRICAL BEHAVIOR OF ELECTRODES

10.1.1 Theoretical Aspects [3–5]

To better understand the small-signal electrical properties of electrodes, it is necessary to expand somewhat on the half-cell overvoltage concepts introduced in Section 9.1. It will be recalled that a space-charge region is formed at the interface between a metal and electrolyte, the charge and potential distributions being governed by the solution to Poisson's equation. A change in the total potential difference resulting from the passage of a current alters the charge distribution in a nonlinear manner. Thus, an accurate large-signal model to account for the displacement current necessarily involves a nonlinear element. For small signals, an incremental capacitance defined by $C_H = dQ/dV$, whose value depends on the steady-state current, enables the small-signal displacement current and voltage to be related.

If the charge-transfer overvoltage mechanism is the dominant cause of electrode overvoltage (this would be the case for an electrode with a small exchange current density), the current and electrode overvoltage are related by [see Eq. 12 of Chapter 9]

$$\frac{J}{J_0} = \exp\left(\frac{\alpha z \eta_t F}{RT}\right) - \exp\left(\frac{-(1-\alpha) z \eta_t F}{RT}\right), \tag{1}$$

where J_0 is the exchange current density, z is the transfer valence, and α is the transfer coefficient. For small-signal conditions, when the steady-state current through the electrode is such that $\eta_t \ll RT/\alpha zF$, the incremental resistance R_t is given by

$$R_t = \frac{\partial I}{\partial \eta_t} = \frac{RT}{zF} \cdot \frac{1}{I_0}, \tag{2}$$

where $I_0 = \text{area} \times J_0$. For larger currents, such that $\eta_t \gg RT/\alpha zF$,

$$R_t = \frac{RT}{\alpha zF} \cdot \frac{1}{I}, \tag{3}$$

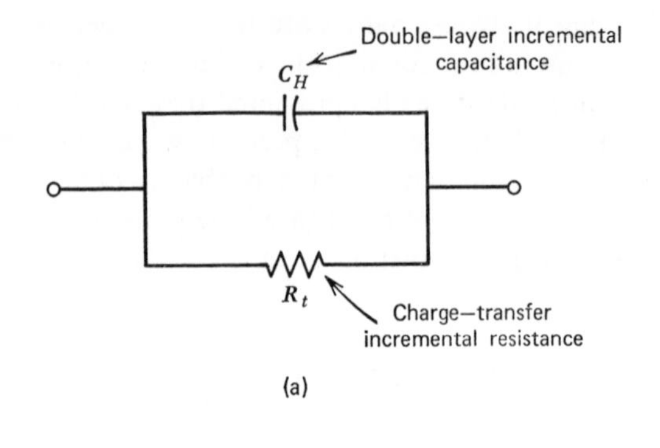

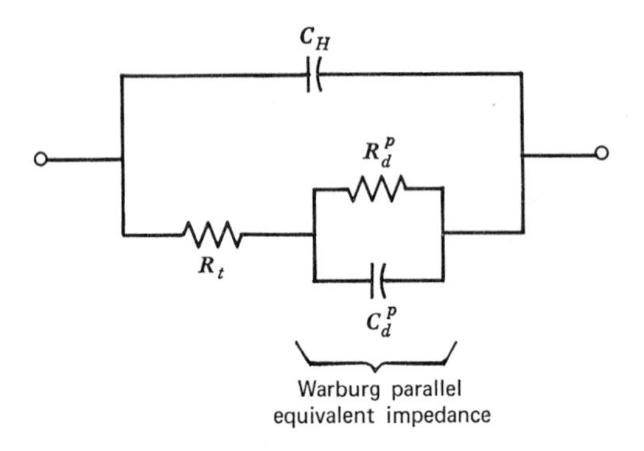

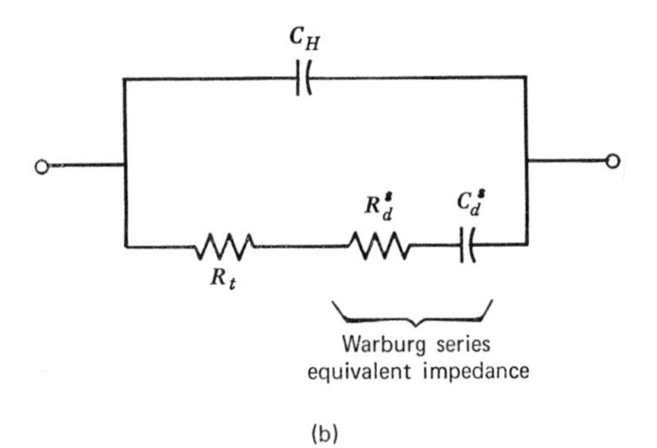

Figure 10.1. Development of a physically based small-signal electrode–electrolyte circuit model: (a) ignoring diffusion mechanisms; (b) including the diffusion (Warburg) impedance in its parallel and series forms.

where I is the steady-state electrode current. For example, in this last case, when $\alpha = z = 1$ and $I = 100\ \mu\text{A}$, then $R_t = 260\ \Omega$. Since R_t is inversely proportional to I, R_t increases to $2600\ \Omega$ when I decreases to $10\ \mu\text{A}$.

Thus far, as illustrated in Figure 10.1(a), the small-signal model of an electrode consists of two parallel linear elements that are frequency-independent but that depend nonlinearly on the steady-state electrode current. To account for the effects of diffusion, it is necessary, as a first approximation, to introduce the additional two elements shown in Figure 10.1(b), both of which are frequency-dependent. The origin of these extra elements will now be considered.

When the electrode overvoltage is controlled by the diffusion of ions to or from the electrical double layer, the diffusion overvoltage η_d is given by [see Eq. 15 of Chapter 9]

$$\frac{J}{J_s} = 1 - \exp\left(\frac{-|\eta_d|zF}{RT}\right), \tag{4}$$

in which, for generality, the valence z of the ion has been included. Hence, by differentiation, the incremental diffusion resistance becomes

$$R_d = \frac{RT/zF}{I_s - I}, \tag{5}$$

where I_s is the electrode saturation current corresponding to the maximum current that the electrode will pass for a given reaction.

Assuming that the diffusion and charge-transfer effects are additive and that conditions are very close to equilibrium ($\eta \approx 0$), it follows from Eqs. (2) and (5) that the total incremental resistance $R_c = R_t + R_d$ is given by

$$R_c = \frac{RT}{zF}\left(\frac{1}{I_s} + \frac{1}{I_0}\right). \tag{6}$$

Further, when the steady-state electrode current I is such that $\eta \gg RT/\alpha zF$, the total incremental resistance is given by the sum of Eqs. (3) and (5):

$$R_c = \frac{RT}{zF}\left(\frac{1}{I_s - I} + \frac{1}{\alpha I}\right). \tag{7}$$

It follows from Eqs. (6) and (7) that if the electrode current is increased from zero, thereby increasing the deviation from equilibrium conditions, the incremental resistance initially remains constant. For larger currents R_c decreases with increasing current. It is of particular importance to note that Eq. (4) is valid in the case of a time varying current only if the rate of variation is sufficiently slow for steady-state conditions to be always present. Thus, Eqs. (6) and (7) can only be applied when the measurement frequency is very low: at higher frequencies it is necessary to consider reactive effects arising from the diffusion mechanism.

Suppose that a sinusoidally varying emf is applied to an ideal metal–electrolyte electrode. A direct result of the emf will be to produce a sinusoidally varying concentration of the reacting ion species at the interface and to cause a concentration wave to propagate out into the electrolyte. Damping and perhaps spreading of the wave cause the amplitude to decrease with distance from the interface. Furthermore, since the damping increases as the frequency is raised, the depth of penetration decreases at high frequencies, thereby causing the concentration gradient to increase at the interface. Since the electrode current is proportional to the interface concentration gradient, it is reasonable to expect that the magnitude of the equivalent impedance arising from the diffusion process will decrease toward zero as the frequency increases.

Warburg [6, 7], it appears, was the first to analyze the concentration distribution resulting from a sinusoidally varying current. By assuming that the penetration depth of the concentration wave (distance from the interface where the amplitude has dropped by $1/e$) was small compared to the diffusion-layer thickness, Warburg solved the diffusion equation and obtained an expression for the concentration as a function of both distance and time. In essence, he showed that the diffusion impedance could be represented by a series R–C combination in which both elements varied as the inverse square root of the frequency.

It can be shown* that for conditions close to equilibrium (i.e., the steady-state component of the electrode current is very small) and for a single ion species dominating diffusion, the series elements are given by [3, 4]

$$R_d^s = \frac{RT}{z^2F^2} \cdot \frac{1}{\sqrt{2\omega}} \cdot \frac{1}{C_0\sqrt{D}}$$

$$C_d^s = \frac{z^2F^2}{RT} \cdot \sqrt{\frac{2}{\omega}} \cdot C_0\sqrt{D}, \tag{8}$$

where D is the diffusion coefficient, ω is the angular frequency, and C_0 is the ion concentration under equilibrium conditions. It follows from Eq. (8) that

$$R_d^s C_d^s = \frac{1}{\omega}. \tag{9}$$

* This problem is essentially the same as calculating the ac diffusion impedance of a p–n junction diode. By solving the diffusion equation, the ac impedance of a p–n junction diode can be shown to have the same form as Eq. (10) with $R_d^s \propto 1/\sqrt{\omega}$ (see, for example, J. F. Feldman, *The Physics and Circuit Properties of Transistors*, Wiley: New York, 1972, pp. 323–326).

Hence, the diffusion, or *Warburg impedance*, as it is often referred to, can be written

$$Z_w = R_d^s + \frac{1}{j\omega C_d^s}$$
$$= R_d^s(1 - j); \qquad (10)$$

that is, $|Z_w| \propto 1/\sqrt{\omega}$. From Eqs. (8) and (10) it follows that as $\omega \to \infty$, the Warburg impedance approaches zero. This is in agreement with the qualitative arguments presented earlier. Furthermore, it should be noted from Eq. (10) that the current through, and voltage across, the Warburg impedance always differ in phase by 45°, independent of the frequency.

An alternative and perhaps more physically meaningful circuit representation of the Warburg impedance is the parallel R–C combination. It is a well-known result of circuit theory that a series R–C circuit can be transformed into an equivalent parallel combination. When this is done for the elements given by Eq. (8), it is found that [3]

$$R_d^p = \frac{RT}{z^2F^2} \cdot \sqrt{\frac{2}{\omega}} \cdot \frac{1}{C_0\sqrt{D}}$$
$$C_d^p = \frac{z^2F^2}{RT} \cdot \frac{1}{\sqrt{2\omega}} \cdot C_0\sqrt{D} \qquad (11)$$

and that

$$R_d^p C_d^p = \frac{1}{\omega}. \qquad (12)$$

It is most important to note that the results given above for the frequency-dependence of the series and parallel elements are only valid if the penetration depth of the concentration wave is small compared to the diffusion depth. For very low frequencies this assumption is no longer valid, and as will be noted from Eq. (10), Z_w approaches infinity as ω tends to zero (i.e., the dc incremental resistance is infinite). This is obviously at variance with our previous discussion of the dc incremental resistance. Evidently, an exact expression for the Warburg impedance should yield the value given by Eq. (5) when this limit value for ω is substituted.

Resistance polarization, arising, for example, from the bulk resistance of the electrolyte, can be included in the circuit model through the simple addition of the series resistor R_B, as shown in Figure 10.2(a). At very high frequencies it is evident that R_B and the double-layer capacitance C_H determine the electrode–electrolyte impedance and the circuit model reduces to

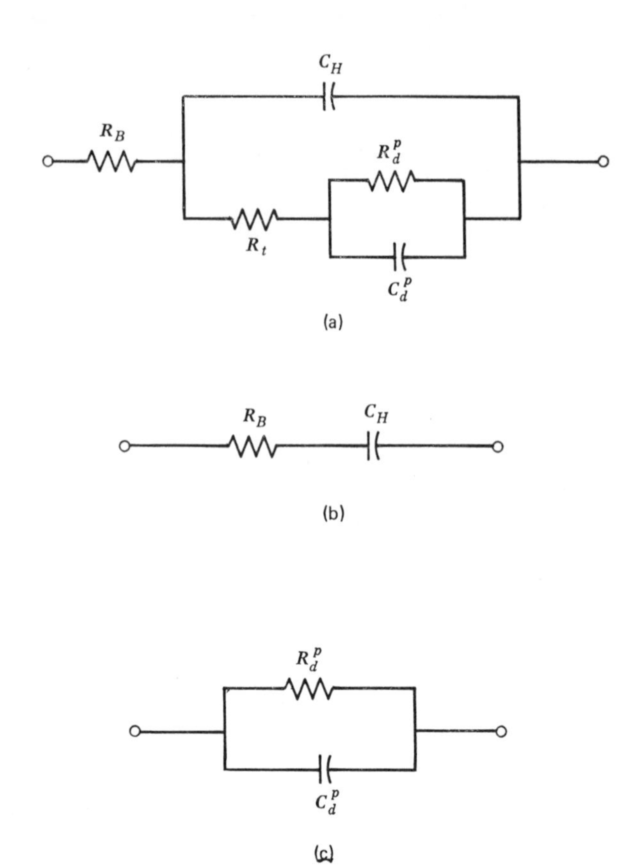

Figure 10.2. Model of Figure 10.1 including resistance polarization effects: (a) complete model; (b) high-frequency approximation; and (c) low-frequency approximation.

that shown in Figure 10.2(b). For this condition the high-frequency current is entirely the result of the displacement of charge (non-Faradic current) rather than the transport of charge across the double layer (Faradic current).

For very low frequencies, the Warburg impedance becomes large and dominates the total electrode impedance, so that the circuit model reduces to that shown in Figure 10.2(c). Evidently, under these conditions the Faradic component of current is large compared to the non-Faradic component.

In concluding this brief introduction to a physically orientated circuit model of an electrode it should be pointed out that no account was taken of possible reaction and crystallization overvoltage effects. It can be shown [3] that both these effects result in R–C elements in series with Z_w, but unlike the Warburg equivalent elements, their values depend on frequency in a rather complex manner. This makes it difficult to identify the contribution such effects make to the impedance characteristics of a given electrode system.

10.1.2 Experimental Behavior

Measurement of the impedance characteristics of an electrode–electrolyte system can be performed either through the use of ac bridge techniques, yielding directly the equivalent R–C series or parallel element values, or by means of phase and amplitude measurements, from which the R–C equivalent elements can be calculated. Frequently the electrode arrangement consists of two identical electrodes immersed in the electrolyte, in which case the impedance of a single electrode is simply half the total measured value. Alternatively, if the electrode to be measured is small in area by comparison to the other electrode, its impedance will dominate and the measured impedance will be essentially that of the small electrode.

Generally it is desired to eliminate the bulk resistance of the electrolyte, so that the results are presented in a form that is independent of the geometrical arrangement of the measurement. The component of R_B arising from the electrolyte can be found by calculation if the geometry is simple and the electrolyte resistivity is known. A second method consists of measuring the change in impedance that occurs when the electrode separation is altered. This is possible when a simple plane parallel arrangement of identical electrodes is used [8]. Finally, R_B can be determined by measuring the series equivalent resistance at a sufficiently high frequency, so that the model of Figure 10.2(b) applies. However, it should be noted that this last method may yield a somewhat higher value than the other methods, since it also includes resistance polarization effects directly associated with the electrode.

Experimental results are often expressed in terms of the series equivalent R–C values (denoted by R_{eq} and C_{eq}) and are plotted on a log–log graph as a function of frequency. The results enable the circuit element values of Figure 10.2(a) to be found. For example, at very low frequencies,

$$
\begin{aligned}
R_{\text{eq}} &\simeq R_d^s \propto \frac{1}{\sqrt{f}} \\
C_{\text{eq}} &\simeq C_d^s \propto \frac{1}{\sqrt{f}},
\end{aligned}
\tag{13}
$$

while for very high frequencies, if R_B is included,

$$
\begin{aligned}
R_{\text{eq}} &\simeq R_B \\
C_{\text{eq}} &\simeq C_H,
\end{aligned}
\tag{14}
$$

thereby enabling some of the elements to be directly determined.

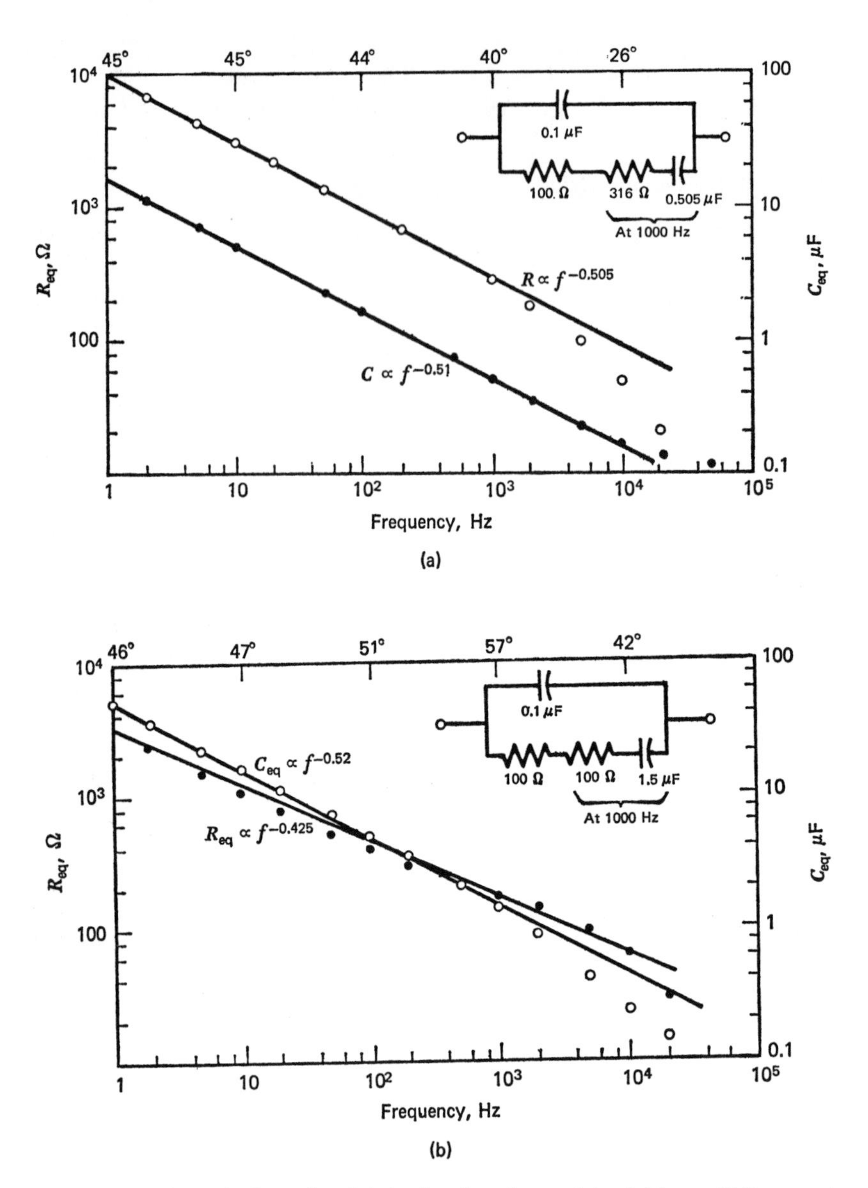

Figure 10.3. Theoretical predicted behavior for the model of Figure 10.2, assuming particular values of the elements; values of the phase angle δ for various frequencies are indicated along the top horizontal axes.

Figure 10.3 illustrates the frequency-dependence of R_{eq} and C_{eq} for two sets of circuit values that were chosen to correspond roughly to those that might be expected in practice. It will be noted that for both graphs both R_{eq} and C_{eq} can be reasonably accurately represented by a power-law-dependence over a wide range of frequencies; that is, $R_{eq} \propto \omega^{-m}$, and $C_{eq} \propto \omega^{-n}$, where m and n are essentially frequency-independent. Furthermore, it will be noted that the phase angle given by $\tan \delta = \omega C_{eq} R_{eq}$ remains reasonably close to the low frequency limit value of 45°, up to frequencies where R_B and C_H become dominant.

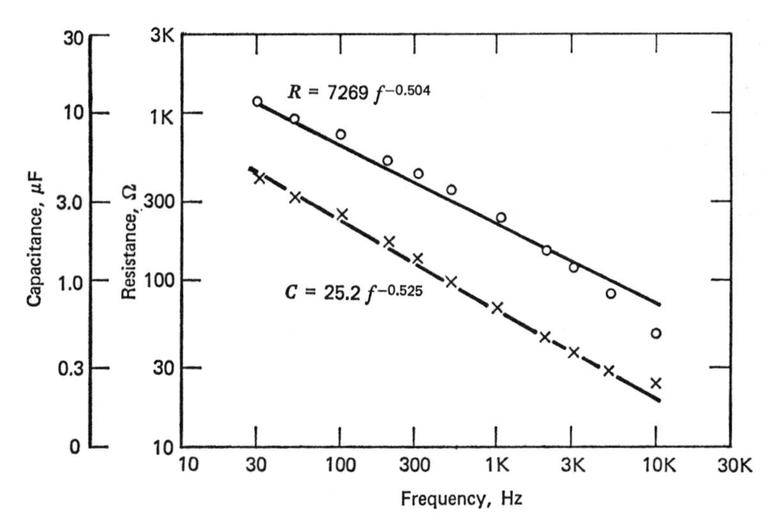

Figure 10.4. Experimental results obtained with a pair of parallel 0.157-cm^2 stainless-steel electrodes immersed in 0.9% saline measured under small-signal (0.025 mA/cm^2) conditions (reproduced, with permission, from L. A. Geddes, C. P. da Costa, and G. Wise, *Med. Biolog. Engng.*, **9**, 511–521, Sept. 1971).

Experimental results on a variety of electrode systems [1] confirm the general nature of the above predictions. For example, Geddes et al. [8] have measured R_{eq} and C_{eq} as a function of frequency for stainless-steel electrodes immersed in saline of various concentrations. The results obtained in 0.9% saline, measured under small-signal conditions are shown in Figure 10.4. Comparison with the theoretical results of Figure 10.3(a) show a remarkable similarity: not only are the slopes similar but also the deviations of experimental results from the power-law-dependence follow a pattern similar to that predicted from the circuit model.

Not all electrodes exhibit values of m so close to 0.5 as in the above example. For instance, it has been observed that platinized platinum electrodes in 0.9% saline [9] have a value of 0.366, while platinum-iridium electrodes in the same solution [10] have a value of 0.79. It is found that most irreversible electrode–electrolyte systems for bioelectric potential measurements have m-values in the range 0.2–0.8. On the other hand, electrodes of the reversible type (e.g., Ag–AgCl) exhibit only a small reactive effect, so that their impedance remains essentially constant.

An interesting aspect of the experimental results concerns the observation that the phase angle δ is almost independent of frequency, even though the value of m differs substantially from 0.5. Fricke [11] first pointed out that the phase angle for a variety of irreversible electrodes is related to m by

$$\delta = \frac{m\pi}{2}\,. \tag{15}$$

By making use of previously published experimental results for a variety of electrodes whose values of m ranged from 0·06 to 0·87, Fricke established that this simple relation is valid when the value of m for a given electrode is

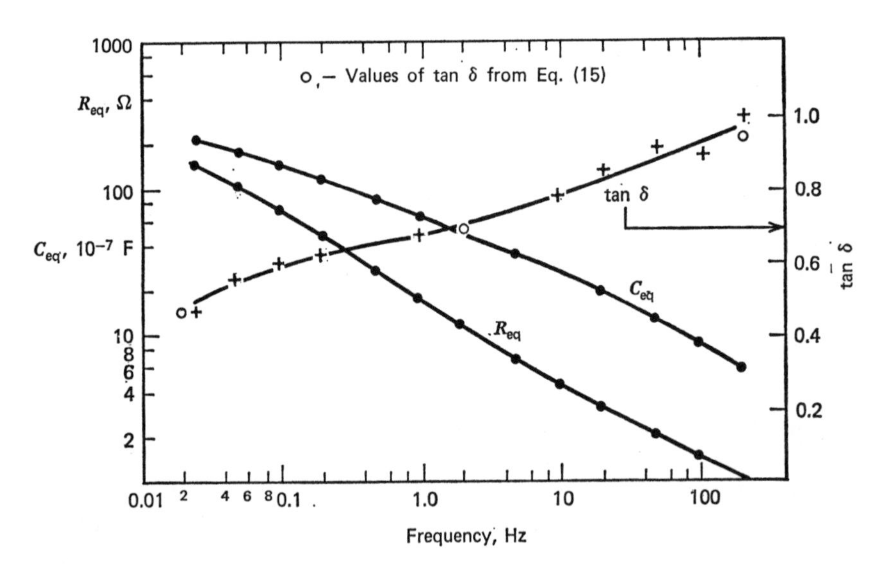

Figure 10.5. Experimentally measured R_{eq} and C_{eq} variation with frequency for Pt electrodes in physiological saline. The value of tan δ calculated from Eq. (15) are shown as open circles, the values calculated from $\omega C_{eq} R_{eq}$ are shown as crosses (reproduced, with permission, from H. P. Schwan, pp. 556–557, in Digest of Tech. Papers, 6th Int. Conf. Med. Electron. Biolog. Engng., Tokyo, 1965).

essentially independent of frequency. Schwan [12, 13], through a series of measurements on large-area Pt electrodes immersed in physiological saline, showed that Eq. (15) can also be applied when m is a slowly varying function of frequency. The results obtained by Schwan for R_{eq} and C_{eq} are shown in Figure 10.5. Also shown is the value of tan δ calculated from measured values of C_{eq} and R_{eq}, compared with the value calculated from Eq. (15) using the values of m derived from the slope of the C_{eq} curve.

It is of importance to note that the circuit model and measurements described thus far are only valid for small signals. If a sinusoidal emf is applied to an electrode, it is found that when the amplitude is small the current is directly proportional to the applied emf. Because of the nonlinear polarization properties of electrodes, it is found that at higher amplitudes the proportionality no longer holds, and in addition, the current is no longer sinusoidal- (i.e., harmonics are produced). Such effects have been extensively studied by electrochemists [4] and used for measuring reaction rates.

The current density at which these nonlinear effects become apparent is a function of frequency. In fact, it increases with increasing frequency. Experimentally it is found, as illustrated in Figure 10.6, that C_{eq} increases and R_{eq} decreases as the current density used to make the measurements is raised. Thus, the electrode impedance becomes smaller at higher current densities.

The reason for this behavior can be understood by noting that an irreversible electrode normally displays both nonlinear and asymmetrical characteristics, similar to a p–n junction diode. As a result, when a sinusoidal emf is applied, a rectification-type phenomenon occurs, causing a dc component of current to flow through the electrode. Effectively this results in a shift in the operating point to a region where the incremental impedance is smaller.

10.1.3 Electrode Response to Complex Waveforms

So far our discussion has been limited to the behavior of electrodes under sinusoidal conditions. In practice, bioelectric signals are generally of a complex form: often nonperiodic and sometimes of a transient nature. The problem of determining the response of an electrode to such a signal is made more difficult by the fact that the small-signal model has frequency-dependent circuit elements.

Cole [14] was the first to study this problem and to show that for certain ideal input waveshapes the Fourier transform method could be used to obtain analytical solutions. The first step in this method consists of performing a Fourier transform* of the applied emf (or current) waveform to determine its spectral density (i.e., the signal is mapped from the time to the frequency

* See Eqs. (10) amd (11) in Chapter 2.

domain). Dividing the spectral density by the electrode impedance and then performing an inverse Fourier transform to return to the time domain, the electrode response is obtained.

An alternative, although less rigorous, approach consists of deriving an approximate circuit model with frequency-independent elements. The difficulty here, however, is that no single circuit model suffices for all input waveshapes. For example, the values of the circuit elements for a square-pulse input depend on the pulse duration, so that the circuit model with fixed elements only holds if certain constraints are placed on the nature of the input.

The electrode response to constant current and constant voltage* pulses is sketched in Figure 10.7(b) and (c), assuming that the small-signal frequency-dependent model of Figure 10.7(a) is valid. It will be noted that for the constant-current pulse the initial change in potential enables the value of R_B to

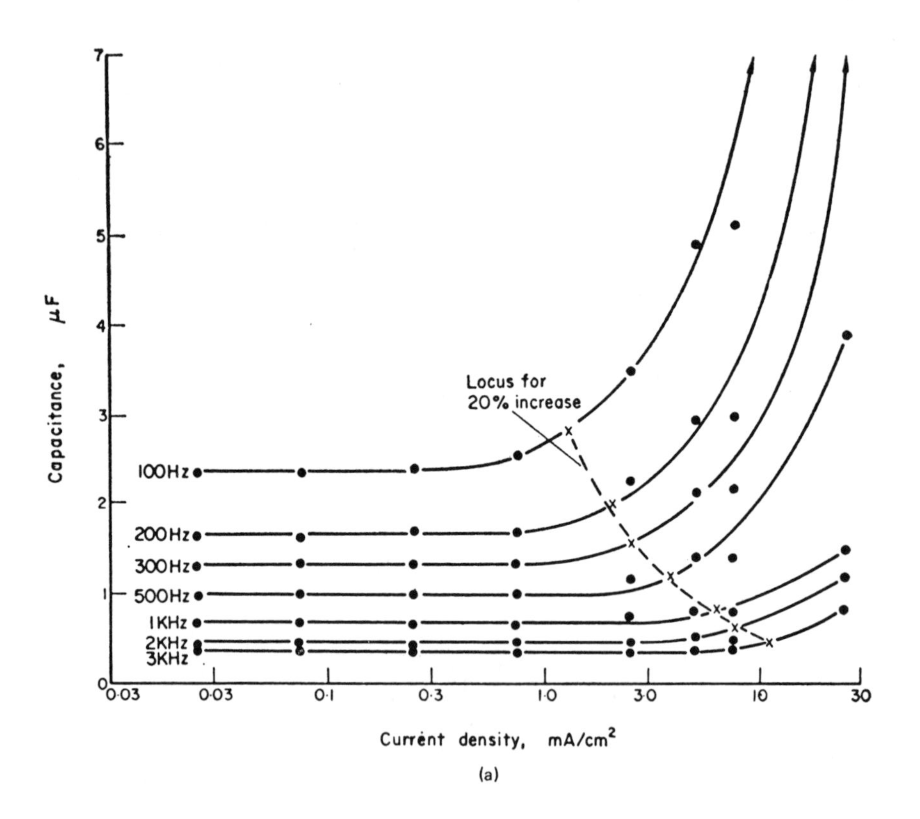

(a)

* Generally referred to by electrochemists as the *galvanostatic and potentiostatic response*.

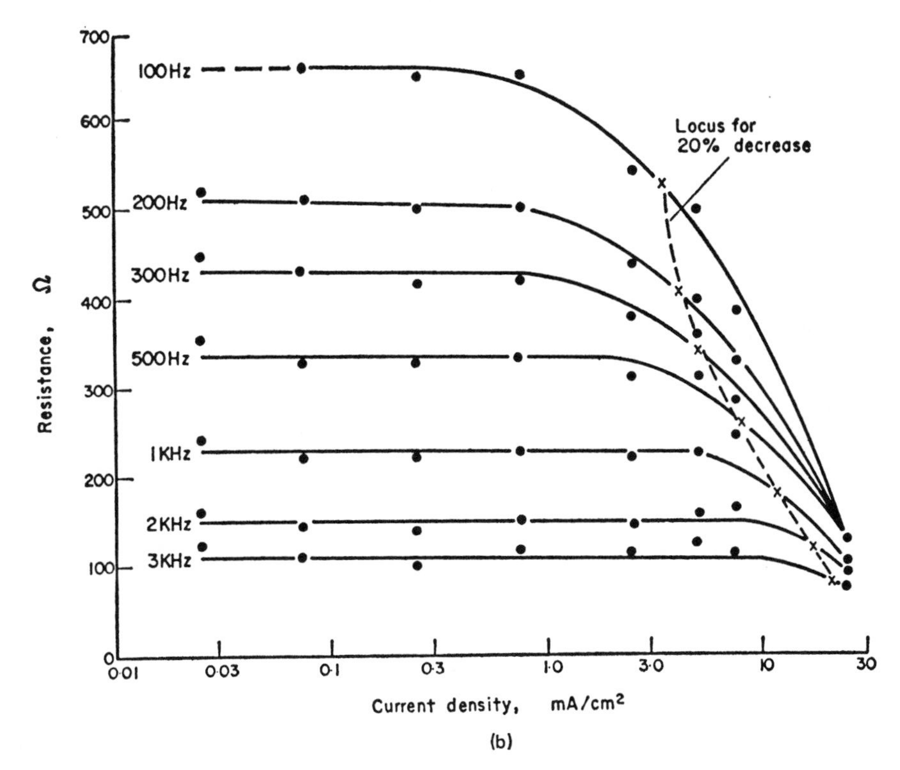

Figure 10.6. Dependence of the series equivalent capacitance and resistance on current density for a stainless-steel electrode of 0.157 cm² area in 0.9% saline: (a) variation of C_{eq}; (b) variation of R_{eq} (reproduced, with permission, from L. A. Geddes, C. P. da Costa, and G. Wise, *Med. Biolog. Engng.*, **9**, 511–521, Sept. 1971).

be found. Furthermore, when the current through the Warburg impedance is small, the initial slope of the voltage curve is given by I/C_H, enabling the value of C_H to be determined. It will also be noted that the frequency dependence of C_d and R_d cause the voltage response to deviate significantly from an exponential form. As a result, in the simplified model of Figure 10.7(d), the elements R and C are functions of the pulse duration.

At higher current densities, additional problems arise in attempting to characterize in a reasonably simple way the electrical properties of certain electrodes. For instance, the response to positive and negative pulses may differ because of the irreversible nature of the electrochemical processes. Moreover, the response to a pulse of a given duration may be a sensitive function of the pulse repetition rate. Weinman and Mahler [15] have detailed

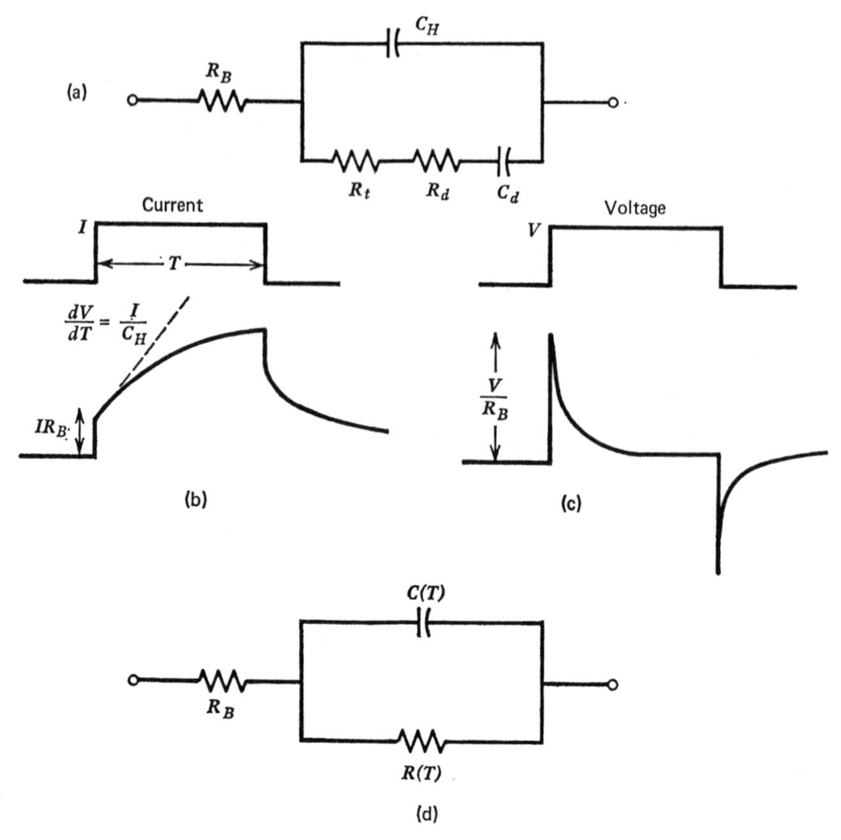

Figure 10.7. Metal electrode response to small-signal constant-current and constant-voltage pulses: (a) small-signal frequency-dependent circuit model; (b) approximate current pulse response; (c) approximate voltage pulse response; and (d) approximate circuit model.

some of the nonlinear and hysteresis effects associated with tungsten electrodes. They report that with a 1 mS, 120 mA/cm^2 positive pulse the value of R in Figure 10.7(d) changes from 18 kΩ at 1 pulse/sec to 360 kΩ at 20 pulses/sec. For negative pulses of the same duration, as long as the pulse interval was greater than 15 times the pulse duration, the behavior of the electrode remained essentially independent of the repetition rate.

The current densities at which such effects occur are considerably greater than the densities that are normally* encountered in an electrode during the

* Large-signal effects could occur with a metal microelectrode under certain circumstances.

recording of biopotentials (typically several milliamperes per square centimeter are required). It follows that if a recording electrode is used for both stimulation and recording, it may be necessary to select carefully the proper electrode material so that recovery from the stimulus waveform will be fast enough to insure accurate recording of the biopotential.

Although most of this section has been devoted to the properties of metal electrodes, this was not intended to imply that electrodes of the second kind are unimportant for the transduction of biopotentials. Indeed, Ag–AgCl electrodes, for example, are generally found to have electrical characteristics superior to those of metal electrodes and are often used for both recording and stimulation. As noted previously, properly chlorided Ag–AgCl electrodes are found to have only a small reactive component, so that their impedance remains essentially independent of frequency [1, 16]. An even smaller reactive component has been reported by Nencini and Pasquali [16] for carbon–manganese dioxide electrodes. They find that such electrodes have a faster pulse response and recovery than Ag–AgCl electrodes. Furthermore, this electrode is reversible to oxygen in that current flow in one direction causes the MnO_2 to be reduced to a lower valent state, while reversing the current causes the material to be reoxidized.

10.2 MACROELECTRODES [1, 17]

This section is primarily devoted to discussing the properties of comparatively large-area electrodes for the transduction of such clinically important biopotentials as ECG, EEG, and EMG. No attempt will be made to present an exhaustive survey of the various types and their properties—this has already been achieved in the excellent monograph by Geddes [1]; rather, specific designs will only be considered when they provide a convenient means of illustrating a certain property.

Macroelectrodes for biopotential measurements can be conveniently divided into two general categories: those that make use of a metal–electrolyte interface (direct-contact types) and those that rely on capacitative coupling (contactless types). The former, unless they are of the subcutaneous form, normally make use of an electrode jelly or paste to reduce and stabilize the electrode interface effects. The latter class of electrode is contactless in the sense that no metal–electrolyte interface is involved, so that no Faradic current can flow. Such an electrode, as discussed in Section 10.2.4, relies on capacitative coupling between the biological surface (the skin) and a conductive plate.

In what follows we shall be concerned with those electrode properties that are of concern in the choice or design of an electrode assembly. Specifically, the following aspects will be considered: electrode impedance and its variation, electrode dc offset voltage, electrode noise and drift, sensitivity to mechanical and electrical disturbances, and human factors.

10.2.1 Electrode Impedance

A discussion of measurement electrode impedance is only significant in so far as it could influence the accuracy of measurement. Three important aspects of this influence can be identified. The first, and most obvious, is the signal attenuation that can arise from amplifier loading. This requires that the amplifier differential input impedance be large compared to the effective source impedance. The second aspect concerns errors arising from differences between electrode impedances when averaging resistors are connected directly between the electrodes, as may occur for certain ECG measurements. The third aspect, also arising from differences in electrode impedance, concerns the reduction in the effective common-mode rejection ratio of the amplifier. This will now be considered in more detail.

Nearly all biopotential measurements involve careful consideration of interference arising from electrostatically or electromagnetically coupled noise. Typically, in the measurement of EEG or ECG, interference often arises from electrostatically coupled 60-Hz signals originating from the lights or other line power sources. Although proper grounding and shielding may serve to reduce these sources, it may not eliminate them: as a result, it is necessary to see what additional steps can be taken to reduce these sources of interference.

Huhta and Webster [18a] have made a very thorough investigation of 60-Hz line interference in ECG measurements and have suggested ways in which these problems can be reduced or eliminated. The reader is particularly urged to consult this excellent paper for an overall view of the problem. We choose to concentrate on one aspect that is particularly influenced by the electrode impedance.

Figure 10.8 shows an ECG measurement system in simplified form and illustrates the manner in which 60-Hz interference can arise from capacitive coupling of the patient to a power line. The small ac current that flows via this coupling results in a common-mode signal that can be several orders of magnitude larger than the millivolt ECG signal. Generally, it is not the intrinsic common-mode rejection ratio of the amplifier that limits the system capability to reject the interference; rather, it is the effective common-mode rejection of the system including the electrodes.

In the circuit model of Figure 10.8 the generator E_c represents the common-mode interference signal. For simplicity, suppose that the electrode impedances Z_1 and Z_2 are real and are denoted by R_1 and R_2. Then, as will be seen, it is

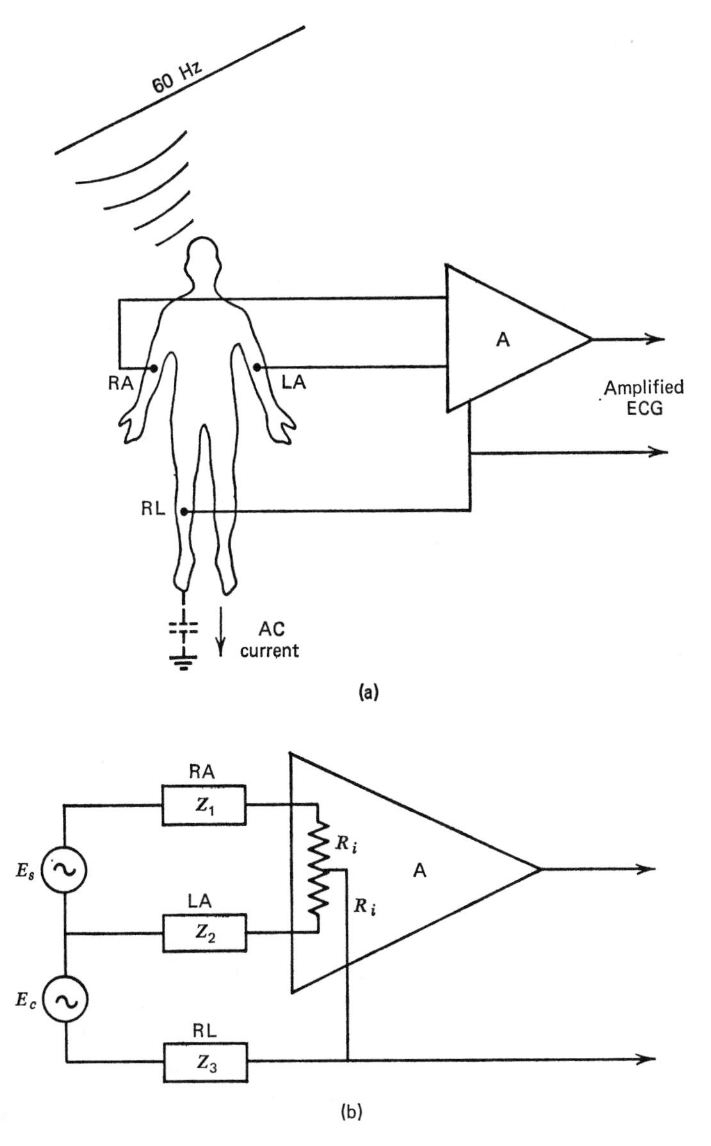

Figure 10.8. Simplified ECG measurement arrangement showing how line frequency interference can arise: (a) physical arrangement; (b) equivalent circuit used in calculating the effective common-mode rejection ratio of the system. The impedance of the right-leg electrode, Z_3, is neglected in the calculations.

the difference in electrode resistances together with the amplifier common-mode input resistance that determines the effective common-mode rejection of the system.

It can be seen from the figure that the interfering signal gives rise to a differential input signal equal to

$$E_i = E_c\left(\frac{R_i}{R_1 + R_i} - \frac{R_i}{R_2 + R_i}\right),$$

where $R_i/2$ is the amplifier common-mode input resistance. If the common-mode rejection ratio of the amplifier is J, then the total equivalent differential input signal arising from E_c is simply the sum of E_i plus E_c/J. If $R_i \gg R_1, R_2$, this sum can be expressed as

$$E_i' \simeq \frac{E_c(R_2 - R_1)}{R_i} + \frac{E_c}{J}.$$

Hence, the effective common-mode rejection ratio J' of the amplification system given by

$$\frac{1}{J'} = \frac{1}{J} + \frac{R_2 - R_1}{R_i}.$$

It therefore follows that the susceptibility of a differential amplifier to common-mode signals is degraded by the difference in electrode impedances. For example, if $R_i = 10$ MΩ, $J = 1 \times 10^5$ (100 dB) and the electrode resistances are 10 kΩ with a maximum of 20% variation between electrodes ($R_2 - R_1 =$ 2 kΩ), the effective common-mode rejection ratio is 5×10^3 under worst-case conditions.

An additional aspect of electrode impedance imbalance arises when the "augmented" ECG lead arrangement is used without buffer amplifiers. Shown in Figure 10.9(a) is the electrode and averaging resistor configuration for the AVR lead measurement. The purpose of resistors R is to obtain a potential equal to the average $(V_{LL} + V_{LA})/2$, where V_{LL} and V_{LA} are defined in Figure 10.9(b). Thus, ideally the potential difference presented to the amplifier should be equal to $(V_{LL} + V_{LA})/2 - V_{RA}$. This will only be achieved if the impedance imbalance between the left-leg and left-arm electrodes is small compared to R and the amplifier differential input impedance is considerably greater than $R/2$. These conditions can be expressed by

$$\big|\,|Z_{LA}| - |Z_{LL}|\,\big|_{max} \ll \frac{R}{2} \ll Z_{in}.$$

The low values of averaging resistors used in the past (5–50 kΩ) are inconsistent with accurate augmented lead measurements using conventional ECG electrodes [17, 18b, 19]. A simple, although more expensive, solution

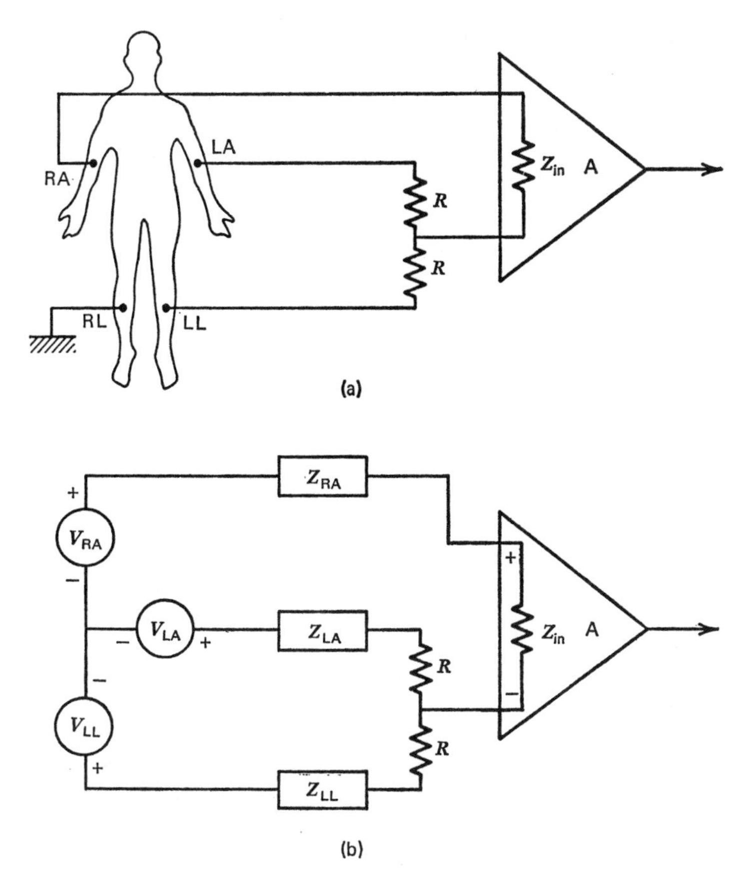

Figure 10.9. Augmented ECG lead arrangement: (a) circuit for AVR measurement; (b) equivalent circuit representation.

to this problem is to use buffer amplifiers connected directly to the electrodes and perform the summation at the amplifier outputs.

The above discussion underscores the desirability of using low-impedance electrodes with their correspondingly smaller differential impedance. Furthermore, an amplifier should be used whose differential and common-mode input impedances are large enough to avoid loading effects and which enable a sufficiently large effective common-mode rejection ratio to be obtained.

It is important to note that with surface electrodes a large, and sometimes dominant, resistance can arise from the outer dry layers of the skin. For example, metal plate electrodes when placed in contact with dry skin may initially show impedances of 50 kΩ or greater, with considerable variability between subjects. Depending on the electrode site, perspiration may develop under the electrode, causing electrolytic communication between the metal and underlying body fluids with a considerable drop in impedance. To establish a reliable low-impedance contact, an electrode jelly or paste is normally used that consists of a proprietary mixture of various compounds together with sodium chloride. Essentially, the medium is a fairly low resistivity electrolyte that permeates the outer horny layers, thereby providing effective electrical contact between the electrode and underlying body fluids.

The resistivity of commercially available pastes and jellies generally lies in the range 5–400 Ω-cm [1, 17, 20, 21]. Assuming a contact area of 1 cm^2 and an effective electrolyte thickness of 1 mm, the series resistance for a 400 Ω-cm jelly is only 40 Ω. Hence, as suggested by the work of Lewes [21], the electrode-jelly resistivity is not normally significant; of greater importance is the ease with which it can be removed, freedom from any adverse skin reactions, and ability to remain effective over long periods of time.

An alternative method for decreasing the effect of the horny layer makes use of an electrode with a large number of fine metal points that painlessly pierce the outer skin layer to achieve contact with the tissue fluids. A stainless-steel electrode of this type with approximately 1000 points has been described by Lewes [22], who reports that the multipoint electrode exhibits roughly the same impedance as a conventional metal plate electrode of the same area with an electrolyte jelly or paste. The primary advantage of this electrode is its ability to establish immediately a low-impedance contact without requiring any electrode paste, thereby enabling ECG recordings to be made with essentially no time lost for skin preparation and cleanup.

The properties of bare metal electrodes for ECG measurements were recently examined by Bergey et al. [23], who concluded that stainless-steel electrodes exhibited the best stability and freedom from motion artifacts. The authors suggested that the fairly high electrode impedances ($\sim$ 50 kΩ for a 4-cm^2 stainless-steel electrode) required special precautions to avoid electrostatic and magnetic interference. In fact, they used a buffer amplifier mounted directly on the electrode with a surrounding electrostatic shield.

Geddes et al. [24a] have measured the properties of dry silver electrodes 1.7 cm in diameter attached to subjects for electro-oculogram (EOG) measurements. They found that a pair of such electrodes when attached by light compression exhibited an initial total circuit resistance in the range 0.5–5 MΩ, depending on the subject. The resistance decreased with time, dropping to about 0.1 of its initial value in an average time of 3.3 min. With a junction-gate FET source follower mounted in the electrode holder, these electrodes proved satisfactory for EOG measurements and, in particular, for determining the linearity of the horizontal component of the EOG [24b].

Another form of dry electrode of particular interest is the spray-on electrode described by Roman [25]. Essentially, this electrode consists of a 0.004-in silver-plated wire attached to the prepared skin surface by spraying on a mixture containing a conductive adhesive and silver powder. The assembly is then coated with an insulating cement. Developed primarily for aerospace monitoring, the electrode can be attached in 20 sec (including skin preparation) and has been found to be particularly suitable for ECG recording from exercising subjects.

The impedance characteristics for a variety of electrodes measured while attached to a subject are shown in Figure 10.10 [20]. Over the normal range of interest for ECG or EEG recording the impedance magnitude remains

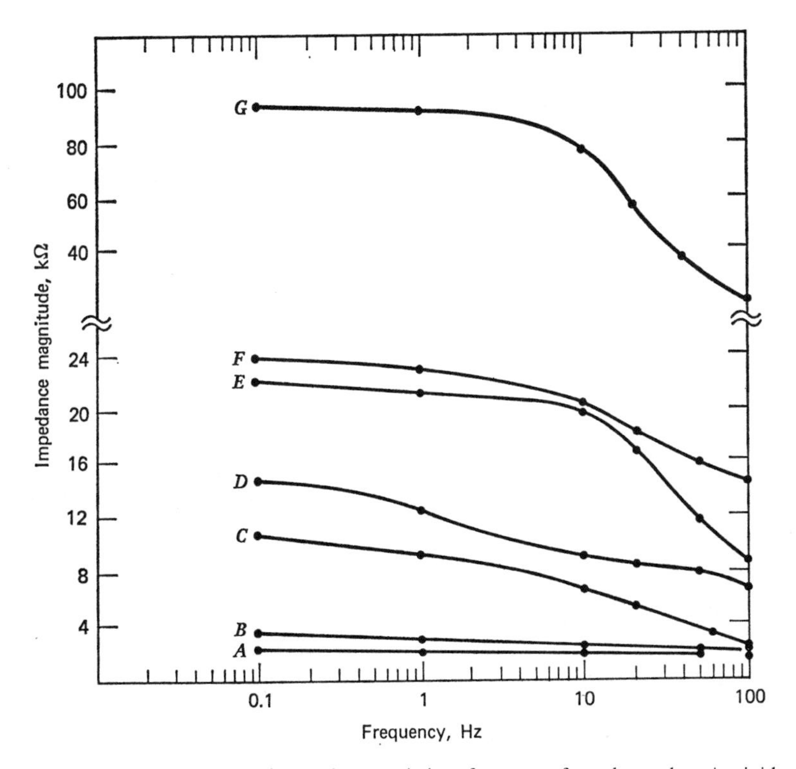

Figure 10.10. Measured impedance characteristics of some surface electrodes: A, rigid-cup self-adhesive electrode (Boter et al., *Med. Biolog. Eng.* **4**, 91 [1966]); B, Sanborn metal plate electrode with jelly; C, Newmark metal plate electrode used with conducting plastic; D, Hiller Ltd., multipoint electrode used dry; E, Smith and Nephew, Ltd., self-adhesive multipoint chest electrode used with jelly; F, self-adhesive gauze electrode (Drachard Ltd.) used with jelly; G, spray-on chest electrode [25] (redrawn, with permission, from D. W. Hill, and R. S. Khandpur, *World Med Instrumentation*, **7**, 12–22, May 1969).

fairly constant, indicating that the reactive impedance is significantly smaller than the resistive component. At somewhat higher frequencies the impedance starts to fall and the electrode starts to behave more like the classical metal–electrolyte electrode described in the last section.

A somewhat more informative impedance graph, consisting of the reactance plotted against resistance for various frequencies [26], is shown in Figure 10.11. The two electrodes, a 15-mm suction-cup electrode and a Beckmann

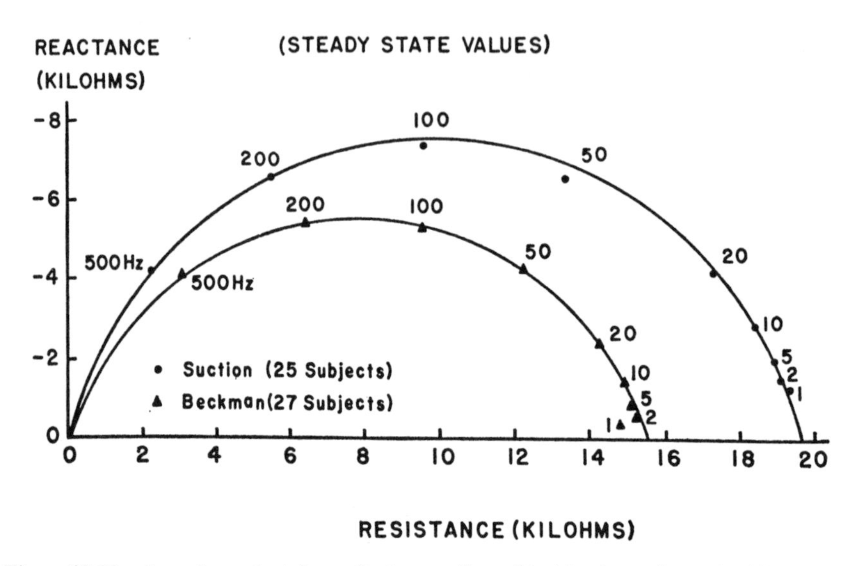

Figure 10.11. Impedance loci for a Beckman silver chloride electrode used with paste, and a 15-mm suction-cup electrode used with paste. The mean steady-state (30 min) values are shown for the number of subjects indicated (reproduced, with permission, from J. J. Almasi and O. H. Schmitt, *Ann. N.Y. Acad. Sci.*, **170**, 509–519, 1970).

sintered silver chloride electrode, were both used with electrode paste. As with most electrodes, following attachment to the subject, the impedance initially falls but eventually reaches a steady state. The measurements used were the steady-state values obtained after approximately 30 min. It will be noted from the graph that at low frequencies the resistive component is dominant for both types of electrode.

Before turning to the stability and noise aspects of surface electrodes some mention should be made of the work reported by Almasi and Schmitt [26] concerning the variation of ECG electrode impedance between subjects and with body location. From the measurements on 25 subjects they predict that over the frequency range 1–10 Hz, the impedance magnitude for approxi-

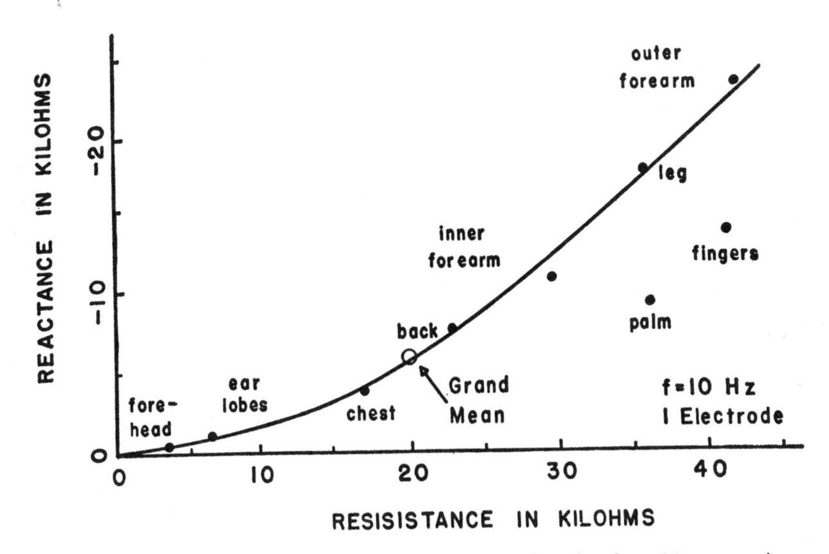

Figure 10.12. Components of impedance related to body location for a 15-mm suction-cup electrode used with paste. Each measurement was made 2 min after applying the electrode. Each point on the graph is the geometric mean over 20 subjects (reproduced, with permission from J. J. Almasi and O. H. Schmitt, *Ann. N.Y. Acad. Sci.*, **170**, 509–519, 1970).

mately 2% of the population may exceed 0.1 MΩ. Furthermore, as illustrated in Figure 10.12, considerable variation with body location was observed. The authors recommend that in order to avoid significant amplifier loading errors with those subjects that exhibit abnormally large electrode impedances, the amplifier input impedance should be 20 MΩ or greater. It should also be noted that for those ECG lead selections that use summing resistors (augmented leads), the use of unity gain buffer amplifiers prior to the summation is almost essential if distortion is to be avoided.

10.2.2 Noise and Drift in Macroelectrodes

As with all transducers, noise and drift set certain fundamental limits to the performance that can be achieved with bioelectrodes. Whether or not these limits are of significance depends of course on the type of measurement involved. For example, ECG measurements on a stationary subject normally pose no problems, since the electrode noise level is roughly two orders of magnitude less than the R-wave amplitude. However, when the subject is active, depending on the degree of activity, considerable interference may arise not only from EMG activity but also as a result of electrode noise produced by the mechanical motion of the electrode assembly. Generally, EMG interference can be reduced by placing the electrodes on the chest rather than on the limbs. Furthermore, the effects of mechanical movement can be reduced by using a lightweight electrode of the proper design.

The primary reason for movement artifact with a metal plate electrode is the disturbance of the electrical double layer at the electrolyte–metal interface. By using a recessed electrode in which the metal (usually Ag–AgCl) is separated from the skin by an appreciable thickness of electrolyte, most of the noise can be eliminated. For an electrode of this type, movement of the skin with respect to the electrode disturbs only the electrolyte-paste–skin interface leaving the paste–metal contact unaffected.

A considerable variety of recessed electrodes of both the disposable and reusable varieties have been described in the literature [1, 27], and a number of these are commercially available. They generally use either a chlorided silver disk (or wire) or a silver–silver chloride pellet formed by compression of silver and silver chloride powders and bonded to a silver wire. Such electrodes can exhibit excellent electrical stability and freedom from movement artifact. A further feature, of special importance for those measurements demanding either a dc or very low frequency response, is the small drift rate and offset potential between pairs of carefully prepared (and perhaps selected) electrodes. Offsets of less than 1 mV and drift rates of less than 0.1. mV/h have been reported [28, 29].

With most ECG-type electrodes offsets of several tens of millivolts (and occasionally more than 100 mV) and drift rates of around 20 mV/h are often observed [27, 30]. Even though the low-frequency cutoff (3-dB point) of ECG amplifiers is about 0.05 Hz, it can be readily shown that such drift rates introduce only about 20 μV of baseline change. The situation is rather different for EEG recording, where the signals are in the 50-μV range. If the same low-frequency cutoff is retained, the baseline drift becomes comparable to the signal. Fortunately, it happens that for most EEG measurements a cutoff of 0·5 Hz is acceptable and this, when employed, greatly attenuates the effect of electrode drift.

Unfortunately, there appears to be a lack of any systematic investigation of surface electrode noise and the manner in which it depends on surface preparation and electrode design. But is seems reasonable to expect that, in common with most electronic devices, surface electrodes should exhibit a low-frequency $1/f$-noise characteristic. Strong [27] has pointed out that large differences in the peak–peak electrode noise signals can occur in practice. Some electrodes exhibit noise in excess of 50 μV, while for others the noise may be in the fractional microvolt range. Strong concludes that reusable electrode types generally exhibit lower noise than the disposable types.

In concluding this subsection, some mention should be made of the impedance characteristics of recessed electrodes. For Ag–AgCl electrodes the impedance is a function of the chloride-layer thickness [1]. As the thickness increases, the impedance initially falls, reaches a minimum, and then increases. The initial decrease can be explained on the basis of the changed charge-transport processes, while the subsequent increase appears to be a direct

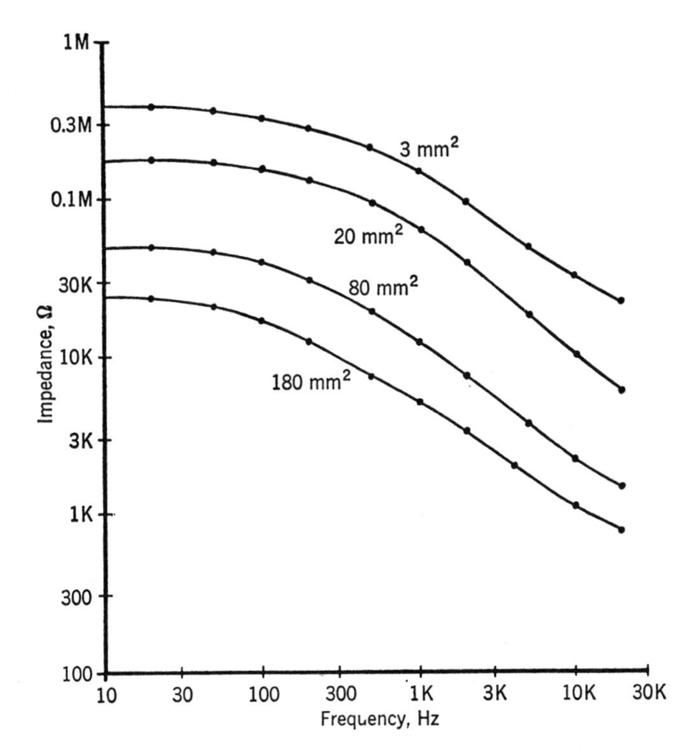

Figure 10.13. Impedance characteristics of silver disc recessed electrodes of various areas (reproduced, with permission, from L. A. Geddes, L. E. Baker and A. G. Moore, *J. Electrocardiology*, **1**, 51–56, 1968).

result of the high resistivity of silver chloride ($\sim 10^5$ Ω-cm). The impedance characteristics of silver-disk recessed electrodes of various areas have been studied by Geddes et al. [31]. It can be seen from Figure 10.13 that the impedance decreases as the area increases. Theoretically, $|Z|$ should be inversely proportional to the area; in practice, because the current density is not entirely one-dimensional, this may only be approximately true.

10.2.3 Properties of Needle and Wire Electrodes [1]

Hypodermic-needle electrodes inserted subcutaneously are frequently used as a convenient and reliable means for obtaining ECG recordings from animals. They are also used for human ECG recording during surgery as well as for emergency situations when speed of electrode application is of paramount importance. A further important application is in clinical and research electromyography, where one or more needle electrodes may be inserted into a muscle to obtain a fairly localized recording of the EMG.

Examples of needle electrodes are illustrated in Figure 10.14. For monopolar EMG recording, a hypodermic needle with an insulated wire (perhaps

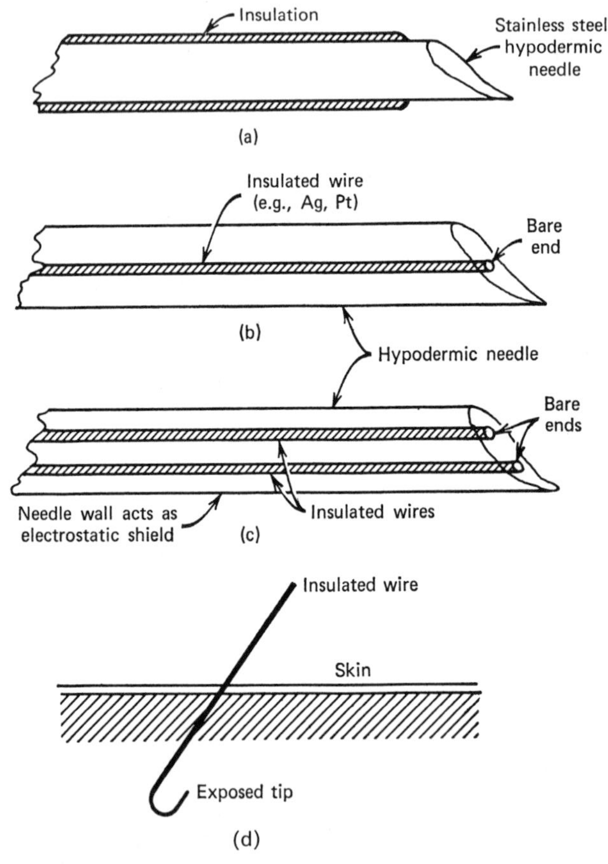

Figure 10.14. Examples of needle and wire electrodes. (a) simple insulated needle electrode; (b) unipolar EMG electrode; (c) bipolar electrode; and (d) hook-type insulated wire electrode.

Ag or Pt) threaded through it and exposed at the end [Figure 10.14(b)] is both simple to insert and reliable. A large-area surface electrode on the skin provides a suitable indifferent reference. The bipolar (differential) needle electrode shown in (c) enables localized EMG recordings to be made. As with the monopolar electrode, the needle wall acts as an electrostatic shield, thereby considerably reducing the susceptibility to 60-Hz line frequency interference. Furthermore, if the inner wires of the bipolar electrode are twisted, electromagnetic interference can be almost eliminated.

Fine wires, insulated except at the tips, are also used for EMG measurements. Such an electrode can be inserted so that the end forms a hook, thereby preventing the electrode from working its way out during movements [Fig. 10.14(d)]. Methods for inserting such electrodes by means of a hypodermic needle have been described by Scott [32] and Parker [33].

Of considerable importance are the impedance characteristics of the above-mentioned electrodes. Generally, it is found that the impedance falls off with increasing frequency, roughly in a $1/f^m$ manner. The nonplanar geometry of most electrodes does not always result in a simple proportional relationship between impedance and surface area. The results reported by Geddes [1] shown in Figure 10.15 give an approximate idea of the impedance dependence

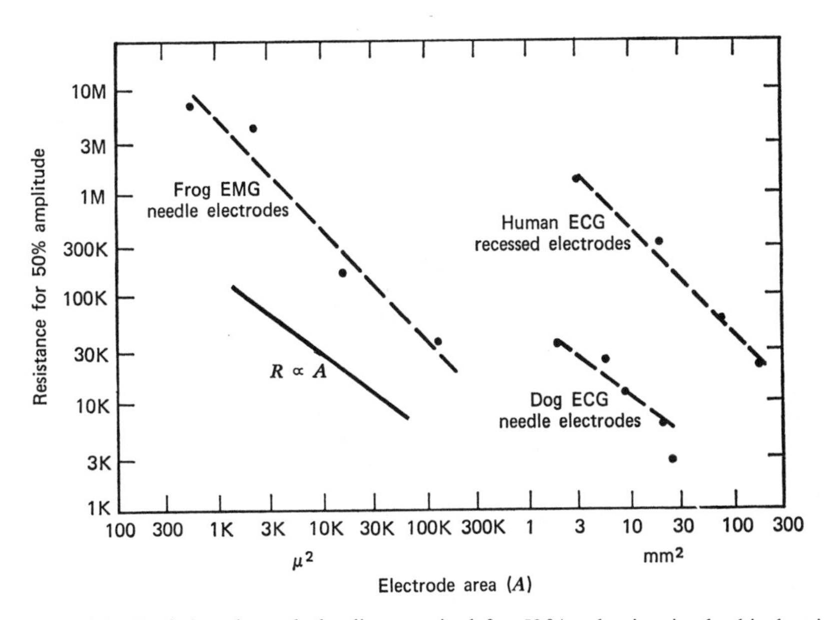

Figure 10.15. Resistive electrode loading required for 50% reduction in the bioelectric signal amplitude versus electrode area (reproduced, with permission, from L. A. Geddes, "*Electrodes and the Measurement of Bioelectric Events*", Wiley, New York, 1972).

on area. The graph is a plot of the resistive loading required to effect a 50% reduction in the bioelectric signal amplitude versus electrode area. As expected, the recessed surface ECG electrode displays a considerably higher impedance than a needle electrode of the same surface area. It is also of interest to note that for all three electrode types the resistance for a 50% amplitude reduction is roughly proportional to the surface area.

10.2.4 Contactless Electrodes

The measurement of a biopotential does not necessarily require that contact be made to the regions between which the potential difference occurs. A class of electrode that enables an ac potential to be recorded by capacitive coupling was first described by Richardson [34, 35] in 1967. The current that flows in such an electrode system involves the displacement rather than the transport of charge around the circuit.

An ECG electrode of the type described by Richardson is illustrated in Figure 10.16. It consists of a metal with a thin insulating layer on one side that is in intimate contact with the skin. In principle, no physical contact is necessary, since a thin air layer could still provide sufficient capacitive coupling, but in practice, a contact is necessary to eliminate artifacts arising from variations in the skin–electrode separation. Also shown in Figure 10.16 is a circuit model consisting of two series capacitors: one representing the

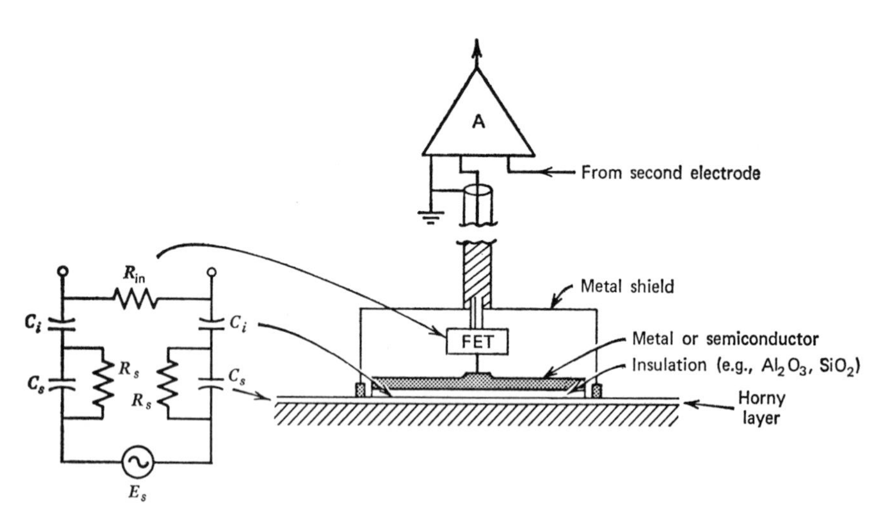

Figure 10.16. Contactless electrode and the circuit model for two such electrodes in intimate contact with skin.

insulator–electrode capacitance and the other representing the equivalent capacitance of the horny layer. In parallel with this second capacitor is a resistance corresponding to the leakage through the horny layer. Evidently, for a moist surface, this resistance will be small compared to the capacitive reactance over the frequency range of interest.

The first electrode described by Richardson used a disk of aluminum that was anodized so as to form thin a layer of Al_2O_3 on the surface. Aluminum oxide is a good insulator with a relative dielectric constant of approximately 10.0. Richardson's ECG electrodes had an area of 6 cm^2, a total capacitance of 6000 pF and a dc insulation resistance of greater than 4000 MΩ. To achieve an adequate low-frequency response for clinical ECG measurements (0.05 Hz), an input resistance of greater than 500 MΩ is required. Richardson et al. achieved this with a field-effect transistor source follower stage mounted within the electrode housing. By using a metal shield around the electrode, electrostatic interference, which is so troublesome in high-impedance circuits, was virtually eliminated.

In a later paper Richardson et al. [36] reported that the anodized aluminium electrodes suffered from noise and instability problems that probably arose from chloride absorption from the skin followed by corrosion. Anodized tantalum electrodes were found to be considerably superior in this regard. Comparative tests with tantalum electrodes against standard ECG paste electrodes indicated that high quality ECG records can be obtained that are essentially free from 60-Hz interference.

An alternative form of contactless electrode, making use of standard silicon integrated-circuit technology, has been described by Wolfson and Neuman [37a]. It consisted of low resistivity n-type Si with a 2000-Å thermally grown SiO_2 layer covering a 0.25-cm^2 area and having a capacitance of 4000 pF.

Much higher capacitances can be obtained using materials such as $BaTiO_3$ ($\varepsilon_r \simeq 1500$), TiO_2 ($\varepsilon_r \simeq 100$), and Ta_2O_5 ($\varepsilon_r \simeq 25$). David and Portnoy [37b] used RF-sputtered films of these materials on highly polished n-type Si slices to form ECG electrodes. Using a standard operational amplifier with a 100-MΩ input leakage resistor, they demonstrated that a cutoff frequency of less than 0.05 Hz could easily be achieved with an electrode area of about 1 cm^2.

The advantages of barium titanate ($BaTiO_3$) ceramic for EEG recording by capacitive coupling have been discussed by Matsuo et al. [37c]. They used a $BaTiO_3$ disk (9 mm in diameter and 0.25 mm thick) coated on one side with silver. The electrode, whose capacitance was 0.02 μF, was supported in a holder that also contained a junction-gate FET source follower. For EEG measurements an electrode paste was used to insure stable capacitive coupling to the skin; however, the authors suggest that for ECG measurements, the much larger signal levels make this unnecessary. Among the advantages claimed for this electrode are stable noise characteristics; the absence of any corrosive effects; and, by virtue of the insulation properties, protection of the patient from any shock hazard.

10.3 MICROELECTRODES

Electrodes for the measurement of potentials at the cellular level must meet some rather exacting requirements. For an electrode to measure accurately an intracellular potential it is evident that penetration of the cell membrane by the electrode must not disturb the normal intra- or extracellular processes to any significant extent. Specifically, the electrode must not poison the cell, it must not allow the cytoplasm to leak out, and it must not remove or inject appreciable numbers of ions and thereby disturb the intracellular concentrations. In extracellular recording, several authors [38, 39] have emphasized the importance of the taper and tip geometry and have pointed out that in the case of brain depth measurements, too large a taper angle can result in measurements that lack consistency. It has also been pointed out that a relatively long active tip area may be required to measure properly the spike potentials.

Intra- and extracellular potentials are measured with either glass or metal microelectrodes. Glass microelectrodes consist of a fine capillary drawn down to a diameter of around 1 μm and filled with a highly conductive solution (e.g., 3M KCl). An equilibrium is established between the filling solution and the intra- or extracellular fluid, enabling a reasonably accurate estimate to be made of the resting potential. On the other hand, no such well-defined equilibrium is established with metal microelectrodes, so that their primary application is for measuring action potentials and other dynamic events. That the electrical properties of the two microelectrode types differ considerably will become evident from the detailed description presented below.

10.3.1 Metal Microelectrodes

Structure. A metal wire formed to a fine tip at one end and insulated except for the tip region is a commonly used form of microelectrode [see Figure 10.17(a) and (d)]. Alternative forms consist of a glass micropipette filled with a metal [40] [Figure 10.17(b)], a glass rod drawn to a fine tip and coated with a thin metallic layer and outer insulation [41a] [Figure 10.17(c)] and a photoengraved Si–SiO_2 structure incorporating a gold-plated film at the tip [41b, 41c] [Figure 10.17(e)].

One of the most difficult aspects of metal microelectrode fabrication is that of achieving a specific geometrical configuration with good reproducibility.

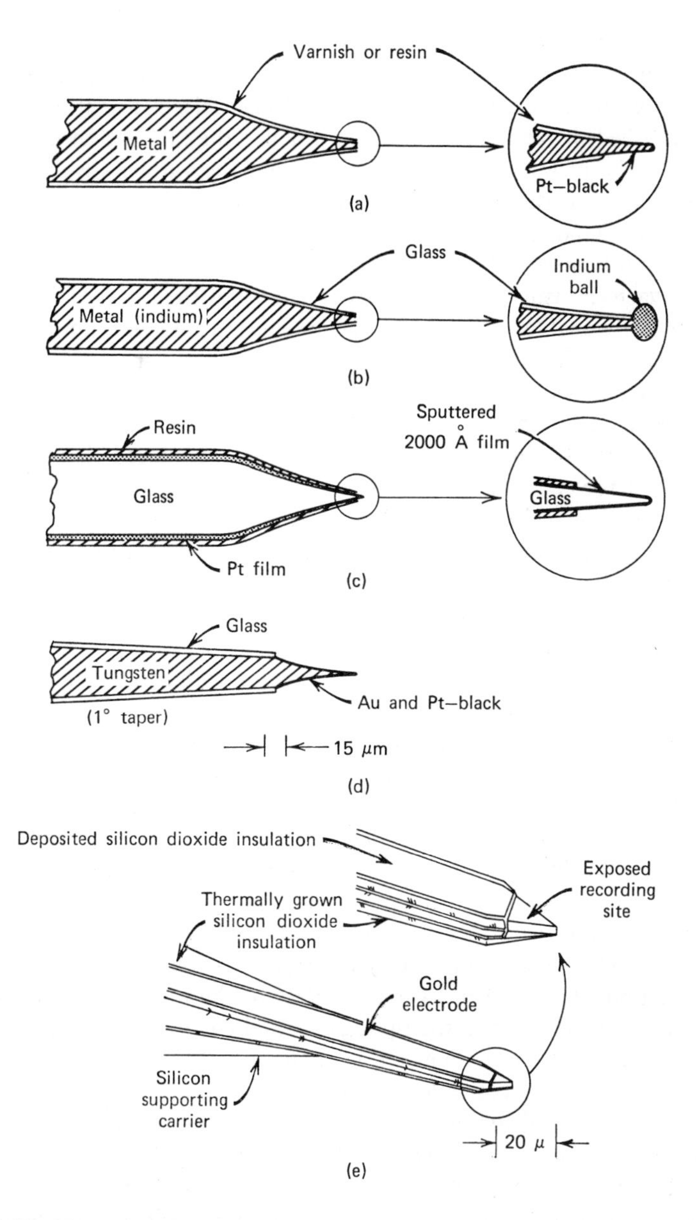

Figure 10.17. Examples of metal microelectrodes: (a) varnish- or resin-insulated etched metal wire electrode; (b) indium-filled glass micropipette; (c) platinum-sputtered and resin-insulated glass electrode; (d) glass-insulated etched tungsten wire electrode [39]; and (e) gold-plated microelectrode fabricated on Si–SiO_2 using photoetching techniques (reproduced, with permission, from A. Starr, K. D. Wise, and J. Csongradi, *IEEE Trans. Biomed. Eng.*, **BME-20**, 291–293, July 1973).

A large part of this problem arises with the insulation layer, in particular with the difficulty of leaving uncovered a well-defined length of the tip. Even though detailed descriptions of metal-microelectrode fabrication have been published, it remains true that in practice the fabrication is somewhat of an art. The metal-filled microelectrode and the varnish-insulated microelectrode have received plenty of attention in the various reviews [1, 38, 40]. On the other hand, the glass-insulated metal-wire electrode has not received the attention it merits. The durability of the glass insulation in comparison with the varnish insulation and the extra degree of rigidity that it imparts to the metal wire enables microelectrodes to be fabricated with a fine taper and excellent mechanical properties. Such electrodes are especially valuable in brain depth studies.

The first description of a glass-insulated metal-wire electrode appears to be that of Wilska [42] in 1940. However, it should be noted that heat-pulled platinum microelectrodes were described by Taylor [43] some 15 years before. The heat-pulling technique involves placing a comparatively large gauge platinum wire in a quartz capillary and pulling the combination (at a temperature high enough to soften the quartz) to a fine tip. This technique differs from Wilska's method in that the latter involves a preformed metal tip and the glass is collapsed onto the metal.

For an electrode to have a long exposed region with a fine tip and a gradual taper, it is essential that the wire used have considerable mechanical rigidity. Platinum–iridium seems to be fairly satisfactory in this regard. Following the work of Wolbarsht et al. [44] in 1960 and that of Ballintijn [45a] in 1961, Guld [45b] made a careful and methodical study of the factors governing electrode shape and arrived at a method of fabrication that resulted in improved reproducibility. More recently, a very comprehensive account of the fabrication, use, and electrical and mechanical properties of glass-insulated platinum–iridium electrodes has been published by Salcman et al. [46]. These electrodes were fabricated by inserting a pre-etched Pt–Ir wire into a glass micropipette and then fusing the glass to the wire using a microforge. Removal of the glass from the tip region resulted in a recording area consisting of a cone, 5 μm in diameter at the tip and 20 μm long.

Tungsten or tungsten carbide is particularly suited for applications demanding a high mechanical strength and durability. The first description of a glass-coated tungsten microelectrode appears to be that of Baldwin et al. [47] in 1965. More recently, Merrill and Ainsworth [39] described in some detail the technique for making such electrodes in a reproducible manner. A brief summary of the method and experimental results is given below.

The first stage in the fabrication consists of shaping a 127-μm straightened tungsten wire by two etching steps. In the first, the wire is etched electrolytically so as to produce a gradual taper of 1–2°, along an 8-mm length. A second electrolytic etch of the exposed tip region is performed to increase the angle

[Figure 10.17(d)] and thereby improve its mechanical strength. The next stage in the fabrication consists of collapsing a borosilicate glass capillary onto the wire by placing the combination in a horizontal glass micropipette puller. Such a device heats the glass over a small region and applies a well-defined tension at the same time. It results in a thin glass layer covering the entire metal wire. Removing the glass from the tip region in a controlled manner was achieved by inserting the tip into a bead of molten glass, allowing the combination to cool, and then withdrawing the electrode. A clean fracture is produced at the junction with the bead, and, since the metal contracts more than the glass, the bare tip can be withdrawn without damage. By this means from 2 μm to more than 100 μm can be exposed in a well-controlled manner. The final stage in the fabrication consists of plating the tip with platinum black to achieve a low impedance. It appears that platinum black does not adhere particularly well to tungsten but that it adheres well to gold. Consequently the solution to this problem is to electrolytically coat the tungsten with gold followed by platinum black. As illustrated in Figure 10.18 the platinum-black layer reduces the electrode impedance by more than an order of magnitude compared to bare tungsten.

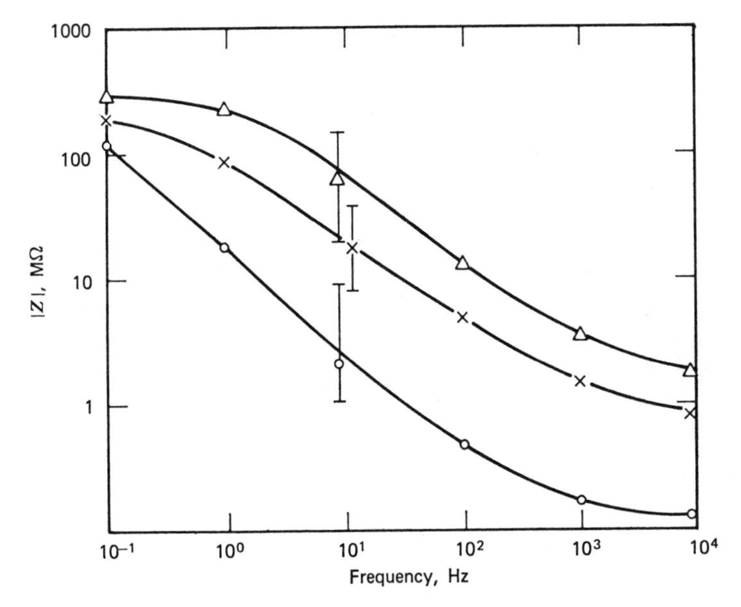

Figure 10.18. Impedance characteristics of electropointed tungsten microelectrodes: Δ, unplated; χ, plated with bright Pt; o, plated with Pt-black. Dimensions of the exposed conical tip before plating were as follows: length, 20 μm; diameter, 6 μm. The plating thicknesses were between 1 and 2 μm. Bars at 10Hz indicate the range of impedance values enocuntered with electrodes of the same nominal dimensions (reproduced, with permission, from E. G. Merrill, and A. Ainsworth, *Med. Biolog. Engng.*, **10**, 662–671, Sept. 1971).

Electrical Characteristics [38]. An insulated metal microelectrode immersed in a fluid and penetrating a cell membrane together with a small-signal circuit model are illustrated in Figure 10.19. The resistance R_s of this model (sometimes called the *spreading resistance*) arises from the electrolyte resistance in the immediate vicinity of the metal tip. The three-dimensional nature of the current flow makes it difficult to calculate the value of this resistance exactly. A rough estimate can be made by considering the tip region to be represented by a conducting sphere having a radius equal to that of the tip.

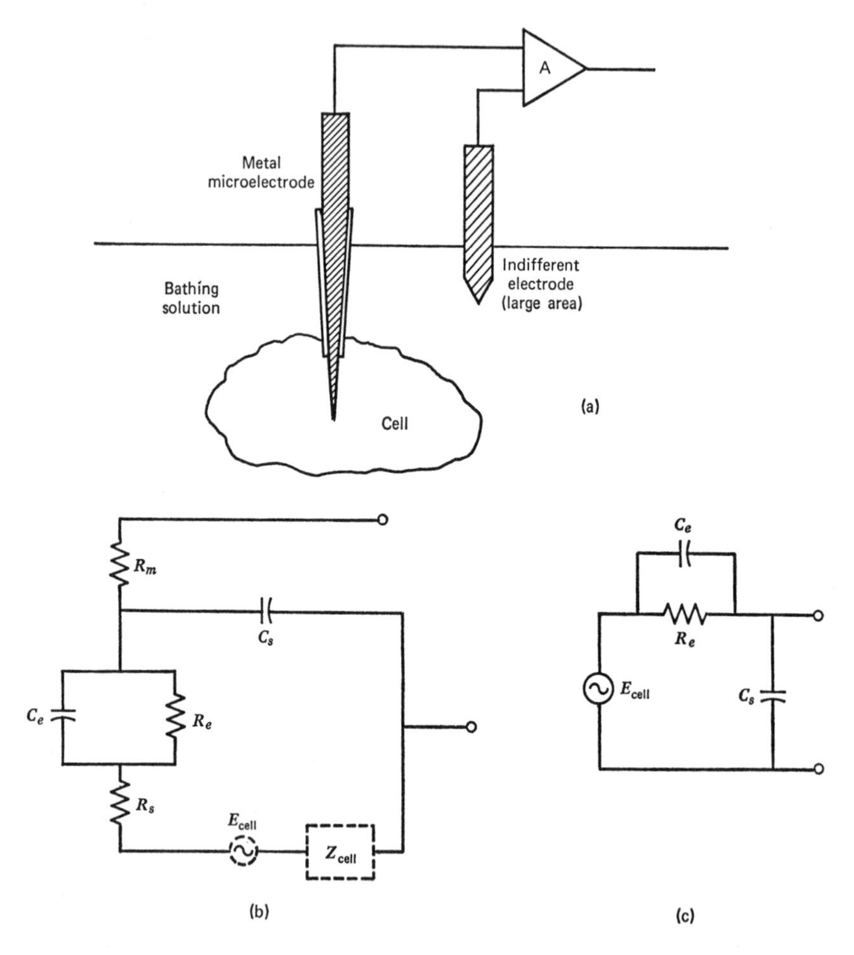

Figure 10.19. Circuit model of a metal microelectrode measurement system: (a) physical arrangement for intracellular measurement; (b) circuit model, ignoring the indifferent electrode; and (c) approximate circuit model.

By integration, it can be readily shown that the resistance of a sphere of radius r immersed in an infinite medium of resistivity ρ is given by

$$R_s = \frac{\rho}{4\pi r}.$$

For a 0.5-μm-radius tip immersed in physiological saline ($\rho = 72\ \Omega$-cm), this equation yields a spreading resistance of 120 kΩ. Since most metal microelectrodes have a surface area considerably greater than that of a 0.5-μm sphere, this value should perhaps be taken as an upper bound. Except at very high frequencies, R_s is generally very small compared to the magnitude of the metal–electrolyte impedance. The same is also true of R_m, the bulk resistance of the metal. Even for the sputtered platinum film on glass electrode illustrated in Figure 10.17(c), R_m is less than 1 kΩ.

The three most important elements in the circuit model are the metal–electrolyte parallel components R_e and C_e, both of which are frequency-dependent, and the capacitance associated with the metal–insulation–electrolyte boundary. The latter, of course, depends on the depth to which the electrode is immersed.

It is generally found that both R_e and C_e decrease with increasing frequency in the manner described earlier in this chapter (i.e., a $1/\omega^m$ dependence). The impedance for a bright metal electrode may be in the range 100–1000 MΩ-μm^2 at 1 kHz. A decrease in the impedance by two orders of magnitude is often observed when the exposed tip is platinized. For example, a 10-μm^2 area electrode may exhibit a 100-MΩ impedance at 1 kHz, which perhaps decreases to 1 MΩ following the deposition of a Pt-black layer. Hence, in order that signal attenuation be avoided, for small area electrodes and electrodes that are deeply immersed (large C_s), plantinization may be essential.

The final element in the model—namely, C_s—shunts the signal to be measured and is therefore particularly significant for signals containing high-frequency components when the metal–electrolyte impedance is large. Its value depends on the permittivity and thickness of the insulator as well as on the depth of immersion. If the insulator thickness is a constant fraction of the electrode diameter at any point along the electrode length (i.e., the ratio of the outside radius R to the metal radius r is constant), the capacitance per unit depth of immersion will be simply the capacitance per unit length of two coaxial cylinders. This is given by

$$C_s = \frac{2\pi\varepsilon_0\,\varepsilon_r}{\ln(R/r)} \quad \text{(in F/m)}$$

$$= \frac{0.55\,\varepsilon_r}{\ln(R/r)} \quad \text{(in pF/cm)},$$

where ε_r is the relative dielectric constant. For most glasses and varnish-type insulation layers $\varepsilon_r \simeq 4.0$. Hence, if the insulation thickness is 10% of the radius (i.e., $R/r = 1.1$), then $C_s = 23$ pF/cm and the 1-kHz capacitive reactance is 7 MΩ/cm. Evidently, for a deeply immersed electrode of small tip area the shunting effect may seriously distort the high-frequency components of an action potential unless steps are taken to neutralize C_s. Negative capacitance amplifiers, as described in the next subsection, achieve this and thereby effect a very considerable improvement in the high-frequency response.

It was mentioned ealier that accurate measurement of cell resting potentials cannot be performed using metal microelectrodes [48]. It has been suggested by some authors that the reason for this is the very large resistance of metal microelectrodes under dc conditions, making amplifier input loading a serious problem. Although the dc resistance is large—perhaps 10^9 Ω—it is still fairly small compared to the input resistance of modern electrometer amplifiers, so that no real problem should arise from this aspect. The main reasons for the difficulty are the failure of the metal microelectrode to establish a well-defined equilibrium and the uncertainty concerning the electrode potential dependence on ionic concentration.

A further important aspect of metal microelectrodes, especially significant for measuring small amplitude (10-μV range) extracellular spike potentials, is their intrinsic noise characteristics. Although details of the noise generation mechanism are still incompletely understood, it is certain that the RMS noise cannot have a value less than that generated by a pure resistance equal to the real part of the electrode impedance. According to Nyquist's theorem, at a frequency f, the mean square noise voltage $\overline{\delta e^2}$ generated by random fluctuations in an impedance Z_e over an incremental bandwidth df centered about f is given by

$$\overline{\delta e^2} = 4kT\mathscr{R}(Z_e)\, df, \tag{16}$$

where k is Boltzmann's constant, T is the absolute temperature, and $\mathscr{R}(Z_e)$ is the real part of Z_e at the frequency f. By integrating Eq. (16) the total RMS noise voltage over a bandwidth extending from f_1 to f_2 can be found:

$$\begin{aligned} E_{\mathrm{RMS}} &= \sqrt{\int_{f_1}^{f_2} \overline{\delta e^2}} \\ &= \sqrt{4kT \int_{f_1}^{f_2} \mathscr{R}(Z_e)\, df}. \end{aligned} \tag{17}$$

For the simplest situation in which $\mathscr{R}(Z_e)$ is independent of frequency, Eq. (17) reduces to

$$E_{\mathrm{RMS}} = \sqrt{4kT\mathscr{R}(Z_e)(f_2 - f_1)}, \tag{18}$$

which is plotted in Figure 10.20.

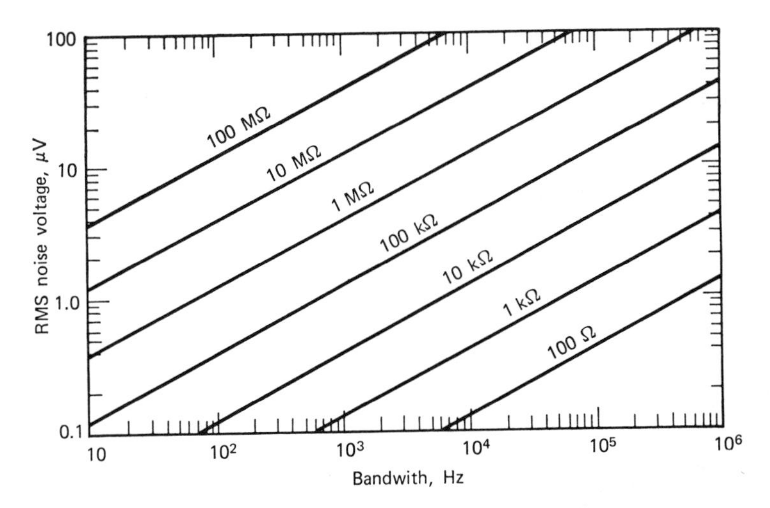

Figure 10.20. RMS noise voltage at 37°C generated by an ideal resistance, as a function of the measurement bandwidth.

For metal microelectrodes, $\mathscr{R}(Z_e)$ is generally found to vary as $1/f^m$, so that the narrow band RMS noise voltage decreases as $1/f^{m/2}$. For a bandwidth defined by the upper and lower cutoff frequencies f_2 and f_1, if $\mathscr{R}(Z_e) = R_0/f^m$ and $0 < m < 1$, it can easily be shown from Eq. (17) that the RMS noise voltage is given by

$$E_{\text{RMS}} = \sqrt{\frac{4kTR_0}{1-m}(f_1^{m-1} - f_2^{m-1})}. \tag{19}$$

Gestland et al. [48] have verified that Eq. (16) represents reasonably well the narrow-band noise characteristics of bright platinum microelectrodes immersed in physiological saline. By measuring the real part of Z_e and comparing it with that calculated from Eq. (16) using the measured value of the narrow-band noise, they found excellent agreement over the frequency range 10 Hz–50 kHz.

10.3.2 Glass Microelectrodes

Structure and Fabrication [1, 40]. For the measurement of both resting and action potentials within a cell, a glass microelectrode, heat-drawn from a capillary tube and filled with a highly conductive solution, is normally used. The structure is generally similar to that shown in the microphotograph of

Figure 10.21, where the nomenclature is also indicated. Typically the tip region has an outside diameter of less than 1 μm and may not be fully visible under the optical microscope. The scanning electron microscope with its very large depth of focus and superior resolution is especially suited for detailed examination of the tip structure. However, a thin conductive coating must be deposited over the surface to prevent charging of the glass surface by the electron beam. Figure 10.22, which shows the tip details for both large- and small-diameter electrodes, indicates that the wall thickness is approximately 10% of the outside diameter for electrode (a).

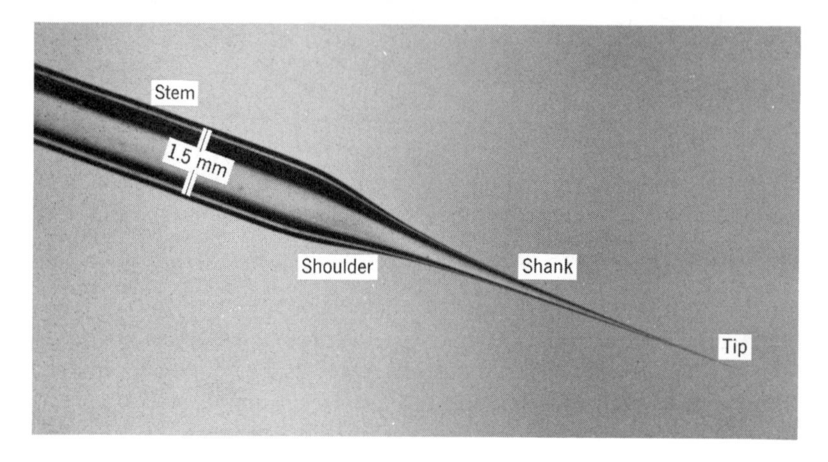

Figure 10.21. Photomicrograph of a typical glass microelectrode: the labels show the nomenclature for the various regions.

With a tip diameter of less than 1 μm, electrodes having consistent geometry can only be produced with the help of an automatic microelectrode puller. Such machines consist of an electrically controlled heater, often in the form of a platinum coil through which the glass capillary is inserted, and a means of applying tension. Most machines [1, 40] have a system for applying an initial tension and a greatly increased tension when the capillary softens. The increased tension, normally produced by means of a solenoid, causes the two halves of the capillary to be rapidly separated and thereby removed from the heat source. Electrodes with tip taper angles in the range 1–15° and diameters of less than 1 μm can be routinely and reproducibly fabricated by this means. Much smaller diameter tips can be produced through the use of solenoid-controlled air jets to produce very rapid cooling of the softened glass during the separation. Chowdhury [49] has described a puller of this type and has reported that electrodes with tip angles of about 11° and diameters down

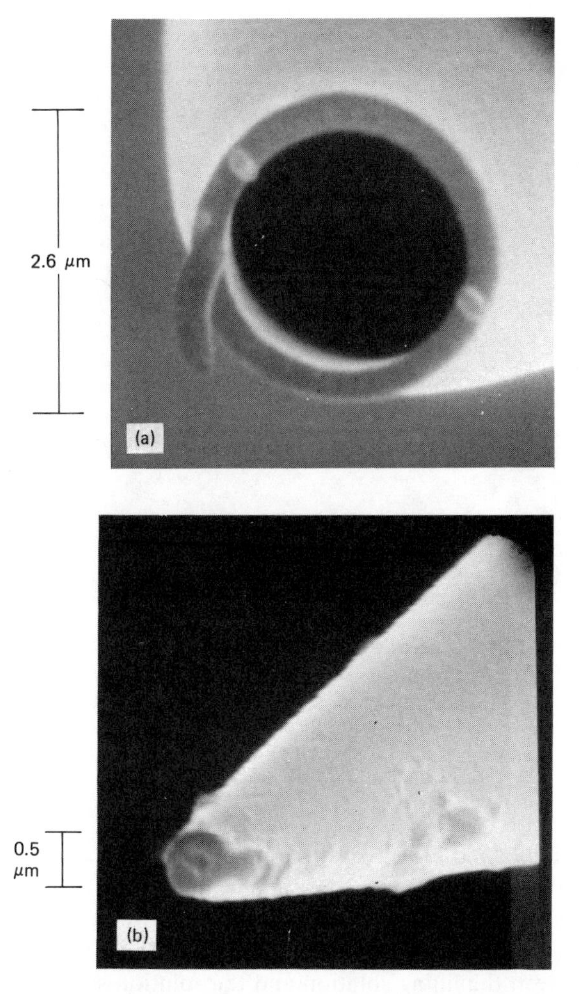

Figure 10.22. Scanning electron microscope picture of a microelectrode tip: (a) large diameter (~ 1 μm) at a beam angle of 82°; (b) small diameter at an angle of 79°. Since both pictures were taken at close to normal incidence, considerable distortion of their taper is apparent. Both electrodes were coated prior to examination with a 1000 Å Au Pd layer (beam energy, 20 keV).

to 500 Å can be fabricated with this technique. The comparatively large tip angle compared to the more conventional electrodes (~2°) insures that the electrode is not too fragile for practical use and its resistance is not excessively large. Such small-diameter electrodes have proved valuable in certain intracellular measurements where the trauma created by larger and blunter electrodes is significant. Such a situation arises, for example, in measuring the

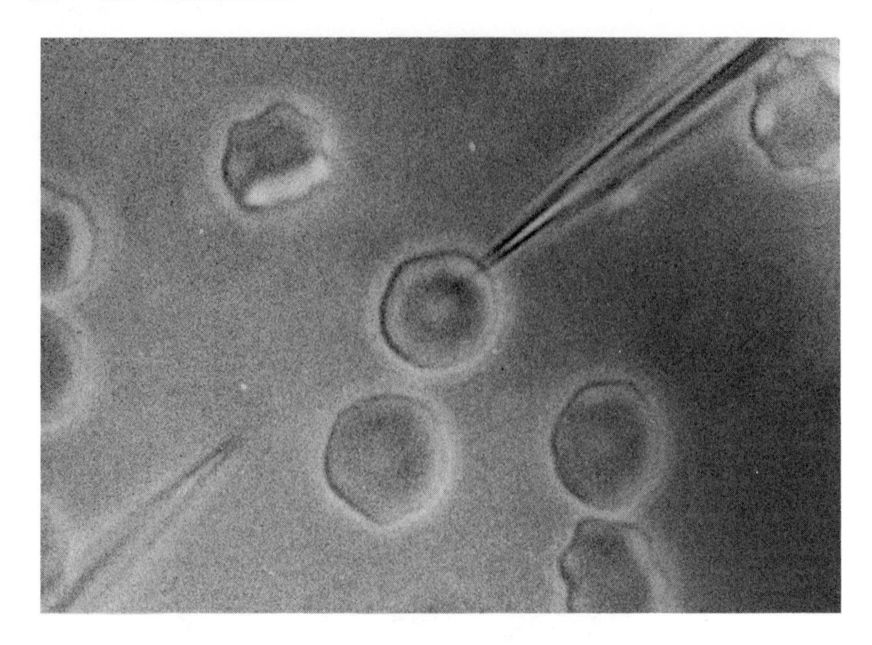

Figure 10.23. Photomicrograph showing a glass microelectrode of a ~ 0.2 μm tip diameter penetrating a red blood cell for the purpose of measuring the resting potential. The external reference electrode is also shown (reproduced, with permission, from A. W. L. Jay and A. C. Burton, *Biophysical J.*, **9**, 115–121, 1969).

resting potential of red blood cells (see Figure 10.23), where diameters of less than 0.25 μm are necessary to avoid significant error [50].

The choice of filling solution is governed primarily by the need to achieve a reasonably low electrode resistance and to insure that the liquid junction potential between the filling solution and the solution surrounding the tip is small. As discussed in Chapter 9, by using a concentrated electrolyte of a type that has nearly equal ionic mobilities, variations in the liquid junction potentials arising from variations in the test solution become small. Generally $3M$ KCl, which has a conductivity of 0.26 $(\Omega\text{-cm})^{-1}$ at 23°C, best meets the requirements. Filling the micropipette is no simple matter: the large surface tension effects that occur in the tip region, the very small flow rates through such a small diameter constriction, and the difficulty in excluding air bubbles, all contribute to the problem. A large variety of solutions have been proposed, some of which have been summarized by Geddes [1].

A problem arising from the use of a very concentrated filling solution is that of diffusion from the tip into a cell. When a $3M$-KCl-filled microelectrode is immersed into a much weaker solution of the same kind, there will, at the instant of immersion, be a very large concentration gradient, causing a rapid efflux of ions into the test solution. As time progresses, the efflux will reduce, eventually settling down to a quasi-steady-state condition in which there is a reduced concentration of ions in the tip region. The steady flow of ions into a cell may, unless the compensatory mechanisms are particularly effective, result in a significant increase in the intracellular concentration. Coombs et al. [51] have studied this problem in relation to motoneurones penetrated by electrodes having a minimum resistance of 5 MΩ. According to their calculations a 5-MΩ electrode filled with $3M$ KCl has a steady-state efflux of approximately 6×10^{-14} mole/sec when immersed in a $0.15M$ KCl solution and will establish in a motoneurone a steady-state Cl^- concentration that is twice the normal value. Such an increase causes a significant change in the inhibitory postsynaptic potential response. Although this example may not be typical for most intracellular measurements, it does underscore the need to use a small-diameter electrode and if possible a less-concentrated filling solution.

Electrical Properties. Figure 10.24 illustrates the penetration of a cell membrane by a glass microelectrode having an Ag–AgCl electrode in its stem to establish electrical contact with the filling solution. Also shown in the figure are two electrical circuit models of differing complexities, the elements of which will be considered in detail following a brief general discussion.

Perhaps the most obvious element in the model is the microelectrode resistance R that arises primarily from the bulk resistivity of the electrolyte in the tip region. Both the spreading resistance of the solution surrounding the tip and the impedance of the Ag–AgCl or other inner reference electrode can be neglected in comparison to R. The capacitance C across the glass wall between the filling and test solutions, depends on the depth to which the electrode is immersed. The resistance and capacitance together form a tapered R–C transmission line that, to a first order, can be approximated by the model shown in Figure 10.24(c).

In measuring the resting potential of a cell, careful consideration must be given to possible errors that might arise from changes in the various sources of dc potential in the model. Associated with the electrode tip are two potentials: the tip potential and the liquid junction potential, both of which are affected by the ion concentrations within and surrounding the tip. To measure the resting potential of a cell, a recording is made of the potential variation that occurs as the microelectrode tip is advanced through the membrane wall. Ideally, the change observed is equal to the resting potential; but in practice errors can result from changes in the tip and liquid junction potentials due to the differing ionic concentrations within and outside the cell. However, no such error results from the internal and external reference electrode potentials: it is only required that they remain stable during the period of penetration.

Tip and Liquid Junction Potentials. According to Schanne et al. [52] a typical glass microelectrode 0.5 μm in diameter made from Pyrex glass (type 7740) and filled with $3M$ KCl, when immersed 2 mm in a $0.1M$ KCl solution, exhibits a resistance of 10 MΩ, a capacitance of 2 pF, and a negative potential of 10 mV associated with the tip region. The potential cannot be explained on the basis of the liquid junction potential, which, for the solutions given

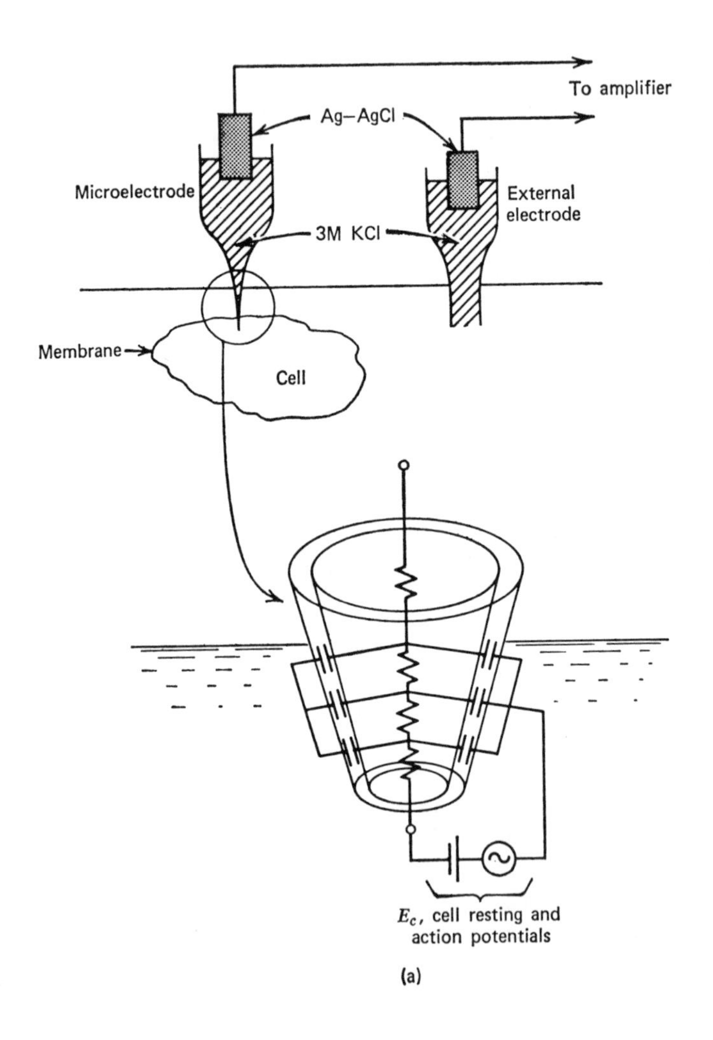

(a)

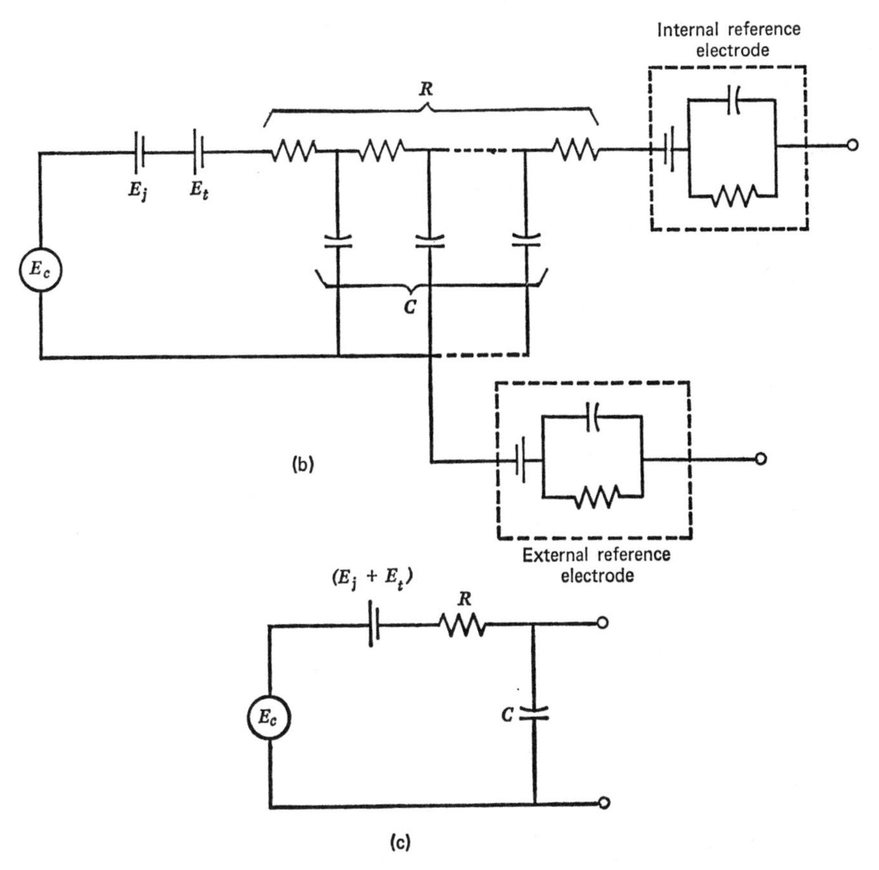

Figure 10.24. Circuit models of a glass microelectrode: (a) physical picture; (b) circuit model; and (c) simplified model.

above, would be less than 1 mV. It is found that the tip potential decreases with increasing tip diameter, increases as the resistivity of the solution surrounding the tip increases, depends on the type of glass used, and is correlated with the electrode resistance.

It seems likely that the tip potential arises from the formation of a hydrated glass layer (see Section 9.4.2) with its associated double layer on the inner tip surface [52–54]. It is known that hydrated glass layers behave as cation exchange membranes that generate, as discussed in Chapter 9, a Nernst potential [55]. It is also known that a hydrated glass has a resistivity many orders of magnitude less than pure glass [53]. Thus, if the hydrated layer does not completely penetrate the tip wall, ion conduction will occur along the wall as well as through the electrolyte. On the other hand, complete penetration of the wall by the hydrated layer will result in direct conduction through the wall, so that ions can essentially bypass the tip region. These two situations are depicted in the circuit models shown in Figure 10.25 [53, 54]. Both models incorporate a Nernst potential E_N, a resistance R_W arising from either the transverse or lateral wall resistivity, and a parallel bulk resistance R_B representing the pathway through the electrolyte in the tip.

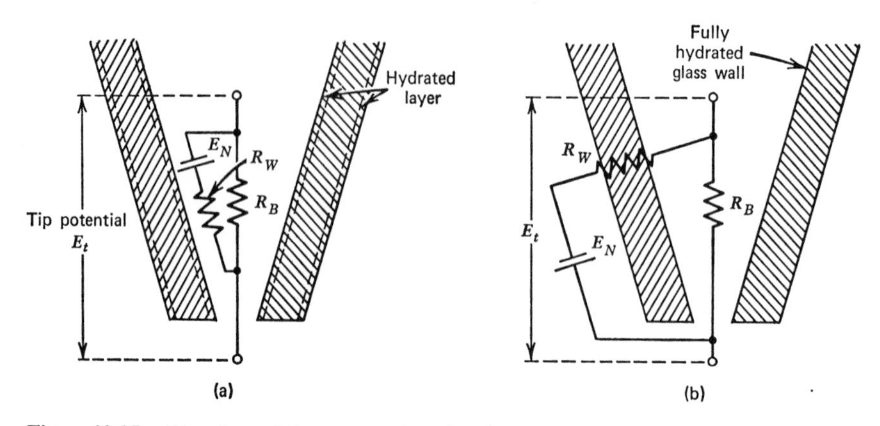

Figure 10.25. Circuit models representing the tip potential: (a) incompletely hydrated wall (after Schanne et al. [52]); (b) Fully hydrated wall (after Agin [53]).

It is evident from the two models that the tip potential has a maximum value of E_N when the tip diameter is sufficiently small for R_W to be much greater than R_B. For this condition the tip potential should change by 58 mV per decade change in the concentration ratio. As the tip diameter increases, so the shunting effect of R_B increases, eventually causing the tip potential to drop to a very small value.

Experimental results obtained by Agin and Holtzman [53, 56] showing the variation in tip potential with concentration for a glass microelectrode filled with 3*M* KCl are shown in Figure 10.26. It will be noted that for simple KCl and NaCl solutions the tip potential decreases and approaches zero as the test-solution concentration approaches that of the filling solution. The slope of the change in the range 1–100 m*M* remains fairly constant, indicating that the ratio R_W/R_B remains constant. The decrease in the slope at higher concentrations has been attributed by Lavallée and Szabo [54] to a decrease in R_B. As will be shortly discussed, R_B depends on diffusion from the tip,

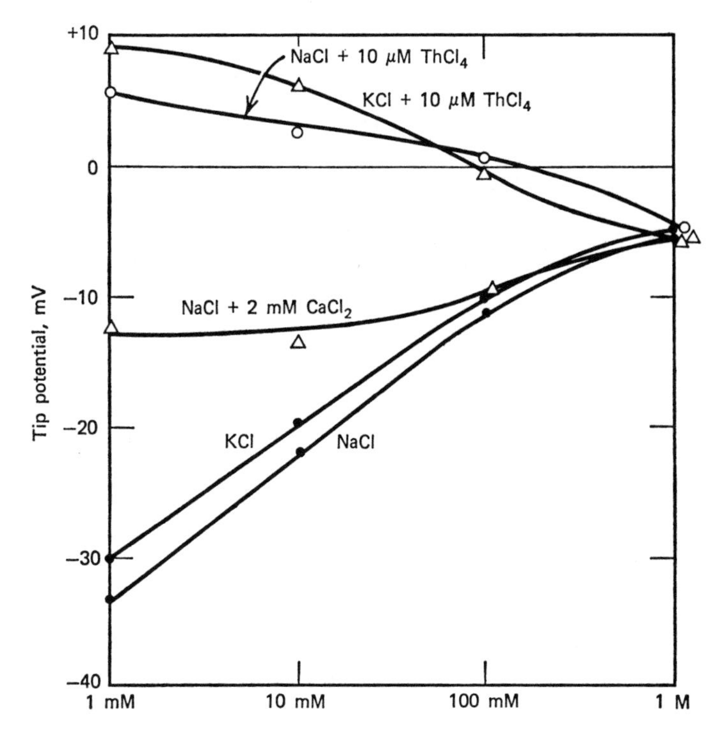

Figure 10.26. Variation of tip potential for 3*M*-KCl-filled microelectrodes in solutions of various concentrations. The results presented are mean values obtained from a large number of microelectrodes. The standard deviation for each point is approximately ±10% (The curves are drawn from data published by Agin [53] and Agin and Holtzman [56]).

so that as the test solution concentration approaches that of the filling solution, R_B can be expected to decrease.

Also shown in Figure 10.26 are the effects of introducing small quantities of thorium or calcium chloride into the test solution. Trace quantities of both substances significantly reduce the tip potential variations [52, 54, 56]. Holtzman [57] has used thorium chloride to reduce the tip potential effect when measuring the resting potential of muscle fibers in a solution of low ionic concentration. Schanne et al. [52] suggest that since thorium is a strongly adsorbed cation, it modifies the double-layer charge distribution, thereby affecting the potential distribution.

Resistance. Calculation of the microelectrode resistance is particulary simple if the diffusion of the electrolyte out from the tip is very small or if the electrode is immersed in a solution identical to the filling solution. As shown

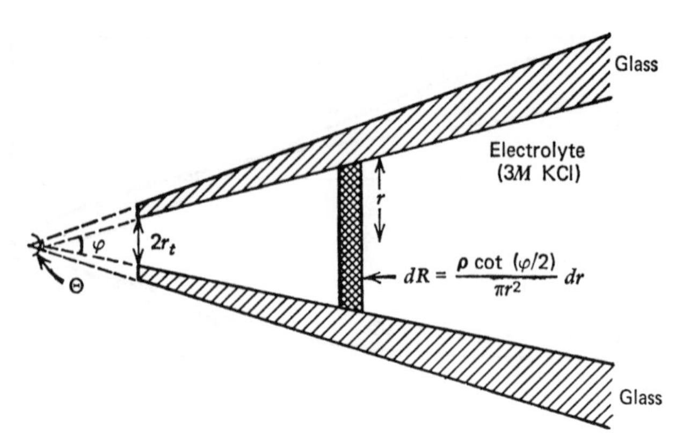

Figure 10.27. Definitions of quantities used in calculating the microelectrode resistance when diffusion effects are absent.

in Figure 10.27, the microelectrode can be approximated by a truncated cone of total angle ϕ and radius r_t, filled with an electrolyte of resistivity ρ. By integrating along the length of the cone, it can be easily shown that

$$R = \frac{\rho \cot(\phi/2)}{\pi r_t}, \tag{20}$$

which for small angles reduces to

$$R \simeq \frac{2\rho}{\pi r_t \phi}. \tag{21}$$

For example, if $\phi = 2° \equiv \pi/180$ rad, $\rho = 3.7\ \Omega$-cm corresponding to $3M$ KCl at 20°C and $r_t = 0.1\ \mu$m, then $R = 13.4\ \text{M}\Omega$.

Such a value would only be observed if the test solution had the same conductivity as the filling solution. For the situation where the tip is immersed in a much weaker KCl solution, diffusion occurs causing the ionic concentration in the tip region to be reduced, thereby increasing the electrode resistance. This is illustrated in Figure 10.28, where for low-resistivity solutions it will be noted that the electrode resistance approaches the value corresponding to equal inner and outer solution concentrations.

A proper analysis of the diffusion effect taking into account the time-varying nature of the concentration in the tip region has not been reported. However, an approximate analysis which assumes that the concentration distribution reaches a steady state has been published by Lanthier and Schanne [57] and Firth and de Felice [58]. The latter authors have shown that if the conductivity

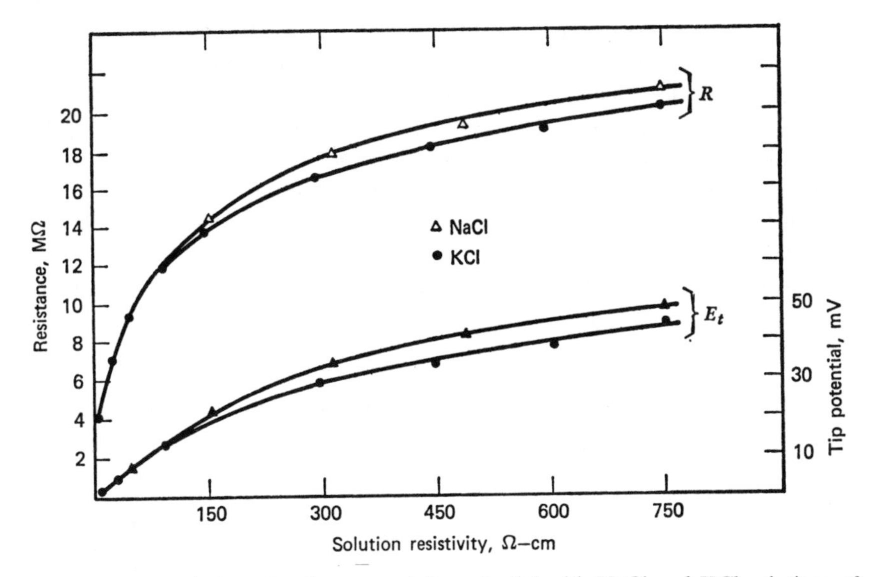

Figure 10.28. Variation of resistance and tip potential with NaCl and KCl solutions of differing resistivity, for a glass microelectrode filled with 3*M* KCl. It should be noted that above 100Ω-cm both R and V_t depend on the ion species in the solution (reproduced, with premission, from O. F. Schanne, M. Lavallée, R. Laprade, and S. Gagne, *Proc. IEEE*, **56,** 1072–1082, June, 1968).

of an ionic solution is assumed to be proportional to the ionic concentration C, the electrode resistance is given by

$$R = \frac{2}{\pi r_t \phi} \cdot \frac{\ln (C_i/C_o)}{K_0(C_i - C_o)}, \tag{22}$$

where C_i and C_o are the concentrations inside and outside the microelectrode and K_0 is the constant of proportionality relating the conductivity to the ionic concentration (i.e., $\sigma = K_0 C$). It should be noted that if L'Hôpital's rule is used to take the limit of Eq. (22) as $C_o \to C_i$, one obtains for small tip angles

$$[R]_{C_o = C_i} \simeq \frac{2}{\pi r_t \phi K_0 C_i}, \tag{23}$$

which, since $\rho = 1/K_0 C_i$, is the same as Eq. (21).

Equation (22) can be expressed in a normalized form by dividing Eq. (22) by Eq. (23):

$$\frac{R}{[R]_{C_i = C_o}} = \frac{C_i}{C_i - C_o} \ln \frac{C_i}{C_o}. \tag{24}$$

It will be noted that the normalized resistance is independent of the electrode structural parameters r_t and ϕ, so that a variety of electrodes can be used to test experimentally the validity of Eq. (24). The results shown [58] in Figure 10.29 for electrodes filled with $3M$ KCl indicate good agreement: each plotted point is the mean resistance for a number of electrodes and the bar indicates the standard deviation. Firth and de Felice [58] found that the agreement decreases as C_i is reduced and becomes relatively poor for $C_i = 0.1M$ KCl. They attributed this to the increased influence of the hydrated wall resistance [59], which is effectively in parallel with the bulk resistance of the tip fluid.

An important application of the dependence of microelectrode resistance on the outside solution concentration is in determining the resistivity of

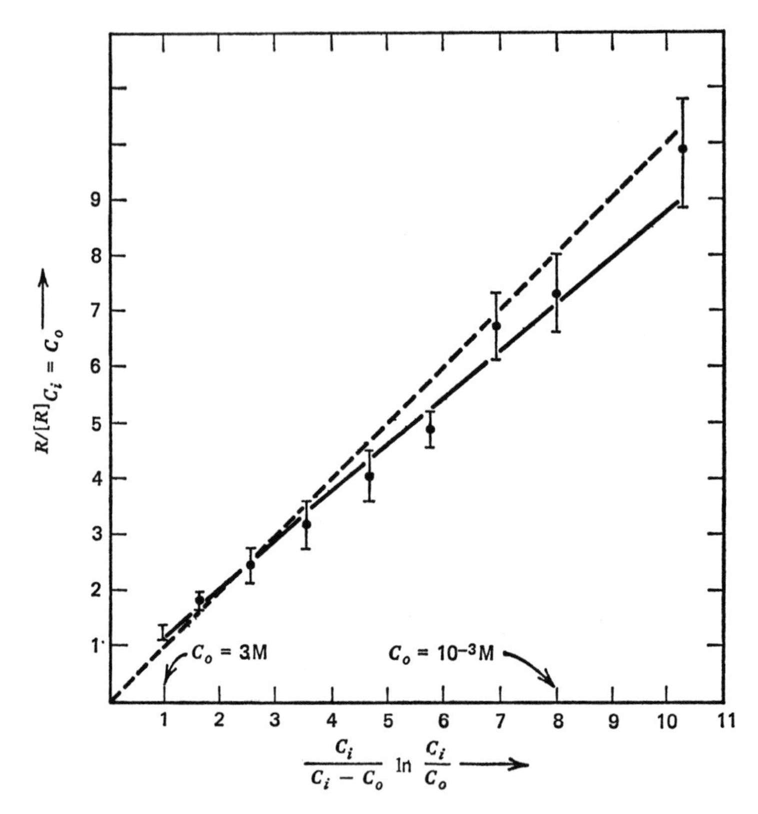

Figure 10.29. Normalized microelectrode resistance plotted against the concentration function as given by the right-hand side of Eq. (24). The electrodes were filled with $3M$ KCl and immersed in a KCl solution whose concentration varied from $10^{-4}M$ to $3M$ (reproduced with permission, from D. R. Firth, and L. J. de Felice, *Can. J. Physiol. Pharmacol.*, **49**, 436–447, 1971).

cytoplasm [60]. By measuring the resistance when the microelectrode tip has penetrated the cell membrane and calibrating the microelectrode in solutions of the same ionic species but varying concentration, the cytoplasmic resistivity can be determined. Schanne [52, 60] has published a detailed account of this method and has pointed out that it has inherent advantages over two electrode or external electrode methods. He has also described a method for automatically measuring the microelectrode resistance as a function of the outside solution resistivity. This greatly increases the speed with which an electrode can be calibrated.

The effect of a pressure difference between the filling and immersion solutions on the microelectrode resistance has also been examined by Firth and de Felice [58]. Both the theoretical and experimental results show that a positive pressure applied to the filling solution decreases the resistance, while a negative pressure increases the resistance. Physically, the effect of a positive pressure is to increase the KCl outflow from the tip, thereby maintaining the fluid concentration in the tip region closer to the filling-solution bulk value. Similarly, the effect of a negative pressure is to decrease the tip concentration through withdrawal of the immersion solution. In the limit, for large positive pressures the electrode resistance decreases to $[R]_{C_i=C_o}$, while for large negative pressures it approaches the value predicted from Eq. (23) when C_i is replaced by C_o. The experimental results shown in Figure 10.30 indicate fairly good qualitative agreement with theory (solid lines), but substantial quantitative disagreement, the reasons for which are not immediately apparent.*

Electrode Capacitance and Methods for Neutralization. The capacitance arising from the glass wall separating the inner and outer solutions can be readily calculated if it is assumed that the ratio of the wall thickness to diameter is a constant throughout the immersed tip length. For a small taper angle, the capacitance per unit length is simply that of two coaxial cylinders:

$$C = \frac{0.55\varepsilon_r}{\ln(R/r)} \quad \text{(in pF/cm)}, \tag{25}$$

where ε_r is the relative permittivity of the glass and r and R are the inner and outer radii, respectively. For example, if $r = 0.1$ μm, $R = 0.15$ μm at the tip; and if $\varepsilon_r = 4.0$, then Eq. (25) yields the value $C = 0.5$ pF/mm. The corresponding electrode resistance for a tip angle of 2° and $3M$ KCl filling solution is 13.7 MΩ.

Although Eq. (25) predicts that the total capacitance depends linearly on the immersion depth, in practice a rather more complex behavior may be

* These are steady-state results; see Figure 7.26 for non-steady-state experimental results.

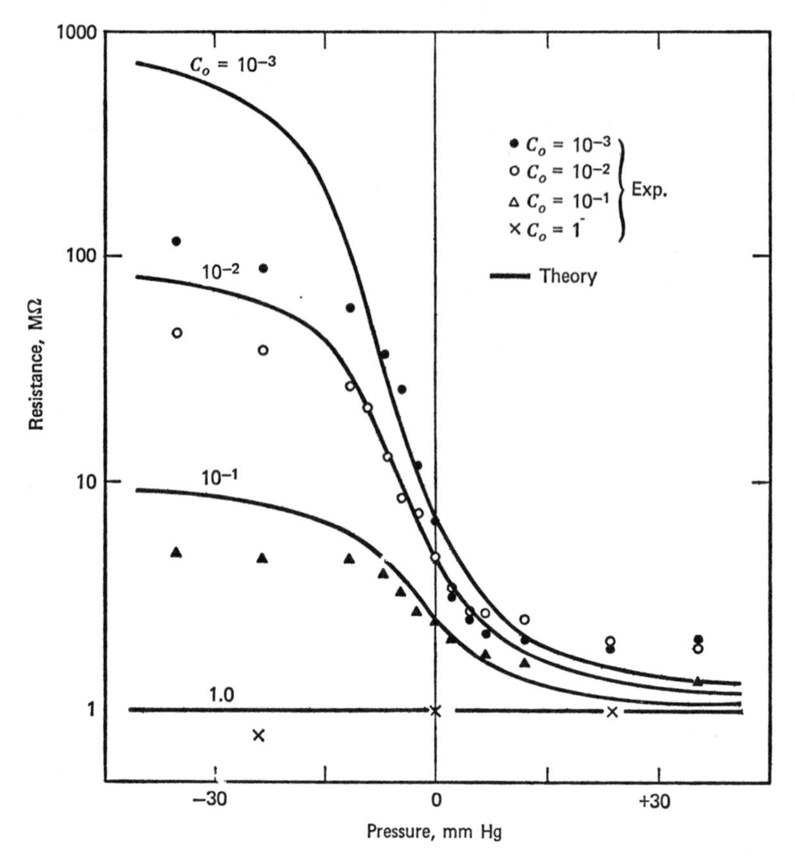

Figure 10.30. Microelectrode resistance variation with pressure: measurements compared to theory (solid lines). The microelectrode was filled with $1M$ KCl and the immersion solution concentration was varied from $1M$ to $10^{-3}M$ (reproduced, with permission, from D. R. Firth, and L. J. de Felice, *Can. J. Physiol. Pharmacol.*, **49**, 436–447, 1971).

observed [52]. The reasons for this may be surface tension effects causing the outer fluid level to be depressed or raised above the average surface level, conduction through the hydrated wall causing the effective thickness to be less than the wall thickness, or deviations from a constant wall thickness to diameter ratio.

Additional capacitances arising from electrode shielding, wiring, and amplifier input capacitances generally cause a substantial increase in the effective capacitive load seen by the signal source. Since this capacitance is in series with the electrode resistance, rather long time constants can result, producing distortion of a fast-rising action potential. Furthermore, it is possible that the relatively large transient current that flows may affect the intracellular ion concentration, thereby changing the cell potential.

To improve the transient response a negative input capacitance amplifier of the type shown in Figure 10.31 can be used. Such an amplifier makes use of positive feedback to, in effect, neutralize the input capacitance, though at the expense of some loss in the stability margin and an increase in the amplifier noise. Amplifiers of this type have been known for many years and were first applied to the problem of microelectrode signal amplification in 1953 [61, 62].

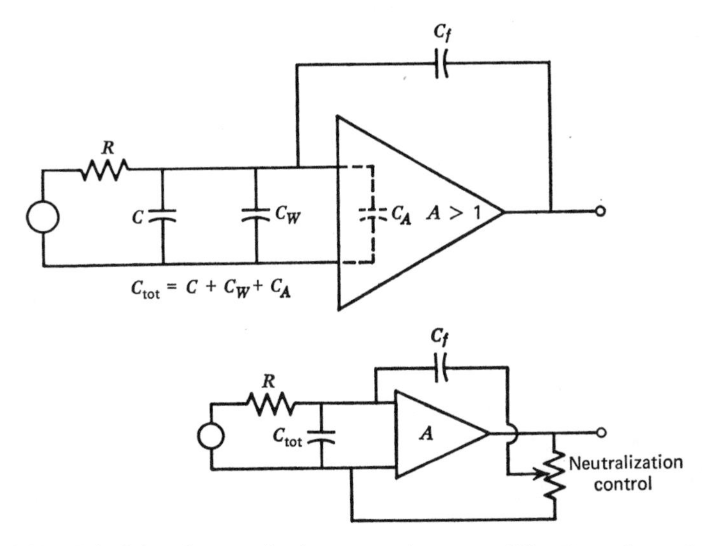

Figure 10.31. Principles of a negative input capacitance amplifier. Inset shows the means normally used to adjust the positive feedback to achieve the best neutralization condition.

Since that time a number of papers have explored the problems of optimum design, stability, and noise performance from both experimental and theoretical aspects [63–67].

If the amplifier of Figure 10.31 has a gain A, which is constant from dc to an infinite frequency, it can be easily be shown that when the feedback capacitance is given by

$$C_f = \frac{C_{tot}}{A - 1}.$$

the effective input capacitance will be zero and the transient response will be perfect. To achieve this condition, either C_f can be varied or, most usually, a variable gain to the feedback capacitor is used (see inset). In practice, perfect compensation cannot be achieved because the finite amplifier frequency response results in a second- or higher-order transfer function with its attendant stability problems and because of the distributed nature of the tip resistance and capacitance [68]. Nevertheless, very substantial improvements in the transient response can be achieved. For example, the amplifier described by Holmer and Lindstrom [69], which used a J–FET input stage, is reported to have a rise-time of 5 μs when close to critically damped. For a 20-MΩ electrode, this corresponds to an equivalent input capacitance of 0.1 pF. Such a performance seems to be more than adequate to insure distortion-free measurement of most action potentials.

A further important aspect of microelectrode amplifier design concerns the input resistance and leakage current. With regard to the former, if the electrode resistance has a maximum value of 50 MΩ, then for a 1% accurate resting potential measurement, the input resistance should be greater than 5×10^9 Ω. A more stringent requirement is set by the maximum current that can be passed through a microelectrode without significantly affecting the cell properties. Since it has been suggested [66] that currents of 10^{-11} A affect the excitability of certain cells, it would seem that a maximum input current of 10^{-12} A should be a design goal. This can be achieved with a carefully designed J-FET input stage [69].*

Electrode and Amplifier Noise. The noise spectrum generated by glass microelectrodes consists of a white- (Nyquist-) noise component arising from the electrode resistance, superimposed on a $1/f$ component [70]. As previously noted, the RMS value of the Nyquist noise emf is given by

$$E_{\mathrm{RMS}} = \sqrt{4\,kTR\Delta f},$$

where Δf is the bandwidth. From Figure 10.20, which is a plot of this equation it can be seen that for a 20-MΩ electrode at 27°C with a measurement bandwidth of 40 kHz, the RMS noise is 120 μV. The actual RMS noise may be considerably greater than this because of a large $1/f$ component. De Felice and Firth [70] have studied this component and the manner in which it depends on the internal and external electrolyte concentrations. They point out that the $1/f$ noise arises from nonequilibrium phenomena at the electrode tip and that it disappears when the inner and outer solutions are identical.

* In this application a J-FET is preferred to a MOST because of its much lower $1/f$ noise and better dc stability.

Significant noise may also arise from the microelectrode amplifier, particularly if a large degree of capacitive neutralization is required. As previously mentioned, one of the penalties paid for the increased bandwidth is an increase in the noise in the form of excess noise (i.e., noise over and above that expected from a simple increase in the bandwidth). Guld [65] has studied the problem of excess noise in an amplifier with a second-order transfer function and has derived an expression for the noise factor F. This expresses the number of times by which the amplifier increases the equivalent input mean square noise generated by the electrode and is given by

$$F = 1 + \frac{R_{eq}}{R} + R_{eq}\frac{C_{tot} + C_f}{\tau_i}$$

$$\simeq 1 + R_{eq}\frac{C_{tot} + C_f}{\tau_i}, \qquad \text{for } R \gg R_{eq},$$

where R_{eq} is the equivalent input noise resistance of the amplifier when the input is shorted, R is the electrode resistance, and τ_i is a characteristic time constant for the amplifier, which, when the amplifier is critically damped, is equal to the input time constant. To obtain some feeling for the magnitude of F, suppose that the short-circuit RMS noise of the amplifier over a 40-kHz bandwidth is 8 μV. From Figure 10.20, it can be seen that R_{eq} is equal to 100 kΩ. If $\tau_i = 2$ μS, corresponding to a rise-time of about 5 μS, the noise figure becomes

$$F = 1 + 0.05\,(C_{tot} + C_f),$$

where the capacitances are expressed in pF. Thus, for $C_{tot} + C_f = 5$ pF, we find that F equals 1.25, corresponding to a 12% increase in the equivalent RMS input noise by the amplifier. When $C_{tot} + C_f$ increases to 50 pF, the value of F increases to 3.5, so that the amplifier noise becomes dominant.

Coaxial and Multibarrel Microelectrodes. When the nature of an experiment demands several microelectrodes in close proximity to one another, it may be prefereable to use either a coaxial or multibarrel electrode assembly. Although this avoids problems associated with the individual manipulation of several independent electrodes, it does constrain the tip positions to a fixed geometrical relationship to one another. Multiple electrode assemblies enable simultaneous recordings to be made from a number of sites in close proximity, cell resting potentials to be made concurrently with microelectrophoretic injection (ion injection by means of a current through the tip) of chemical substances into the cell, and recordings to be made simultaneously with electrical excitation.

A variety of techniques have been described for fabricating multiple electrode assemblies [40, 71–78]. One of the first, described by Coombs et al. [72] in 1955, used a glass partition in a capillary that was then heat-drawn to a tip diameter in the range 0.7–2 μm. With the aid of this double-barreled electrode, electrophoretic injections (or removal) of ions were made simultaneously with the measurement of the resting potential. Multibarrel electrodes, similar to the five-barrel electrode shown in Figure 10.32(a), can be made by fusing together a number of glass capillaries and then heat-drawing the assembly to a fine tip [77]. Coaxial electrodes of the form illustrated in Figure 10.32(b) were first described and used by Tomita [73–75]; subsequently Freygang and Frank [79] employed them to record simultaneously intra- and extracellular potentials from a motoneurone. Electrodes of this type are formed by fabricating two individual microelectrodes designed so that one fits into the other. If the inner electrode has a fairly long tip region, a considerable variation in the relative positions of the two tips can be achieved.

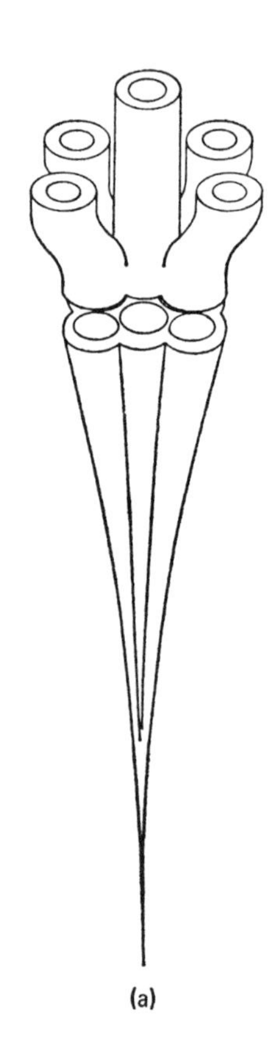

(a)

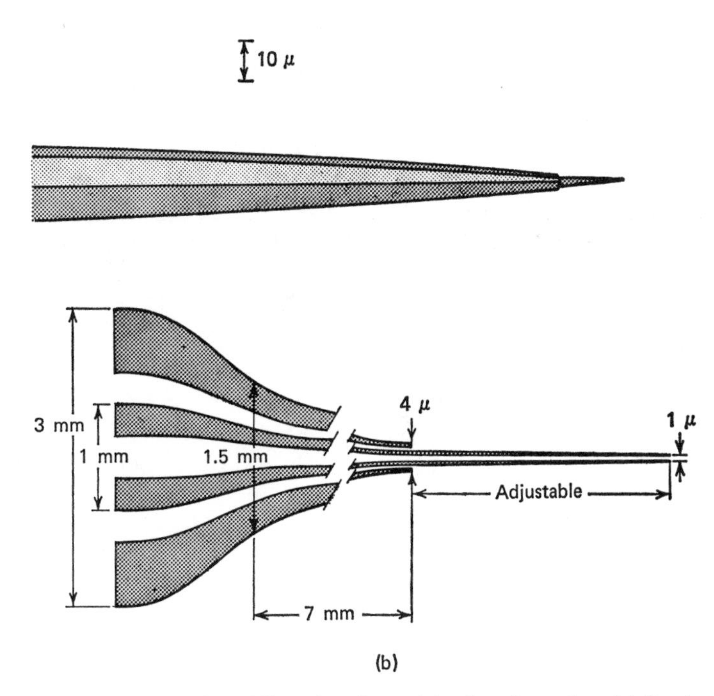

Figure 10.32. Examples of multibarrel and coaxial microelectrodes: (a) five-barrel glass electrode; (b) sketch of a coaxial electrode (reproduced, with permission, from K. Frank, and M. C. Becker, Ch. 2 in "*Physical Techniques in Biological Research*", W. L. Nastuk (ed.), Academic Press, New York, 1964).

Shown in Figure 10.33 is a circuit model for a coaxial microelectrode immersed in a conducting fluid.* It will be noted that in addition to the distributed capacitance to ground and distributed resistance associated with the inner and outer electrodes, there is a distributed interelectrode capacitance, which in the first-order model is represented by capactior C_{12}. If a voltage transient is present on one of the electrodes, a displacement current flows through this capacitor causing a signal to appear on the other. The measurement error that results from this intermixing of the two signals can be especially serious if the rise-times are short; hence, it becomes essential to provide a means of neutralizing the effect of C_{12}.

Two methods of achieving this are illustrated in Figure 10.34, both of

* The model is also valid for a double-barreled electrode. A detailed analysis of this electrode type by Rush et al. [79] has shown that for glasses with resistivities of 10^{14} Ω-cm, the inter-electrode resistance arising from leakage through the glass is around 10^{13} Ω. This resistance, which has not been included in the model, can normally be neglected.

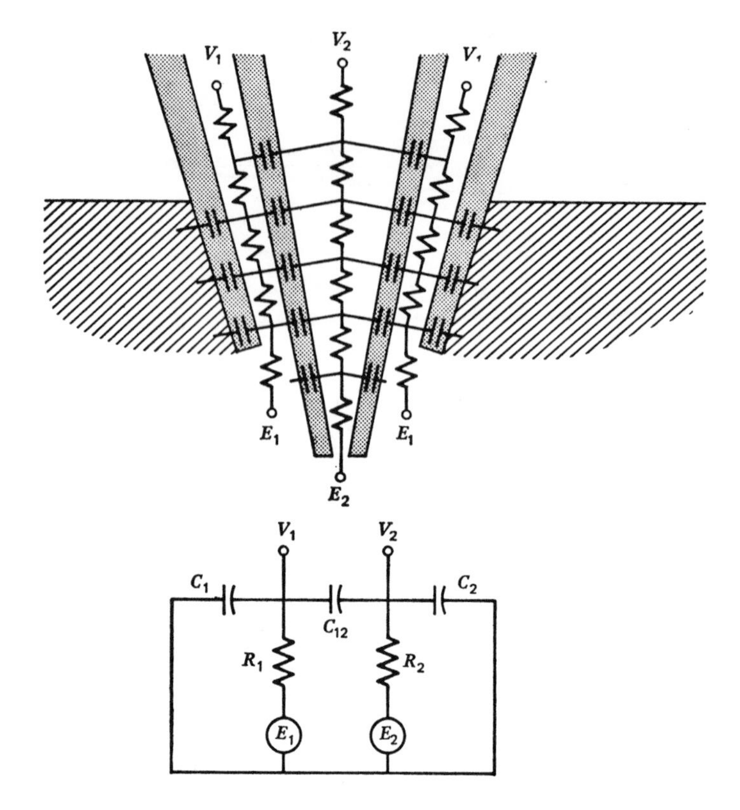

Figure 10.33. Circuit model of a coaxial microelectrode immersed in a conducting medium.

which employ cross coupling of the two channels [71, 80, 81]. In Figure 10.34(a) a portion of the signal from each channel, as controlled by R_{12} and R_{21}, is subtracted from the opposite channel by feeding the portion into the inverting input of the differential amplifier. Compensation for the self-capacitances C_1 and C_2 is provided by positive feedback through C_{f1} and C_{f2}, under the control of R_{f1} and R_{f2}, respectively.

A difficulty with the above circuit is the presence of four controls whose functions are not entirely independent, making it difficult to achieve optimum compensation of all three capacitances. To overcome this difficulty, Hoffman and Schmidt [81] have proposed the somewhat more complex circuit shown in Figure 10.34(b), which provides both single-ended and differential outputs. The most important feature of the circuit is that a single control, R_{12} governs the interelectrode capacitance neutralization, making it relatively simple to trim the system for optimum performance.

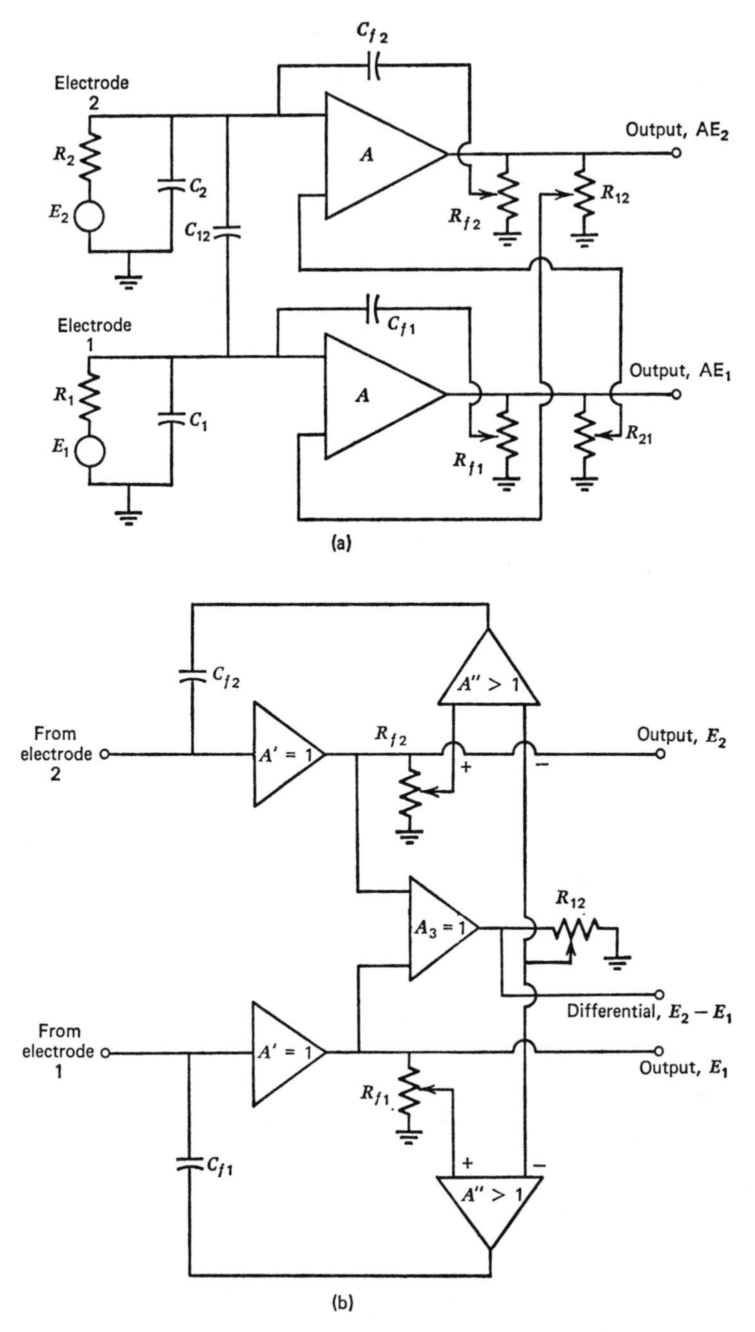

Figure 10.34. Two methods for neutralizing the self- and interelectrode capacitances: (a) essential features of the method described by Tomita [80] and Freygang and Frank [76] using four controls; (b) method described by Hoffman and Schmidt [81] using only three controls.

REFERENCES

1. Geddes, L. A. *Electrodes and the Measurement of Bioelectric Events.* Wiley-Interscience: New York, 1972.
2. Geddes, L. A. "Interface Design for Bioelectrode Systems." *IEEE Spectrum,* **9**, 41–48 (October 1972).
3. Vetter, K. J. *Electrochemical Kinetics, Theoretical and Experimental Aspects.* Academic: New York, 1967.
4. Damaskin, B. B. *The Principles of Current Methods for the Study of Electrochemical Reactions.* McGraw-Hill: New York, 1967.
5. Grahame, D. C. "Mathematical Theory of the Faradic Admittance." *J. Electrochem. Soc.*, **99**, 370C–385C (1952).
6. Warburg, E. "Ueber das Verhalten sogenannter unpolarisirbarer Elektroden gegen Wechselstrom." *Ann. Phys. Chem.*, **67**, 493–499 (1899).
7. Warburg, E. "Ueber die Polarisationcapacität des Platins." *Ann. Physik*, **6**, 125–135 (1901).
8. Geddes, L. A.; da Costa, C. P.; and Wise, G. "The Impedance of Stainless-Steel Electrodes." *Med. Biol. Eng.*, **9**, 511–521 (September 1971).
9. Schwan, H. P. "Determination of Biological Impedances," in W. L. Nastuk, Ed., *Physical Techniques in Biological Research*, Vol. VI, Pt. B. Academic: New York, 1963, pp. 323–407.
10. Ray, C. D.; Bickford, R. G.; Clark, L. C.; Johnston, R. E.; Richards, T. M.; Rogers, D.; and Russert, W. E. "A New Multicontact, Multipurpose, Brain Depth Probe: Details of Construction." *Mayo Clin. Proc.*, **40**, 771–780 (October 1965).
11. Fricke, H. "The Theory of Electrolyte Polarization." *Phil. Mag.*, **14**, 310–318 (1932).
12. Schwan, H. P. "Electrode Polarization Impedance and Measurements in Biological Materials." *Ann. N.Y. Acad. Sci.*, **148**, Art. 1, 191–209 (February 1968).
13. Schwan, H. P. "Electrode Polarization in AC Steady-State Impedance Studies of Biological Systems." Digest of Tech. Papers, 6th Int. Conf. Med. Electron. Biolog. Engng., Tokyo, 1965, pp. 556–557.
14. Cole, K. S. "Alternating Current Conductance and Direct Current Excitation of Nerve." *Science*, 16 February 1934, pp. 164–165.
15. Weinman, J., and Mahler, J. "An Analysis of Electrical Properties of Metal Electrodes." *Med. Electron. Biol. Eng.*, **2**, 299–310 (July 1964).
16. Nencini, R., and Pasquali, E. "Manganese Dioxide Electrodes for Stimulation and Recording." *Med. Biol. Eng.*, **6**, 193–197 (March 1968).
17. Hill, D. W. *Electronic Techniques in Anaesthesia and Surgery*, 2nd ed., Butterworths: London, 1973.

18a. Huhta, J. C., and Webster, J. G. "60-Hz Interference in Electrocardiography." *IEEE Trans. Bio-Med. Eng.*, **BME-20**, 91–101 (March 1973).

18b. Schwartzchild, M. M.; Hoffman, I.; and Kissin, M. "Errors in Unipolar Limb Leads Caused by Unbalanced Skin Resistances and a Device for their Elimination." *Am. Heart J.*, **48**, 235–248 (1954).

19. King, G. E. "Errors in Voltage in Multi-Channel ECG Recordings Using Newer Electrode Materials." *Am. Heart J.*, **18**, 295–297 (September 1964).

20. Hill, D. W., and Khandpur, R. S. "The Performance of Transistor ECG Amplifiers." *World Med. Instrum.*, **7**, 12–22 (May 1969).

21. Lewes, D. "Electrode Jelly in Electrocardiography." *Brit. Heart J.*, **27**, 105–115 (1965).

22. Lewes, D. "Multipoint Electrocardiography Without Skin Preparation." *World Med. Electron.*, **4**, 240–245 (August 1966).

23. Bergey, G. E.; Squires, R. D.; and Sipple, W. C. "Electrocardiogram Recording with Pasteless Electrodes." *IEEE Trans. Bio-Med. Eng.*, **BME-18**, 206–211 (May 1971).

24a. Geddes, L. A.; Steinberg, R.; and Wise, G. "Dry Electrodes and Holder for Electro-Oculography." *Med. Biol. Eng.*, **11**, 69–72 (January 1973).

24b. Geddes, L. A.; Bourland, J. D.; Wise, G.; and Steinberg, R. "Linearity of the Horizontal Component of the Electro-Oculogram." *Med. Biol. Eng.*, **11**, 73–77 (January 1973).

25a. Roman, J. "Flight Research Program. III. High Impedance Electrodes Techniques." *Aerospace Med.*, **37**, 790–795 (August 1966).

25b. Patten, C. W.; Ramme, F. B.; and Roman, J. "Dry Electrodes for Physiological Monitoring." NASA Tech. Note., NASA TND-3414, 1966.

26. Almasi, J. J., and Schmitt, O. H. "Systematic and Random Variations of ECG Electrode System Impedance." *Ann. N.Y. Acad. Sci.*, **170**, Art. 2, 509–519 (1970).

27. Strong, P. *Biophysical Measurements.* Tektronix: Beaverton, Oreg., 1970.

28a. Venables, P. H., and Sayer, E. "On the Measurement of the Level of the Skin Potential." *Brit. J. Psychol.*, **54**, 251–260 (August 1963).

28b. Venables, P. H., and Martin, I. "Skin Resistance and Skin Potential," in P. H. Venables, and I. Martin, Eds., *A Manual of Psychophysiological Methods*, North Holland: Amsterdam, 1967, Chapter 2.

29a. O'Connell, D. N.; Tursky, B.; and Orne, M. T. "Electrodes for the Recording of Skin Potential." *Arch. Gen. Psychiatr.*, **3**, 252–258 (1960).

29b. O'Connell, D. N., and Tursky, B. "Special Modifications of the Silver-Silver Chloride Sponge Electrode for Skin Recording." *Psychophysiol. Newslett.*, **8**, 31–37 (1962).

30. Almansi, J. J.; Hart, M. W.; Schmitt, O. H.; and Watanabe, Y. "Bioelectrode Voltage Offset Time Profiles and Their Impact on ECG Measurement Standards." Digest of Tech. Papers, 4th Can. Med. Biol. Eng. Conf., Winnipeg, 1972, pp. 1a–1b.

31. Geddes, L. A.; Baker, L. E.; and Moore, A. G. "The Use of Liquid-Junction Electrodes in Recording the Human Electrocardiogram (ECG)." *J. Electrocardiol.*, **1**, 51–56 (1968).

32. Scott, R. N. "A Method of Inserting Wire Electrodes for Electromyography." *IEEE Trans. Bio-Med. Eng.*, **BME-12**, 46–47 (January 1965).

33. Parker, T. G. "Simple Method for Preparing and Implanting Fine Wire Electrodes." *Am. J. Phys. Med.*, **47**, 247–249 (1968).

34. Richardson, P. C.; Coombs, F. K.; and Adams, R. M. "Some New Electrode Techniques for Long-Term Physiologic Monitoring." *Aerospace Med.*, **39**, 745–750 (July 1968).

35. Lopez, A., and Richardson, P. "Capacitive Electrocardiographic and Bioelectric Electrodes." *IEEE Trans. Bio-Med. Eng.*, **BME-16**, 99 (January 1969).

36. Lagow, C. H.; Sladek, R. J.; and Richardson, P. C. "Anodic Insulated Tantalum Oxide Electrocardiograph Electrodes." *IEEE Trans. Bio-Med. Eng.*, **BME-18**, 162–164 (March 1971).

37a. Wolfson, R. N., and Neuman, M. R. "Miniature Si–SiO_2 Insulated Electrodes Based on Semiconductor Technology" (Paper 14-6). Proc. 8th Int. Conf. Med. Biol. Eng., Chicago, 1969.

37b. David, R. M., and Portnoy, W. M. "Insulated Electrocardiogram Electrodes." *Med. Biol. Eng.*, **10**, 742–751 (November 1972).

37c. Matsuo, T.; Iinuma, K.; and Esashi, M. "A Barium-Titanate-Ceramics Capacitive-Type EEG Electrode." *IEEE Trans. Bio-Med. Eng.*, **BME-20**, 299–300 (July 1973).

38. Robinson, D. A. "The Electrical Properties of Metal Microelectrodes." *Proc. IEEE*, **56**, 1065–1071 (June 1968).

39. Merrill, E. G., and Ainsworth, A. "Glass-Coated Platnium-Plated Tungsten Microelectrodes." *Med. Biol. Eng.*, **10**, 662–672 (September 1972).

40. Frank, K., and Becker, M. C. "Microelectrodes for Recording and Stimulation," in W. L. Nastuk, Ed., *Physical Techniques in Biological Research*, Vol. V, Pt. A. Academic: New York, 1964.

41a. Brown, V. R., and McCusker, D. R. "A New Thin Film Metallized Glass Microelectrode" (Paper 13A5). Proc. 21st Ann. Conf. Eng. Med. Biol. November 1968.

41b. Starr, A.; Wise, K. D.; and Csongradi, J. "An Evaluation of Photoengraved Microelectrodes for Extracellular Single-Unit Recording." *IEEE Trans. Bio-Med. Eng.*, **BME-20**, 291–293 (July 1973).

41c. Wise, K. D.; Angell, J. B.; and Starr, A. "An Integrated Circuit Approach to Extracellular Microelectrodes." *IEEE Trans. Bio-Med. Eng.*, **BME-17**, 238–246 (July 1970).

42. Wilska, A. "Aktionspotentialentladungen einzelner Netzhautelemente des Frosches." *Acta Soc. Med. Fenn. Duodecim.*, Ser. A, **22**, 63–75 (1940–41).

43. Taylor, C. V. "Microelectrodes and Micromagnets." *Proc. Soc. Exp. Biol. Med.*, **23**, 147–150 (1925).

44a. Wolbarsht, M. L.; MacNichol, E. F.; and Wagner, H. G. "Glass Insulated Platinum Microelectrode." *Science*, 4 November 1960, pp. 1309–1310.

44b. Wolbarsht, M. L., and Wagner, H. G. "Glass Insulated Platinum Microelectrodes: Design and Fabrication," in F. H. Bostem, Ed., *Medical Electronics*, Proc. 5th Int. Conf. on Med. Electron. Univ. of Liège, 1965.

45a. Ballintijn, C. M. "Fine Tipped Metal Microelectrodes with Glass Insulation." *Experimenta*, **17**, 523–524 (November 1961).

45b. Guld, C. "A Glass-Covered Platinum Microelectrode." *Med. Electron. Biol. Eng.*, **2**, 317–327 (July 1964).

46a. Salcman, M., and Bak, M. J. "Design, Fabrication, and In Vivo Behaviour of Chronic Recording Intracortical Microelectrodes." *IEEE Trans. Bio-Med. Eng.*, **BME-20**, 253–260 (July 1973).

46b. Goldstein, S. R., and Salcman, M. "Mechanical Factors in the Design of Chronic Recording Intracortical Microelectrodes." *IEEE Trans. Bio-Med. Eng.*, **BME-20**, 260–269 (July 1973).

47. Baldwin, H. A.; Frenk, S.; and Lettvin, J. Y. "Glass-Coated Tungsten Microelectrodes." *Science*, 11 June 1965, pp. 1462–1464.

48. Gestland, R. C.; Howland, B.; Lettvin, J. Y.; and Pitts, W. H. "Comments on Microelectrodes." *Proc. IRE*, **47**, 1856–1862 (November 1959).

49. Chowdhury, T. K. "Fabrication of Extremely Fine Glass Micropipette Electrodes." *J. Phys. E*, **2**, 1087–1090 (1969).

50. Jay, A. W. L., and Burton, A. C. "Direct Measurement of Potential Difference Across the Human Red Blood Cell Membrane." *Biophys. J.*, **9**, 115–121 (1969).

51. Coombs, J. S.; Eccles, J. C.; and Fatt, P. "The Specific Ionic Conductances and the Ionic Movements Across the Motoneuronal Membrane That Produce the Inhibitory Postsynaptic Potential." *J. Physiol.*, **130**, 326–373 (November 1955).

52. Schanne, O. F.; Lavallée, M.; Laplade, R.; and Gagné, S. "Electrical Properties of Glass Microelectrodes." *Proc. IEEE*, **56**, 1072–1082 (June 1968).

53. Agin, D. P. "Electrochemical Properties of Glass Microelectrodes," in M. Lavallée, O. F. Schanne, and N. C. Hebert, Eds., *Glass Microelectrodes*. Wiley: New York, 1969, Chapter 4.

54. Lavallée, M., and Szabo, G. "The Effect of Glass Surface Conductivity Phenomena on the Tip Potential of Micropipette Electrodes," in M. Lavallée, O. F. Schanne, and N. C. Hebert, Eds., *Glass Microelectrodes*. Wiley: New York, 1969, Chapter 6.

55. Eisenman, G. "The Ion-Exchange Characteristics of the Hydrated Surface of Na^+ Selective Glass Electrodes," in M. Lavallée, O. F. Schanne, and N. C. Hebert, Eds., *Glass Microelectrodes*. Wiley: New York, 1969, Chapter 3.

56. Agin, D., and Holtzman, D. "Glass Microelectrodes: Origin and Elimination of Tip Potentials." *Nature*, **211**, 1194–1195 (1966).

57. Lanthier, R., and Schanne, O. F. "Change of Microelectrode Resistance in Solutions of Different Resistivities." *Naturwiss.*, **53**, 430 (1966).

58. Firth, D. R., and de Felice, L. J. "Electrical Resistance and Volume Flow in Glass Microelectrodes." *Can. J. Physiol. Pharmacol.*, **49**, 436–447 (May 1971).

59. Caillé, J. P., and Gagné, S. "Resistance Electrique de la Paroi d'une Microélectrode." *Can. J. Physiol. Pharmacol.*, **49**, 783–786 (August 1971).

60. Schanne, O. "Measurement of Cytoplasmic Resistivity by Means of the Glass Microelectrode," in M. Lavallée, O. F. Schanne and N. C. Hébert, Eds., *Glass Microelectrodes*. Wiley: New York, 1969, Chapter 14.

61. Solms, S. J.; Nastuk, W. L.; and Alexander, J. T. "Development of a High Fidelity Preamplifier for Use in Recording Bioelectric Potentials with Intracellular Electrodes." *Rev. Sci. Instrum.*, **24**, 960–967 (October 1953).

62. Woodbury, J. W. "Recording Central Nervous Activity with Intracellular Ultramicroelectrodes: Use of Negative-Capacity Amplifier to Improve Transient Response." *Fed. Proc.*, **12**, 159 (March 1953).

63. Yang, C. C., Hervey, J. P., and Smith, P. E. "On Amplifiers Used for Microelectrode Work." *IRE Trans. Med. Electron.*, **ME-10**, 25 (March 1958).

64. Robinson, M., and Weimann, J. "Negative-Capacitance Amplifier Noise." *Electron. Technol.*, **37**, 127–129 (March 1960).

65. Guld, C. "Cathode Follower and Negative Capacitance as High Input Impedance Circuits." *Proc. IRE.*, **50**, 1912–1927 (September 1962).

66. Moore, J. W., and Gebhart, J. H. "Stabilized Wide-Band Potentiometric Preamplifiers." *Proc. IRE.*, **50**, 1928–1941 (September 1962).

67. Schoenfeld, R. L. "Bandwidth Limits for Neutralized Input Capacity Amplifiers." *Proc. IRE*, **50**, 1942–1950 (September 1962).

68. Guld, C. "Factors Limiting Capacitance Neutralizing in Microelectrode Amplifiers." Proc. 2nd Int. Conf. Med. Electron., *Medical Electronics*. Iliffe: London, 1960, pp. 28–32.

69. Holmer, N. G., and Lindstrom, K. "An Electrometer Amplifier with Low Input Capacitance and Large Input Dynamic Range." *IEEE Trans. Bio-Med. Eng.*, **BME-19**, 162–164 (March 1972).

70. De Felice, L. J., and Firth, D. R. "Spontaneous Voltage Fluctuations in Glass Microelectrodes." *IEEE Trans. Bio-Med. Eng.*, **BME-18**, 339–351 (September 1971).

71. Vis, V. A. "A Technique for Making Multiple-Bore Microelectrodes." *Science*, 23 July 1954, pp. 152–153.

72. Coombs, J. S.; Eccles, J. C.; and Fatt, P. "The Electrical Properties of the Motoneurone Membrane." *J. Physiol.*, **130**, 291–325 (November 1955).

73. Tomita, T. "The Nature of Action Potentials in the Lateral Eye of the Horseshoe Crab as Revealed by Simultaneous Intra- and Extracellular Recording." *Jap. J. Physiol.*, **6**, 327–340 (December 1956).

74. Tomita, T., and Kaneko, A. "An Intracellular Coaxial Microelectrode—Its Construction and Application." *Med. Electron. Biol. Eng.*, **3**, 367–376 (October 1965).

75. Tomita, T. "Single and Coaxial Microelectrodes in the Study of the Retina," in M. Lavallée, O. F. Schanne, and N. C. Hébert, Eds. *Glass Microelectrodes.* Wiley: New York, 1969, Chapter 8.

76. Freygang, W. H., and Frank, K. "Extracellular Potentials from Single Spinal Motoneurons." *J. Gen. Physiol.*, **42**, 749–760 (March 1959).

77. Curtis, D. R. "Microelectrophoresis," in W. L. Nastuk, Ed., *Physical Techniques in Biological Research*, Vol. V, Pt. A. Academic: New York, 1964, Chapter 4.

78. Terzuolo, C. A., and Araki, T. "An Analysis of Intra- Versus Extracellular Potential Changes Associated with Activity of Single Spinal Motoneurones." *Ann. N.Y. Acad. Sci.*, **94**, 547–558 (1961–1962).

79. Rush, S.; Lepeschkin, E.; and Brooks, H. O. "Electrical and Thermal Properties of Double-Barreled Ultra Microelectrodes." *IEEE Trans. Bio-Med. Eng.*, **BME-15**, 80–93 (April 1968).

80. Tomita, T. "A Compensation Circuit for Coaxial and Double-Barreled Microelectrodes." *IRE Trans. Bio-Med. Electron.*, **BME-9**, 138–141 (April 1962).

81. Hoffman, C. J., and Schmidt, E. M. "A New Approach to the Cross-Neutralized Microelectrode Amplifier." *IEEE Trans. Bio-Med. Eng.*, **BME-17**, 161–163 (April 1970).

Index